WORLD POPULATION AND
WORLD FOOD SUPPLIES

The Shasta Dam, California: a great multi-purpose scheme
(*Bureau of Reclamation, California Projects*)

WORLD POPULATION
AND
WORLD FOOD SUPPLIES

BY

SIR E. JOHN RUSSELL
D.Sc. F.R.S.

Formerly Director of the
Rothamsted Experiment Station

LONDON
GEORGE ALLEN & UNWIN LTD
RUSKIN HOUSE MUSEUM STREET

*Printed in Great Britain
in 10 pt Times Roman type
by Unwin Brothers Ltd
Woking and London*

PREFACE

There is at the present time much anxiety about food supplies for the world in general and for Britain in particular. It is no new thing. It was felt even in the 1830's, when the population of England and Wales was only about 15¼ million compared with nearly 44 million to-day, when the country was largely agricultural and long before the destruction of agricultural land so characteristic of this century had begun. Fears were expressed that the population was too high and emigration was widely advocated. Malthus's famous *Essay on the Principles of Population*, published in 1798, had exercised a profound effect and set people thinking that in this country at any rate population had outstripped food resources.

Happily these gloomy forebodings were falsified by three developments hardly foreseeable at the time: changes in our agricultural system; the introduction of fertilizers—the first and for long the only application of science to agriculture—and the opening up by new methods of regions not previously regarded as capable of producing food. These proved so successful that nothing more was heard of the food problem till near the end of the 19th century; food was plentiful and very cheap; if people did not feed well it was largely because they lacked the knowledge of what to choose out of the large variety available. Prices were indeed so low that British farmers were unable to compete and for the last twenty years of the century our agriculture was not only depressed but apparently almost unnecessary: "British agriculture is dead," a high official of the Board of Agriculture was heard to say, "and the business of the Board is to give it a decent burial."

Then in 1898 came a rude shock. Sir William Crookes, in his presidential address to the British Association at Bristol, pointed out that the world's wheat eaters then numbering 516 million would by 1931 probably number 746 million and would require 3·3 thousand million bushels of wheat compared with the 2·3 thousand million then being produced. There seemed no possibility of increasing the wheat area sufficiently to produce anything like that quantity and in consequence mankind faced grave risks of hunger. It is impossible for people of this generation to realize the terrific shock caused by this pronouncement. The 19th century had been a period of tremendous progress which unlike that of the 20th century had engendered feelings of intense pride in achievement, of unbounded optimism and unshakeable belief in the progress of mankind onward and upward for ever. To be told that it might all end in a few years in hunger or starvation was a shattering blow.

Crookes pointed a way out: the synthetic manufacture of nitrogenous fertilizers, which he claimed could give the necessary increase in output of wheat.

Again, however, the gloomy expectations were not fulfilled. When the 1930's came there were such gluts of food on the world market that wheat had to be burned in the Argentine, and farmers everywhere suffered serious financial distress.

This unexpected increase in wheat production had resulted not from Crookes' suggested method but from the development of a new science, plant genetics and its associate plant breeding, which hardly existed in Crookes' day. It produced new varieties of crops which could grow in regions hitherto

5

deemed unproductive and it allowed a great extension of the area of cultivation. New implements and procedures were devised to overcome the practical difficulties. The successes achieved were so marked that the Hot Springs Conference of the United Nations held in 1943 confidently passed resolutions urging all Governments to aim at higher standards of nutrition for their peoples, and no difficulties were anticipated when the implementing body showed that this would necessitate as a minimum a well-balanced increase of 1 to 2 per cent per annum in world production of basic foods in excess of population growth.

These hopes, however, have not materialized. Instead, the Food and Agriculture Organization of the United Nations, a body which collects statistics from most countries of the world, has uttered repeated warnings that world food production since 1939 has not even kept pace with the growth of world population. A few countries have, on the average, more food per head than they had fifteen years ago, but most have less; so, far from improving, the nutritional status of the world as a whole has declined.

For the third time, therefore, fear of world hunger or even starvation has spread, and a number of books have appeared on the subject in Great Britain and America, some developing to the full the sensational possibilities of the situation, which it must be admitted are considerable, others more soberly (but often with less popular appeal) discussing ways and means by which the danger may be averted. The new factors that have come into play destroying for a time the older hopes of progress have been the material destruction and wide-spread impoverishment resulting from the war, and the social upheavals which in so many countries have hampered food production. Political theory, especially nationalism, has in many countries become almost an obsession, sweeping aside laws of economics and other considerations and setting up national systems which will almost certainly result in a lower standard of living and which can be maintained only by skilful propaganda backed by force.

Meanwhile, however, scientists and technologists are more vigorously than ever before seeking new and better methods for bringing more land into cultivation, for intensifying output from land already in use, and for reducing the very considerable wastes and losses of foods that now take place. And, just as in 1898 the new science that was to falsify Crookes' prediction was hardly recognized, indeed hardly born, so now there are sciences and techniques in little more than embryo stage that may completely dispel the present fears. Less than 10 per cent of the world's land surface is cultivated; ways can still be found of expanding into the 90 per cent at present untilled. But, as the better methods are more easily applied in advanced countries where political and economic conditions do not hamper their use, so we may expect the greatest advances to be made there.

In the following chapters I have dealt with the countries of most importance from the point of view of food production and consumption: those which must import, those which can export, and those using some methods of organization or technique which may be useful elsewhere. I have endeavoured to show what each is doing to increase its contributions to the world food market or to reduce its dependence thereon. I have visited, at least once, almost all these lands to study the problems on the spot; and each chapter has been

6

read by a competent expert in the country concerned so as to minimize errors of fact or of perspective. Self-sufficing countries making no important contribution or demands on the world market have been omitted, and to my regret I have had to omit also the U.S.S.R. and satellite countries partly because, as a group, they seem to fall into this self-sufficing non-contributing category, but chiefly because I was not satisfied with the information I could get about them. Between 1930 and 1939 I made four visits to the U.S.S.R., studying its agriculture, and, indeed, began a book on the subject. But from 1939 onwards the information available to me has been too unsatisfactory to embody here. Russian publicists and permitted visitors, however, always declare that life in the U.S.S.R. is entirely satisfactory and free from any food problems; all I can say at present is that we may be able to draw supplies of grain and other foods from them, but with some uncertainty since political considerations may always override economic factors.

In spite of present difficulties the picture that finally emerges is one of tempered optimism. In all the countries examined there is a considerable gap between the best and the average food producer which can certainly be narrowed, thereby increasing the output of food. And in all countries, even in the most advanced, there is an equally great or even larger gap between the present achievements of the best farmers, and the high yields occasionally obtained as the result of combinations of factors which in Nature occur only rarely, but which if we could discover and reproduce them would make these rare records a more usual perhaps even the normal occurrence. Finally, the possibilities of new scientific achievements are completely unpredictable and although it is a pleasant enough occupation to enumerate them and discourse on their potentialities I have refrained from doing so because the great majority of food producers are small operators with neither the time, the money, nor the knowledge for making drastic changes. Improvements can come only slowly; already the better farmers in many countries are adopting them and our hope must be that the others will follow. Advanced countries able and willing to pay for food will, so far as I can see, always get it.

The less advanced countries are in a more difficult position because they lack the appliances needed for the improvement of their agriculture. Yet all can, if they will, find a basis for co-operation with the countries that can supply them and provide experts teaching how to use them. Each country must work out its own salvation, either by itself or in co-operation with others. I see no prospect whatsoever of running the world as a super Welfare State; our own experience is showing how very costly it is and how liable to induce parasitism. The solution lies in co-operation between the more advanced and the less advanced countries, but co-operation that is mutually advantageous and not hampered by restrictive conditions. Finally, a sound population policy must be adopted to ensure that the numbers do not outstrip the food resources.

The statistics quoted are from the publications of the respective Ministries, the Food and Agriculture Organization, or other acceptable authority; the source is always given. They lack the precision of industrial statistics and should be taken to show orders of magnitude rather than exact quantities. Few farmers, even in Britain, know the precise acreage or yield of their crops; there is a considerable element of estimation, even of guesswork, in arriving at the figures. So long as there is no bias the final results may not be far out. I doubt whether even for our figures the errors are less than about 5 or 10 per cent. In peasant countries the figures are subject to considerably larger error; it may be as much as 25 per cent or more, and there may be a definite bias, especially where the agricultural officer is suspected of being in league with the tax collector. But the trends are probably true and the general picture may be accepted as being fairly reliable, at any rate, it is the best we can get.

I owe much to many kind friends in many different countries for help and criticism in preparing this book; I have indicated some of the names in the relevant chapters. I wish, also, to thank the School of Rural Economy of Oxford University for permission to use their library and to thank their librarian, Mr. Shepherd, for much help, and Mr. John Smithwhite for preparing the diagrams.

Campsfield Wood,   E. JOHN RUSSELL
Woodstock. Oct. 1953.

The statistics are quoted as issued. Those from F.A.O. and foreign countries are in metric tons (2,205 lb.); those from British and Commonwealth sources are in long tons (2,240 lb.). The difference of 2 per cent is within the error of the statistics and for that reason and to facilitate reference I have left them as they are and not converted them to a common basis.

CONTENTS

PREFACE   *page* 5

I *The Problem: Feeding the World's Population*   13

II *The United Kingdom. Eire*   24

III *Methods of Increasing Food Production*   59

IV *Northern Europe's Intensive producers: The Netherlands, Denmark, Sweden, Finland*   78

V *France; the peasant producers of the Mediterranean lands: Spain, Portugal, Italy, Israel, Egypt*   132

VI *Africa's Southern Regions: the White Man's Farming*   182

VII *Africa: the Central Regions: Eastern Group; African Peasant and European Farming*   232

VIII *Africa: the Central Regions: Western Group; African Peasant Farming*   271

IX *Asia. India and Pakistan; Problems of Growing Population*   317

X *Asia. China, Japan, Indonesia and the Rice Exporting Countries*   344

XI *The Food Exporters: (1) The United States, Canada*   353

XII *The Food Exporters: (2) Australia, New Zealand*   399

XIII *Potential Suppliers: the South American Countries*   446

XIV *Trends in Food Production*   468

LIST OF FIGURES   502

INDEX   504

A*

ILLUSTRATIONS

The Shasta Dam, California: a great multi-purpose scheme   *Frontispiece*

Plate   Facing page

1. The wheat harvest, Cheddington, Bucks   64

2. Harvesting a crop of oats and peas for silage, Eashing, Surrey   64

3. A farm in Northern Ireland   64

4. Bog reclamation, Eire   64

5. Improvement of hill pasture: Cahn Hill, Cardiganshire   65

6. Reclaiming the heath, Elveden, Suffolk   65

7. Improvement of a lowland meadow by a hormone spray to kill weeds   65

8. Intensive strip grazing   65

9. The North East Polder reclaimed from the Zuyder Sea   128

10. Intensive horticulture in Westland, the Netherlands   128

11. Korinth Cooperative Butter Factory, Funen   128

12. Typical Danish Farms, Spanager, Near Køge, Zealand   128

13. Farm in South Sweden   129

14. Drying Hay on racks in North Sweden   129

15. The Svalov Plant Breeding Station: experimental plots of Autumn wheat   129

16. Neighbours helping with the harvest ("Talkoo work") Finland   129

17. Farm and forest work combined, Finland   192

18. Terracing in the Mediterranean region, Vineyard at Pinhão, Douro Valley, Portugal   192

19. Reclaimed Pontine Marshes, Torre Campanaria   192

20. Planned Settlement in Israel—Nahalal   192

21. Wild Veld, S. Africa: 10 to 15 inches rainfall   193

22. A good grass for binding soil and withstanding drought: *Pennisetum clandestinum* (Kikuyu grass)   193

23. Virgin bush, near Njoro, Kenya   193

24. The same cleared and seeded down   193

25. A Kikuyu settlement, Odongo Reserve, Kenya   320

26. A demonstration farm to teach better methods: Wakamba Reserve, Kenya   320

27. Breaking ground with a hand plough, Nigeria   320

28. Improving the native farming, Nigeria   320

29. The barrage at Sansanding. French Niger irrigation scheme   321

30. Irrigating guava trees, Banfora, Ivory Coast   321

31 Treading out rice by human labour, Travancore, S. India   321

32. Making cattle manure into blocks for fuel, Uttar Pradesh, India   321

Plate   Facing page

33. The Damodar Valley Project: restoring eroded lands in the head
    water regions near Hazaripur   352

34. Taking fish from temple tank, Hiran Minar, Nr. Lahore, Pakistan   352

35. Former productive wheatland ruined by salt brought up through
    faulty irrigation   352

36. Terraces for rice cultivation, Szechwan province, China   352

37. Strip cropping on the contours to prevent erosion, Winona Co.,
    Minn., U.S.A.   353

38. Rehabilitating eroded lands: corral on community pasture, Nr.
    Donavon, Sask.   353

39. A Combine threshing wheat out of the swath, Regina Plains, Sask.   353

40. William James Farrer's Paddock and field laboratory, Lambrigg,
    Nr. Canberra, where he bred wheats from 1889 onwards   353

41. Reclaiming the Ninety Mile Desert: Australia   416

42. After supplying the missing trace elements and seeding down the
    "desert" is converted into good dairy farms   416

43. Good dairy farms, Pukekohe, N. Island, New Zealand   416

44. Aeroplane being loaded with phosphatic fertilizer for application
    from the air, New Zealand   416

Chapter 1

THE PROBLEM:
FEEDING THE WORLD'S POPULATION

One of the first difficulties in the problem of feeding the world's population is that no one knows precisely how many people there are in the world, nor how fast they are increasing. A good deal is known about the populations of the United Kingdom, Europe, the United States, and the British Commonwealth, though even for these countries few censuses have been taken since 1939, so that the present populations can, in general, only be estimated. The U.S.S.R. also had a census in 1939, but has since acquired great territories from its Eastern European neighbours and from Finland, so that future censuses will not for any of these countries be comparable with the old. Elsewhere the position is even worse. China has never had censuses but only estimates, and the business of framing these used to be described as a kind of parlour game unencumbered by any rules. Great areas of Africa and South America also lack precise population data.

The League of Nations' Statistical Branch, and the more recent Food and Agriculture Organization—henceforward referred to simply as F.A.O.—have collected and examined the available evidence and arrived at figures which represent as well as is at present possible the order of magnitude of the populations of the different countries. They estimated the world population at 2,408 millions for 1950, made up as shown in Table I:

TABLE I. *Estimated world population in 1937 and 1950 and densities in 1950*

	Area in sq. miles (millions)	Population (millions) 1937	Population (millions) 1950	Percentage increases	Density per sq. mile 1950
Asia (excluding U.S.S.R.)	10·38	1,139	1,273	12	122
Europe (excluding U.S.S.R.)	1·90	371	394	6	207
U.S.S.R. (1)	8·59	189	203	7	24
Africa	11·78	169	198	18	17
America (9·37):					
North	7·30	140	166	19	23
Central	2·07	39	50	28	25
America:					
South	6·86	84	110	31	16
Oceania	3·30	11	13	20	4
World (2)	52·18	2,142	2,407	12	46

(*F.A.O. Stat. Year Book*, 1951.)

The white population of the world is about 750 to 800 millions.

(1) The U.S.S.R. census for January 17, 1939, gave the population as 170 millions and the area as 8,173,550 square miles. The war-time accessions taken from Europe raised the area in 1946 to 8·71 square miles, and the population to 193·2 millions.

(2) Ice-covered regions are excluded. Adding these in the total land surface comes to about 56 million square miles.

For present-day discussion the total is rounded off by F.A.O. to 2,400 millions.

As shown in Table I, about half the world population lives in Asia, about 16 per cent in Europe, and about 7 or 8 per cent each in the U.S.S.R., North America, and Africa. The densities per square mile vary considerably, ranging from 207 to 3.

The distribution of the world's population is, however, even more uneven than these figures suggest. Human settlement is possible only where sufficient fresh water is available, either from rain, wells, or an ever-flowing river, and so is usually restricted to river basins or to a belt stretching a few hundred miles inland from the coast, the distance depending on the position, height, and topography of the mountains.

Asia's population is in the main compacted into three regions: about a third are in India and Ceylon; more than a third are in China, largely in the Yang-tse and Yellow River valleys; and the rest in the islands and peninsulas: Japan, Indo-China, Java, Malaya; the interior of the continent is largely desert. North America's population is mainly in the east; towards the west are deserts that even American ingenuity has failed to tame, while to the north settlement thins out considerably above 45° N. latitude. Australian settlement closely follows the coast line, the depth of the belt depending on the distance to which the rain penetrates; beyond, lie semi-arid regions, very thinly populated, and farther inland still, the desert. Europe alone is free from deserts, partly because so much of its winds are moisture laden from the Atlantic, partly because its mountains happen to run east and west, and so do not intercept the rain as would have happened had they run north and south. Even in Europe there is much compacting of population in the north-west and in the British Isles, in Italy, and, before the war, in parts of Germany. C. B. Fawcett[1] points out that nearly two-thirds of the world's population are crowded on to one-eighth of the available land, living in four major regions put out in Table II:

TABLE II. *The four major human regions (C. B. Fawcett)*

	Area in million sq. miles	Population (millions)	Density per sq. mile	Acres per head
Europe and European U.S.S.R.	2·8	520	186	3·4
Eastern North America	1·9	130	52	12·3
Far East	1·7	500	292	2·2
India	1·0	400	400	1·6

The total land area per head, however, does not adequately represent the position so far as food production is concerned. Only part of the land in any country is used for food production, rarely more than half in countries outside of Europe, and often less: in India only about 45 per cent, in China and Japan much less; the remaining land is unsuitable for present methods (Fig. 1).

Accurate figures of food production areas in the different countries are not obtainable. Many countries publish statistics showing the areas sown, or alternatively, the areas of arable land including current fallows; the difficulty is about the grass which, even when recorded, is always an indeterminate quantity shading off without a break into waste land. The better quality grass

[1] *Advancement of Science*, 1947, Vol. 4, pp. 140–147. Map on p. 143.

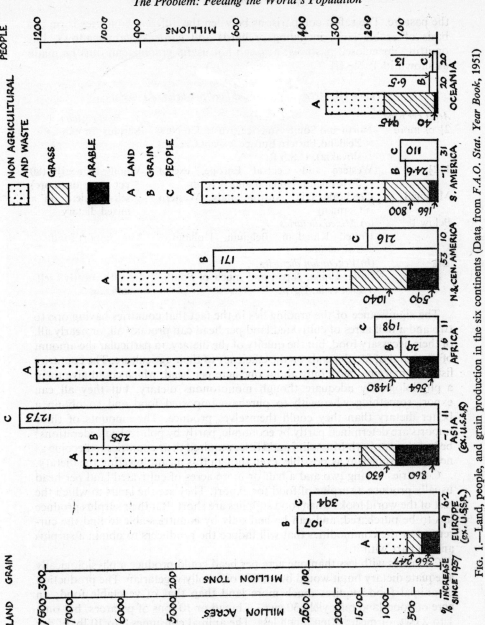

FIG. 1.—Land, people, and grain production in the six continents (Data from *F.A.O. Stat. Year Book*, 1951)

land makes a substantial contribution to the food supply and is usually included in the meadow land; commonly it receives some sort of treatment and can be regarded as tended. More difficulty arises about the grazing land. Much of this receives no attention and some is very poor. The British statistics distinguish between the better lands that rank as permanent grass, and the poor, untended "rough grazings"; but this distinction is not usually made, and it is always uncertain how much food-producing value should be assigned to the pasture. The safest comparisons between the different countries is on the basis of arable land, including orchards and gardens *plus* meadows, but omitting unenclosed pastures; a rough but useful grading can thus be made as shown in Table III.

TABLE III. *Areas of cultivated land per head of population*

Acres per head	Countries	Food position
2½ or more	North and South America, Australia, New Zealand, Eastern Europe (except Czechoslovakia), U.S.S.R.	Surplus for export
1–2½	Western and Central Europe, except Switzerland, Holland and Belgium	Wholly or nearly (80 per cent or more)
Marginal	Czechoslovakia, Austria, Italy, Western Germany	self-sufficient on a mixed dietary
Below 1	(*a*) *Mixed dietaries*	
	United Kingdom, Belgium, Holland, Switzerland	Must import food
	(*b*) *Vegetarian dietaries*	
	India, China, Japan and much of South-East Asia, Egypt	Usually nearly self-sufficing

The significance of the grading lies in the fact that countries having one to two and a half acres of cultivated land per head can produce all, or nearly all, of their necessary food, but the quality of the dietary, in particular the amount of meat and of fat, depends on the efficiency of their agriculture. The countries listed as marginal have only about one acre per head, which could give them a physiologically adequate though monotonous dietary, but they all can export something wherewith to purchase imported food and so obtain a better dietary than they could themselves produce. The amounts of these imports are determined partly by economic, partly by political considerations; before the war both Mussolini and Hitler required their countries to become as nearly self-sufficient as possible, even though this meant lowering the dietary.

Countries having two and a half or more acres of cultivated land per head usually produce a surplus of food for export. They are the lands to which the rest of the world looks when food supplies are short. But their surplus produce has to be purchased, and can be had only by countries able to find the currencies or the commodities that will induce the producers to obtain a surplus and to part with it.

Countries with less than one acre per head could produce a physiologically adequate dietary but it would be mainly or wholly vegetarian. The production of animal food requires much more land than that of vegetable food; an acre of good land may yield 30 cwt. of bread or 10 tons of potatoes, but only 1 to 2 cwt. of meat; often much less. The animal consumes 5 to 10 lb. of dry matter in its food for every pound of dry matter of human food that it produces. The countries in this group fall into two categories. Great Britain, Belgium, Holland, and Switzerland have developed international trade on a sufficient scale and character to induce surplus countries to supply them with the foods they need; they therefore maintain a mixed dietary of rather high quality, and the more they can intensify their production, the more secure this remains. India, China, and the other Asiatic countries, however, cannot do this; they therefore have largely eliminated meat from their dietaries and live almost entirely on vegetable foods. In this way India manages on about 0·8 acres per head, China on about 0·5, Japan on less. But for all countries in this group there is an element of precariousness in the food supplies. Countries in the first category depend for their food supplies on the smooth working of international trade; they would have suffered greatly in the war and the disturbed post-war period had it not been for Marshall Aid from America. Food supplies for countries in the second category depend on the smooth working of Nature's cycles; regular falls of rain as and when needed, freedom from more than average incidence of pests, diseases, or other disasters. Any breakdown may lead to serious shortages; famines have always been on the doorstep both in India and China.

Broadly speaking, about two-thirds of the world's population grow their own food, and probably about 80 per cent live in rural areas in which the food consumed has all been grown locally. The remaining 20 per cent—some 450 or 500 million people—are dependent to a greater or less extent on food transported from a distance.

In many countries the area of cultivated land is decreasing, it being taken for a variety of other purposes. The loss may be partly offset by bringing into cultivation land at present unused, but this is not usually as good as the land that is lost. The output from the cultivated land in advanced countries is, however, increasing, and this has hitherto more than made good the reduction due to shrinkage in area. Unfortunately, intensification of agriculture is more difficult in the less advanced countries.

THE RATE OF GROWTH OF THE WORLD'S POPULATION

Detailed studies of the world population and of the rates of natural increase in the various countries have been made by A. M. Carr-Saunders, by the office of Population Research, Princeton University, by F.A.O., and other investigators.[1] The Princeton figures indicate that in the period 1930, the world average increase was 12 per thousand per annum, the F.A.O. figures indicate that between 1937 and 1950 it had averaged about 10 per thousand. The data are too uncertain to allow the conclusion that the increase is slowing down. But the rate of increase has varied considerably in different countries, and at different periods. Latin America has the highest rate of increase: 16 per thousand as the excess of births over deaths about 1930 according to Kirk; later the birth-rate continued at about 40 per thousand, but the death-rate fell to 17 per thousand, so that the net increase became 23 per thousand, at which figure it stood as the average for the period 1937 to 1950. Asia's birth-rate is also 40 to 45 per thousand, but the death-rate is 25 to 32 per thousand, so that the increase in population is only moderate and the expectation of life only about 27 years. Europe, on the other hand (excluding the U.S.S.R.), had the lowest actual increase during this period—

[1] A. M. Carr-Saunders: *World Population*, 1936. Dudley Kirk: *Europe's Population in the Inter-war Years* (League of Nations, Princeton University Press), 1946, p. 255. *F.A.O. Stat. Year Book*, 1951.

which had, of course, included the war and mass movements of refugees; only 5 per thousand as compared with about 10 per thousand before the war.

The rates of increases in population in any particular country do not remain constant, but vary, and the changes follow the same course in all countries. In unimproved peasant conditions, birth-rates and death-rates are both high and the population remains fairly steady, fluctuating up and down according to food supplies, pestilences, wars, etc. As conditions of life improve, people live longer, the death-rate falls but the birth-rate remains high—the population therefore increases. With further rise in the standard of life, the death-rate continues to fall, necessarily at a decreasing rate, but the birth-rate falls also and so the increase in population slackens. In the fourth and final stage the birth-rate falls to the level of the death-rate or even below it, and consequently the population no longer increases but begins to decline.

Along with the change in rate of increase goes a change in the structure of the population. The period of high birth-rates is one with a preponderance of young people; in consequence, the communities often show great enterprise and ability to colonize as happened in Great Britain in the 19th century. With falling death-rates and falling birth-rates the older people become proportionately more numerous, with a larger proponderance of women, as they live longer than men. Moreover, the fall in the birth-rate is not uniform; it is almost invariably greater among the educated, higher income, and therefore presumably more intelligent groups than among the others.[1] All this causes great changes in the character and outlook of the community.

These changes are well illustrated by the course of events in Great Britain for which full statistics are on record.[2]

The Royal Commission on Population (1949) showed that the population of Great Britain rose from about 7 millions in 1700 to an estimated 49 millions (the census figure was 48·8 millions in 1951), the main reason being a fall in the death-rate. In the early part of the period both birth- and death-rates were high and the difference between them only small. Then in the second half of the 18th century the death-rates began to fall but the birth-rates did not, and so came the steep rise in population of the 19th century; for England and Wales it rose from 8·9 millions in 1801 to 32·5 millions in 1901;[3] in addition, great numbers of people migrated to North America, Australia, New Zealand, and South Africa,[4] so that these all became English-speaking

[1] For a discussion of the question whether deterioration in quality may result, see A. M. Carr-Saunders, *Biological Basis of Human Nature*, London, 1942; Cyril Burt, *Intelligence and Fertility*, London, 1946; and G. Thomson, *Trend of National Intelligence*. A good summary is given in *Population Policy in Great Britain, A Report by Political and Economic Planning* (P.E.P., 16 Queen Anne's Gate, S.W.1, 1948. The Royal Commission on Population did not deal with the question, but stated that it required further investigation.

[2] Registrar General's Ann. Reports, H.M.S.O.; Rept. of Royal Commission on Population, H.M.S.O., 1949. Much of the information is collected in a readable form in "Matters of Life and Death," Reg. Gen., H.M.S.O.

[3] There was a further but slower rise to 40·0 millions in 1931 and 43·74 millions in 1951.

[4] Kirk (loc. cit., p. 279) states that the number of emigrants from the British Isles usually varied between about 150,000 and 230,000 per annum, with no clearly marked trend for the years 1846 to 1930; the total number in this period was 14·3 millions, and the average per annum 175,000. Then in 1930 came a dramatic fall and from then onwards the average rate was only 32,000. The Report of the Royal Commission on Population, 1949 (Table VII,

countries. In the 1870's, however, the birth-rate began to fall, and continued to do so till finally it fell faster than the death-rate, and so we attained our present low rate of increase. The main cause, and in the view of the Commission, probably the only cause, of the fall in birth-rate was the spread of deliberate family limitation. Couples married in the mid-Victorian period produced on the average 5½ to 6 live-born children, those married in 1925–29 about 2·2—which is less than the 2·4 necessary to maintain the population; manual workers averaged 2·49 and non-manual workers 1·73. Later statistics up to 1947 suggest an increase of family size among the non-manual workers, but a continued decline among some sections of the manual workers; on the average the family size appears to have slightly enlarged. The Commission predicts with confidence that, apart from the effects of emigration and immigration:

(1) the total numbers of population will continue to grow in the near future, perhaps for another generation;
(2) the population of working age will remain at about its present level for at least the next 30 years, but thereafter will form a smaller proportion of the whole;
(3) the population of young adults (15–39) will show a fall of about 1·4 million in the next 15 years;
(4) the number of people over 65 will steadily increase over the next 30 years, the increase amounting to at least 2·3 millions and very probably much more. The proportion of old people to the total will increase considerably. Some uncertainty arises from the circumstance that mortality rates will continue to decline, but it is impossible to say by how much. All one can be sure about is that more people will continue to reach the age of 65, and to live longer after they have passed it, and that more of them will be women.[1]

There are already 5·5 million people over 65 in our population of 50·7 millions, and they are expected to number at least 8 millions in 25 years time. Already over 4 millions receive old age pensions from the State; for the years 1949 to 1952 the numbers were:

		Millions
At March 31st	1949	4·119
"	1950	4·162
"	1951	4·193
At December 31st	1952	4·204 (prov.)

(Rpts. of Min. National Insurance Cmd. 8882.)

---

p. 15), gives the net figures, allowing for migrants coming into the country; these are much lower, the net loss varying from 12,000 to 86,000 a year. But from 1930 onwards the stream was reversed; the net gain averaged 65,000 a year from 1931 to 1941. In 1951 the net gain reached the record total of 505,000. Many of the men and women who had gone out (often at public expense) proved unsuitable and had to come home again.

[1] In England and Wales the expectancies of life at birth has increased as follows:

	1871–1880	1891–1900	1938–1939	1945
Males	41·4	44·1	61·8	62·6
Females	44·6	47·8	65·8	68·6

(Registrar General's Reports). Males who attain the age of 60 have the "expectation" of another 14 years and females of 18 years. For further discussions see "Population Policy in Great Britain," a report by Political and Economic Planning, 1948, and A. M. Carr-Saunders, *World Population*, Oxford, 1936. The health statistics are discussed by Percy Stocks, *British Med. Jour.*, Jan. 7, 1950: "Fifty Years of Progress as Shown by Vital Statistics."

The numbers will certainly increase and their growing voting strength will enable them to secure larger pensions; the shrinking number of workers of the future will have a steadily growing number of ineffectives to support.

In Europe, as in the United Kingdom, the population rose greatly during the 19th century; Carr-Saunders[1] estimated that the total in Europe including European Russia was 187 millions in 1800; it had risen to 401 millions in 1900 and 542 millions in 1939, an annual rate of 0·9 per cent—also in spite of much emigration.

TABLE IV. *European countries. Population increase between* 1937 *and* 1950. *Millions*

North-West Europe

	1937	1950	Percentage Increase in 13 years
Belgium	8·35	8·64	3·5
Holland	8·60	10·11	17·5
Denmark	3·75	4·27	14·0
Norway	2·92	3·26	11·7
Sweden	6·28	7·02	11·7
France	41·20	41·93	1·8
United Kingdom	47·29	50·37	6·5

Southern Europe

	1937	1950	Percentage increase in 13 years
Portugal	7·42	8·49	14·4
Spain	25·04	28·29	13·0
Italy	42·37	46·27	9·2
Greece	7·11	7·96	12·0

Central Europe

	1937	1950	13 years
Switzerland	4·18	4·69	12·0
Austria	6·75	6·91	2·4
Germany (1)	57·57	69·00	20·0

Eastern Europe

	1937	1950	13 years
Poland	31·6 (2)	25·0	−20
Czechoslovakia	14·43	12·34	−14
Bulgaria	6·54(2)	7·23(2)	10·6
Rumania	15·51	16·10(2)	4·0
Yugoslavia	15·72(2)	16·25	3·0
U.S.S.R.	188·6(2)	203·0 (2)	7·4

(1) Rough estimate only, no data being available for the Soviet zone.
(2) Unofficial estimate.
(*F.A.O. Stat. Year Book*, 1951.)

By about 1930 most countries in Western Europe were settling down to low birth-rates, low death-rates, and a low natural increase as in Great Britain; in Kirk's tables only the Netherlands had a birth-rate as high as 22·7 per thousand and a natural increase of 13·3 per thousand; for all other countries the birth-rates varied between about 15 and 19 and the natural increase about 5 to 7 except for France (1·8) and Sweden (2·6). Eastern Europe, on the other hand, had much higher birth-rates—30 to 35 per thousand—and the natural increase ranged between 14 and 16 except for Czechoslovakia, where the birth-rate was only 22 and the natural increase 8 per thousand. Southern Europe came between the two with birth-rates about 26 to 30 and natural increases about 10 to 14 per thousand. The U.S.S.R. completely overtopped all other countries with a birth-rate of 45 and a natural increase of 23 per thousand.[2]

The war, however, has caused considerable change. Detailed vital statistics

[1] A. M. Carr-Saunders, *World Population*. Further information about population changes in Europe during and since World War II are given by Gregory Frumkin in *Population Changes in Europe Since 1939* (Allen and Unwin, 1952).

[2] Kirk, loc. cit., pp. 263 *et seq.*

are not available in all cases, but F.A.O. population figures show that all countries in Western Europe excepting only France and Belgium are gaining population at the rate of about 1 per cent per annum, Holland still leading with a gain of about 1·3 per cent; the Southern European countries also have increases of the same order except Italy which is lower. Germany apparently has a much higher rate of increase, but the figures are only approximate estimates (Table IV). France never had in the 19th century a steep rise of population like that of Great Britain, indeed the increase was among the slowest in Europe, and by 1850 was already slackening and threatening to become a decrease. John Stuart Mill, in his *Political Economy* published in 1848, thought this was an advantage to France, but he was writing at the time of the terrible Irish famine when the dangers of peasant over-population were being shown with appalling clearness. But later events have caused the French Government to stimulate an increase in births—between 1931 and 1940 there had been an actual excess of deaths over births—and a system of family allowances (*prestationes familiales*) has been set up which had at first some success; the birth-rate rose from 1946 to 1950: since then, however, it has again fallen. The position still gives ground for much anxiety (Table IV).

Eastern European countries, on the other hand, which before the war were increasing rapidly in population, are no longer doing so; Poland, Czechoslovakia have actually smaller populations, but how far this is due to war casualties and how far to losses of territory and people to the U.S.S.R. it is impossible to say. Bulgaria alone is maintaining an increase at the rate of about 0·8 per cent per annum. The natural increases, however, had fallen considerably between 1930 and 1939 (Table V).

TABLE V. *Rates of natural increase per thousand of populations of Eastern Europe*[1]

	1930–31	1939	*Decline*
Bulgaria	13·9	8·0	5·9
Greece	14·1	10·5	3·6
Poland	16·0	10·7(1938)	5·3
Rumania	14·1	9·7	4·4
Yugoslavia	15·2	10·9	4·3
Mean	14·7	10·0	4·7

Statistics for the U.S.S.R. are incomplete and not always very reliable. No census was taken till 1897 and no detailed statistics are available since 1926–27. R. R. Kuczynski,[2] using data derived from ecclesiastical registers, estimated the birth-rate for the period 1867 to 1895 at about 50, and the death-rate at about 36; the figures for the year 1936–37 are 39 and 24 respectively. By 1935 the birth-rate had apparently fallen to 30, as the result of the widespread practice of abortion. The Government then intervened, abolished abortion, and took other steps to raise the birth-rate; for 1937 the rate was given as 38·3 and the death-rate at 17·8.[3] Apparently the

1 Kirk, loc. cit., p. 60.
2 Brookings Inst., Washington.
3 Infant mortality rates under one year for 1940 are given as about 150, compared with 40 in England and Wales at the same period. All the above rates are per thousand.

U.S.S.R. is in for a period of considerable population with a higher proportion of young people than in Western Europe. A rapid fall is expected later by demographers.

Assuming that the present trends continue, the population pattern of Europe and the U.S.S.R. will change considerably in the next twenty years. The forecast as set out in the *Political Economic Planning* volume is given in Table VI.

TABLE VI. *Estimated populations of Europe and U.S.S.R. if present trends continue*

	Millions		
	1940	1955	1970
British Isles	50·2	50·2	46·8
Europe:			
Western and Central	163·6	166·0	159·0
Northern	20·1	20·5	19·5
North, West, and Central	234	237	225
Europe:			
Southern	77·5	84·1	86·5
Eastern[1]	87·7	98·5	105·0
South and East	165	183	192
All Europe, except U.S.S.R.	399	419	417
U.S.S.R. (pre-war area) adjusted for war losses	174	{ 216 { 192	251 } 222 }

(*P.E.P. Report*, loc. cit.)

The result of the shorter expectation of life and the higher birth-rate in Eastern Europe and the U.S.S.R. as compared with Western Europe, is to raise the proportion of younger people in the total population and in the labour force, thus giving the impression of a young people's country. The expected proportions of young men aged 15 to 34 in the total manpower aged 15 to 64 are:

	1940	1970 *expected*
	per cent.	*per cent.*
Europe:		
North, Western, and Central	48	39
Southern and Eastern	56	44
U.S.S.R.	61	51

But no one can foretell what may happen in the meantime.

Statistics for Asia are, with two or three exceptions, very incomplete. Both birth-rates and death-rates are high: for India and Japan they were, about 1940 and 1950:

---

[1] The figures for Eastern Europe were not adjusted for war losses, which in the case of Poland were considerable, 4·6 millions out of 35·4 millions, 13·6 per cent (Kirk, p. 69).

	Rates per thousand					
	Birth rate		Death rate		Natural increase	
	1940	1948	1940	1948	1940	1948
India	31·4	25·4	20·7	16·0	10·7	9·4
Japan	29·5	28·3 (1)	16·5	10·9 (1)	13·0	17·4 (1)

(1) 1950.

(*P.E.P. Report.*)

The U.N. Dept. Social Affairs Report for 1952 gives for Asia birth rates 40 to 45 and death rates 25 to 32 per thousand.

but the population increases vary greatly in the different countries.

In India, where the highly efficient medical and other services inaugurated by the British have saved many lives that would otherwise have been lost, the population increase has been considerable: it was no less than 15 per cent during the decade 1931–40 as against 10 per cent in the previous decade. In Malaya in the same decade it was about 30 per cent. In Java, under Dutch organization, the population increase was some 19 per cent between 1920 and 1930. Elsewhere in south-east Asia great increases are reported. On the other hand vast areas of China, Manchuria, and other countries, where no such services were available, have had little if any increase in population— F.A.O. estimates that the 22 provinces of China increased only from 452 millions to 463 millions between the period 1937 and 1950. The overall increase for all Asia cannot be accurately stated, but it is estimated to be of the order of 10 per cent for the last decade.

Data for Africa are incomplete. In the survey made by Lord Hailey's Commission the view was expressed that the population might not rise much in the near future. F.A.O. estimates that increase is going on at the rate of 1·4 per cent per annum. For parts of Africa much higher figures are given. A sample census taken in 35 districts of Southern Rhodesia in 1949 led the Director of Census and Statistics to conclude that the natural increase of the African population was 2·81 per cent per annum—at which rate it would double itself in 25 years—while the rate for Europeans was 1·97 per cent. African birth-rates are among the highest in the world, and in the regions under British control measures are taken to reduce infant mortality and general death-rates; a rise in the natural increase may therefore be expected.

For Latin America the birth-rate in 1952 still remained at about 40 while the death rate had fallen to 17 per thousand.[1]

The problems of food production differ in the different countries according to the soil, climatic, and other conditions, but they have been most fully studied in some of the advanced countries and we shall accordingly begin with them.

[1] U.N. Rpt., 1952, v. *supra.*

Chapter 2

THE UNITED KINGDOM

The feeding of the people of the United Kingdom is really a marvel of organization, but it is accomplished so smoothly that few people recognize its great complexity. No other advanced country except Holland and Belgium has so great a density of population or makes heavier demands on its people for sustained work, and no country is so dependent on outside sources for its food supplies. Only the highly efficient systems of distribution developed before the war could have ensured the even course of supplies that made most people in those days think of food as a kind of natural dispensation of no particular concern to themselves.

Up to the 1870's the United Kingdom had been largely self-supporting in food except in times of bad harvests. But the development of rail and steamer transport in and to North America and Australasia, led to the production, by inexpensive pioneer methods, of enormous quantities of grain and beef which were shipped to this country in exchange for much-needed manufactured goods. They were sold at prices far below those at which they could have been produced at home, and many of our farmers were driven out of business leaving their farms derelict. The bad harvest of 1879 followed by the economic disasters of the 1880's and 1890's are still remembered in the countryside and still tinge the countryman's outlook.

New systems of agriculture were worked out, generally on the ecological basis of producing those things best suited to the conditions, and new methods were developed; recovery slowly set in. But the position in regard to self-sufficiency had completely altered. The population had in the meantime greatly increased and had become accustomed to a much higher standard of living, particularly to more meat and dairy products, which require much land for their production. But the area of cultivable land was steadily shrinking and it was no longer possible to produce the whole of the food needed; considerable quantities had to be imported. Fortunately the exports of goods and services, and income accruing from overseas investments, sufficed to pay; and regular supplies of food were forthcoming that had an appearance of being secure for ever. So we arrived at our pre-war dietary, which for the great majority was both satisfying and pleasing (Table VII).

The total amounts of food supplied annually on an average during the pre-war years 1934–38 are given in Table X.

These gave a total supply of 52 million million calories, allowing an average of 3,000 per head per day, which is adequate for full health. About 30 per cent of these calories were produced at home and the rest imported.

The 1914–18 war had shaken this system of heavy importation of foods, but recovery was proceeding. Then came the second war; imports on the peace-time scale became impossible because of the submarines, and we were thrown much more on our own resources. The most strenuous efforts were made to increase our food production and valuable experience was gained as to how much food could be grown here when all economic limitations were set aside.

24

TABLE VII. *Food supplies, lb. per head per annum moving into civilian consumption in the United Kingdom*

	Pre-war	1943	1951	1952
Dairy products (excluding butter) total as milk solids	38·3	50·0	54·8	51·6
Meat (including canned meat, bacon, and ham) (edible weight)	110·0	86·4	76·5	84·6
Fish, poultry, and game (edible weight)	32·7	21·6	30·1	28·4
Eggs and egg products (fresh eggs equivalent)	28·3	25·6	27·6	26·3
Oils and fats (visible) (fat content)	46·9	39·1	49·5	45·1
Sugar and syrups (sugar content)	98·1	66·7	92·4	87·6
Potatoes	181·9	248·8	239·6	238·1
Pulses and nuts	9·5	6·0	10·3	9·5
Fruit (fresh equivalent)	124·0	68·5	111·1	105·4
Vegetables (including tomatoes) fresh equivalent	120·4	126·4	130·0	121·3
Grain products	210·1	248·9	221·1	219·8
Tea, coffee, and cocoa	11·9	9·6	11·0	11·0

Nutrients supplied by the above foods—grams per head per day (U.K.)

		Pre-war	1943	1951	1952
Proteins:					
animal	gm.	43·5	39·8	43·4	42·7
vegetable	gm.	36·8	45·5	42·5	41·0
Total	gm.	80·3	85·3	84·9	83·7
Fat (from all sources)	gm.	130·0	115·3	125·6	122·5
Carbohydrates	gm.	377·5	370·0	387·0	378·7
Calories (M. Food factors)		3,000	2,860	3,020	2,950
Calories (F.A.O. factors)		3,110	2,950	3,130	3,060

Corrected values in *M. Food Bull.*, 720, September 1953.

The figures for nutrients supplied do not quite agree with those given by *F.A.O.* because of differences in the conversion factors. The British Ministry of Food use the factors computed by the Accessory Food Factors Committee of the Medical Research Council adopted in the 1944 Report on Food Consumption Levels in the United States, Canada, and the United Kingdom and in later Reports (*M.R.C. War Memo*, No. 14). *F.A.O.* uses rather higher values: these are adopted for all other countries in this book.

After the war the present period of austerity set in, resulting partly from the impoverishment caused by the war and partly from the reorganization of the national life on a more egalitarian basis and therefore lower level of well-being. Economic limitations proved inescapable and have ruled out many of the previous imports; we now have either to produce or go without. A new factor has come into play: some of the countries that formerly supplied us with food are now consuming more of it themselves, so that unless they increase their outputs we shall have to forgo their contributions to our supplies. Thus a continuance of supplies from them can be secured only if we can offer sufficient inducement to them to make the necessary effort, which means the payment of higher prices.

During the pre-war period when imports were physically possible on a very large scale, and were in fact only partially restricted, British farmers naturally concentrated on systems of husbandry most easily carried out and therefore most closely adapted to their surroundings; the control was ecological.

The United Kingdom is unusual in its wide range of natural conditions. It lies at the northern limit of the wheat belt of Europe, but the effect of the warm Atlantic winds is to allow the growth of plants that otherwise would be found only in more southerly climates. The effect is naturally most pronounced in the south-west and decreases in passing to the north-east: Cornwall and Devon can grow palms, grapes, and early vegetables, while north-east Scotland is so cold that aphids cannot thrive, in consequence potatoes escape the destructive aphid-borne virus diseases afflicting them in most of England; north-east Scotland thus became a reliable source of disease-free seed.

The rainfall varies in somewhat the same way as the temperature. The hill country lies mostly in the north and west: here most of the rain is caught, and over a considerable part the annual rainfall ranges from 30 to 60 inches, mounting to some 130 inches at Seathwaite in Cumberland. East of a line drawn from Berwick-on-Tweed to the Isle of Wight, however, the rainfall is less, in many areas being only 20 to 24 inches.

The soils also vary greatly. The newest rocks are in the east, the oldest form the hills of the north and west; earth movements have caused a general downward tilt from the west, so that geological formations which are on the surface in the west lie buried deep below the surface in the east and south. All of the main geological formations occur in Great Britain, but owing to this tilt they out-drop as belts or other areas of only limited extent. Over much of the country the soils have been transported by ice from regions further north and are not derived from the rock immediately below them: not infrequently, however, they are formed from similar rock elsewhere.

The consequence of these variations in temperature, rainfall, and soil is that Great Britain has an unusually large number of agricultural regions, each with some distinctive characteristics that make it appropriate for some special agricultural system or products. Farmers have usually discovered these empirically. Agricultural science and engineering developments have shown how to modify the local conditions to make them better suited to particular crops, and how to modify the crops so that they may be better adapted to the local conditions; the bridge is thus built from both ends. But it still remains true that the farmer achieves his best results when he can work with Nature and not against her, the resources of science being employed to enhance conditions already partly favourable. This means in practice that much of our land in the wetter western regions is better used for grass than for grain crops, while grain is more appropriate for the drier eastern regions; also it accounts for the obstinate persistence of large areas of waste and marginal lands classed as rough grazings: if the changed conditions brought about on reclamation involve too much constraint of Nature they are liable to be impermanent, and reversion may be rapid unless constant and usually expensive measures are taken.

Of the 60 million acres of the United Kingdom little more than half is actually cultivated, but a further 30 per cent of rough grazing brings the total in agricultural use to 80 per cent. This is also the value for England and

Wales; in Scotland the figure is a little lower and in Northern Ireland higher. The proportions of cultivated land differ more widely: they are 65 per cent in England and Wales and in Northern Ireland, but only 22 per cent in Scotland. Three-quarters of the cultivated land of the United Kingdom is thus in England and Wales (Table VIII).

TABLE VIII. *Land utilization in the United Kingdom*

		England and Wales	Scotland	Northern Ireland	United Kingdom
Arable land	1939	8·93	2·94	1·04	12·91
War-time peak	1944	14·57	3·37	1·34	19·27
	1950	13·94	3·21	1·20	18·36
	1951	13·68	3·19	1·13	18·00
Permanent grass	1939	15·71	1·62	1·44	18·77
	1944	9·76	1·05	0·93	11·74
	1950	10·51	1·19	1·08	12·77
	1951	10·79	1·20	1·14	13·13
Total cultivated	1939	24·64	4·56	2·48	31·68
	1944	24·32	4·42	2·26	31·01
	1950	24·44	4·41	2·28	31·13
	1951	24·47	4·39	2·27	31·13
Rough grazing	1939	5·54	10·46	0·53	16·54
	1944	5·57	10·76	0·71	17·03
	1950	5·47	10·92	0·70	17·10
	1951	5·44	10·91	0·71	17·07
Total land area		37·34	19·46	3·35	60·15
Non-agricultural use	1939	7·16	4·44	0·34	11·93
	1951	7·43	4·16	0·35	11·91
Per cent agricultural use	1951	80	77	90	80

(*Min. Agric. Statistics*, 1945 and 1953.)

The area of non-agricultural use includes woodlands and forest, waste and moorland used for sport only and not attached to farms for grazing, land held by the Services, roads, built-up areas, gardens, and holdings less than 1 acre.

TABLE IX. *Arable crops England and Wales and United Kingdom. Million acres*

	England and Wales			United Kingdom			
		War-time arable peak			War-time peak		
	1939	1943	1950	1939	1943	1950	1951
Wheat	1·68	3·28	2·39	1·77	3·46	2·48	2·13
Other grain	2·37	4·36	4·35	3·54	6·10	5·81	5·65
Potatoes	0·454	0·957	0·867	0·704	1·39	1·24	1·05
Sugar beet	0·337	0·404	0·419	0·345	0·417	0·429	0·425
Fodder crops (1)	0·923	1·44	1·20	1·38	1·97	1·45	1·63
Fruit	0·302	0·284	0·311	0·321	0·316	0·346	0·345
Vegetables (2)	0·251	0·358	0·495	0·317	0·375	0·508	0·420
Total tillage area	6·86	11·54	10·38	8·79	15·05	12·82	12·20
Temporary grass	2·07	2·48	3·56	4·12	4·22	5·53	5·80
Total cropped area	8·93	14·02	13·94	12·91	19·27	18·36	18·00

Production, million tons

Wheat	1·55	3·25	2·51	1·64	3·45	2·60	2·32
Other grains	2·00	3·71	3·90	2·97	5·20	5·16	5·83
Potatoes	3·31	6·77	6·68	5·22	9·82	9·51	8·28
Sugar beet	3·47	3·66	5·12	3·53	3·76	5·22	4·53

(1) Includes swedes, turnips, mangolds, brassicas, vetches, green rye, peas, and beans.

(2) Excluding potatoes but including glasshouse and crops not primarily for sale. (*Min. Agric. Stat.*, 1945 and 1953.)

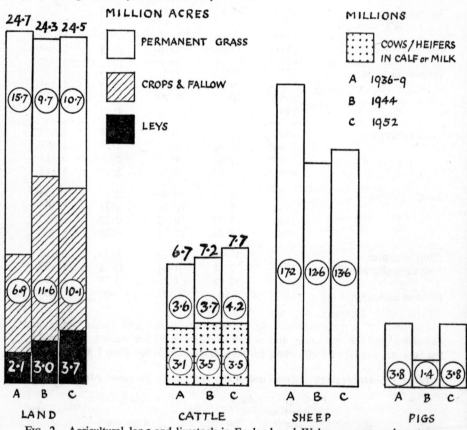

Fig. 2.—Agricultural land and livestock in England and Wales, pre-war and post-war. (Data from *Min. Agric. Statistics*, 1953)

During the pre-war years when agricultural production was determined almost entirely by economic factors, about 60 per cent of the cultivated land of the United Kingdom and rather more than that of England and Wales was in permanent grass; of the remainder, grain crops occupied about half, cultivated root and row crops about a quarter, and clovers and rotation grasses the remaining quarter (Table IX). Adjustment to changing economic conditions was made by varying the proportion of permanent grass land; as these conditions became more difficult, more and more arable land was laid down to grass. In the economically favourable conditions of the 1860's and 1870's the arable land of England and Wales had formed about 60 per cent of the total cultivated area; in the depression before the 1914 war it fell to 40 per cent; in the 1929–38 period it was 37 per cent, and livestock products then accounted for about 60 per cent of the total value of agricultural production. Out of 32 million acres of cultivated land in the United Kingdom less than 4 million were used for the production of direct human food; the rest was devoted to the animals. Their numbers are given in Table XIII; in relation to the area of cultivated land they were among the highest in the world. (Fig. 2.)

THE PRE-WAR DIETARY: HOME PRODUCTION AND IMPORTS

The pre-war dietary required about 1·8 acres of land per head for its production at average British yields of those days. The different constituents varied greatly in the area needed; all the wheat, potatoes, fruit, and vegetables

TABLE X. *Home production and net imports of chief foods, United Kingdom.*
Million tons

Pre-war, 1934–38	*Population 47·1 millions*		
	Home production	*Net imports*	*Total supply*
Wheat and flour	1·74 (¹)	5·47	7·21
Other grains	2·89	4·34	7·24
Meat, bacon and poultry	1·39	1·49	2·88
Including beef and veal	0·590	0·593	1·18
Lamb and mutton	0·193	0·350	0·543
Pork and bacon	0·383	0·448	0·831
Milk (whole)	8·32	—	8·32
Cheese	0·046	0·142	0·188
Eggs (fresh equivalent)	0·295 (²)	0·227	0·522
Sugar	0·455	1·731	2·186
Fats and oils	0·178	1·315	1·493
Including butter	0·048	0·481	0·529
Total calories million million per year	16·5	36·5	53·0
Per cent calories	31	69	100

(*Food Balance Sheets, F.A.O.*, 1949.)

could have been grown on about a quarter of an acre; the rest of the area was needed for the livestock products. The amount of cultivated land per head was only 0·6 acres. It was thus impossible for our farmers to produce anything like the whole of our dietary, and in fact they produced only about one-third of it. They did not, however, produce one-third of each of our foods, but concentrated attention on those affording the best return for their labour, especially foods not easily brought in from overseas like milk, potatoes, and bulky vegetables, or for which consumers were willing to pay a good price: nice fruit, new-laid eggs, and high-quality meat and cheese. We were thus

¹ *Min. Agri. Stat.*, 1947, Pt. 2 give 1·65 m. tons as pre-war production: ·73 m. for human food, ·66 m. tons for livestock, ·14 m. tons for seed and ·12 for other purposes. The total consumption by human beings was 6·00 m. tons: the home supply was thus 12 per cent of the total: for all purposes, however, it was 24 per cent of the total.
² Later estimates indicated that this figure is too low; 0·390 being better (Table XV).

fully or almost self-sufficing for milk, potatoes, and vegetables (except early vegetables), and nearly so for fish; we produced over two-thirds of our eggs and nearly half our meat, about a fifth of our sugar and fruit, but only one-ninth of our flour and even less of our "visible" fats, i.e. butter, margarine, and lard. Expressed in terms of nutrients we produced 63 per cent of the animal protein we consumed, but only 25 per cent of the vegetable protein, 45 per cent of the total protein and 31 per cent of the total calories.[1]

These quantities of foods, though produced on our own land, were not obtained entirely from our own resources. A considerable importation of potassic and phosphatic fertilizers had been necessary, but against this was an export of nitrogenous fertilizer. About a quarter of the starch- and protein-equivalents fed to our animals had had to be imported,[2] in spite of the fact that they received the produce of some 90 per cent of our land. Some of this import was primarily to supply the fermentation and oil industries, and agriculture took only the by-products, but a good deal of it was for direct agricultural use.

THE WAR PERIOD: CONTROL BY PHYSICAL LIMITATION

When war broke out it was necessary to curtail the heavy imports of human and animal food and to produce more at home. Selection of imports became necessary, and grain, which made heavy demands on shipping space, was the obvious choice for curtailment, though some of the more concentrated foods, dried eggs, dried milk, meat, cheese could still come in. Fortunately, during the inter-war period the science of human nutrition had greatly advanced and a well-founded food policy could be devised on which to base a programme of home production and import. An adequate supply of calories was a first essential and had to be provided at home whatever the cost. Milk, meat, and eggs would supply protein and fats; some of these could still be imported. Vegetables and fruits would supply vitamins and mineral substances: owing to their bulky nature they could no longer be imported, and in order to save transport and farmland, people were encouraged to grow them in their own gardens: a vigorous campaign was launched in which the Women's Organizations played a very important part and it achieved great success.

Our accustomed dietary had supplied on the average about 1·1 million calories per head per year. The calories and nutrients normally supplied per acre by the chief crops are given in Table XI. Potatoes and sugar beet supply six or seven million per acre, grain about three million, grass anything from two to eight million according to the management, but these have to be transmuted into human food by animals, and the conversion is from our point of view extremely wasteful, ranging from about 20 per cent for dairy cattle and pigs down to 7 per cent for beef cattle: the overall value for our grass-land is about 9 per cent. The values for protein conversion vary from 10 per cent for beef cattle to over 30 per cent for poultry. (Table XI.)

1 Economic Survey, 1949, Cmd. 7647, p. 13.
2 Norman Wright (*Empire Jl. Expt. Agric.*, 1940, Vol. 8, pp. 231–48) estimated the import at 22·7 per cent of the starch equivalent and 27·4 per cent of the protein equivalent.

TABLE XI. *Nutrients produced per acre by the chief crops reasonably well farmed*

	Dry matter	Cwt. per acre Starch Equiv.	Protein Equiv.	Millions per acre calories
Cereals, grain	18	14	1·7	2·92
Potatoes	43	32	1·5	6·67
Sugar beet:				
Sugar	35	35	—	7·35
Pulp and tops	46	26	3·1	
Mangolds	60	32	2·0	6·67
Kale	42	27	4·2	5·63
Beans	17	13	3·9	2·71
Grass	25–60	10–25	1·0–4·0	2·1–5·25
Grass intensively managed		up to 40		up to 8·3

Total crop production, U.K., 1945.

Starch equiv. m. tons		Calories for human consumption m.m.	
for human food	3·2	from crops	12·9
for animal food	19·3	from animal products	7·3
	———		———
	22·5		20·2

From the 19·3 m. tons S.E. the animals produced 1·8 m. tons S.E. of human food.

Total consumption: home production and import.

Starch equiv. m. tons		Calories m.m.
Human beings		55
Animals	22·8	95

(F. Yates and D. A. Boyd, *Agric. Progress*, 1949, Vol. 24, pp. 14–24, for the first three columns.)

1 lb. starch equivalent = 1,860 calories; 1 ton starch equivalent = 4·17 million calories. Min. Food values: 1,814 and 4·06 million respectively.

TABLE XII. *Relative efficiency of farm animals as converters of calories and protein equivalent into human food*

High percentage conversion				Low percentage conversion		
		Protein Percentage of protein (1)				Protein Percentage of protein
	Calories	equiv. fed			Calories	equiv. fed
Dairy cows	19·4	23	Beef cattle		6·8	10
Pigs	18·5	12	Sheep		7·6	13
Fowls	9·7	32				

(1) Protein equivalent = (N in digestible protein + one-half of non-protein N) × 6·25.

(F. Yates and D. A. Boyd, loc. cit.) See also I. Leitch and W. Godden, *Commonwealth Bur. Anim. Nutr. Tech. Comm.*, No. 14, 1941.

Dairy cows head the list for calorie conversion and come second for protein conversion. Beef cattle on the other hand are very wasteful converters. Pigs and poultry are much more efficient, but unfortunately their foods are so nearly like our own that during the war we were able to consume much of what they would otherwise have had: like the prodigal son we were fain to feed on the "husks that the swine did eat."

The agricultural policy was, therefore, to plough up much of the grassland and increase greatly the acreage of grain, potatoes, and to a less extent sugar beet; to improve the remaining grassland; to concentrate on dairy cattle but to sacrifice pigs and poultry, and to reduce beef production—much of this, however, had to continue since as many male as female calves are born. So the numbers of pigs fell catastrophically from 1940 onward, and there were great falls in numbers of sheep and poultry, but the total numbers of cattle remained as before and, indeed, after 1942 began to rise. (Table XIII, Fig. 7.)

TABLE XIII. *Livestock in England and Wales and United Kingdom before, during and after the war. Millions*

	England and Wales			United Kingdom		
	Pre-war average			Pre-war		
	1929–38	1943	1952	1939	1943	1952
Total dairy cattle (cows and heifers)	2·93	3·45	3·53	3·88	4·32	4·46
Other cattle	3·46	3·60	4·20	4·99	4·94	5·7
All cattle	6·39	7·05	7·73	8·87	9·26	10·2
Sheep	17·15	12·93	13·59	26·89	20·38	21·6
Pigs	3·18	1·38	3·84	4·39	1·83	4·93
Poultry	56·43	29·12	68·54	74·36	50·73	94·54

(*Min. Agric. Statistics.*)

In the First World War the additional grain had been secured at the cost of both meat and milk. In the second, while meat production fell, the milk supply was kept up and, indeed, slightly increased; this was the result of the advances in the science and practice of agriculture during the intervening years.

The over-riding need to safeguard the bread supply necessitated the fullest possible use of home-produced wheat for this purpose. Prior to the war, a large proportion had been fed to poultry and only 44 per cent was used as human food; the rate of flour extraction was only about 72 per cent so that considerable quantities of offal were available for cattle and pigs. This was drastically changed during the war: wheat could no longer be fed to poultry and the extraction rate was raised to 85 per cent, greatly reducing the available offals. By 1943–44 no less than 80 per cent of the home-grown wheat was used for human food, and in addition the flour was "diluted" with a certain amount of barley meal:[1]

Wheat. Million tons

	Production	Used as human food	Per cent used as human food
Pre-war	1·65	0·73	44
1943–44	3·45	2·78	80
1945–46	2·18	1·40	64

(*Min. Agric. Statistics.*)

[1] In 1942–43 and 1943–44 the quantities of barley used for "flour dilution" were 0·282 and 0·142 million tons respectively.

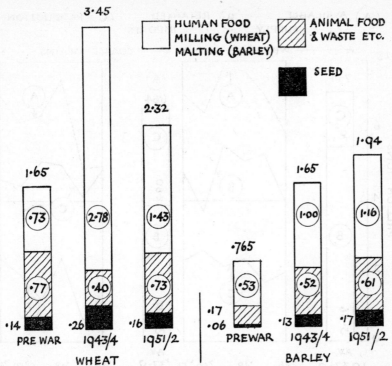

FIG. 3.—Utilization of home-grown wheat and barley, United Kingdom pre-war, war-time and post-war. Note that the quantity of home-grown barley used for malting is not far short of the quantity of home-grown wheat used for milling. (Data from C.E.C. Reports *Grain Crops*, 1953)

In consequence a great saving in imports of wheat and other edible grains became possible: instead of 5 million tons of pre-war days the import fell below 4 million tons in the years 1942 to 1946.[1] (Fig. 4.)

It was also necessary to ensure food supplies for the animals, and large amounts of barley and oats in addition to fodder crops were grown for them. The quantities of the imported feeding stuffs fell from the 5·1 million tons of pre-war days to an average of 0·2 million tons during the years 1942 to 1944.

This change over from grass to arable meant a considerable reorientation of British farming. Before the war only about 3 million acres out of 24½ million cultivated in England and Wales were devoted to crops for direct human consumption, the remaining 21½ being used for the production of animal food. In 1944, however, 5 million acres were used for direct human food and only 19·3 million acres for animal food.

The carrying out of this policy necessitated a colossal amount of work by farmers, agricultural experts, and officials. Much reorganization of systems of farming and agricultural technique was needed which would have been impossible but for the high level of ability and mental adaptability of the "A" farmers, about 60 per cent of the whole, who set the standards, and the relatively small number of "C" men (about 5 per cent) who were unable to

[1] C.E.C. Rpts., *Grain Crops*, 1953.

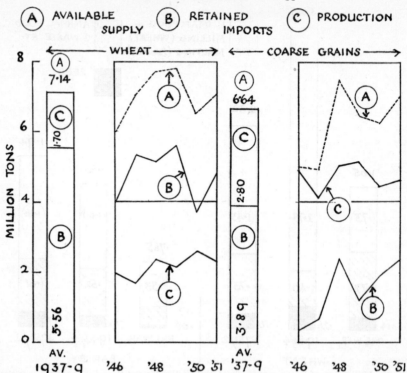

Fig. 4.—Production and import of wheat and coarse grains, United Kingdom, pre-war and post-war. (Data from Report of Commonwealth Economic Committee: hereafter called C.E.C.: *Grain Crops*, 1953.)

follow. The necessary change in equipment was very great, and many farmers lacked the ploughs and other implements needed for the new programme. The draft power was quite inadequate and large numbers of tractors were needed. Public provision was made on a lavish scale, but this widely extended use of machinery not only enabled cultivations to be done in time but increased the output per man, which by 1943 was some 10 or 15 per cent higher than it had been before the war.

Much scientific work was also needed and duly accomplished. Fertilizers and feeding stuffs were scarce and scientific rationing schemes were designed and operated. Protection of crops and animals against diseases and pests was organized on a better scale than ever before.

By 1943 the output of wheat and potatoes in the United Kingdom had practically doubled, other grains had increased by 70 per cent, and sugar beet by 33 per cent as compared with the ten years before the war.

The permanent grass land, which before the war occupied 18·8 million acres and formed 60 per cent of the cultivated land, was now reduced to about 40 per cent—11·7 million acres—and the arable land increased by 6·3 million acres, 5·6 million being in England and Wales: this was put mostly into tillage crops.

Several peaks were reached in 1943 and 1944 particularly in acreages of grain, potatoes, and fodder crops in England and Wales:

England and Wales. Million acres

	Pre-war 1929–38	1943	1944	1949
Wheat	1·56	3·28	3·06	1·90
Sugar beet	0·318	0·404	0·418	0·413
Mangolds	0·249	0·279	0·300	0·267
All tillage	7·11	11·54	11·59	10·23

Yields, however, did not keep pace with the increased acreage and some of the land was not really suitable for the crops, nor were all the farmers; there was also a shortage of fertilizers. Outputs of animal products also fell. (Table XV.)

While all these farming changes were going on the general public was playing its part. The national dietary was drastically altered to fit in better with the possibilities of home food production. Austerity set in. By 1941, perhaps the worst year, the consumption of meat, fish, poultry, and game had fallen from the pre-war 142·4 lb. per head per annum to 105·6 lb.; of sugar from 98 lb. to 67 lb.; of fruit and vegetables from 244 lb. to 169 lb.; of eggs and egg products from 28 lb. to 25 lb.; and of oils and fats from 47 lb. to 42 lb.—though a still lower level—36 lb.—was reached in 1947. On the other hand consumption of cereals had increased from 210 lb. to 257 lb. per head; that of potatoes also increased and continued to do so, rising to 286 lb. in 1947, while consumption of milk and its products rose slightly (from 38·3 to 40·7 lb. reckoned as milk solids).[1]

By 1944 the results of the double change, the lowering of the dietary to one requiring less land for its production, and the increased output from the farms, had increased our degree of self-sufficiency of the staple foods although there was a lowering of self-sufficiency for the more agreeable foods. (Table XIV.)

TABLE XIV. *Per cent of self-sufficiency—1944 compared with pre-war (1934–38)*

Increases	Pre-war	1944	Decreases	Pre-war	1944
Wheat flour	12	44	Condensed milk	70	53
Sugar	18	27	Dried milk	61	21
Fruit	26	61	Cheese	24	7
Other vegetables	92	99	Meat	45	35
Eggs	60[1]	63	Fats	7	2

(*How Britain was Fed in Wartime*, H.M.S.O., 1946.)

[1]Later estimates indicate that 70 per cent would be a better pre-war value. (Table X, p. 29.)

Throughout the whole war and post-war period the dietary had been physiologically adequate and the nutritional health of the nation remained good.

It must be admitted, however, that while the calories produced on British farms during the war and after are more numerous, they are of less agreeable and cheaper quality than before the war. The gross output expressed in money terms at constant prices shows only a slight improvement since pre-war days in spite of all the great efforts put into the work. But whereas the pre-war output had necessitated a large import of animal feeding stuffs the war-time

---

[1] The consumption of liquid milk increased as the result of the welfare services, but that of the milk products decreased.

output did not. The reduction by 85 per cent in the cost of imported feeding stuffs (calculated at uniform prices) accounted for the major part of the increase of net output.[1]

The Post-War period. Control by economic pressure

With the ending of the war, agricultural policy had to be changed. Ominous signs of overcropping were beginning to appear. The great increase in tillage area had not been balanced by a corresponding increase in production of farm-yard manure. Large amounts of straw were produced by the grain crops but no method practicable on a farm could be devised for converting it into anything as good as farm-yard manure; stacks accumulated on farms, and in some districts straw was even burnt to get rid of it: a most wasteful procedure.

The only good substitute for farm-yard manure is a crop of grass and clover, and it became necessary to sow down some of the tillage land; by 1951 nearly three million acres had been so treated.

In particular it proved impracticable to maintain the 1943 peak of 3·5 million acres of wheat. Some of the districts in which it had been grown were so unsuitable that the costs of production and the risks of failure were unjustifiably high, while in favourable districts the wheat crops had had to follow each other so quickly that fungus diseases accumulated in the soil, especially "Take all" (*Ophiobolus graminis*) and "Eye spot" (*Cercosporella herpochitroides*) and in 1948 became a cause of real anxiety.[2] Against these the surest remedy[3] is to stop growing wheat and barley for a time and take special steps to keep down weed grasses susceptible to attack, especially couch and water grass (*Agrostis*).

Weeds also became serious pests as a result of the too-frequent growth of cereal crops on the same land. The broad-leaved annuals that infest spring corn could be kept down by the new selective weed killers: some striking results were obtained. But the wild grasses infesting winter corn—*Agropyron* (couch), *Agrostis*, wild oats, slender foxtail—cannot as yet be thus kept down; they are destroyed only by good stubble-cleaning methods, but the difficulties increased when the proportion of cereals increased.

The potato acreage did not reach its limit in 1944; it rose to 1·548 million acres in 1948. But this also could not be maintained. On some of the land other crops could be grown more advantageously. In the specially suitable districts of Lincolnshire and the Fens crops of 12 to 15 tons per acre are common, and even 27 tons per acre have been obtained; the average for the whole country, however, is only 7–8 tons per acre, showing that much unsuitable land has been pressed into service. It is hardly possible to increase the frequency of potato cropping in the favoured districts. Nearly 30 per cent of the arable land in the Holland division of Lincolnshire, and over 25 per cent of that of the Isle of Ely had been put into potatoes. In many areas there

---

[1] *Agric. Stat. U.K.*, Pt. II, 1939 to 1945–46, p. 30. For a full account of this period see "How Britain was Fed in Wartime." The Scottish agricultural activities are described in "Agriculture in Scotland" (1939–48), Cmd. 7717, 1949.

[2] The season happened to be favourable to these diseases, a moist summer having followed a mild winter.

[3] A preventive measure against "Take all" devised by F. P. Chamberlain is described by S. D. Garrett and W. Buddin in *Agriculture*, 1948, Vol. 54, p. 425.

and elsewhere the potato eelworm is dangerously increasing; and there is no cure except to withhold potatoes for a period. The problem is under investigation but no practicable solution is in sight.

A further difficulty is the treatment of the gluts. The normal yield about suffices for the normal consumption, but in good seasons embarrassingly large quantities are obtained which the markets cannot absorb and which, therefore, are left on the farms.[1] They can be used as fodder when adequate numbers of livestock are kept, but many potato growers have only few animals. The establishment of factories similar to those in Germany and Holland for making potato flour, alcohol, and other products would be a solution, but factories require regular supplies and cannot be worked on gluts alone: in any case special varieties are grown for them.

The cultivation of sugar beet is still extending and it is free from the problem of gluts. In good districts yields are often 12 to 16 tons per acre, but the average is only 9½ tons per acre, suggesting that much is now grown in less suitable districts. The largest acreage is in Norfolk where its cultivation has been skilfully woven into the business of winter milk production. But here also too frequent cropping of the same land encourages the eelworm against which, as in the case of potatoes, there is no remedy, except to withhold the crop for a period.

As a result of these difficulties the area under wheat fell from its war-time peak of 3·46 million acres to 2·48 million acres in 1950 and to 2·13 million acres in 1951–52: the acreage of other grains fell from the peak of 6·1 million acres to 5·81 million in 1950 and to 5·65 million in 1951–52 and the area under potatoes also fell. The land thus liberated was put into grass; not all of it, however, into permanent grass as would have happened before the war: in spite of labour difficulties the total cropped area including rotation grasses fell but little and this was made possible by the increasing use of tractors, with their accompanying trains of well-designed and well-made implements.

Mechanization proceeded rapidly during the war and it has continued ever since; by January 1952 the number of agricultural and horticultural tractors in England and Wales was estimated at 325 thousand, an increase of 145 thousand since 1946 and of about a quarter of a million since 1939.[2] It was further estimated that about £60 million per annum was being spent by the farmers of England and Wales on re-equipment, much of it in machinery and implements.[3] As a result farm operations can now be done far more expeditiously than before, a matter of vital importance in cultivation: the land can be tilled and the seeds sown at the most propitious time, and harvests can be got in with the minimum of loss. Further, the amount of labour required is reduced. (Plates 1 and 2, p. 58.)

[1] In 1948 the production in the United Kingdom was 11·8 million tons against a usual 9 million tons, and the ensuing glut caused great embarrassment.

[2] Other increases were:

	Thousands			*Thousands*	
	1946	1952		1946	1952
Petrol and oil engines	155	222	Potato planters	5·7	17·0
Electric motors	48	107	Combine harvesters	3·2	16·5
Milking machines	40	81	Pick-up balers	1·7	11·4

("Agric. Econ. Res. Instit. Oxford," in *Westminster Bank Review*, Nov. 1952.)

[3] "National Income and Expenditure, 1946–51," H.M.S.O., Aug. 1952.

This continued increase in mechanization does not appear, however, to have increased the output per man per year beyond the peak of 1943–44; there is a tendency now to use it for reducing the hours of labour. F. C. Wragg estimates that for the Bristol province the increased performance per man equivalent between 1944 and 1952 was less than 2 per cent in spite of the greatly increased mechanization:

	1939	1944	1952
Performance per man equivalent	100	110	111

(*Jl. Farmers' Club*, 1953, Pt. 4. 201–216. See also H. T. Williams, *Agric. Econ. Soc.*, July 1953.)

By 1947 farmers, remembering the terrible slump of the 1930's, were becoming nervous of the future. But a dollar crisis supervened: imports had to be cut, they were reassured by the passing of the Agricultural Act which assured markets for their produce at prices related to the cost of production. Although the tillage acreage of 1943 was not maintained there was an impressive increase in food production in the United Kingdom over that of pre-war days. In 1950 the production of bread grains was a million tons above that of pre-war, of potatoes 4 million tons, and sugar beet 1¼ million tons; much more fruit also was being grown; 2¼ million tons more of oats, barley, and rye were grown, the grass was improved and, in consequence, 400 million gallons more milk was being produced, and 130 thousand tons more eggs; output of beef was back to pre-war levels (Table XV), with this highly significant difference: that the result had been achieved largely on our own resources; the import of feeding stuffs had been reduced from the pre-war 5 million tons to about 2 million tons, though it was a good deal higher than during the war. F. C. Wragg gives the following quantities of starch equivalent supplied to the livestock in the United Kingdom:

	Pre-war = 100		
	1943–44	1950–51	1951–52
Home produced	119	123	124
Imported	17	42	41
Total	92	101	101

(*Jl. Farmers' Club*, 1953, Pt. 4, pp. 201–216.)

TABLE XV. *United Kingdom production of animal products. Thousand tons*

	Thousand tons				
	Pre-war	1943	1949	1950	1952
Carcass meat	1,209	787	900	1,073	1,284
Including beef and veal	605	478	528	636	607
Mutton and lamb	211	159	140	147	166
Pig meat	393	150	232	290	511
Milk, thousand million gals. (1)	1·78	1·71	2·17	2·17	
Eggs, thousand million (2)	6·67		8·05	8·45	
Thousand tons	389	266	423	516	

Annual Abs. of Stat., 1938–50, except for milk and eggs (*M. Ag. Stat.*), and 1952 (C.E.C. Report: *Meat* and *M. Ag. Stat.*)

(1) June to May of following year.

(2) Estimates of egg numbers are liable to a considerable error but the trends are probably correct.

The numbers of beef cattle and pigs rose till 1950 and those of pigs continued to increase; by 1952 the pre-war output of meat had already been somewhat exceeded. Some 3½ million sheep had perished in the terrible winter of 1946–47 and the numbers already lowered by the war fell to 16·7 millions: later they recovered up to about 22 millions but they seem unlikely to return to the pre-war 27 millions: partly because of the difficulty of getting shepherds, partly because of the worrying by dogs: a risk that becomes greater as new building estates are opened up in country districts in consequence of which a ring of sheepless country tends to surround them.[1]

By 1950 milk production was fully sufficient for liquid consumption even with the heavy subsidy[2] and any further quantities go for manufacture of processed milk, butter, cheese, etc. The resulting produce is much dearer than imported Danish, as British farmers are paid higher prices—74 per cent higher in 1951–52.[3]

These increased outputs of livestock products resulting from the additional grassland have furnished calories to the dietary, numerically less than when arable crops had been grown but intrinsically more valuable. There has been a net increase, but by 1950 it had only just caught up with the growth of population so that in spite of all the efforts of farmers and their advisers the contribution of British agriculture to the total calorie supply of the nation was still only 40 per cent as in 1943. The comparison is unfair, however, because the calories of 1950 were altogether more agreeable than those of 1943. The magnitude of the effort is better shown by the fact that by 1951 the farmers of England and Wales were producing the equivalent of food for 17 to 18 million people, and as they and their workers numbered little more than one million this amounts to about fifteen persons fed per agricultural operator. Counting in Scotland the number fed becomes about nineteen or twenty millions, and that is about the number for which Great Britain can provide food on present methods.

The continued increase in livestock products has more than offset the fall in value of the field crops. The value of the agricultural production has been estimated as follows:

| | 1948 = 100 | | |
	1950	1951	1952 (1)
Gross output	111	117	118
Farm crops	107	100	98
Livestock products	124	128	132
Net output	108	113	115

(Years beginning June 1st)

(1) Unofficial estimate.
(*Economist*, March 28, 1953.)

[1] In 1952 straying dogs killed 5,844 sheep (Minister's reply to Question in the House, March 19, 1953. This is only a small part of the damage and takes no account of stillbirths, loss of condition, and other injuries. Other losses reported to the House were the killing of 20,273 poultry and 17 cattle; and injury to 4,729 sheep, 3,021 poultry, and 50 cattle. In another year about 7,000 sheep were said to be killed. *The Times*, February 28, 1953: Private Members Dogs (Protection of Livestock) Bill.

[2] In 1953 the State was paying £46·5 million for school and other "welfare" milk in addition to the trading loss of nearly £40 million on the Ministry of Food's milk transactions (*The Times*, March 17, 1953).

[3] Survey, Econ. Comm. for Europe (1953).

Notable as they are, these achievements do not represent all that British farmers are expected to do. The continuing adverse balance of overseas payments necessitated further efforts to break the stagnation in area of tillage crops, and in 1952 the Ministry of Agriculture asked for: (*a*) another million acres of grassland to be ploughed up and put into coarse grains for which a subsidy of £5 per acre would be paid; (*b*) a 5 per cent increase in yields of tillage crops; and (*c*) a 15 per cent increase in grassland productivity; the whole effort to result in four years' time in an increase of 60 per cent over the pre-war production of food, and in particular an additional output of 250 thousand tons of meat, mostly pig meat.[1]

The Post-War Dietary

Immediately after the war, food imports were resumed first with a continuance of the lend-lease arrangement whereby the United States had helped us considerably during the war, then with the generous Marshall Aid and a substantial loan which was quickly expended; Canada also helped with a loan and aid came from New Zealand, Australia, and South Africa. The result was that we were able to import larger quantities of food for the improvement of our dietary than would otherwise have been possible. More important, however, was the fact that recovery continued, and by 1950 the position of the national dietary in comparison with pre-war was as follows:

> Better: Liquid milk, flour, potatoes, vegetables.
> Equal: Fats (except butter), eggs.
> Worse: Meat, poultry and game, butter, sugar, fruit.

The most significant change, however, was in the sources from which our imports came.

Before the war the United Kingdom imported food and feeding stuffs from a large number of countries and was the chief buyer in the world market, taking some 40 per cent of the total trade: very little, however, from the United States. During the war the Continental supplies were cut off, and large quantities came from the United States, much of it on Lend-Lease arrangements; there were also greatly increased supplies from Canada, Australia and New Zealand. Since the war supplies from the United States have practically ceased, but Canada, Australia, and New Zealand have sent us more than ever. In 1948 our chief suppliers of food, and the percentage of imports they sent us were as follows:

Wheat and flour. Canada (78 per cent), Australia (20 per cent).

Meat (including bacon). New Zealand (34 per cent), Argentine (31 per cent), Australia (16 per cent), Canada (11 per cent).

Butter, cheese, and processed milk. New Zealand (51 per cent), Australia (20 per cent), Denmark (14 per cent).

Eggs (including processed eggs). Canada (32 per cent), Denmark (18 per cent), Australia (16 per cent), China (12 per cent).

Sugar. Cuba and San Domingo (53 per cent), British West Indies (18 per cent), Australia (10 per cent).

Oils and fats. British West Africa (50 per cent), Argentine (14 per cent).

[1] White Paper Cmd. 8556, November 1952.

Fruit. Citrus: Palestine (44 per cent), Spain (20 per cent), South Africa (16 per cent), Sicily and Italy (10 per cent). Canned: Australia (85 per cent), South Africa (13 per cent). (K. G. Fenelon, *Britain's Food Supplies*, 1952, p. 178.)

As the population of the United Kingdom continues to increase, and its area of good cultivable land to diminish, it is of supreme importance to know whether these countries can continue to send similar large amounts of food. It is equally important to know whether countries which before the war used to send large quantities of food but no longer do so, could again supply us: the chief of these, and their contribution to the total import before the war were:

Wheat and flour. Argentine (15 per cent).
Meat (bacon). Denmark (13 per cent).
Dairy produce. Denmark (17 per cent), Netherlands (15 per cent).
Eggs. Netherlands (11 per cent).
Sugar. Mauritius (11 per cent).
Oils and fats. India (14 per cent).
Fruit. Citrus: Brazil (11 per cent).
      Canned: Straits Settlements (11 per cent).
(K. G. Fenelon, loc. cit.)

It may at once be said that Denmark and the Netherlands are on this list simply through British Import restrictions, and India because her growing population precludes any export of food.

For all countries the problems of food exports change in character as their populations grow and as they develop industries. It still remains true, however, that our present import restrictions exclude supplies from countries that could produce them but in view of these restrictions are not doing so. If the restrictions were lifted supplies would be increased.

By 1950 the following degrees of self-sufficiency had been attained for the United Kingdom:—

Home production, per cent of total requirements, United Kingdom

	Pre-war	1950		Pre-war	1950
Wheat flour	11	29	Carcass meat	51	52
Coarse grains	38	70	Bacon and ham	34	45
Sugar (refined)	16	22	Eggs (shell)	71	82

(K. E. Hunt, *Changes in British Agric.*, Oxford Inst. Agric. Econ., 1952.)

POSSIBILITIES OF FURTHER FOOD PRODUCTION IN THE UNITED KINGDOM

The tremendous efforts made during and after the war had resulted, by 1943, in an increase in the home contribution towards the total calorie requirement from the pre-war 31 per cent to 41 per cent, with some lowering of quality; and by 1950 in an improvement in quality (not yet, however, a return to pre-war standards) and maintenance of the 40 per cent contribution, in spite of a rise in population from the pre-war 47 million to about 50 million in 1950 and a shrinkage of the area under crops and grass by nearly 900 thousand acres between 1936 and 1949. But the effort required had been

B*   41

colossal. Consumption of nitrogen and potassic fertilizer had trebled, the number of tractors had gone up six times, considerable direct subsidies were paid for particular operations, in spite of which the cost of producing the resulting food was so great that a further and much larger subsidy was given to lower the price to the consumer. (Table XVI.)

TABLE XVI. *Effort expended in increasing home production of food.*
United Kingdom

	Pre-war	1943	1950
Percentage of calories produced	31	41	41
Equivalent to feeding, million people	14½	19½	20
Number of full-time workers, thousand United Kingdom	685	724	717
Number of full-time workers, thousand England and Wales	525	543	575 (1)
Fertilizer used, thousand tons:			
N	60	171	213
P_2O_5	170	303	461
K_2O	75	73	234
Tractors, thousand	60		325
Direct subsidies, £ million			24·37 (2)
Expenditure on United Kingdom Agric. Depts. £ million	8·9	—	63·7 (3)

(1) The numbers fell later: they were down to 554 thousand in 1951.
(2) The figure for subsidies includes only direct payments to farmers for carrying out costly operations: hill farming, drainage, marginal production, etc.: it does not include the food subsidies made to meet the difference between the prices paid to farmers and the prices charged to consumers. In 1950–51 the food subsidies amounted to £410 million, of which £246 million were in respect of home-produced food and £164 million in respect of imported food (Chancellor of Exchequer answering Mr. Hurd, May 1950). At December 1953, agricultural production subsidies were £40 million (*The Economist*, December 5, 1953).
(3) Financial Secretary to Treasury in House of Commons April 30, 1953.

This was the effort required to raise the home contribution from 30 to 40 per cent of the total food supply. A higher contribution could be obtained but almost certainly the cost per unit would be proportionately greater through the operation of the law of Diminishing Returns. Whether the 40 per cent could be raised to 100 per cent is of purely academic interest as the data are insufficient to work out the relation between the quanta of effort and the quanta of result. Some of our best farmers are probably near the stage where further output on present methods would involve financial loss,[1] but many ordinary farms are still far from the position and could advantageously produce more, though additional output would necessitate a considerable infusion of new capital.

Fortunately the stage at which the Law of Diminishing Returns begins to operate is not fixed but can be raised. Repeatedly it has happened in the history of farming that some change in the system or the introduction of some new method or appliance has increased the output from the same

[1] This question is discussed by C. H. Blagburn, "Some Economic Aspects of Increasing Farm Output," Univ. of Reading, Dept. Agric. Econ., 1951.

expenditure of effort. Accounts of achievements of this kind form a staple part of farmers' conferences and of the best of the farmers' journals.

The difficulties of increasing output from our land are, however, considerable.

Leaving out all holdings of less than five acres, some 75 per cent of the farmers of England and Wales, and also of the United Kingdom, have less than a hundred acres of land; more than half of these have less than fifty acres. Most of the farms are worked by the farmer and his family; only about 20 per cent of them in England and Wales employ more than two regular workers and only about 10 per cent employ more than four.[1] Many of the farmers have only limited capital, and milk which is paid for monthly, is their chief stand-by; but their herds are small and often not very economic. Although they can give individual attention to each cow it does not appear from the records of the Milk Marketing Board that their yields are higher than those obtained on the larger farms. Broadly speaking the output per man tends to be greater on the large farms than on the small ones, while output per acre tends to be greater on the small than on the large ones. Some of the small farms of the Land Settlement Association have had very high outputs per acre but there are many cases where this is not so.

Owing to the great variety of conditions in the United Kingdom it is impossible to lay down any general rule as to the optimum size of the farm.[2] The hill farms of the west and north tend to be small, many of the arable farms of the east and south are large but interspersed with small ones. The large farmers though fewer than the small ones have the largest share of the land. Both they and the small farms tend to decrease in number; on the other hand the group of farms ranging from 100 to 300 acres shows remarkable stability and has suffered but little change for many years. (Table XVII.)

TABLE XVII. *Numbers of agricultural holdings, and areas of cultivated land per head, 1895 to 1951*

England and Wales

	Number of holdings, thousands			Area of crops and grass Total	Population millions	Area per head of population, acres
	Between 1–100 *acres*	100–300 *acres*	*Above 300 acres*			
1895	388	68·3	21·0	27·8	30·7	0·90
1939	284	66·4	11·9	24·6		
1951	300	64·7	12·7	24·5	43·7	0·56
Change between 1895 and 1951	− 88	−3·6	−8·3	−3·3	+13	
Per cent fall	22·7	5·2	39·5			

(1) In 1951, 0·56.

Valiant efforts have been made by County Councils and bodies like the old Land Settlement Association to establish more small holdings because of

[1] F. C. Wragg, *Jl. Farmers' Club*, 1953, Pt. 4, pp. 201–16.
[2] Much detailed information about the finances of farms of various sizes is given in "Farm Incomes in England and Wales, 1944–45—1947–48," Min. Agric., H.M.S.O., 1951. Strange as it may appear there are even now scattered holdings in some parts of England. At Yetminster, Dorset, 27 farms out of the 35 in the district were in 1952 in 93 separate pieces, one of them was in 19 pieces (Yetminster Farm Boundary Rept., Min. Agric., 1952).

their social importance in the countryside, but the fall in number still continues. What is unexpected is the fall in number of large farms. In an age when consolidation and amalgamation have so profoundly changed commerce and industry in Great Britain farming has remained essentially a small family affair. This is not peculiar to Great Britain; as we shall see it is a universal condition, and will be discussed later, but its effect is that agriculture requires different treatment from other enterprises. The number of large farms may increase as mechanization extends, but not infrequently in the past farms joined up by one man have been separated again by his successors.[1]

The great variation in size and circumstances of the farms results in marked differences in the quantum of effort needed to obtain a given result. Detailed studies on this subject have been made for many years by the Economics Department of the School of Agriculture at Cambridge, at Wye by J. Wyllie, and by others elsewhere. C. V. Dawe of Bristol University reporting on eighty farms in the south-western counties showed that the average number of hours required to produce 100 gallons of milk was 20 per annum but the range was from 10 to 40: the two extreme farms both had the same yield per cow—600 gallons. Reports by C. H. Blagburn, at Reading University College, give similar instances. The fundamental difficulty in comparing different systems of farming is to find some common denominator to which the products can be reduced. Calories serve for cereals, potatoes, and sugar beets, but not for vegetables, fruit, milk, or meat, and prices have no meaning in these days of subsidies and controls.

A State Advisory Service has been set up with a view to raising the general efficiency of the farming, especially at the lower levels, well below the operation of the Law of Diminishing Returns.

NORTHERN IRELAND[2]

Northern Ireland is important as the nearest source of food for Great Britain, and it is of interest as demonstrating a distinctive and satisfactory solution of the problem of the small peasant farmer. Like the rest of Ireland it has no minerals and no important forest reserves; agriculture is its only natural resource. The growth of population early necessitated the breaking up of the large estates that formerly existed and their conversion into small farms; these were as in other peasant countries becoming smaller and the redundant population was driven to emigrate. It was the usual problem of the peasant farm embittered by religious and political strife.

The solution adopted was to establish Congested Districts Boards with power to forbid fragmentation of farms below certain limits, and with funds to purchase land for new small farms or for enlarging those that had already become too small for economic working. At the same time industries were developed to absorb the redundant farm population; some of these take

[1] Instances are given by C. S. Orwin, *A History of British Farming* (Nelson, 1949, pp. 112 *et seq.*): an excellent short guide to the subject. The difficulty goes back to very early times: "Woe unto them that lay field to field," said Isaiah.

[2] A comprehensive survey of Northern Ireland is given in *Belfast in its Regional Setting*, Belfast, 1952, published for the British Association.

farm products as raw materials and work them up into higher priced commodities, others are quite independent of agriculture and depend on imported raw materials. The best known is the ship-building industry, a triumph of business organization, as practically everything needed has to be brought in from outside: even London had been unable to build ships in these conditions, yet Belfast continues to do so with great advantage to all concerned. In its trail are a number of light industries, electrical and others. Flourishing linen and tourist industries have also been developed. Northern Ireland has thus established a balanced and stable economy that affords a good standard of life to its growing population.

Northern Ireland includes a highland belt 1,000 to 2,000 feet elevation on its eastern and northern coast, and another of similar height in the west; in between is the River Bann system of valleys and lowlands with the great Lough Neagh; there is also an extensive low-lying area east of the Belfast–Newcastle line. The climate is moist and cool, free from extremes of heat in summer or cold in winter; fuchsias grow untended and flower abundantly throughout the country. Mean maximum temperatures in July are about 65° F., and minimum about 50° to 58° F.; the January mean maxima range from about 34° F. to 48° F.; both spring and summer come late. Up to 700 feet altitude the season of active growth is from June to September: at 1,500 feet it is a month shorter. The rainfall varies from about 32 inches a year in the low-lying eastern district to about 40 inches in the west, and rising to 50 or 60 inches in the mountains.

The number of wet days is high, evaporation and hours of sunshine are both low.

The total area of Northern Ireland is 3·345 million acres, utilized as follows:

	1939	1951	*Percentage change*
Cultivated:			
Arable	1·036 ⎱	1·128 ⎱	+10
Permanent grass	1·441 ⎰	1·143 ⎰	−21
Rough grazing	0·533	0·710	+33
Total in farm use	3·011	2·982	−1
Other use and waste	0·343	0·372	
Total	3·354	3·354	

The population in 1951 was 1·37 millions, 40 per cent of whom live in the open countryside.

The area of cultivated land per head of population is 1·7 acres.

There were in 1951, 83,854 holdings of more than 1 acre in extent aggregating 2·27 million acres; 60 per cent were 30 acres or less in size, 20 per cent were between 30 and 50 acres, 15 per cent between 50 and 100 acres, leaving only 5 per cent above 100 acres. Most of the land is in farms ranging from 25 to 60 acres, but generally 30 acres or less; these form the basis of Ulster's agriculture; there are about 60,000 of them. The farms are nearly all owned by the farmers or will be when their annual payments under the Land Purchase Acts are completed, and most of the work is done by the farmers, their wives, and families, there being relatively few hired agricultural workers; only about 14 thousand full time and 10·5 thousand part time or seasonal.

The climatic conditions are very suitable to grass, roots, potatoes, and oats; these combine to make livestock farming the chief agricultural enterprise.

TABLE XVIII. *Areas, yields, and production of chief crops in Northern Ireland pre-war (1939), peak war production (1943), and 1951*

	Area thousand acres			Production thousand tons			Yields per acre Average
	1939	1943	1951	1939	1943	1951	1939–45
Oats	291·4	469·7	316·4	270	394	295	18·0 cwt.
Wheat	2·9	13·8	1·3	3·0	12·1	1·4	19·1 cwt.
Barley	3·5	14·4	2·9	3·1	12·9	3·3	18·0 cwt.
Mixed corn	0·4	15·4	4·5	0·4	13·6	4·4	18·3 cwt.
Rye, beans and peas	0·6	2·6	1·0				
Potatoes	115·1	197·5	144·1	864	1,285	1,197	6·7 tons
Turnips	23·4	23·6	11·6	385	336	178	15·5 tons
Other root and green crops	4·2	10·5	10·2				
Flax	21·2	93·4	20·9	4·5(1)	17·5(1)	4(1)	28·2 stones
Fruit	8·1	10·1	10·1				
All tillage crops	470·8	850·7	522·9				
Rotation grass	565·2	490·6	605·6				
(Including hay)	(212·1)	(238·4)	(257·4)	315	400	419	31·1 cwt.
Total arable	1,036	1,341	1,128				
Permanent grass	1,442	910·4	1,143				
(Including hay)	(223·3)	(180·5)	(180·5)	419	387	327	39·7 (hay)
Total cultivated	2,478	2,252	2,272				
(Including grass)	(2,007)	(1,401)	(1,749)				
Rough grazing	533·6	699·6	710·0				
Total farm use, million acres	3·01	2·95	2·98				

There is but little fallow land: the conditions are too wet.

(1) Scutched fibre.
(*Agric. Stat. N. Ireland.*)

The areas of crops and their yields are given in Table XVIII. The area of cultivated land has shrunk since pre-war days as elsewhere in the British Isles, and an increase in the area of rough grazing is recorded at the expense of the permanent grass, but this may represent a change in classification rather than in condition. Grass is by far the most extensive of all crops accounting for 80 per cent of the cultivated land before the war, 62 per cent in 1943, and 77 per cent in 1951. During the war much was ploughed up and the tillage crops increased from 471 thousand to 851 thousand acres, but this large area of tillage crops has not been maintained, and it had by 1951 fallen to 523 thousand acres, only 10 per cent above the pre-war value; in 1952 there was a further fall of 10·6 thousand acres in spite of the subsidy of £5 per acre for ploughing up old grass land. The cropping returned mainly to the pre-war pattern, excepting that the area of potatoes was still in 1950 about 30 per cent greater than pre-war (representing, however, a great fall from the peak war-acreage), the area of rotation grass at 606 thousand acres was only 7 per cent above that of 1939.

The summers being moist and cool, and evaporation low, the grass rarely suffers from drought; it remains green for most of the year. Considerable care is now taken about the leys; selected strains from Stormont and Aberystwyth are widely used and much high-class seed is brought in from Britain. The mixtures include rye grass (imported as well as local seed), cocksfoot, rough-stalked meadow grass, Montgomery and other clovers, red and white. The leys are hayed for the first year or so, afterwards they are used for grazing. The permanent grass is mostly used for grazing; meadows for hay form only about one-sixth of the whole, but they have the unusual feature that they give higher yields per acre than the leys: 40 cwt. against 32 cwt.

The grazing season extends roughly from mid-March or April to the end of October; then come about seven months when dairy cattle have to be housed though store cattle can be left out provided they have some shelter. Much hay is needed for the winter feeding; silage, however, is becoming increasingly popular; it is made with molasses in pits, covered if possible. Dried grass is also used but the cost of fuel is considerable.

The climatic conditions do not in general favour seed production, but rye grass seed is somewhat exceptional in requiring moist conditions for proper filling out; considerable quantities of high quality are grown for home use, for shipment to Great Britain, and export elsewhere.[1] Northern Ireland claims to be the largest producer in the world.

Of the arable land rather more than half is in grass, rather more than a quarter in oats, about one-eighth in potatoes, and the rest in roots, flax, and other crops. This distribution conforms generally with the northern pattern of agriculture as seen in Scotland, Sweden, and Finland, where half the arable land is in grass for three or four years and the other half in crops; in the old days cereals and fallow, but with more and more invasion by potatoes and root crops. Actually there is no uniform rotation of crops: the common one is 7 years, 4 in grass followed by 3 tillage crops, 2 of which are cereals with potatoes and other roots in between. But other rotations up to 10 years are practised. Varieties of oats specially suited to the local conditions have been raised by the Plant Breeding Division of the Ministry of Agriculture, and more and more of the seed is treated with organo-mercury compounds for protection against fungus diseases. The present average yield of 18 cwt. per acre may reasonably be expected to increase; good farmers in good districts often get up to 30 cwt. per acre. Practically all the oats are fed to the livestock. Next in importance to oats come potatoes. The damp,

---

[1] All the same, the English growers declare that their rye grass seed, ripened and harvested under drier conditions, is of better quality and of higher germination capacity than that of Northern Ireland.

cool conditions and the long hours of daylight favour the production both of ware and of seed, while the wetness, the cold, and the high winds discourage aphids which carry virus diseases. The output far exceeds the home demand and there is a considerable surplus for shipment, about half as ware and half as seed. The Arran varieties are the most popular, but some excellent new varieties have been raised at Stormont by the Ministry of Agriculture staff and, of special interest, by a practical farmer, Mr. John Clarke of Ballycastle, Co. Antrim, who has the artist's eye for a potato and raises new varieties on his own farm without calling in the aid of professional geneticists: he produces the "Ulster" sorts. The Ministry staff closely inspects crops intended for seed and issues certificates of grading and purity. Most of the seed is shipped to Great Britain or exported to Mediterranean countries; the quantities have increased considerably:

	1939	1950
Shipment of seed potatoes	18·3	117·8 thousand tons
Value, thousand £	97	1,335

To ensure continued freedom from disease and eelworms potatoes for seed are not usually grown on the same land more frequently than once in seven years.

The area under root crops, especially turnips, is decreasing as in Great Britain, the yields per acre being too low in relation to the cost of production. Trials are being made of the Danish fodder beets with promising results. Some of the kale varieties are also proving useful.

Flax is one of Northern Ireland's specialities: it continues to be grown there long after other districts in the British Isles have given it up, and it supplies material for the linen industry famous throughout the world. It is grown only for fibre, which must be of high quality; this necessitates pulling the crop before the seed is ripe; in consequence the seed cannot be used for sowing though it could be crushed for oil. This has not proved economic and the seed is in fact wasted, being partly decomposed during the retting in the farmers retting pond or "dam"—an operation which announces itself to the traveller by the evil-smelling amines it contributes to the atmosphere. The whole process of production and retting requires considerable skill, but this has become traditional in Northern Ireland; indeed, it is not uncommon for a farm worker to hire a suitable piece of land from a farmer and grow and sell the crop himself.

Seed for the new crop is purchased from Norfolk and other eastern and southern counties of England where healthy vigorous supplies can be produced. Thus, the interesting situation arises that Northern Ireland exports rye grass seed to the eastern counties and imports flax seed from them.

Apples are successfully grown in the region about the south-east of Lough Neagh, in the north of Co. Armagh and the south-west of Co. Antrim. Bramley's Seedling is the chief variety and the produce is largely sent to Britain. This is a comparatively recent development; in the 1920's the orchards were in a bad state but they were cleaned by proper spraying. Other branches of horticulture and market gardening, including mushroom culture, are expanding, and there has long been an important rose-growing industry.

Flax, seed potatoes, rye grass seed, and apples are valuable cash crops, helping considerably in financing the general farm operations.

As in other advanced agricultural countries, the consumption of fertilizers has greatly increased and in 1950 it was about three times what it had been before the war.

Livestock large and small are, however, the basis of Northern Ireland agriculture accounting in 1950–51 for some 86 per cent of the total value of the farm output. The numbers of animals have been, in thousands:

	Total cattle	Dairy cattle	Sheep	Pigs	Poultry
1939	753	270	894	627	10,220
1943	832	324	683	257	15,430
1951	961	331	672	585	17,838

Cattle are the traditional source of income for Northern Ireland farmers. In the old days they were shipped to England as two or three-year-old stores, but more intensive methods are now adopted. Two cattle industries have been developed: meat production and dairying.

For meat production dual purpose Shorthorns or Aberdeen Angus cattle are, fattened on grass during the summer, and the surplus over home requirements shipped to England for slaughter. Winter beef production was increasing considerably before the war, using purchased feeding stuffs, but as these became scarcer and dearer the practice was given up. The summer-fattened cattle on the other hand have greatly increased in number: they rose from 187,000 in 1940 to 311,000 in 1951. They form a major item of agricultural shipments. The method is wasteful as the animals lose condition on the journey: an animal weighing thirteen or fourteen hundredweight when it leaves the farm may lose up to one hundredweight before it reaches the slaughter-house in Great Britain. The obvious remedy would be to establish proper packing houses in Northern Ireland and ship carcasses instead of live animals to England; both countries would benefit as England would receive more meat and Ireland would retain the slaughter-house residues which could be worked up into valuable pig and poultry feeds. The fear has been expressed, however, that the beef would have to be chilled and this would lower its market value.

Northern Ireland is among the few countries where small farmers go in for beef production; usually this is regarded as more suited to the large farmer.

The other cattle industry is dairying. Non-pedigree Shorthorns are generally used, but the numbers of Ayrshires and Friesians are increasing. Almost every farmer keeps cows; usually about one to each three acres: on farms ranging from 15 to 50 acres it would not be uncommon to find 5 to 15 cows, often more when followers are counted. Over the whole country the density of cattle population is 1 per 2¼ acres, which is higher than in England or Scotland. Sales of milk off the farms have greatly increased: in 1940 they amounted to 40·4 million gallons and in 1949–50 to 88·9 million gallons.[1] Much more could undoubtedly be produced.

[1] *Agric. Dept. Annual Rpt.*, 1951.

The average milk yield is about 400 gallons per lactation, but as usual, the good farmers do much better, obtaining up to 800 gallons or more. Before the war the milk went to Co-operative Creameries; it now goes instead to Government Milk Depots. The farmer deposits his three or four churns by the roadside and the depots do the rest: the churns are picked up by the depots' lorries, pasteurized, and bulked; during the summer months (August to October) the milk is sent in large tankers over to Great Britain by the ferry service, the drivers bringing back the empty tankers from the preceding day. During the rest of the year, when Great Britain has sufficient milk from local sources, the milk remains in the factory for processing: most of it is condensed, dried, or converted into infant or invalid foods. The farmer receives the same price in either case.

Farmhouse production of butter—the old "firkin" butter—has practically ceased. Factory production amounted in 1949–50 to 86,880 cwt.: but this was insufficient for local needs and 71,800 cwt. had to be imported. Before the war production had been rather less: about 70,000 cwt., but imports had been very much higher: about 250,000 to 300,000 cwt. The adoption of British rationing considerably curtailed consumption.

Sheep are found mainly in the hill districts: the bedraggled hedges and poor fences of the lowland farms limit the numbers that can be kept there. The commonest breed is the Black-face; on lowland farms the ewes are generally crossed with a Border Leicester ram, and the resulting Greyface may be further crossed with a Suffolk or other breed and the lambs fattened. Under the old system of management the numbers of sheep had been falling, but this production of fat lamb is rapidly expanding as the grasslands and the fences improve.

Pigs are of great and growing importance. Their numbers fell drastically during the war owing to lack of feeding stuffs, but by 1951 they were nearly back to their pre-war level. The Pig Marketing Scheme of 1933 caused great changes in the farmers' pig policy. At that time the pigs were slaughtered on the farm and sold for what they would fetch. The new policy was for production of Wiltshire bacon at factories: this necessitated a change of breed from the old Ulster White to the Large White: the animals are grown to bacon weight—about 220 lb. This new policy has proved very successful: the numbers of bacon pigs rose from 280,000 in 1933 to over 750,000 in 1939 and is still rising.[1] Pig recording and litter testing are being carried out.

Poultry are widely distributed and generally in charge of the women of the farm household: specialist poultry farms are rare. It says much for the energy and skilful enterprise of the womenfolk that the eggs produced suffice not only for Northern Ireland's consumption but for a large shipment to Great Britain, bringing in nearly £10 million a year. Before the war the birds were fed largely on imported grain: this is now being in part replaced by home-grown oats and chat potatoes. The factor limiting expansion of output, however, is the labour supply, the farmer's wife being an extremely busy person; but increasing use is made of labour-saving and protective devices such as the deep litter system, debeaking, etc. The number of birds one person

[1] The work is often divided, small farmers breeding the pigs and selling them when 8–12 weeks old to larger farmers who fatten them.

can look after under these improved conditions is about 7,000 compared with 1,000 when they were kept in ordinary houses. The quantity of eggs marketed increased from 1 million cases (of 360 eggs) in 1939 to 1·71 million in 1949: the shipments were 855,000 and 1·27 million respectively.

Supply of all hired labour is scarce and wages high owing to the standards set by industry. Mechanization is greatly increasing on the farms and the introduction of the small Ferguson tractor has been a great help to farmers; the number of farm tractors rose from 858 in 1939 to 15,719 in 1950. The prevailing high prices for farm produce and the loan facilities offered by the Ministry have enabled many farmers to erect new buildings or adapt old ones to the requirements of modern dairying and pig-keeping. Indeed, fears have been expressed that the small farms are becoming over-capitalized.

Shipments of farm produce from Northern Ireland are considerable: in 1951 they were valued at over £36 million. (Table XIX.)

TABLE XIX. *Quantities and values of food shipped from Northern Ireland,* 1951

	Quantity	Value £ million		Quantity	Value £ million
Fat cattle	224,000 head	11·0	Canned foods	21,950 tons	2·75
Milk: manufactured	Equiv. 30 m. galls.	3·0	Potatoes ware	119,739 tons	1·17
Milk liquid	6·1 m. galls	0·76	Potatoes seed	117,821 tons	1·35
Fat sheep	123,000 head	0·66	Apples	9,882 tons	0·309
Eggs	43·2 mill. doz.	9·84	Rye grass seed	13,682 tons	1·21
Poultry	5,893 tons	—			
Bacon and ham: edible	17,850 tons	3·67			
Meat for manu- facturing	700 tons	0·11			

The figures represent the sums paid to the producers and the packers.
Direct subsidies amounted to £4·4 million.

Against these shipments must be set imports of most of the wheat and a good deal of the butter required by the human population, and much of the feeding stuffs required by the animals. Imports of feeding stuffs, however, are much less than they were; before the war they amounted to about 700,000 tons a year, including much maize; now they are about 200,000 tons; efforts are being made to lessen them still further by producing more livestock food at home. On balance the country is more than self-supporting, and the large shipments of food show that the 1·7 acres per head of agricultural land is used to good advantage.

The organization of agriculture has been satisfactorily accomplished. The scientific, educational, and advisory services function well. There is a strong faculty of agriculture at Queen's University of Belfast. Greenmount Agricultural College provides special instruction for men, and Loughry College at Cookstown for women; the Central Research Institute is at Hillsborough, Co. Down. The freedom from drought and absence of a dry season removes one of the great difficulties confronting livestock farmers elsewhere. The Land Acts have succeeded in stopping fragmentation of the holdings, though as free sale is permitted there seems nothing to prevent the successful farmers from buying up their neighbours—which, however, would not necessarily reduce the output of food.

A special feature of the small farming system of Northern Ireland, distinguishing it from the small farm systems of Holland, Denmark, Sweden, Finland, and New Zealand, is that Co-operative Societies have never developed to any marked extent. The Northern Ireland farmer is too much of an individualist to accept the discipline they impose. Instead, the Ministry of Agriculture serves his needs. This was established in 1922 when the Government of Northern Ireland was set up. It was guided first by James Scott Gordon, its Permanent Secretary from 1922 to 1933, afterwards by George Scott Robertson who died in 1948. Its activities accord with the psychology of the Northern Irish farmers; its various Boards cover all the main branches of farm production, assuring the farmers fair prices for their produce and protection against exploitation.[1] The tourist in Northern Ireland in search of scenery often misses the fertile tracts with the neat prosperous farms and is apt to get an impression of poverty of the small farmers: the untidy landscape, the small irregular unkempt fields, bedraggled hedges, gates and fences mended with bits of barbed wire, the only solid features being the very substantial round stone pillars, two feet or more in diameter, from which to hang a gate: all these combined with unattractive villages, austere chapels, lack of desirable country houses, and of beautiful churches make a striking contrast with the English countryside. But let the visitor attend a Market Day, or an Annual Fair and he will see numbers of motor-cars, and if he is fortunate enough to be invited into a farmhouse he will be treated with a warmth of hospitality that may give a wrong impression of the usual standard of living. The farm may be only thirty acres in extent, but it is the farmer's own; the land and buildings would probably sell at anything up to £100 an acre, and the live and dead stock may be worth as much. And yet the recorded money income does not seem to be great: a survey in 1948–49 showed that the average value of the gross output per acre was £25 17s. 5d. and the average net profit £8 6s. 11d. (Plate 3, p. 58.)

The geological history of Northern Ireland was such that all the formations between the Chalk and the Lower Lias got somehow left out, and so there are no local supplies of the beautiful building stones of the Oolite and the Upper and Middle Lias that tempted men to carve and to develop the mason's craft, nor did Presbyterian austerity permit the union of craftsmanship with religion that gave so much to the English village churches. The age of village craftsmanship missed Northern Ireland.

Good farmers recognize that the farm output, high as it is and apparently stationary at present, can certainly be raised: some of the estimates are as high as 50 to 100 per cent. Useless hedgerows occupy much valuable land, much more drainage could be done, and more use made of fertilizers and lime. Land lying just above the level of present cultivation, but used by a former generation of farmers, could once more come into use as rural conditions are improved. Reclamation by deep ploughing is already being done

[1] An account of the Dept. is given by A. E. Muskett in *British Agric. Bull.*, Vol. 5, No. 19, and the operations of these Boards are described in General Rpts. of the Ministry of Agric., Belfast, issued annually.

in counties Tyrone and Londonderry with aid from the Ministry.[1] More extended use of artificial insemination would greatly improve the cattle both for beef and milk production and would, moreover, do away with many of the present 5,000 bulls. A livestock improvement scheme has been in operation for some time and is proving effective. The remarkable thing is that on such small farms so much has been achieved during the past twenty-five years and this holds out promise for much more.[2]

THE IRISH REPUBLIC: EIRE

Ireland has some of the best land in the world for the raising and fattening of cattle and this is of growing importance in view of the threatened shortage of beef for the non-dollar countries. It owes its superiority partly to its topography and partly to its position in the Atlantic. Topographically it is sometimes likened to a saucer; a fringe of mountains or high land borders the sea, some of the lower slopes are very fertile: Wicklow has been called the garden of Ireland. On the land side to the east and south (but not the west) is a belt of level or gently undulating fertile land some forty miles wide in places and practically all in grass and tillage. The centre is low-lying: some is rich, the plain of Boyle in Roscommon is famous for its grazing, as also are great tracts of Meath, Westmeath, and Limerick: but there are great areas of bog—Eire has over two million acres in all—much of which has not yet been cut. The west is very poor.

The rainfall is highest in the western mountains where over large areas in Galway and Kerry it exceeds 60 inches a year. Elsewhere, on the high coastal rim, it is less, often nearer to 40 inches; in the coastal area near Dublin it is less than 30 inches. On the central lowlands it ranges between 30 and 40 inches. It is well distributed throughout the year and the summer visitor hoping for sunshine may be disappointed.

Temperatures are mild. In the western regions the winters are comparatively warm and the summers cool. In the centre and in Dublin the temperature range is greater but nowhere are the winters really cold or the summers hot.

These conditions are eminently suitable to the growth of grass, oats, and potatoes, and these are everywhere the chief crops. The grass is always green: the "Emerald Isle" really deserves its name—but the bogs are not. The total area of the whole island is 20·37 million acres, but some 15 per cent of the land and 30 per cent of the population are in Northern Ireland; the Free State comprises 17·02 million acres utilized in 1951 as follows:

Arable	Grass	Woodland	Mountain, bog, and built-up areas
3·65	8·0	0·3	5·1 million acres

The arable land was cropped as shown in Table **XX**.

[1] The Ministry prepares the land for cropping, the farmer finds the manure and the seed, does the sowing or planting, and all subsequent work. The estimated cost per acre is about £28, roughly half for the Ministry's work and half for the farmer's, for which alone he pays.

[2] Further information about the agriculture of Northern Ireland is given in the *British Assoc. Rpts.* for 1952: J. Morrison, "Animal Husbandry"; J. C. Baird, "Crop Husbandry," and A. E. Muskett, "Education and Research."

TABLE XX. *Areas, yields, and production of chief crops, Eire*

	Thousand acres			Yield cwt. per acre			Million tons		
	Average			Average			Average		
	1934–38	1944	1951	1934–38	1944	1951	1934–38	1944	1951
Oats	581	945	620	19·6	16·6	17·6	0·574	0·792	0·576
Wheat	193	642	282	18·3	16·0	18·6	0·178	0·555	0·248
Barley	131	168	167	20·0	18·2	21·0	0·132	0·155	0·175
Potatoes	334	413	321	7·7	7·3	8·6(2)	2·58	3·06	2·77
Turnips	151 (1)	144	129	16·0		17·1(2)	2·44		2·21
Hay	2,126 (1)	1,898	1,936	58·0		46	4·66		4·45

(1) 1940. (2) tons.

(*F.A.O. Stat. Year Book*, 1951, and Central Statistics Office, Dublin.)

About half the arable land is in temporary grass; of the remainder, oats occupy the largest area followed by wheat and potatoes; barley, turnips, mangolds, and other crops have smaller areas. The climatic conditions are unsuited to wheat and some has to be imported; the total requirement is about 600 thousand tons a year of which before the war less than 200 thousand were grown in the country and more than 400 thousand tons were purchased from abroad. During the war importation on this scale was impossible and home production was so increased that it practically covered requirements: production of oats also had to be increased to replace some of the 300 thousand tons of maize previously imported for animal food. Grain production which before the war was a little under 900 thousand tons a year rose in 1944 to 1½ million tons. But, as in Britain, it was found impracticable to maintain this high output; by 1948 production of grain was down to 1·3 million tons and by 1951 it was about 800 thousand tons: wheat production was 248 thousand tons, necessitating an import of 290 thousand tons—considerably less than before the war, but high in view of Eire's adverse balance of payments.

The production of potatoes had somewhat increased and is about three million tons per annum of which some two million tons are fed to the live-stock. About 10 per cent is used for seed, and another 10 per cent is estimated to be wasted, so that the amount actually available for human food was estimated by F.A.O. in 1948 to be 583 thousand tons, an average of 430 lb. per head per year compared with 250 lb. per head in the United Kingdom.

Yields of all tillage crops are high: those of potatoes are exceeded only by Belgium and the Netherlands; those of oats and barley by these same two countries and Denmark, and in the case of barley by the United Kingdom also. Eire's freedom from drought is an important factor in attaining this high productivity.

The numbers of livestock have been, in millions:

	Cattle	Sheep	Goats	Pigs	Poultry	Turkeys
1939	4·06	3·05	0·12	0·93	16·0	1·01
1948	3·92	2·06	0·06	0·45	17·1	1·12
1950	4·32	2·38	0·05	0·64	18·0	1·28
1951	4·38	2·62	0·048	0·56	18·8	1·30

(*F.A.O. Stat. Year Book*, 1951, and Dept. of Agric., Dublin.)

As elsewhere in Europe, the numbers of animals fell considerably during the war. By 1948 only poultry and turkeys had recovered; by 1950, however, the numbers of cattle and of poultry were greater than in 1939 while sheep and pigs though increasing has not yet reached pre-war numbers and goats were further decreasing. Beef cattle are the most important of the animals; they are mainly exported to Britain as stores, an arrangement advantageous alike to the Irish and the British farmer. Calculated as meat, some 70 per cent of the beef cattle were exported before the war and 30 per cent consumed at home: in 1948 only 60 per cent were exported. The production and export of livestock products have been, in thousand tons:

Average 1934–38	*Beef* (1)	*Pig meat*	*Poultry etc.* (2)	*All meat and offal*	*Eggs*	*Butter*	*Other milk products*
Production	177	101	25	379	66	63	34
Export	133	41	7	218	19	24	18
1948							
Production	159	48	27	284	52	50	78
Export	95	nil	11	123	15	nil	25
1951							
Production	201	58	34	331	49	49	17

(1) Live animals calculated as meat equivalent.
(2) Includes rabbits and game.
(*F.A.O. Food Balance Sheets* and *Dept. Agric., Dublin.*)

Production and export of all these products, excepting poultry and milk products other than butter, were less in 1948 than before the war: export of butter and bacon had ceased. By 1952 the export of beef and of live cattle as compared with 1938 was:

	1938	1951	1952
Carcass beef, thousand tons	0·2	16·3	25·5
Live cattle, thousand	702	490	482
(Carcass beef, production, thousand tons	42	69	71)

(*Dept. Agric., Dublin Statistics* and C.E.C. Rpts. *Meat*, 1953.)
There were also small exports of pig meat and of butter (5·8 and 0·04 thousand tons respectively).

It is not clear why this should have happened. Eire not only suffered no damage during the war but acquired large sums of money from the United Kingdom.[1] It is, however, more important to know whether the pre-war level of exports can be regained and if possible increased.

The livestock industries are somewhat localized. Most of the dairying is in the south, especially Cork and Tipperary; much of the cattle raising is in the west; the animals travel eastwards and may change hands two or three times on the journey so that the original breeder gets much less than the final selling price. The animals remain for a time on the fertile eastern farms and are then shipped to Birkenhead either fat or as forward stores: as in Northern

[1] The 1939–45 war is not recognized in Eire but is spoken of as "The Emergency." On the other hand, the embargo imposed by Great Britain during the civil disturbances is called "The Economic War."

Ireland there is no large-scale slaughter. The popular breeds are the Short-horn, Aberdeen Angus, and their crosses, also some Herefords. The black Kerry cattle are found in the mountains of the west but not in the more fertile plains of the east and south. The sheep are mostly in Galway and Roscommon.

The good Irish pastures are a beautiful sight; rich green in colour, luscious in growth. The soils are almost everywhere deficient in phosphate but this is corrected by the better farmers; yields per acre of 400 to 500 gallons of milk or of 4 cwt. live weight increase of cattle are regularly expected. The pastures are not disfigured by mole hills or ant hills, indeed, there are said to be no moles in Ireland and not many ants. Re-seeding with some of the Glasnevin strains of grasses bred by Prof. M. Caffrey and with others from Aberystwyth and New Zealand has been shown to raise the output from some of the moderate land provided the suitable legume is included.

Most farms are small; practically all farmers own their own land, having been greatly helped by the Land Purchase Acts of the British Government from 1891 onwards; the process is continuing under the present regime. There are some larger farms, however, in the fertile districts of the east and south with good farmhouses and a standard of living almost forgotten in England; they have possibilities of greater output than at present. But the Irish farmer in general wants something more than a life of unalloyed food production: he loves horses, and is deeply interested in the local hunt and the local steeplechase.

The west country, on the other hand, is much poorer; it is rain-sodden and boggy, forsaken by those who can leave it; the farmers that remain are poor, their villages even less attractive than those in the east. Much of the country is saddening: the bogs depressing, some at times even dangerous when they are so placed that they can overflow and slip down the hill doing much damage as they go. Plans for improving and developing the country have been drawn up, but it is difficult to see where the money is to come from.

Economic considerations, however, do not entirely dominate life in Eire. Much of the country is very beautiful: the rain has softened the outlines of the hills and made endless lakes and streams forming some of the most attractive scenery in the British Isles. But it has also produced vast stretches of bogs and it has made the mild climate so enervating that the vigorous labour needed to develop the country soon becomes wearisome; one easily slips into that state of wistful sadness that is part of the charm of Ireland, and which the Anglo Saxon has never been able fully to appreciate or to understand.

The population problem differs from that of almost all other countries in Europe. The birth-rate is high—Eire being a Catholic country—and the death-rate fairly low, but there is so much emigration that for many years the population fell: at one time undivided Ireland had about 10 million people; in 1941 Eire had 2·99 million and Northern Ireland 1·28 million; by 1951 Eire had lost a further 400,000 and its population was down to 2·59 millions only. Northern Ireland had gained 110,000, and its population numbered 1·37 million. The depopulation of Eire has been specially marked in the west. It is the result of lack of opportunity not of general food shortage; in point of fact the average dietary is good: before the war it supplied 3,390 calories per day, in 1949–50, 3,340, and the target for 1960 is 3,300; these are among the highest figures in the world. Nor is the rate of emigration related to poverty of natural resources; it has been as marked from the good as from the poorer districts. Dublin city and county alone have gained population since 1891.[1]

Further efforts are being made to expand the work of the old Congested Districts Board in developing the resources of the country so as to stem the depopulation. A Land Rehabilitation Project was started in 1949 with an allocation of £40 million to be spread over ten years; among its operations are the draining of wet land, rehabilitation of abandoned land now covered with scrub or strewn with boulders, utilization of bog land after the peat (locally called "turf") has been cut and removed for fuel; altogether it is hoped to improve or reclaim some 4½ million acres. A Government-sponsored body, the Bord na Mona, is responsible for the exploitation of the peat bogs: it has a research station at Newbridge, near the Curragh. The great Bog of Allan in the central lowlands, some 240,000 acres in extent, supplies machine-cut peat for the generation of electricity at Portarlington.

A survey of land utilization possibilities is desirable for deciding what proportion of the available resources should be used for the intensification of output from land already farmed, but not to its full capacity, and what should be used for the reclamation of land at present waste. Intensification is usually the more remunerative, though it may be unspectacular: reclamation, however, often makes the more popular appeal. Both types of work are necessary. The Department of Agriculture has a small group of competent soil and grassland experts capable of organizing the survey required.

The consumption of fertilizer is low and could advantageously be considerably increased. Some of the soils in the west have almost reached the limit of exhaustion, and practically all the soils are deficient in phosphate, some so seriously that animals suffer from aphosphorosis. Lack of potash is widespread. Cobalt deficiency leads to trouble on the free-draining granite soils of the west and in places in the east;[2] other deficiencies of trace elements have been observed. At least half the land is acid; fortunately limestone is abundant and plant has been set up for grinding 1½ million tons annually, the quantity deemed desirable, though at present only about 300,000 tons are used. It has been estimated that suitable dressings of limestone and of fertilizer combined with better technique of grass and tillage management would raise output from existing farms by 50 to 100 per cent. Serious difficulties arise from the circumstance that much of the poor land is in the congested districts of the west; the better land of the east is usually more thinly populated.

Reclamation is necessary to provide more farms, so reducing the need for emigration. More than a million acres are considered to be reclaimable. Much abandoned and bush-covered land has been prepared for cultivation by bulldozers. Bog land of this high moor type, from which peat has been removed, can be converted into grassland if the cutting had stopped suffi-

---

[1] T. W. Freeman, *Geog. Rev.*, Jan., 1943, Vol. 33.

[2] The grass *Molinia* counteracts the harmful effects, possibly because of its high nutritive value when young (see B. Thomas and H. W. Dougall, *Agriculture*, 1939–40, Vol. 46, pp. 277–281.)

ciently above the water level to allow of a drainage system; more difficulty arises with the "blanket bogs" of the west. A great area adjacent to Lough Corrib, in Galway, is planned for reclamation by lowering the water table about nine inches. Reclamation, however, is only the first stage: land once reclaimed has to be kept in full use or it rapidly reverts to the wild. (Plate 4.)

Some new enterprises are being tried in the west. Sugar beet has been introduced, also fodder beet to reduce the need for purchased grain for the pigs. Improvement of the grass is encouraged so as to increase the amount of winter keep and so lessen the need for selling so many of the animals in autumn when prices tend to be low. Tomato growing in cold glasshouses has been started in Galway; there seems scope for other vegetables also.

The Co-operative Creameries started by Horace Plunkett and Fr. Finlay have greatly benefited the middle group of farmers (30–100 acres) in the dairy districts of the south. The smaller farmers of the west, however, lacked the capital to start them and so the Government did it. Vans carrying separators are sent round, stopping like buses at stated times at certain cross-roads; they take milk from the farmers assembled there, separate it, return the skim milk and carry the cream to the creamery. They also receive eggs, but not pigs.

The marketing of livestock is not done co-operatively. Most of the cattle are sent alive to Great Britain, either fat or as forward stores. An abattoir has, however, been set up in Dublin for the export of chilled beef instead of live animals.

Along with these technical improvements go others of social importance. Attractive houses, provided with electricity, are being built and other amenities introduced. An appeal is made to nationalist sentiment; the teaching of Gaelic is compulsory in schools and the hope was entertained that it would become the general language of the country and usher in the revival of the old Irish culture that would keep people on the land. So far, however, the young people do not appear to be attracted; prosperous relatives in America and high wages in England continue to lure them away, and although some able ones remain behind striving to develop the country they tend to look forward rather than backward. Ireland faces the same problem as various other countries: how to fit the culture and political ideas of the old days into the modern chemical and machine age. So far no solution is in sight.[1]

[1] Further accounts of Ireland are given in: T. W. Freeman, *Ireland*, Methuen, 1950; E. Estyn Evans, *Irish Heritage*, Dundalgan Press, Dundalk, 1942; R. Lloyd Praeger, *A Botanist in Ireland*. The *Base Line Reports of the Congested Districts Board* give accounts of the conditions about 1891.

Chapter 3

METHODS OF INCREASING FOOD PRODUCTION IN THE UNITED KINGDOM

One of the greatest obstacles to the improvement of agricultural output has been the steady shrinkage in area of cultivated land. This is a modern phenomenon. Throughout most of the 19th century the area of cultivated land in England and Wales was steadily increasing: it reached its maximum of 28 million acres in 1891. Since then it has steadily fallen; at the beginning of the First World War, in 1914, it was 27·1 million acres; by 1939 it had shrunk to 24·6 million acres and by 1944 there was a further drop to 24·3 million acres. From then onwards to 1951 there was a slight reversal as some of the land taken for military purposes during the war was returned to agricultural use. The average annual loss in England and Wales during successive ten-year periods steadily increased from 1892 to 1928, it then fell off and from 1944 onwards the process has been reversed and there has been an actual gain:

Average annual net losses of agricultural land, England and Wales

	1892– 1901	1901– 1910	1910– 1919	1919– 1928	1928– 1937 (1)	1937– 1944	1944– 1951
Thousand acres	26	23	54	125	72	66	21 gain

(1) The Scott Committee (1942) put the loss for the 12 years 1927–38 at 794,800 acres, while the Ministry of Agriculture estimate is 880,000 acres. Dudley Stamp (*The Times*, March 17, 1949) put the average annual loss from 1939–48 at about 50,000 acres. The statistics have no high order of accuracy, but the trends are probably correct.

The losses between 1939 and 1944 were unevenly distributed throughout the counties. The northern hill counties suffered most heavily: Yorkshire lost over 83,000 acres out of nearly 2½ million, Northumberland lost nearly 45,000 acres out of 640,000, Westmorland over 25,000, and Cumberland over 24,000. Some of the land was taken by the military, some for afforestation and some for housing and buildings; precise details of the fate of the land are not available. On the other hand, some of the south-eastern arable counties had by 1944 actually increased their areas of cultivation, though not on the scale of the northern losses: Hampshire gained 18,600 acres, Surrey 14,000, Somerset 12,400, while a number of others showed smaller gains.

The loss during the next 60 years is not expected to be less than two million acres.[1]

[1] Lord Carrington, House of Lords, July 1, 1953, speaking for the Government. Some 70 per cent is for housing. The quantities of food produced in gardens and allotments in the peak year 1942 were estimated to be in thousand tons: potatoes 490; other vegetables 1,147, fruit 191 (*Domestic Food Production*, H.M.S.O. 1950). Later less definite estimates (1953) are about two-thirds less for fruit and vegetables and 20 per cent less for potatoes. Domestic poultry, however, are estimated to produce about 20–25 per cent of the total egg production of the country.

In view of the serious position thus created special importance attaches to the reclamation of waste and marginal lands.

For generations past there have been enterprising farmers and land-owners who have delighted in bringing the waste land into cultivation. The time and labour involved have usually been considerable, but in recent years they have been much reduced by three important developments: improvements in soil and plant analysis, whereby soil deficiencies can be estimated rapidly and with sufficient accuracy; the production of new strains of grasses, clovers, and other crops better suited to hard conditions than the older sorts; and the development of the crawler tractor and its accompanying implements, the bulldozer, heavy ploughs or cultivators like the Prairie Buster, the Jumbotrac, and other machines which have greatly facilitated the labour of clearing and breaking up waste or derelict land. These appliances were widely used during the war; some of the reclamations were very costly but they gave valuable information about methods of bringing waste land into use and of maintaining it in productive condition.

(a) The Rough Grazings

There are five and a half million acres of rough grazings of England and Wales, and eleven million acres in Scotland. They are wild lands, usually high lying, untended, retaining their native vegetation and not divided into fields. The distinction between rough grazings and permanent pasture is not sharp, and the same piece of land may be classed sometimes as one and sometimes as the other.

The first modern survey of these rough grazings was made in 1936 by Sir George Stapledon and W. Davies who estimated that about one-third of the one and a half million acres thus classed in Wales was capable of considerable improvement: the proportion is probably not very different for England, and it seems safe to assume that in England and Wales some one and a half or two million acres of this class of land could be brought into much better use.

Some of this land is much more hopeful than the rest, and a study of the native vegetation gives a good indication of the degree of suitability for agricultural plants. The order of tractability is roughly:

> *Best: Agrostis*, especially if some wild white clover is present;
> Bracken;
> *Nardus-fescue;*
> *Molinia;*
> *Poorest:* Heather.

Agrostis and bracken are usually associated with fairly dry soil of some depth and not too heavy; *Molinia* and heather with wet, heavy soil and heavier and more unkindly subsoil: heather also with peat. This order of merit has long been recognized in the countryside: the Welsh hill farmers speak of "Gold under bracken, silver under gorse, copper under heather," while the Scottish hill farmers, with perhaps a shrewder sense of values, speak of "Famine under heather."[1]

On the *Agrostis* and bracken lands two general methods of improvement can be adopted. In the first, the natural vegetation can be gradually displaced by useful grasses and clovers by altering the soil conditions so as to make them more suitable for these than for the original plants. This is done by drainage to facilitate soil aeration, by addition of lime to neutralize soil acidity, and by addition of phosphatic fertilizer, especially basic slag, which greatly stimulates the development of clover. Surface cultivation is done, and a renovating seed mixture may be harrowed in. The native vegetation, weakened by the competition of the new plants, suffers further through the trampling of cattle that have come to graze. This method of altering the balance of competition is well suited to *Agrostis* land, especially if some white clover is already there;[2] it was developed at Rothamsted on the Park grass plots, and later at Cockle Park: it is less expensive but slower than the alternative method. Proper management of the grazing is essential: grazing by sheep alone is unsuitable as they are too selective in their feeding and are liable to cause deterioration of the pasture; cattle also must be used.

The second method is to get rid of the wild vegetation by ploughing it well in: ten inches deep for bracken, less for *Agrostis*, but in any case completely burying it. Limestone and slag are added[3] and an inexpensive mixture of grasses and wild white clover is sown, to be replaced later by a better mixture: alternatively, a mixture of rape, turnips, and cocksfoot is sown as pioneer, to be followed by the permanent mixture of grass and clover. Nitro-chalk is added (1–2 cwts. per acre) to increase the growth and also to hasten the decomposition of the ploughed-in material. This method is speedy and effective but it costs considerably more than the first, and it entails much outlay for the purchase of the necessary cattle: unless the grass is adequately grazed it rapidly deteriorates. This method was worked out by Sir George Stapledon and his colleagues at Cahn Hill and elsewhere.[4] (Plate 5.) A third method[5] is a combination of both: to plough up and re-seed a small area leaving it open in the midst of a larger wild area. The cattle graze both areas: the sown grass and clover furnishes protein and minerals; the wild vegetation provides the bulky material of which they have need, and may also supply nutrients or necessities lacking in the sown mixture. Animals given the full range use both kinds of herbage but seem to spend more time on the wild than on the sown grasses.

Subsidies up to 50 per cent of the capital cost have been made available under the Hill Farming and Live Stock Rearing Acts.

Considerable areas have been reclaimed. Montgomery has been one of the active counties, having reclaimed some 7,000 acres, mostly of rough grazings,[6]

[1] R. G. Stapledon and W. Davies, *A Survey of the Agriculture and Waste Lands of Wales*, Faber and Faber, 1936.

[2] Moses Griffiths records the conversion of a *Molinia-Nardus* tract in this way to a very useful sward in *Journal of Farmers' Club*, 1950, Part 3, pp. 32–50.

[3] About 2 tons per acre of limestone and 6 to 10 cwt. medium quality basic slag per acre.

[4] R. G. Stapledon, *Journal Ministry of Agriculture*, 1934, Vol. 41, No. 6.

[5] J. W. Gregor, *Scottish Journal of Agriculture*, 1946, No. 2, October.

[6] W. Ellison, *Journal of Farmers' Club*, 1949, Part 3, pp. 33–47, and *Marginal Land in Britain*, Bles, 1953. See also Moses Griffiths, *Journal of Farmers' Club*, 1950, Pt. 3, and with J. F. H. Thomas and R. Line, *Reclaiming Land for Agriculture*, Crosby Lockwood, 1951.

much of it by re-seeding. Land which formerly carried only one sheep per acre, has had its productivity raised four times and made to carry rather more than one head of cattle per two acres[1] in summer, yielding some 100–150 lb. increase in live weight, about half of which is meat, as well as providing some winter grazing.

The improved herbage persists, however, only so long as it is properly grazed by cattle, and this necessitates fencing and provision of a supply of water, besides the acquisition of the cattle. This last item presses heavily on the hill farmers, most of whom are small men of limited resources. Several systems are adopted. One is "agistment," i.e., the taking in of cattle from lowland farmers for boarding during the summer months. This provides a regular money income, and avoids the necessity for buying cattle and for feeding them during winter—always a costly business in the hills, as hay-making is precarious. Another method is to breed young animals, preferably well-chosen crosses, having them born in early spring when the grass is beginning to grow and selling them to lowland farmers in autumn when the grass is finished. Ellison estimates that, from 1,000 acres so improved, an additional 250 store cattle annually could be supplied to lowland farmers. Other farmers prefer dairying, selling milk if they are near enough to a collecting point, or, alternatively, cream, the skim milk being fed to young calves reared for sale. Exmoor provides good examples: some 1,800 acres re-seeded by the Earl of Fortescue are now carrying about 150 cows, their calves, and followers.[2]

The essential condition for success is that the livestock population should be sufficiently heavy during summer to consume all the grass except any that may be made into silage, and sufficiently light in winter to avoid the necessity for over-grazing or for purchasing much food. The summer season can be lengthened by growing fodder crops or leys to provide food in autumn.

The system fits in well with lowland farming, as it leaves more land there free for cropping and for the production of winter food; the link provided by agistment is beneficial to both parties.

(b) *The Dry, Light Lands*

The light waste lands stand at the opposite end of the fertility scale from the hill lands: they suffer from excessive dryness, from a tendency to be blown away by high winds, and from a remarkable suitability for the propagation of rabbits.

The most important tracts are in the eastern and south-eastern counties, overlying the chalk or on the Lower Greensand that underlies it; elsewhere the chief areas are in the Bunter sandstone regions of Staffordshire. Those near London are used for residential purposes, golf, or other recreational activities, those farther away are either open heaths, former sporting estates, or taken by the Forestry Commission. Until recently afforestation was considered the best way of utilizing this land, and conifers and other soft

---

[1] One head of cattle is the grazing equivalent of seven sheep.

[2] This useful piece of reclamation is described in the *Farmer and Stock Breeder* of January 2, 1945. The old reclamations of John Knight (1760 to 1840) are described by C. S. Orwin in an interesting volume, *The Reclamation of Exmoor Forest*, Oxford University Press, 1929. Post-war economic results are recorded by V. Baker (University of Bristol Agric. Econ. Dept.) in *Exmoor: an Economic Survey* (in 1947–48).

woods certainly grow well. But so do lucerne and cocksfoot with suitable manuring, and some remarkable reclamations have been achieved.

The most extensive has been that of the Earl of Iveagh at Elveden, in Suffolk, where 8,000 acres of very poor brekland formerly devoted almost entirely to sport, 3,000 of them absolutely derelict, have been brought into production. The land was surrounded with a rabbit-proof fence, levelled, and broken up with heavy cultivation implements. The wild vegetation must, as in the hill country, be completely buried, and, as in the hill country, the bracken land is the most tractable and the heather land the least, though the difference is, perhaps, not so marked. As in the hills also, the soil is acid, sometimes extremely so, in spite of the fact that the chalk is so near the surface; it is also extremely deficient in plant food and, unlike much of the hill land, in organic matter also. Acidity and poverty in plant foods are easily remedied by dressings of chalk and of fertilizers; lack of organic matter presents greater difficulty, but fortunately is of less consequence for leguminous crops than for others. The Elveden cropping scheme is, therefore, to begin with corn crops for the first two years, during which the meagre supplies of organic matter derived from the ploughed-in vegetation may be expected to persist, these give an immediate cash return; then comes inoculated lucerne mixed with cocksfoot—the best companion for lucerne here because it is drought resistant and grows well—this mixture remains for three to five years and is followed by a cereal crop, then sugar beet, and, finally, a cereal crop undersown with the lucerne-cocksfoot mixture again. This mixture not only provides large quantities of animal food but much enriches the soil and improves its texture, giving it more cohesion. (Plate 6, p. 59.)

The crops are mainly converted into milk of which some 300,000 gallons were produced in 1950 on land which before the war was yielding nothing but game birds and rabbits—of the latter about three to the acre were caught and sold. In addition there was a herd of 500 beef cattle and two flocks each of 500 ewes.[1]

Similar methods were used during the war by the War Agricultural Executive Committee under its Executive Officer, Roger Sayce, for the reclamation of much other waste light land in West Suffolk, and since the war more of this work has been done by private contractors. The light fen land, however, required different treatment. The dykes had to be cleaned, concrete roads constructed to make the farms more accessible and mitigate their isolation which had made them very unattractive to the women. Special technique was required for the first ploughing to prevent the implements becoming bogged. Potatoes were the first crop, then followed two crops of stiff strawed oats or wheat, and afterwards sugar beet, of which some ten tons per acre were often obtained—though they were liable to suffer from eelworm. The land is always prone to weeds, which it is hoped the new weed killers will suppress; it is very liable to wind erosion: leys of three or four years' duration and belts of trees as windbreaks are recommended as protection.

[1] *The Elveden Enterprise*, George Martelli, Faber and Faber, 1952. By a terrible tragedy the herds suffered greatly in the epidemic of foot and mouth disease in May 1952.

For the Duke of Grafton's reclamation of similar soil at Euston, Thetford (also using lucerne), see *Journal Royal Agricultural Society*, 1943, Vol. 104, pp. 85–89.

In reclaiming sandy wastes in Devon, potatoes were grown for the first one or two years, then oats or rye, then a grass-clover mixture was sown. In wet conditions, however, potatoes were very liable to fail and so were omitted; strong strawed oats or rye were sown and the grass-clover mixture followed at once.[1]

(c) The Derelict Land

A considerable area of land had been enclosed and cultivated but was later abandoned because of some unsuitability.[2] Much of it was brought into cultivation during and after the war when a suitable scheme of utilization had been devised. Mr. Rowland Dudley took over 1,300–1,400 acres of almost derelict land on the chalk near Andover, and transformed it into an excellent farm through realizing that the soil's deficiency was potash, and, this being supplied, excellent crops of grain and of lucerne would grow. Some successful improvers have put their experiences on record: they make most interesting reading;[3] few ways of life can be more satisfying to young people of energy and enthusiasm than the building up of a productive farm out of derelict land.

INTENSIFICATION OF OUTPUT

The most hopeful way of increasing food supplies is by more intensive cultivation of the land already in use: this is true not only for the United Kingdom but for large parts of the rest of the world. The great need is to transform the old peasant system into a more productive modern form, and this often involves far-reaching changes in the structure of village life destroying its old self-sufficing character, and making it dependent for its essential appliances on industries often far distant from the village and completely out of contact with it. The transformation has long been accomplished in the United Kingdom and North-West Europe; elsewhere it is in very different stages, in some countries it has hardly begun. It is always difficult and rarely accomplished smoothly. But it must be brought about, for the peasant systems are incapable of much improvement: only the modern systems can be intensified, as shown by the fact that only in the agriculturally advanced countries have yields per acre increased since pre-war days; elsewhere, they have remained stationary or even fallen.

The first step is to establish a system of land tenure that encourages high productiveness, then to develop a system of good farming. In Great Britain and North-West Europe, as in other regions of well-distributed rainfall, the fallows, which under the peasant system occupied some 30 to 50 per cent of the land, were replaced by fodder crops, potatoes, sugar beet, and others; grasses and leguminous crops were cultivated, the latter being specially important as the basis of soil fertility.[4] More food for animals is thus produced,

[1] F. R. Horne describes the reclamation of some 40,000 acres in Devon in *Journal Royal Agricultural Society*, 1943, Vol. 104, pp. 90–100.

[2] In the *National Farm Survey of England and Wales* (H.M.S.O., 1946) the area of enclosed land lying derelict in 1941–43 was estimated at 232 thousand acres.

[3] Among others see Frances Donaldson, *Four Years' Harvest*, 1945; Alan Bloom, *The Farm in the Fens*, 1944; George Henderson, *The Farming Ladder*; P. J. O. Trist, *Land Reclamation: the Record of Achievements in Essex*. All these are published by Faber and Faber.

[4] R. E. Slade has shown that lucerne properly grown can provide all the nitrogen needed to yield abundant crops: wheat 35 cwt., barley 30 cwt., potatoes 12 tons, all per acre (*J. Roy. Soc. Arts*, 1951, Vol. 99, pp. 501–11).

1 (left) The wheat harvest, Cheddington, Bucks. (*Farmer and Stockbreeder*) [p. 57]

2 (right) Harvesting a crop of oats and peas for silage, Eashing, Surrey. (*The Times*) [p. 37]

3 (left) A farm in Northern Ireland. (*Courtesy of Govt. of N. Ireland*) [p. 52]

4 (right) Bog reclamation, Eire. (*Courtesy of Dept. of Agric., Dublin*) [p. 58]

5 (left)
Improvement of
hill pasture: Cahn
Hill, Cardiganshire.
The lighter parts on
which the animals
congregate have
been improved the
darker parts, which
they are avoiding,
have not. (Author)
[p. 61

6 (right) Reclaiming
the heath, Elveden,
Suffolk. (Courtesy of
Earl Iveagh) [p. 63

7 (left)
Improvement of a
lowland meadow by
a hormone spray to
kill weeds: left-hand
part sprayed. (Plant
Protection Ltd.)
[p. 71

8 (right) Intensive
strip grazing: the
front wire shows
the width of the
strip to be grazed
next day. (I.C.I.)
[p. 74

and this enables more animals to be kept and so the agriculture improves by the old ascending spiral: more crops, more livestock; more livestock, more manure; more manure, more crops. In all well-farmed countries the livestock population is high: before the war the farm animals of Great Britain consumed twice as many calories as did the human population—though in the main the calories were derived from grass, straw, roots, coarse grains, and industrial residues which the human population could neither use nor avoid producing.

There are limits to the intensification thus attained and these are raised by increasing the amount of plant food in the soil. Few natural soils contain sufficient food for modern varieties of crops, efficiently cultivated by modern methods. Diagnosis of soil deficiencies is now both rapid and accurate: it is accomplished by analysis of the soil and of the plant, and the conclusions reached are checked by properly conducted field experiments. The deficiencies are made good by the addition of fertilizers and manures. The results are so satisfactory that consumption of fertilizers is rapidly increasing, especially in the more advanced countries. Far more fertilizer could with advantage be used—one ton of fertilizer nitrogen with the necessary phosphate and potash gives an average of ten additional tons of starch equivalent, sufficient to feed forty persons for a year.[1] The kind and quantity required depends not only on the soil but on the water supply, and like other modern aids to production they must be used with knowledge and discernment. World consumption increased between 1938 and 1952 by 80 per cent for nitrogenous and by 70 per cent for phosphatic and potassic fertilizers:

Million metric tons plant food used as fertilizer, world consumption

	1938	1951	1952
Nitrogen (N)	2·40	3·90	4·38
Phosphoric acid (P_2O_5)	3·50	5·60	5·92
Potash (K_2O)	2·50	4·20	4·33

(Excluding U.S.S.R.)
(*F.A.O. Rpt.*, 1953.)

This rapid increase in the use of fertilizers has aroused anxiety on two important questions: will the supplies last? Will the fertilizers damage the soil or adversely affect the crops? In neither case is there any reason for fear. The nitrogen fertilizers are made from the nitrogen of the air; this passes through cycles in the plant, the animal and the soil which ultimately return it to the air. The only material actually consumed is the source of energy: approximately five tons of coal, or its energy equivalent, is needed for the fixation of one ton of nitrogen.[2] Phosphatic fertilizers consume rock phos-

[1] F. Yates, in *Four Thousand Million Mouths*, ed. F. Le Gros Clark and N. W. Pirie, p. 58 (1 cwt. starch equivalent = 208 thousand calories). For fertilizer consumption in U.K. see Table XVI, p. 42. Information on fertilizer practice in England and Wales during 1942–43 is given in surveys by F. Yates, D. A. Boyd and I. Mathison (*Empire Jl. Expt. Agric.*, 1944, Vol. 12, pp. 162–176 and later by B. M. Church (*ibid.*, 1952, Vol. 20, pp. 249–256).

[2] F. C. O. Speyer, *Empire Jl. Exp. Agric.*, 1953, Vol. 21, pp. 49–54. In 1952 the installed world capacity of the nitrogen industries was 6·4 million metric tons a year, of which ammonia synthesis represented 78 per cent and by-product ammonia 8·5 per cent, about 15 per cent is used in industry.

C

phate, of which supplies are almost indefinitely large; and also sulphur of which supplies are smaller and at present hampering further expansion of superphosphate manufacture. New sources are being exploited: oil refineries are supplying an increasing quantity. But sulphur is not essential and alternative processes are being devised; quantities of pyrites are now used.

The recovery of phosphate in the crop does not usually exceed 25 per cent and may be less: the remainder stays in the upper layers of soil in a form not available to crops on our present methods of management. A small amount gets out to sea in sewage but this is probably taken up by plankton and seaweed some of which serves as food for fishes. Potash is available in enormous amounts. Calculations of visible supplies of phosphate and of potash differ, but even allowing for generous rates of use they run into thousand of years.

There is no evidence that fertilizers properly used injure the soil or the crop. But they can do harm if wrongly used. The case is exactly parallel to that of a high-class motor-car: in the hands of a skilled driver it can accomplish great things, but an ignorant person may easily run into disaster. The properties of the various fertilizers are well known and have been amply documented; but in new conditions proper field tests must always be made before their use is advocated. For their full effectiveness they require a suitable soil reaction and this usually necessitates dressings of lime. They do not supply organic matter: other provision must be made for this.

The old crop varieties are rarely able to respond fully to the improved conditions that can now be attained and new and more prolific varieties are being produced. The results obtained in the different countries are set out in later chapters.[1]

Improvements in the dairy herds of the country are being brought about by artificial insemination whereby a good bull can in his active lifetime produce several thousand daughters endowed with higher milk yielding ability than their dams—this being inherited through the sire.[2] Simultaneously, there have been notable efforts to reduce disease, especially tuberculosis, mastitis, and contagious abortion. The result has been an increase in milk yield per cow; not only has the fall during the war been completely recovered but the pre-war average has been well passed:

		War-time Average			
	Pre-war	1940–44	1948–49	1949–50	1950–51
Average gross yield per cow (gallons) (June–May)	542	470	567	581	586

(*Min. Ag. Stat.* The average yield from cows supplying the Milk Marketing Board was higher: it was 650 gallons in 1952 and had been increasing at the rate of about 3 per cent per annum.) (Fig. 5.)

It must be admitted, however, that much of the increase in yield is due to a change-over from dual purpose animals to more purely milk breeds thereby sacrificing beef production. The percentages of the different types in the herds of England and Wales are estimated to have been:

1 For England and Wales, see F. R. Horne, *Agric. Progress*, 1948, Vol. 23, pp. 501–511.
2 For Danish results see p. 103.

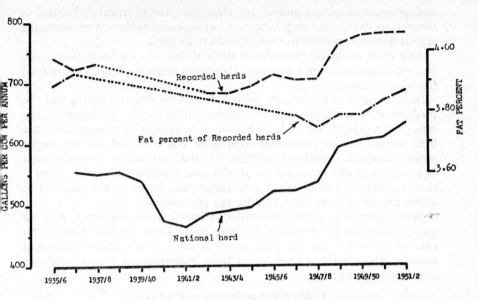

FIG. 5.—Increasing output of milk per cow, and raising of fat content, England and Wales. (E. D. Ashton, *Empire Jl. Expt. Agric.*, 1954, Vol. 22, pp. 1–9.)

Type	1908	1935–36	1951–52
Beef	17	13	13
Dual purpose	75	73	35
Dairy	8	14	52
Total milk production (million gals.)	1,000	1,300	1,700

There are wide differences in economy of milk production. In ordinary practice 3½ lb. of concentrated foods are commonly fed throughout the year for each gallon of milk produced, i.e. about one ton per cow. But M. M. Cooper at the Wye College Farm gives 1½ lb. only[1]; many other farmers are equally economical. The limit of production is not nearly reached yet. It is unlikely, however, that our farmers will do much more than supply the demand for liquid milk owing to the relatively low price paid for milk for manufacture. To produce at home all the dairy products consumed in 1951 would have required about four million million gallons of milk, double the actual output. Unless prices were to rise heavily the sums paid to the farmers for the additional milk would have to be very low.

Improvements in the beef supply result from fertilizing the cow with semen from a beef-producing bull. The possibility has been opened up by J. Hammond and others at Cambridge of transfering an ovum from a good cow to another one, then fertilizing it from a good beef bull, and so obtaining a much better calf than the cow used as incubator could herself have given. Since a cow produces some 1,700 ova during her lifetime the possibilities of

[1] *Agric. Progress*, 1952, Vol. 27, Pt. 1. 3·3 lb. was the average in the Milk Marketing Board's enquiry of 1947–49. See also W. R. Trehane, *Jl. Roy. Soc. Arts*, 1953, Vol. 101, pp. 403–7.

multiplying a first-class animal are great once the practical difficulties of transfer are overcome—they have been in the case of rabbits. The incubating animal does not transmit its own qualities to its guest.

As a result of the development of artificial insemination lower-grade bulls become redundant—there are some thousands of them—leaving more food for other animals.

Improvements in poultry are being achieved by progeny testing and the production of sex-linked crosses whereby pullets can be produced for egg laying and cockerels for table birds. Improved systems of management have been worked out or introduced from other countries and the egg output greatly increased. Addition of antibiotics to the food has cut down the losses of young birds and increased the growth rate, especially when the ration is short in protein. The Shinfield investigators are, however, not prepared to advise the use of these substances for egg production.

Better varieties of crops are continually being introduced which, with the same expenditure of labour and fertilizer, give a larger product. Much more efficient protection can be given to crops and animals against pests and diseases. The combined result of all these improvements is that yields per acre have gone up:

United Kingdom, average yield per acre

	Pre-war average 1935–39	Average 5 years 1940–44	Average 3 years 1948–50	1951
Wheat, cwt.	18·1	19·1	21·5	21·7
Barley, cwt.	16·7	17·4	19·8	20·3
Oats, cwt.	16·3	16·7	17·9	18·3
Potatoes, tons (1)	6·8	7·1	7·4	7·9
Sugar beet, tons	8·8	9·0	10·8	10·7

(*F.A.O. Stat. Year Book*, 1951.)

(1) G. V. Dyke and P. R. D. Avis adduce evidence by sampling methods that the estimates are probably about 1¾ tons per acre too low. (*J. Ag. Sci.*, 1953, Vol. 43, pp. 450–455).

These are averages, but good farmers regularly get higher outputs, and there are occasional extraordinarily high records which can neither be explained nor repeated. Some of the results are:

	Present average	Good farmers expect	Present highest record	
Wheat, cwt. per acre	21·5	30–35	70	Turrell Bros., Wiggenhall, Kings Lynn
Potatoes, tons per acre	7·4	10–12	27	1950, Lincolnshire
Milk, lb. per cow	6,180	8,000–10,000	33,184	A. Drexler, Manor Farm,
lb. butter fat			1,800	Kidlington, Oxon.
			(5·4%)	

These records show that we are still far from having reached the physical limits of production.

Control of Wastes and Losses

From the time of sowing the seed to the time when the crop is finally eaten by human beings or by animals it is perpetually liable to attack by insects, fungi, bacteria, viruses, and other pests. There have always been plant diseases: wheat has suffered from very early times;[1] bunt was a cause of serious losses in England in medieval days. Plant diseases are almost certainly increasing. Modern transport is so rapid and widespread that a crop disease appearing in any one country is soon carried to every other country where that particular crop is grown, and if the conditions are favourable, it multiplies and may do serious damage. The process began directly transport became more rapid. The introduction of steam ships and the great shortening of time for ocean voyages in the first half of the 19th century was accompanied by the introduction into Ireland of the potato blight fungus *Phytophthora infestans*, which caused the terrible famine of the 1840's—the effects of which still persist. In the same period the grape mildew appeared in France, causing serious losses to the wine growers. Both diseases may have come from America. At the beginning of this present century wart disease of potatoes (*Synchtrium endobioticum*) suddenly appeared in Cheshire coming, apparently, from Czechoslovakia, and gradually spread across England causing serious destruction till immune varieties were discovered and used for breeding new varieties. About the same time American Gooseberry Mildew appeared, also in the Cheshire district, and spread to the fruit growing regions with much loss to growers. Other Western European countries suffered invasions. Some of the new attacks were difficult to understand. The downy mildew of hops was formerly known only in Japan: suddenly in 1920 it appeared in many parts of Europe, including the hop garden at Wye College; now it is widespread. All countries suffer directly they are opened up and movement begins. *Macrocarpa* was introduced into Kenya and proved most valuable: suddenly a fungus, *Monochaetia unicornis*, appeared and caused a dangerous canker; it spread, and threatens to put the tree out of cultivation. Where it came from is a mystery: previously it was known only as a herbarium specimen. Another valuable product of Kenya, pyrethrum, suffers considerably from a bud disease caused by a fungus *Ramularia bellunensis* previously known only in Italy, where it is apparently harmless, and in Cheshunt glasshouses where, however, it attacks marguerites.

Instances could be multiplied where some new pest or disease has turned up unexpectedly, no one knows whence. Quarantine arrangements are in force in most countries with the view of preventing the entry of diseases and pests.

The best way of dealing with a disease is to select or breed crop varieties resistant to it, but this is complicated by the circumstance that the fungus also can change, and produce a mutant capable of attacking the varieties resistant to the ordinary forms; the rust of wheat affords a good example (p. 379). Virus diseases, in particular, appear capable of considerable increase: new ones are recorded almost every year. "Virus yellows" was unknown in East Anglia before sugar beet was introduced; now it causes considerable loss. Virus disease of apples and plum trees, of broccoli, and cauliflowers have appeared. Potatoes have long suffered.

The insect population in field and orchard is very mixed: some members are harmless, some are destructive, others prey upon the harmful forms. They

[1] Solomon prayed for protection against "blasting (i.e. rust), mildew, locust, and caterpillar" in his dedication of the Temple. Theophrastus and Virgil also refer to plant diseases.

settle down to some sort of equilibrium which, however, is always shifting according to the weather and other conditions. An insect potentially harmful may, in fact, do little damage because its numbers are too low, but a shift in the conditions may favour it, enabling it to increase so much that it does serious damage. C. B. Williams at Rothamsted has devised statistically-based methods by which fluctuations in numbers can be forecasted. Massee of East Malling has long issued warnings to fruit growers of impending attacks based on observations of changes in insect population.

If only it could be done, the best way of dealing with injurious insects would be to encourage the multiplication of their predators. This has not been accomplished on any general scale though there are successful instances of the introduction of a predator, especially in a closed community such as an island, or a cultivated region surrounded by desert. But the converse may happen: Nature's complex mixed population may become simplified by smoothing out Nature's complexity of conditions and harmful forms may then increase. V. B. Wigglesworth[1] has pointed out that the small fields of Britain, the wide range of crops in a small area, the hedgerows, and mixed road-side verges encourage a variety of insects including pests and predators; but if the conditions are made more uniform by enlarging the fields, removing the hedges, and having one uniform pattern of road-side vegetation the balance may be broken with consequences that cannot be forecasted. America has done more in the way of unifying and simplifying conditions than we have—and suffers more from insect pests.

Modern chemical technology has produced a number of remarkably effective substances for destroying insects and fungi. They do not kill everything indiscriminately but are far more potent against some forms than against others. The tar oil washes destroy insect eggs on apple and plum trees in winter and soon became very popular among fruit growers. But they also destroyed predatory insects that had kept down the numbers of fruit tree red spider mites: these, therefore, multiplied and became a serious pest for the first time in the experience of many orchardists. When D.D.T. was first introduced from Switzerland it was rightly hailed as a great scientific triumph: it acted magnificently against houseflies, tsetse flies, grain weevils, tomato moth, and other destructive insects. But it soon lost some of its glamour—new strains of houseflies appeared which were resistant to it. Other resistant insects multiplied considerably as it killed their competitors and their predators: among these were woolly aphis and red spider mite which flourished and became serious pests. In consequence of these difficulties the insect populations are now studied as a whole, and before any new insecticide is distributed its effect on the general equilibrium is investigated. Under proper advice insecticides and fungicides can advantageously be used, and the methods of applying them have been so greatly improved that smaller quantities are needed than before with the result that less incidental damage is done.

A new group of insecticides has recently been introduced: the systemic insecticides and fungicides. These are not sprayed on to the plant but fed to it: they pass to the leaves making them poisonous to particular insects attacking them. An instance of their use is given on page 302.

[1] Advancement of Science, 1950, Vol. 7, pp. 154–161.

Many broad-leaved weeds growing in cereals or grass can be destroyed by spraying at an early stage with certain chemicals: the cereals escape damage because the substance does not adhere to them. Two groups of chemicals are used: direct poisons which kill on contact, and substances of hormone type, non-poisonous and therefore safer in use, but when taken up by the plant and translocated within it they cause fatal physiological disturbances. These substances are extraordinarily effective against many common weeds, and they are widely used in Great Britain, Canada, the United States, and elsewhere. Few pests are more widespread and cause so much loss as weeds, especially in the early stages of growth, and one of the many advantages of mechanization is that it allows of more rapid cleaning operations than would otherwise be possible. But once the corn is up, or in a meadow, cultivation is impracticable and these modern herbicides are proving a great boon. The question whether they may ultimately harm the soil or the crop, and their effect on the natural fauna, is under investigation.[1] In the meantime they are being increasingly used: something like 100 million acres of crop were sprayed in 1952, chiefly in North America, the United Kingdom and North-West Europe. (Plate 7, p. 59.)

Animal diseases are steadily being brought under control. The old method is instant slaughter to avoid spread; it is effective but costly.[2] The modern method is to apply diagnostic tests so as to catch the disease early, then to segregate and give the appropriate treatment. Vaccines are widely used against mastitis, one of the worst diseases of dairy cows; swine-fever, so destructive of pigs; and for a number of other diseases. Immunization by the appropriate serum is extensively practised. Great gains may be expected as these methods spread. Estimates of loss always have a considerable speculative element; but, before the war, the loss of milk due to disease in England and Wales was estimated at 200 million gallons per annum. Cows should remain in the herd for six or seven lactations: at present the average is only about three and a half, thus necessitating the maintenance of a considerable number of animals for replacement.

Variation in achievement in our live-stock husbandry is enormous.

IMPROVEMENT OF GRASSLAND

Grasses of various sorts grow readily in most parts of Great Britain: indeed, in the wetter western parts of the country they grow so freely that grass husbandry is largely practised for the raising of livestock and the production of milk. In times of economic difficulty farmers everywhere tend to put their land into grass or even to leave it to "tumble down" to a spontaneous covering of grasses, clovers, and weeds such as occurred on a large scale in the crises of the 1880's and the 1930's. The resulting mixture can be grazed: it gives but meagre returns but costs almost nothing and there may still be a small profit while arable cropping is resulting in loss.

Land covered with wild vegetation gains some nitrogen and organic matter

[1] For a fuller discussion of these wastes and losses see *Untaken Harvest*, Geo. Ordish, Constable, 1952, and E. J. Russell, *Inter. Conf. on Crop Protection*, Fernhurst, 1951.

[2] The outbreak of Foot and Mouth Disease in England in the spring of 1952 necessitated the slaughter of 84,496 cattle. In a normal year some 7 to 10 thousand cattle are slaughtered for this disease and bovine tuberculosis. (Rpt. to Council, R.A.S.E., 1953.)

but, in so far as it is grazed, it loses phosphate and lime. The soil ultimately becomes impoverished in these elements; also it tends to accumulate wire-worms, leather-jackets, and other insects that may do considerable damage when it is again used for arable crops.

This easy growth of grass and the fact that it gives some kind of return, even when it receives no attention, has rather encouraged the idea that it can look after itself and needs none of the care usually devoted to arable crops. So the grassland has been much neglected and the effects are cumulative: yields per acre of grass, both temporary and permanent, have, with some exceptions, fallen since they were first recorded in 1886, in marked contrast with yields of arable crops which have risen.

A poor, neglected grass field generally contains a large number of different plant species. In the prevailing poverty nothing can grow vigorously enough to crowd out its neighbours: any seed that falls has some chance to germinate and grow. One of the poorest pieces of grass in the country, the Rothamsted Park grass plot, that has been hayed every year since 1852 and received neither fertilizer nor manure during the whole period, contains some fifty different species of plants. The adjacent manured plots all contain fewer species: the manuring has favoured some more than others; they have therefore developed, crowding out the less-favoured ones, and a new equilibrium has been set up. The flora of a grass field is thus very unstable: it can be considerably modified by suitable treatment, and the science of grassland improvement consists largely in discovering the reactions of the different elements of the flora to given changes in conditions. Manuring and soil reaction are among the most potent factors affecting the flora. Adequate dressings of phosphate and if necessary potash, but no nitrogen, are more favourable to the leguminous plants which can obtain their own nitrogen than to the grasses which cannot: a highly leguminous herbage therefore develops. Nitrogenous manuring, on the other hand, favours the grasses; the particular species that finally dominate depend on the reaction of the soil.

The grazing animal introduces a further complication by perpetually cutting off the leaves of plants that it likes and so eliminating plants that cannot quickly throw up new shoots. But plants that it does not like are left to grow and to produce seed: docks and thistles may thus become important components of the herbage. The grazing effect, however, is complex: it depends on the stage of growth of the plant, on the duration and intensity of the grazing, and on the kind of animal and its manner of grazing.

Drainage, acidity, cultivation, all affect the equilibrium, shifting the balance in favour of some and against other species. One has to think of a grass field as the scene of a perpetual competition in which man can intervene effectively by altering some or other of the many conditions influencing the growth of the different species of plants. This intervention constitutes grassland management.[1]

Only few of the many species of grasses found in Great Britain have much feeding value. Some, like the annual poas, have too short a life, others, like

[1] The effect of manuring on the chemical and botanical composition of the hay crop is well shown by the Rothamsted experiments, and of grazing on the floral types by the Jealott's Hill experiments.

crested dogstail, are too wiry, and yet others like Yorkshire fog are disliked by animals in some circumstances. The richest pastures in the country contain mainly three or four species of plants only, mostly rye grass and white clover with varying but usually smaller amounts of cocksfoot, timothy, meadow fescue, or others, according to the conditions. Rye grass, in general, is the best of these; it is native to this country but its cultivation as a farm crop was introduced from Flanders in the 17th century.

A striking example, and an early one, of the improvement of grassland by a simple change in conditions is afforded by the Cockle Park experiments, initiated in 1892 by William Somerville, on a poor, heavy boulder clay. A dressing of 10 cwt. basic slag per acre sufficed to bring up so much clover, previously hardly perceptible in the mat of *Agrostis* and other worthless grasses, that it dominated the whole herbage. Many thousands of acres of poor pasture land had their productiveness increased 50 to 100 per cent or more by this simple and inexpensive method. Although the herbage was very valuable per ton, however, the total weight per acre was not great, and the live weight increase obtained even after improvement was usually only of the order of 50 lb. per acre.

The method was much less effective on grassland of better quality where there was already a certain amount of clover in the herbage. Some improvement was effected by nitrogenous manuring: in particular, a dressing of $1\frac{1}{2}$ to 2 cwt. of nitro-chalk brought on the grass two or three weeks earlier, and so shortened the expensive winter feeding season. The problem of improvement of this kind of herbage had already been studied in New Zealand, and in Holland, and from 1930 onwards it has been much demonstrated by the staff of Imperial Chemical Industries at Jealott's Hill and on farms in various parts of the United Kingdom. The underlying principles are: first, the encouragement of heavy growth of herbage by liberal manuring, in particular nitrogenous manuring, but always supported by sufficient phosphate, potash, and if necessary, lime to ensure full growth; and second, to feed or cut the herbage at the stage of optimum feeding value, i.e. when the percentages of protein, mineral matter, and digestible carbohydrates are still high, and before any seed or large amount of fibre has formed. This process usually, in English conditions, has to be repeated three or four times in the season, and of course any necessary cultivation or mole draining must be done to allow the grass to make its fullest growth.

Considerable care is required in managing the grazing. It is far more difficult than in the days of the old "stick-and-dog farmers," who simply turned a bunch of animals loose in a grass field and let them find what food they could. Once grazing begins, it has to be rapid and complete; there must be no large amount of herbage unused, and any that is left should be removed by cutting. Cattle, however, soil the herbage with their excrements. In an open field ten cows in a grazing season of 180 days may soil an acre of grass which they thereupon are very unwilling to eat.[1] The animals are, therefore, allowed access to the grass only for a short time, but they are crowded on to it sufficiently densely to ensure that it shall be cleared as completely as possible.

[1] D. B. Johnstone Wallace and K. Kennedy (*Journ. Agric. Sci.*, 1944, Vol. 34, pp. 190–7) showed that a cow dungs 12 times and urinates 9 times daily, soiling on an average 24 square feet daily.

They are then removed before they have had time to do much soiling and they are turned into a field where the soiling will not matter.[1]

The first method, called rotational grazing, consisted in setting up a number of paddocks, each of about an acre in extent which could take about ten cattle for a few days. They were then moved on to the next. The paddocks had to be permanent and each required stout fences and a supply of water. Considerable improvement became possible when easily movable electric fences were more widely used; these consist simply of one or two strands of barbed wire charged with high-tension electricity and carried by little insulators on light posts easily driven into the ground. The animals quickly learn to respect the electric charge: one touch of the wire with their sensitive noses— their testing organ—suffices to keep them away. (Plate 8.) The fences are easily moved: more easily in New Zealand than in England because the New Zealand farmer can buy light aluminium barbed wire while the British farmer cannot; it is possible to shift them daily and fold the cattle just as was done with sheep in the old days. The close-folding method has also been successfully developed in Holland, Denmark, and New Zealand: the animals are packed so closely that they clear the grass in a single day; the soiling is thus still further reduced. The packing of the animals is astonishingly dense: a rate of 100 per acre is not uncommon:[2] they must, of course, be dishorned. Having had their fill of this luscious herbage they are turned on to a poorer field for the rest of the 24 hours. Table XVIII shows some of the results obtained by these different methods.

TABLE XVIII. *Outputs from grassland under old and new methods of management*

Management	Yield of milk gallons per acre	Cow grazing days per acre	Starch equivalent cwt. per acre
Good traditional	200		10–12
Rotational grazing (1), higher manuring	387	129	17
Close folding (1), manured as above	487	171	21
R. E. Slade's farm (p. 77)			25–30

(1) Jealott's Hill results: R. A. Hamilton, *Proc. Fert. Soc.*, 1950, No. 8. For other results see "N. Ireland," J. T. Kernohan, *J. Brit. Grassland Soc.*, 1947, Vol. 2, No. 2; P. A. Linehan and J. Lowe, *ibid.*, Vol. 1, No. 1; R. R. Turner, *ibid.*, 1948, Vol. 3, No. 2. "Holland," W. D. Hay, *Agriculture*, 1948, Vol. 55, pp. 286–9.

While, with skill and patience, it is possible to improve almost any grass the quickest way is often to plough it up and reseed with a carefully chosen mixture of grasses and clovers. The advantage of this method is that special strains can be used to meet particular requirements: the farmer need no longer depend on whatever happens to be growing in the field. Numerous strains have been produced at the plant breeding station, Aberystwyth, first

[1] During grazing experiments at Drayton it was observed that cattle kept approximately an 8-hour day: 8 hours were spent in grazing, during which time the animal walked about 2 miles, and 8 hours were spent lying down and chewing the cud, the other 8 were spent in sleep, etc.

[2] J. M. Hopkins, *New Zealand Jl. Agric.*, Dec. 1948; R. A. Hamilton, *Proc. Fert. Soc.*, No. 8, 1950. M. E. Castle and A. S. Foot (*Agriculture*, 1949, Vol. 56, pp. 1–6) give details about the fences and water supply.

under Sir George Stapledon and, later, T. J. Jenkin, and much information has been obtained at the Grassland Research Station, first at Drayton, and now at Hurley, Berkshire, by William Davies and his colleagues as to the most suitable for any particular conditions. Only few species are needed: rye grass, cocksfoot (especially in dry conditions), and timothy (for moister conditions) are the chief, with white and red clovers. Usually these grasses are left down only for a few years. When they have passed their period of maximum productiveness they are ploughed up and a succession of arable crops is taken before sowing down again. This alternate grass and arable husbandry is called ley farming; it is more productive than the old permanent grass and permanent arable farming. It is an old method and has long been practised in the west and north of Great Britain. The modern form differs from the old in that the ley is made up of properly selected strains of grasses and clovers, and it has become the central pivot of the rotation.

These new leys are considerably more productive than the old pastures (Table XIX). They have the further advantage that they can be adapted to a remarkable degree to meet varying requirements.[1] Their composition can be varied at will; and can differ in various fields; growth can be retarded by sowing under a nurse crop or hastened by sowing without any cover, or modified by early or late nitrogenous dressings. Much staggering thus becomes possible in utilizing the herbage: already it is possible to extend the grazing season from the usual 26 or 30 weeks to something nearer 45: from early March almost up to February. William Davies is optimistic enough to believe in the possibility of having grass in every month of the year. The dead periods of the present grazing systems are being filled out: the rye grass and clover mixture which yield well in spring and autumn, but not so well in summer, can be supplemented by mixtures of timothy, meadow fescue, cocksfoot, and wild white clover which have a longer season of productiveness.

TABLE XIX. *Liveweight increases of grazing cattle, lb. per acre*

Good pastures	*Permanent pasture*	*Ley*
Leicestershire (1945–1949)	301–422 (1)	286–427
Hereford (1945)	404	660
Leicestershire (1945–1949)	219–340	252–401
Essex (1946)	332	408
Second-class pastures		
Bedford (1944–1948)	146–250	144–356
Sussex (1945–1947)	184–264	242–476
Durham (1946–1947)	268–328	299–323

(Results collected and summarized by T. E. Williams.)

Old style	*Starch equivalent cwt. per acre*
Poor pasture (Cockle Park)	5·5
Poor pasture + basic slag	11

(1) Linehan (loc. cit.) estimated that some of these Leicestershire pastures supplied 30–33 cwt. per acre of starch equivalent.

[1] They require also less seed, only about 12 lb. to 16 lb. per acre instead of the 30 to 40 lb. of the older and more complex mixtures.

Experiments with sheep at the Grass Land Improvement Station, Drayton, in 1946, have given useful data showing how greatly white clover improves the feeding value of the herbage. The results per acre were:—

	Old pasture	Timothy	Timothy and white clover	White clover
Live weight increase lb.	265	257	554	559
Herbage (dry matter) consumed lb.	4,828	3,887	7,209	6,250
Starch equivalent (maintenance and live weight increase) lb.	1,820	1,560	3,110	2,960
Sheep grazing days	1,020	878	1,550	1,430

These high outputs are attainable only by proper use of fertilizers. There must be little or no soil acidity: the pH should not be below 5·5 and is better to be about 6·5. All three fertilizer constituents are needed, but especially nitrogen, of which grass contains a considerable quantity and to which it responds well so long as sufficient phosphate and potash are given. In the I.C.I. folding experiments quoted above the dressing per acre was 4 cwt. of superphosphate, 1–3 cwt. muriate of potash, and 7¼ cwt. nitro-chalk in four doses; a dressing of 2 cwt. early in spring, followed by another after each cutting or grazing.

Among the ordinary crops grass is equalled only by marrow stem kale in the amount of fertilizer nitrogen it can advantageously receive provided always it is kept properly grazed or cut: even after it ceases to make further growth its protein content may still increase. Late dressings, especially, have this effect. In one of the I.C.I. experiments grass without nitrogen but with ample phosphate, potash, and lime manuring, yielded 10·8 cwt. of starch equivalents per acre utilized by the grazing animals and 14·5 cwt. per acre starch equivalent in the hay crop, a total of 25·3 cwt. per acre: while the addition of 10½ cwt. per acre nitro-chalk applied in four dressings raised this to 40·9 cwt. starch equivalent per acre: 24·3 cwt. being utilized by the animals and 16·6 cwt. contained in the hay crop. Phosphatic fertilizers have no such dramatic effect on these good swards as on the poor boulder clay, such as that of Cockle Park; they may give increases of 10 to 25 per cent, but they are needed to bring out the full effect of the nitrogen.

Good as they seem to us, these new and improved strains of grasses and clovers do not altogether satisfy the grazing animals. Often when sated with the rich vegetation they will eagerly devour some weed—docks or wild grasses—offered to them, or if they get the chance will wander on to poorer or wild ground in search of plants that have been excluded by the grass expert.[1] "Bloat" has often been reported where there is too much clover in the mixture and Dutch investigators have shown that the improved herbage lacks something required for chewing the cud, tends to overtax the kidneys, and may depress the milk yields.[2] The difficulty is partly met by allowing the animals sufficient access to unimproved verges or to less intensely managed grass.

[1] Interesting observations are reported by R. G. Stapledon in *Agriculture*, 1948, Vol. 55, p. 231. The palatability of some of these grasses is discussed by W. E. J. Milton in *Empire Jl. Expt. Agric.*, 1953. Vol. 21, pp. 116–122.
[2] B. Sjollema, 5th Internat. Grassland Congress, 1949.

Increasing output of grass by using more vigorous strains or by more liberal application of fertilizers is in any case likely to intensify deficiencies of trace elements or others; these may have to be supplied.

Both temporary and permanent grass deteriorate rapidly if they are allowed to grow too old, and this must be prevented if necessary by mowing. The grass is too short to be made into hay in the usual way: it can be picked up by an implement of the buck-rake type and either made into silage or dried artificially—the picker-up, the pit silo, and the drier rank in importance with the electric fence in modern grassland management.

Ensilage is an old process introduced into England from America in the wet seasons of the 1880's when haymaking was impossible.[1] The modern methods are a great improvement on the old: A. I. Virtanen's method (always called A.I.V. for short), requires the use of sulphuric acid which is inconvenient but it involves only little loss of feeding material, while the molasses method, which is easier to carry out, entails some loss. The final product is so good as winter food and so easily made that it is becoming increasingly popular.

Artificial drying, however, gives a better product. A number of driers of various types and sizes are now obtainable. Many large farmers are setting up their own and using them also for drying combined grain: some smaller farmers are running a joint dryer, and the Milk Marketing Board is experimenting with a co-operative scheme. About 10 to 15 cwt. of coke or 70 to 80 gallons of oil are usually needed to produce one ton of dried product: the final moisture content is about 6 per cent, but more is rapidly absorbed up to 12 per cent; the crude protein content is about 16–20 per cent.[2] R. E. Slade, farming near Bishops Stortford, has obtained some remarkable yields of dried grass:

Cwt. nitro-chalk per acre	Crude protein in dried grass per cent	Total weight dried grass cwt. per acre
0	11	35
4	15	41
8	17	50
12	18	60

(*Jl. Roy. Soc. Arts*, 1951, Vol. 99, pp. 501–11.)

[1] The old methods are described in papers of the *Journ. Roy. Agric. Soc.* for 1884; see also E. J. Russell and H. E. Annett, *Journ. Agric. Sci.*, 1908, Vol. 2, pp. 382–391.

[2] Commercial samples sometimes contain less because the grass has been allowed to grow old.

Chapter 4

NORTHERN EUROPE'S INTENSIVE PRODUCERS

Partly for climatic reasons, and partly because of its topography and its history, the most productive region in Europe is in the north-west: it includes Denmark, the Netherlands, South Sweden, and Norway, followed by Belgium, West Germany, North France, and Switzerland. Output per man and output per acre are alike higher than in any other part of Europe. Next, in order, come East Germany, Czechoslovakia, Hungary, Italy, Spain, and Southern France; while still lower are Poland, the Balkan States, U.S.S.R., Greece, and Portugal. During their period of independence Latvia, Estonia, and Lithuania came nearer to Western standards than did the surrounding countries. The high output per man in the north-western region enables one agricultural worker to feed more people, and to feed them better, than is possible in the less productive regions; a smaller agricultural population, therefore, suffices and a larger number can be spared for industry, commerce, and the professions. In the north-west and central regions about 25 to 30 per cent of the population are dependent on agriculture and suffice to feed the rest of the people; in the eastern regions the proportion rises to 70 or even 80 per cent.

Europe can thus be divided into zones of productiveness centring round Great Britain: the most productive being nearest the centre, the less productive lying beyond, and the least productive on the periphery. In this same order come the other characteristics associated with high productiveness: standard of living and health, higher expectation of life but lower birthrate, and, ominously for the future, a lower net reproduction rate.

From the point of view of food production the important difference is that the most productive group make livestock their main concern and import grain, while the less productive group have grain as their chief product and livestock is of secondary importance. There is, in fact, a rather rough inverse relation between productiveness and the area under grain: before the war only 8·5 per cent of the cultivated land of Denmark was in bread grain (wheat and rye); in Poland the proportion was 40 per cent and in the U.S.S.R. 45 per cent.

As the standard of living varies with the agricultural productiveness it is not closely related to the area of agricultural land; indeed, the number of acres required to produce food for one person varies much less from country to country than the standard of living. Most European countries, except Holland and Belgium, had, before the war, between 1·3 and 2 acres of agricultural land per head of population. Those with about 2, exported food: Denmark with 2·1 exported livestock products; Poland, the Danubian countries, and the U.S.S.R. exported grain; Germany and others with about 1·5 acres were approximately self-sufficing—though the self-sufficiency was attained by adjusting the dietary to the production possibilities.

78

TABLE XXI. *Production of foods in the different regions of Europe, average 1933–37*
Million tons per annum

	N. and W. Europe	Central and Eastern	Southern	Danubian	Continental Europe (1)	United Kingdom
Bread grains	12·9	21·7	13·9	10·5	59·0	1·7
Other grains	13·9	15·7	9·3	14·8	53·7	2·75
Meat	3·75	4·7	1·7	1·0	11·13	1·4
Dairy produce (2)	38·6	38·7	16·5		94	7·9
Oils and fats (3)	0·98	1·4	1·1	0·46	4·0	0·16
Sugar	2·17	3·48	0·64	0·36	6·65	0·55

(1) Excluding U.S.S.R.

(2) Whole milk equivalent.

(3) All visible fats, edible and inedible, including butter.

The sugar is calculated on raw basis in tons of 2,000 lb., the other foods are in metric tons of 2,204·6 lb.

N. and W. Europe.—France, Belgium, Netherlands, Switzerland, Denmark, Norway, Sweden, Finland.

Central and Eastern.—Poland, Czechoslovakia, Austria, Germany.

Southern.—Portugal, Spain, Italy, Greece.

Danubian.—Hungary, Yugoslavia, Roumania, Bulgaria.

Home production as percentage of consumption
1934–39

	United Kingdom	Continental Europe (1)	N. and W. Europe	Central and Eastern	Southern	Danubian
Grain	31	91	75	92	94	118
Meat	47	101	107	97	95	107
Dairy	42	105	114	97	—	102
Oils and fats	11	67	54	53	90	119
Sugar	21	95	78	116	76	97

(1) Excluding U.S.S.R.

(*Cmd. 6879/1946.*)

The pre-war pattern of European agriculture is shown in Table XXI. North-Western Europe produced surpluses of meat and of dairy produce (also fruit and vegetables) but insufficient grain, sugar, oils, and fats. Central and Eastern Europe were practically self-sufficing in meat and dairy produce (achieved by a low rate of consumption), but not in grain or in oils and fats. They produced, however, a considerable surplus of sugar for export. The Danubian countries had surpluses of all products except sugar. Before the war these surpluses were sent to the north-west and the south in exchange for goods and services; in consequence, Europe as a whole was nearly self-sufficing in food; there was a deficit of 9 per cent only in grain, and of 5 per cent in sugar; the only serious shortage was in oils and fats, where it amounted to 33 per cent. As against this there was a net export of dairy produce amounting to 5 per cent of the production, and a smaller net export of meat, both mainly to Great Britain. There were thus two dominant movements in the European trade in food stuffs: the movement of grain and sugar from east to west; and of livestock products, vegetables, and fresh fruit from the west mainly to Great Britain. The quantities of the different commodities were, in million metric tons:

Annual average 1934–39	*All grain*	*Wheat* (2)	*Meat*	*Dairy produce*	*Oils and fats*	*Sugar*
Home production	112·7	59·0	11·13	94·0	4·0	6·65
Import	11·1	3·7	−0·07 (3)	−3·6 (3)	2·1 (4)	0·52
Total available	123·8 (1)	62·7	11·06	90·4	6·1	7·2

(*World Food Shortage*, Cmd. 6879, H.M.S.O., July 1946.)

(1) Of this, 57·9 m. were for human food, 47·4 m. for feeding to animals, and 18·5 m. for seed and other uses.
(2) Includes rye and 35·2 m. tons flour. Average extraction rate, 72 per cent.
(3) Export.
(4) Includes also stock changes.

So long as the exchange of goods between East and West Europe worked smoothly Europe was assured of its food. There was considerable scope for improving yields in Eastern Europe, which would have permitted a rise in the standard of living there and at the same time ensured the extra supplies which in due course the west would require.

All this has been changed by the last war. The amount of destruction was far greater than in the first: indeed the ravages are not even yet healed. Even in the second season after fighting had ceased food production was down by 25 to nearly 50 per cent, in spite of generous help given by the United Nations Relief and Rehabilitation Administration (U.N.R.R.A.) (Table XXII).

TABLE XXII. *Food production in Europe, pre-war and 1945–46*
Million tons annually

Average	*All grain*	*Wheat*	*Meat*	*Dairy produce*	*Oils and fats*	*Sugar*
1934–39	112·7	59·0	11·1	94	4·0	6·6
1945–46	85	31·3	6·4	64	2·6	3·6
Percentage fall	25	47	42	32	35	45

Farmers were doing their best to retrieve the situation but the bitter winter of 1946–47 caused heavy losses of stock and winter-sown crops; while rains and floods in spring, and serious droughts in the summer, greatly lowered the cereal yields, making the season one of the worst on record.

Later seasons and outputs have been better, but a new difficulty has arisen. It is by no means certain how far the old east-west grain traffic will be resumed. It is still continuing, but on a much diminished scale: in 1938 Western Europe had imported $1,685 million worth of food stuffs from Eastern Europe, but in 1948 $307 million only. This low level of trade injures both sets of countries: Western Europe needs the grain, and Eastern Europe needs capital goods for development of industries to absorb its redundant rural population, but it can pay for them only by exports of agricultural produce. There are several reasons for this falling off. Western Europe cannot supply so easily as before the things that Eastern Europe wants; and the splitting up of the large estates in Eastern Europe has lowered the production of grain, though this might increase again if the new small farms were improved. The chief uncertainty is political. Among the many gains the war brought to Russia one of the greatest has been to secure full control over this east–west movement of food, with the result that the west can no longer rely on Eastern Europe for supplies; although for a time they may be forthcoming they are liable at any time to be cut off. The Soviet Union has already on occasion switched some of its exported wheat to Egypt, Pakistan, and Brazil.

Western Germany has suffered considerably by the partition. Before the war the eastern section was the granary and the west produced livestock products and manufactured goods: the country was nearly self-sufficing, and needed to import only about two million tons of grain. But since the Russian occupation the eastern section has supplied very little and much larger imports have been needed: they have been:

	1949	1950	1951	
Million tons	5·0	2·7	3·75	bread and coarse grains
of which wheat	2·4	1·7	2·7	

(*Grain Crops*, Commonwealth Econ. Cttee., H.M.S.O., 1953.)

A new orientation of the European nations has therefore become necessary. Following the disasters of 1946 and 1947, General Marshall made his famous speech at Harvard, in June 1947, offering financial aid to Europe if a sound plan for recovery of industry, transport, and agriculture could be drawn up and put into operation. Ernest Bevin promptly called the European ministers together at Paris, and the European Recovery Programme was duly prepared; the organization for European Economic Co-operation was set up to assist in carrying it out. The United States Senate made a grant of $5,000 million for the first year and supplemented this later; by 1950 a total of $11,000 million had been given; 1952 was the last year for this Marshall Aid, by which time it was hoped that Europe would be self-supporting once more.

Each country drew up plans and set up "targets" in the usual way, all sufficently above pre-war outputs to allow for the growth of population. In general the agricultural part necessitated imports of fertilizers, feeding stuffs, and implements, especially tractors. These did not become available in the quantities requested, and in the main the "targets" were not attained; the 1949 wheat harvests surpassed that of pre-war only in Great Britain (15 per cent), Sweden (5 per cent), and Turkey (25 per cent). In France the harvest fell below that of pre-war by 15 per cent and in Belgium by 20 per cent. But a great deal was done. By 1950 the areas of bread grains, coarse grains, and potatoes were nearly up to pre-war levels and the area of sugar beet was 31 per cent higher. (Table XXIII.) More important still, the yields in North-West Europe and the United Kingdom were higher than pre-war, due in part at least to improvements in their already advanced agriculture. The total food production for all Western Europe, however, was not yet up to pre-war levels, and in the meantime the population had risen and it was necessary to continue imports on a substantial scale; during 1950 nearly $2,000 million were allocated for imported foods.[1] Efforts at improvement were still pressed forward: more fertilizers were used, and more tractors became available.

Consumption of fertilizers, cwt. per acre of agricultural land (1) *in Western Europe*

	Pre-war	1947–48	1949–50	1950–51
Nitrogen (N)	6·0	7·1	8·5	(9·4)
Phosphate (P_2O_5)	10·4	11·0	12·9	(14·3)
Potash (K_2O)	7·8	9·0	10·6	(11·4)
Total	24·2	27·1	32·0	(35·1)

(1) Omitting rough grazings.
(*Economic Progress and Problems of Western Europe*, O.E.E.C., June 1951.)

TABLE XXIII. *Area under crops, and quantities produced in O.E.E.C. countries Pre-war* = 100[2]

	Area			Production		
	1947	1949	1950	1947	1949	1950
Bread grains	89	94	97	60	96	102
Coarse grains	100	97	97	82	98	99
Potatoes	100	97	97	91	102	121
Sugar beet	105	122	131	78	119	155
Fodder roots	97	92	89	72	85	102
Oil seeds	165	231	244	217	383	371

(*Economic Progress and Problems of Western Europe*, O.E.E.C., June 1951.)

The number of tractors in the O.E.E.C. countries rose from 194,000 in 1938 to 724,000 in 1950: nearly half the increase was in the United Kingdom, but the increase in France was from 35,000 to 130,000, and in Germany from 21,500 to 103,000.[3]

The numbers of livestock were slightly above pre-war and the output of their products was higher. The food position continued to improve and, adding

[1] *Economist*, December 10, 1949. The value of imports is given by O.E.E.C. (loc. cit.) as follows:

Food and agricultural imports of ten member countries
Million current dollars quarterly rates

	1948	1949 1st 3 qtrs.	1950 3rd qtr.	1950 4th qtr.
Imported from participating countries	349	429	497	602
U.S.A. and Canada	532	493	232	308
Other sources	1,290	1,181	1,006	1,108
Totals	2,171	2,103	1,735	2,018

[2] The actual pre-war areas and outputs were:

	Million acres	Million tons
Average 1934–38:		
Bread grains	55·64	33·51
Coarse grains	44·86	30·00
Potatoes	10·66	56·82
Sugar beet	2·40	3·40 (sugar)

(*Economist*, October 16, 1948.)

[3] O.E.E.C., loc. cit.

all foods together, F.A.O. estimated that in 1950–51 the total output in the O.E.E.C. countries was 111, and the output of livestock products 108, compared with 100 in each case before the war.

In Eastern Europe, however, recovery has been slower. Poland alone had increased its acreage of wheat, but as the yield had fallen the total output fell also: the acreage of rye and of other grains also fell. (Table XXIV.)

TABLE XXIV. *Acreage of chief crops, pre-war and* 1950

Poland

	Million acres Average		Cwt. per acre Average		Million tons Average	
	1934–38	1950	1934–38	1950	1934–39	1950
Wheat	3·3	3·7	11·7	9·9	1·96	1·85
Rye	13·2	12·7	10·2	10·1	6·85	6·50
Other grains	8·1	7·0			4·93	3·54
All grains	24·6	23·4			13·74	11·89
Potatoes	6·8	6·5	5·5	5·5 tons 38·0		36·8
Sugar beet	0·55	0·71	10·6	8·9 tons 6·0		6·4

(*F.A.O. Stat. Year Book*, 1951. It should be remembered that Poland lost 18·5 million acres as the result of the war.)

The available data indicate similar falls in other Eastern European countries. The result was that, in spite of recovery by the O.E.E.C. group, Europe as a whole had not attained its pre-war level of food production at the time of the F.A.O. second world survey in 1952. The population had gone up from the pre-war 371 millions to 394 millions in 1950, but neither areas nor outputs of food crops, except sugar beet, had increased:

Area, yields, and production of crops in Europe, pre-war and 1949–51

	Million acres Average		Yield per acre Average		Million tons Average	
	1934–39	1949–51	1934–38	1949–51	1934–38	1949–51
Wheat	73·7	70·0	11·4	11·8 cwt.	42·3	41·6
Other grains	122·1	111·5			75·0	69·2
Potatoes	24·8	23·0	5·4	5·5 tons	135	128
Sugar beet					6·5	8·2

(*F.A.O. Second World Food Survey*, 1952, p. 28.)
The situation had, however, improved by 1953.

North-West Europe will still always have to import grain to feed both its animal and its human populations, and apparently more and more of this will come from North America.

THE NETHERLANDS

The Netherland country is a remarkable example of what men can do in wresting land from the sea and the rivers: nowhere in the world has there been better reclamation, or more of it in relation to the total area. Much of the inland part consists of pleistocene sands deposited by the Rhine and the

Meuse. Ice movements during the Ice Age pushed up some of these sands into low hills, and wind-blown sand in late pleistocene times covered up some of the older deposits. Peat was formed in the damp, lower-lying places. Towards the coast, however, much of the present land had until recently lain under the sea and become covered with extensive deposits of marine clays, silts, sand, and shells. As the sea level fell and the new surface appeared intermittent lines of sand dunes were formed along the new coast line and the sea water left behind them was gradually replaced by fresh water in which peat began to form. At a later stage the sea again penetrated, depositing more marine clay which gradually became covered with vegetation giving rise to more peat.

Human settlement began several centuries before Christ; by the 10th century, dykes were being constructed; by the 14th century they were fairly numerous, and the monks actively participated in making them. Dams provided with sluice gates were built across the mouths of some of the smaller streams to prevent the sea entering at high tide and covering the land, hence the prevalence in place names of the termination, "-dam": Amstel, Rotte, Schie, Ee, and others are all streams or tidal creeks. Provision was made for holding the river water ("boezem") during high tide when the sluices had to be shut. In the early 15th century the invention of the windmill pump enabled the lower land to be drained and lakes to be converted into dry land. Extensive use of these two appliances, dams and windmill pumps, began in the 17th century after the expulsion of the Spaniards left the Dutch masters of their own country. About half the country was then waste moors, heaths, and pools, but a period of prosperity set in, and trade with the Indies provided money which enabled thousands of acres to be reclaimed—some 200,000 acres of pools were drained between 1600 and 1640. The pictures of the old painters leave no doubt about the prosperity and cheerfulness of the peasantry. Napoleon's blockade of Europe in 1807 caused much distress but a benevolent society was formed to reclaim and colonize some of the 2·2 million acres of waste. In the bad times of the 1840's the Haarlemmermeer, a stretch of 46,000 acres, was drained (1848–52); its bed of sea clay has now become a prosperous arable region. Adjoining it on the west, on pure dune sand, is now the most famous tulip-growing area in the world; prior to reclamation it had been, like other sandy tracts, a nuisance because of the quantities of dust raised by the wind in the dry summers—the peaty tracts suffered similarly. There was distress again during the crisis of the 1880's when cheap American wheat flooded the world's markets and caused the breakdown of Dutch agriculture. But, again, the remedy was sought in reclamation. In 1888 a society was founded at Arnheim on the model of the already existing Danish society for heath reclamation; it was called the Niederlandsche Heidemaat Schappij, and its purpose was to reclaim some of the 1¾ million acres to which the waste had now been reduced. This is still functioning: before the war some 20,000 acres a year were being reclaimed. Power pumps have replaced the windmills with a gain of efficiency but great loss of picturesqueness. During the war the process of reclamation was reversed and some 627,500 acres were flooded or otherwise put out of action, and 75,000 acres of wood cut down. After the war reconstruction speedily began and once again the area of cultivated land is steadily being increased.

By far the most spectacular of all the Dutch reclamations, and one of the greatest feats of modern times, has been the reclamation of much of the former Zuider Zee. The law authorizing the work was passed in 1918, and operations began in 1923. It was realized that the whole area could not be drained; part had to be left to become a fresh-water lake, which would serve

THE PARTIAL RECLAMATION OF THE ZUYDERSEA

[Courtesy of the Netherlands Embassy]

Fig. 6.—Map showing reclamations in North Holland 1608 to 1952

as a reservoir and also maintain the underground water level in the adjacent land: this is the Ijsselmeer: its area is to be 250,000 acres. A survey of the sea floor showed which parts were fertile clay that could become good farm-land, and which were sand that would serve as village sites; it showed, also, the best locations for the Ijsselmeer and the dykes. In 1930 the Andijk pilot scheme was completed on the west side of the Zuider Zee, and was used as an experimental polder, where methods were discovered for bringing the new land as rapidly as possible into cultivation. A two-kilometre barrage was built linking up Wieringen with North Holland and an area of 50,000 acres of the sea was enclosed. The water was pumped out—causing, incidentally, a great glut of fish in the locality, for as the water level fell they congregated in the deeper parts and were easily captured. The soil contained a good deal of salt which, fortunately, the rain soon washed out. Some of its clay, however, had become a sodium complex which had to be converted into the normal calcium complex before ordinary agriculture could be practised. This was done by adding gypsum (about 1 to 4 tons per acre in several dressings), growing clover, and ploughing in the residues. So the first polder, the Wieringenmeer polder, came into existence.

Meanwhile, the great dyke from Den Oever, in North Holland, to Zurig, in Friesland, was closed on May 28, 1932. The position of the main polders had been decided and in 1937 work began on the north-east polder of 118,000 acres: the surrounding dyke was completed by December 1940 and the pumping out of the water by September 1942. Detailed soil surveys had already indicated where the farmhouses and villages should be located and what rentals could reasonably be asked. The whole area had to be underdrained, but on the sandy soils the drains fulfil the double purpose of removing water in winter and bringing it in during the summer when sub-irrigation ("infiltration") becomes necessary to ensure full growth; this is effected by raising the water level in the ditches. The drains were completed by 1944 but the soil was not yet ready for farming. There was, it is true, no salt problem, the sea water having been largely displaced by the fresh. The Government took over the land, sowed it with grasses[1] and clover to add organic matter and build up soil structure; as the risks of failure diminish the land is let out to tenants in farms of 30 acres on the good, light soils, but more on the heavier soils. The whole polder has been planned on the basis of soil and social studies: the villages are so placed that no farm will be more than four miles away from one. Already a shop and a school have appeared—a church is to come and, meanwhile, services are held in the houses. Ornamental shrubs are provided to start the gardens and free advice is given on how to make the best use of them. Houses and buildings alike are attractive; they are not always up to the old standards because the quality of the materials has fallen off, but the best available are used.

It is expected that about a quarter of the land will remain in pasture (more on the sub-irrigated part) and that Friesian dairy cattle will be kept. Yields of 360 gallons of milk per acre are anticipated.

Lucerne grows well, and on the arable land cereals, flax and roots. The rents in 1950 were 150 to 170 guilders per nectare (110s. to 116s. per acre). A population of 40,000 is expected. (Plate 9, p. 108.)

Not all of the soil is suitable for farming; about 6 per cent of it is too light and is to be afforested, poplars, willows, and alder being grown. Poplars are also planted along the roads for shelter.

Work has already commenced on the south-east polder of 240,000 acres, and on the south-west polder of 135,000 acres.

These great schemes do not exhaust the efforts of the Dutch people to extend their territory. Smaller schemes have long been in progress around the

---

[1] *Lolium per., Phleum prat., Poa triv. and prat. Festuca prat.*

coast of Groningen where accretion of land has proceeded naturally to the stage at which a dyke could be built to prevent further flooding by the sea. Some 160,000 acres of inlet and coast land have been reclaimed since the records began in the 13th century. Another impressive scheme is on the Lauwerszee, south-west of Zoutkamp; it is to bring in 13,000 acres. An improved Schleswig-Holstein method is used. Square settling basins, 400 metres each way, are made in the inter-tidal area by dams of clay, or of wooden piles with brushwood; inside these is a system of ditches. The tide comes in laden with silt which it deposits in the ditches and then flows quietly out. The silt is taken out of the ditches and laid on the mud between them, so raising its level. Numerous algae, *Zostera*, and other plants grow on the mud and help to bind it; various molluscs (*Lamelli branchiates*) play an important part by ingesting clay particles with their food and excreting them as larger particles which settle much more rapidly. The land rises two to four inches yearly. At a certain stage *Salicornia herbacea* comes in, also *Aster trifolium* and *Glyceria maritima*; this last is perennial and forms dense sods, hence is a very valuable reclamation agent.

Much more work of this kind could be done. At low tide much of the Waddenzee is dry and could be dyked, but the bottom is poor sand of little agricultural value. With the growth of population it may still be necessary to take in some of this area for the building of a town. The work is very costly; the estimate in 1950 for the Lauwerszee scheme was about 10,000 guilders per *ha* (£380 per acre) and the rent at £7 10s. per acre. The cost of the Zuider Zee scheme is much more. But the population of Holland is growing. The net reproduction rate is one of the highest in Europe; more land is needed, and, as is pointed out to the visitor, even costly reclamation is cheaper than war as a means of extending territory, besides being more certain.

The third type of reclamation being practised in Holland is that of the moorlands and heaths. Large areas are peat, usually the upper layer is sphagnum, the rest is reed and sedge peat. Before the coal-mines were worked much of this was used as fuel; its removal left a series of pools and barren stretches of sand. The pools are now generally drained and the land cultivated, excepting where its position is such that water would perpetually soak in from the surrounding area making continuous and costly pumping necessary; in that case the pools are left for recreation or as reservoirs. But the sand is made productive; it is levelled, dressed with the sphagnum (*bonkaard*) layer, sand dredged out of the canals, and any available town refuse, and the whole mixed by cultivation. One of the largest schemes is an area of nearly 200,000 acres of "high moor" peat in Drenthe. The reclaimed land is used for arable cultivation; the chief crops are cereals and potatoes, almost all for farina.

An important reason for the striking success of Dutch agriculture is that it is highly specialized and completely suited to its surroundings. Many of the reclaimed farms produce no farmyard manure but use large quantities of fertilizers: a common dressing per acre is 60–100 lb. nitrogen as nitro-chalk, 48–56 lb. P_2O_5 as superphosphate, and 100–140 lb. K_2O. Yields are high: potatoes give 12 to 16 tons per acre, wheat and barley 30 cwt. per acre, oats 36 cwt. per acre, and rye 28 cwt. per acre. Some of the land in Drenthe giving yields of this order was reclaimed in 1875 and has been more than seventy-five years without farmyard manure; it has had only occasional green manuring, yet the yields show no signs of falling. There is much discussion in Holland as to whether organic matter is necessary in the soil or not.

The possibility of utilizing the light sands depends entirely on the position of the water level. Where this is sufficiently near the surface intensive horticulture becomes possible and Holland's special crops are grown to perfection, some in the open, some under glass: bulbs, early vegetables, garden plants, Alicante grapes, and others. In the dune-sand district, between Haarlem and Leiden, good bulb land is sold at fantastic prices and great expense is incurred in making new land. Dunes of calcareous sand are decapitated, the dry upper layers are sold—for stone is scarce and sand commands a high price for road making and other purposes—then, when a level is reached about half a metre or so above the water table, a valuable horticultural holding can be made. The sand is liable to wind erosion, and the holding is divided into many little rectangles by rows of maize, oats, or other plants acting as windbreaks, these little plots make the place look like an experimental garden. Heavy fertilizer dressings are given in addition to farmyard manure purchased from stock farmers, the top soil is periodically put well below to prevent accumulation of pathogenic organisms.

One of the most intensively cultivated regions in the world is in the western part of South Holland, where there are some 7,500 acres of fruit and vegetables, 5,000 acres of which are under glass either as houses or frames. Each house has its rather tall chimney making the area look somewhat like a congestion of miniature factories. (Plate 10.) The average-sized nursery is $2\frac{1}{2}$ to 4 acres. About a third of the gross income from Holland's 330,000 acres of horticultural and garden land is earned in this district: grapes, peaches, plums, and tomatoes are grown in the houses, and cucumbers, salad vegetables, and cauliflowers in the frames. A local experiment station at Naaldwijk deals with the growers' problems. A complicated system of drainage is necessary as the level of the land varies from 0 to 20 feet below high-water mark at Amsterdam, and the ground water level has to be kept from $1\frac{1}{2}$ to $3\frac{1}{2}$ feet below the surface.[1] Sand, also, is carried on to some of the heavier soils to make them more suitable for horticulture.

These light, sandy soils occur largely in the south-west of the country. In the west, centre, and north-west there are considerable areas of clay which are put into grass for dairy cattle. Friesland, in its northern part, is one of the most intensive dairying regions in the world with some 48,000 pedigree milch cattle, 38,000 of which give 1,100 gallons of milk or more a year with an average fat content of 3·84 per cent. It occupies only 10 per cent of the area of Holland, but it produces 20 per cent of the total milk and butter outputs and 50 per cent of the cheese; indeed, it claimed before the war to produce nearly 200 million gallons of milk annually within a circle of twenty miles radius. In the eastern sections of the country the soils are lighter and there is much mixed farming.

The climate everywhere is suitable for crop production; the average annual rainfall is about 28 inches, fairly evenly distributed, but with a minimum in February and a maximum in August; the centre of the country is rather

[1] Drainage and sub-irrigation are controlled by local water boards which are co-ordinated by a special Ministry.

wetter. Evaporation in summer may exceed rainfall, however, and droughts are liable to occur, necessitating sub-irrigation. The mean annual temperature is rather lower in the north (49° F) than in the south (52° F), but nowhere does the mean winter minimum fall below 32° F. Cattle have to be indoors, however, for some five months in the year.

The total surface of Holland, land and water, is 9·88 million acres, and of land surface, including, however, lakes less than 185 acres in extent, is 8·22 million acres. This was used as follows in 1939 and in 1949 and 1950:

	Million acres		
	1939	1949	1950
Arable land	2·16	2·27	2·29
Grass land	3·27	3·25	3·26
Horticulture	0·25	0·33	0·33
Total cultivated (1)	5·59	5·71	5·77

(1) Smaller than the sum of arable, grass and horticulture as horticulture overlaps with grass and orchards and with arable.

(*Rpt. to F.A.O.*, 1951.)

The area of cultivated land increased between 1939 and 1950 by 180,000 acres; the arable had gone up by 130,000 acres and the horticultural land by 80,000: there had been a small decrease in the grassland. In 1950 there were about 282,000 agricultural and horticultural holdings. Nearly all are small: the horticultural are often only 2½–5 acres, many are less; the farms are usually about 50 to 150 acres; mixed holdings come in between. Only a small number of farms exceed 150 acres. Co-operation is effectively organized. The total number of regular workers, including occupiers, was in 1939–40, 735,000, which, however, included 53,000 children under 15; in 1950 the number had fallen to 582,000, the under-fifteens being now down to 5,500. Increasing mechanization has been partly the cause, partly the result.

Nowhere is cultivable land so zealously guarded by law as in Holland. Land classification maps based on soil surveys have been prepared to show what land may, and what may not, be used for non-agricultural purposes, public recreation, building, etc. Much good horticultural land had been threatened at Breda, and elsewhere, but was saved by the survey; unfortunately at Bergen op Zoom much had already been lost before the Act was passed.

The population in 1949–50 was 10·03 millions; the area of cultivated land per head was, therefore, just below 0·6 acres. On this small area it is impracticable for the Dutch people to produce the whole of their food. A choice had to be made, and very wisely the decision was to concentrate on high quality, highly-priced commodities needing great skill for their production, and to rely on outside sources for grains which give relatively low returns per acre, and for oil seeds which, in any case, cannot as yet be grown in sufficient quantity. Before the war considerable amounts of these were imported thus allowing the production of large quantities of dairy and horticultural produce and eggs for export, and of sufficient meat to provide a moderate surplus for export. The areas and outputs of the chief crops are given in Table XXV.

TABLE XXV. *Areas and production of chief crops, pre-war and later*

| | Thousand acres | | | Thousand tons | | |
	1939	1949	1950	Average 1934–8	1949	1950
Rye	533	450	432	499·5	516·8	421
Wheat	294	243	225	429·6	425·3	295
Oats	388	321	348	351·2	423·8	382
Barley	100	116	170	124·0	188·6	232
All cereals	1,314	1,163	1,222	1,404·3	1,554·6	
Potatoes						
edible	227	309	300	3,080	3,064	2,846
industrial	69	123	111	698	1,541	1,205
Sugar beet	109	161	165	1,637	2,943	2,717
Fodder roots	119	141	139		3,444	3,466
Green fodder crops	54	94	67			
Total arable land	2,166	2,268	2,286			
Total cultivated area	5,592	5,706	5,775			

Catch crops are not included in the above Table.
(*F.A.O. Food Balance Sheets*, 1948.)
(*Rpt. to F.A.O.*, 1951.)

About half the arable land was in cereals in 1949 and 1950 and about one-third in roots, including potatoes; the remaining 17 per cent was in temporary grasses, clovers, lucerne, and other crops. Among the latter were 52,000 acres of agricultural and market-garden seed crops, a growing and important industry, having an official control organization, N.A.K., which inspects the crops and issues certificates of purity. 62,000 acres of colza, and some poppy, were grown for oil and, also, some hybrid maize brought in from the United States but now grown from Dutch seed and proving very successful: this is probably the most northerly region in which it is grown. It promises to give considerably higher yields than the ordinary cereals. No regular rotations are practised.

There have been some interesting and significant crop changes since the war. The area of cultivated land has gone up but the increase has been mainly in industrial and fodder crops, potatoes (including seed potatoes), and sugar beet, and in barley alone among the cereals. The area of bread grains, wheat, and rye has shrunk from 827,000 to 657,000 acres. This was the result of price-fixing but it is quite sound from the technical point of view: bread grains are the easiest and least profitable products of arable land, while crops for industry and livestock require more capital and skill to grow successfully and are more profitable and attractive to the competent farmer.

The grassland is being steadily improved; indeed, Holland has some of the most intensively managed grassland in Europe. The grazing season is about six months, from the end of April to the beginning of November. The average pre-war production of the permanent grass was about 2,200 lb. of starch equivalent and 440 lb. crude protein per acre: the quantities needed to yield 3,160 lb. of milk per acre. In 1950 the average was 3,840 lb. milk per acre and 8,326 per cow. Many pastures do much better and yield 6,000 to 7,000 lb. of milk per acre. On the best grass farms tripods are used for making hay, some of the grass is converted into silage and some is dried.

Grass drying is being increasingly practised and loans are readily obtainable for purchase of the plant; 60,000 tons were produced in 1951, 60 per cent of the plants are owned co-operatively. It is very useful in the new Zuider Zee polders for dealing with the large areas of lucerne, clover, and grass that will continue to be grown till the soil has become conditioned for arable crops. The average protein content is 19 per cent and the usual range is 16 to 22 per cent. 100 lb. of dried grass is reckoned equivalent to 75 lb. of imported feeding stuffs.[1]

Nitrogenous fertilizer is freely used; up to 160 lb. nitrogen (N) per acre as nitro-chalk may be given in five or six dressings, but half this is the usual quantity. Close folding is increasingly practised[2] on these good pastures. The grass is so rich in protein that carbohydrate foods, especially sugar beet pulp, also boiled potatoes and potato sludge from farina factories, have to be fed to balance it. As in other countries, however, there is considerable range in quality. About a third of the grassland falls below the average; this occurs mostly on the low-lying acid silts, or on peaty soils which may need drainage, phosphate and lime or, in some cases, reseeding. But the good permanent grass is so good that farmers have shown little interest in leys, and they are but little grown in Holland.

Crop yields are very heavy: over the whole country the general averages have been:

Per acre	Wheat cwt.	Oats cwt.	Rye cwt.	Barley cwt.	Potatoes tons edible	Ind.	Sugar beet tons	Fodder beet tons
Average 1934–38 (1)	24·0	20·4	18·2	23·8	7·4	10·5	15·2	
1949 (2)	34·0	26·4	23·0	32·0	9·8	12·2	18·1	24·4
1950 (2)	25·8	21·6	19·2	26·8	9·4	10·6	16·2	24·6

Permanent Pasture 20 cwt. starch equivalent per acre. (3)

(1) *F.A.O. Statistical Year Book*, 1949.
(2) *Rpt. to F.A.O.*, 1951.
(3) P. Bruin: *Proc. U.N. Resources Cong.* (U.N. Dept. Econ. Affairs), 1951, Vol. 6.

The horticultural land was used as follows:

	Thousand acres 1949	1950
Fruit	160	169·5
Vegetables	116	121
Bulbs	14·8	16·1
Horticultural seeds	31·3	16·1
Flowers, shrubs, trees, herbs	11·3	11·0
Horticultural area (1)	330·6	329·5

(1) The area of crops exceeds the land area because of double cropping. The area under vegetables includes strawberries and melons. The increase in fruit area is less than is shown here because of a difference in the mode of enumeration: the actual gain is about 2,500 acres. Many orchards also carry grass or arable crops.

[1] A typical ration for a cow giving 5½ gallons of milk is 22 lb. hay, 6½ lb. dried grass, 44 lb. grass silage, and 6½ lb. low protein concentrate (e.g. sugar-beet pulp) to balance the protein.

[2] In the experimental tests close folding using electric fences increased yields on the average by 25 per cent, the range being from 15 to 34 per cent.

The areas under glass are included in the above figures. They were:

Vegetables		Fruit		
1949	1950	1949	1950	
4·8	5·5	2·0	2·0	thousand acres

This increasing intensification of Dutch husbandry is shown in the addition, since 1939, of some 30 per cent to the area devoted to horticulture, in spite of a fall of 3,000 acres in the area under bulbs—due wholly to currency difficulties of the buyers and not at all to any fault of the growers.

Standards of production are among the highest in the world: three or four crops a year are regularly grown and the marketing is done by a very ingenious auction arrangement.

One reason for the high output, both on farms and on horticultural holdings, is the skilful control of the water level in the soils. The Dutch grower never fears too much water; his danger is that there may be too little.[1] Another reason is the heavy consumption of fertilizer which, in Holland, is higher than in any country in the world. The amounts used in 1949–50 were:

	N	P_2O_5	K_2O	Sum
Cwt. per acre of cultivated land	0·47	0·42	0·50	1·39
Thousand metric tons	143	125	153	

There has been a marked increase in the use of nitrogenous fertilizer on grassland since rationing was discontinued.[2] Little use, however, is made of organic residues or sewage sludges as manure; sewage is run into the sea wherever possible. Town waste from the Hague is composted and used (95,000 tons in 1949), also smaller quantities from Groningen, Zandvoort, and other towns.

The numbers of livestock are not yet back to pre-war level but the productivity per animal, and the total output, both of milk and of meat, have increased, in spite of the large decrease in the amounts of grains and oil seeds given to the animals. Before the war two million tons of cereals were fed annually; in 1948 716,000 tons only: a remarkable result due to improvements in the quality of the animals and to a better use of the grass than before the war. The numbers of livestock and outputs of their products are given in Table XXVI and Fig. 9, p. 117.

TABLE XXVI. *Number of livestock and quantities of produce, Netherlands*

		Numbers millions				Outputs				
		Including milch				Av. milk yield per	Milk million	Thousand tons		
	Cattle	cows	Sheep	Pigs	Poultry	cow, lb.	tons	Beef and veal	Pig meat	Total meat
1939	2·82	1·57	0·69	1·55	32·8	7,790	5·32	120 (1)	214(1)	351
1948	2·31	1·32	0·43	0·87	17·4	7,436	4·48	77	98	188
1949	2·54	1·44	0·46	1·30	20·3	8,140	5·35	86	164	269
1950	2·72	1·52	0·39	1·86	24·2	8,316	5·50	139	232	400

(1) 1938.

(*Rpt. to F.A.O.,* 1951.)

[1] One sometimes hears growers, part in jest, wondering whether they will not soon use up all the water of the Rhine.

[2] These heavy dressings raise some interesting problems. Magnesium deficiency has resulted on a fairly wide scale and is being met by using potassium magnesium sulphate as fertilizer; copper deficiency is marked on some of the reclaimed soils, especially the peats.

The cattle are chiefly the black-and-white Friesians. Some of them give remarkable yields. The average for full-grown cows (five years and upwards) of recorded herds in 1950 was 11,490 lb. milk, but yields of 15,400 lb. are not uncommon. A dual purpose breed, the red-and-white Meuse–Rhine–Yssel, commonly called the MRY breed, is common in the south and central districts in the region of the rivers after which it is named. These give an average milk yield of 11,000 lb. at five years of age.

Artificial insemination is increasingly used to raise the quality of the animals and to reduce the losses from diseases of the genital tract.

As in many other intensively farmed countries, sheep are decreasing in number. They are now mainly in the island of Texel: the original breed was crossed with English Down and longwoolled sheep and has long become fixed.

Utilization of the food produced

Table XXVII shows the quantities of food produced, exported, and available for home use in the years before the war and in 1950. Production of bread corn—wheat and rye—was in 1950 less than in pre-war, but this was due simply to the badness of the season; in 1949 it had just exceeded pre-war output. Production of oats and barley was, however, greater than before the war. Output of cheese, butter, and potatoes was almost equal to that of pre-war days; while production of fruit, meat, milk, and oil seeds was greater, but of eggs was less. As a round figure the Dutch experts consider that agricultural production was about 24 per cent greater in 1950 than in 1939, while the population had increased by 17·6 per cent.

Prior to the war there had been considerable imports of grain, oil seeds, sugar, and fruit. Against this there were exports of much greater value of dairy produce, eggs, meat, potatoes, vegetables, fruit, including high-class luxury produce,[1] and, of course, the remarkable flowers, bulbs, plants, and seeds for which Holland was famous. By 1950 this pattern was generally restored but there was more processing. Imports of grain and oil seeds still continue, but on a reduced scale: it is a remarkable achievement that output of livestock products now exceeds that of pre-war days though the import of feeding stuffs is only one-third of what it was. Exports would be possible on an even greater scale than before the war, but they are gravely impeded by the trade restrictions now imposed by the British and other Governments. It is greatly to be hoped that these may soon be lifted. The amplified processing includes the development of factories for making potato farina, milk food products, sugar products from home-grown and imported raw sugar, biscuits and pastry, synthetic wool from skim milk, strawboard from surplus straw, and others. (Figs. 7 and 8.)

During the war the population suffered much hunger. The marked improvement in agricultural output has provided much more food and by 1950 the dietary was equal in nutritive value to that of pre-war days. The supplies of food per head of population per year are given in Table XXVIII.

[1] It was not unusual in the 1930's for early strawberries to be gathered in the morning, sent by air to London, and to be served with cream at a garden party in the afternoon.

TABLE XXVII. *Production, consumption, and export of chief foods, Netherlands*
Thousand tons

	Production		Net export (1)		Available	
	Average 1934–38	1950	Average 1934–38	1950	Average 1934–38	1950
Bread grains (wheat and rye)	926	716	−719	−741	1,645	1,457
Feeding and industrial grains	488	614 (2)	−1,293	−968	1,781	1,582
Fed to livestock					2,037	
Vegetables	820		275	332	545	
Potatoes	3,080 (3)	2,846 (4)	373	671 (5)	2,707	2,175
Meat	368	412	32	49	336	363
Eggs thousand tons	120		71		49	
millions	2,208	1,775		1,113		662
Milk, whole	5,173	5,723			5,173	5,723
Condensed and powdered	167	213	143	170	24	43
Cheese	121	129	65	70	56	59
Butter	98	93	50	64·6	48	28·4
Visible fats and oils	435		−574	−370	1,009	
Oil seeds	21	45	−709	(6)		
Sugar	235		−82	−268 (7)	317	
Fruits, fresh and dried	220		−135	98	355	
Population, millions					8·5	10·0

(*F.A.O. Food Balance Sheets*, 1949, for 1934–38 figures; *Govt. Rpt. to F.A.O.*, 1951, for 1950 production figures.)

(1) A minus sign (−) indicates an import.

(2) Barley, oats, maize and rice. The quantity fed to livestock includes 571,000 tons of wheat and rye.

(3) Includes private gardens while (4) does not.

(5) Includes 152,000 tons farina; none in 1934–38.

(6) Import of 160,000 tons of oil cakes.

(7) Raw sugar. Against this are to be set as exports:

Refined sugar	178 thousand tons
Confectionery and sugar products	66·4
Chocolate confectionery	17·3
Biscuits, pastries	9·7

TABLE XXVIII. *Supplies of food, lb. per head of population, Netherlands*

Average	Cereals	Potatoes	Sugar	Boneless meat	Milk	Vegetables	Fruit
1936–38	238	242	65	52	320	147	93 (1)
1950	221	308	79	41	440	136	116 (1)
1950 per cent of pre-war (2)	86	147	119	78	139		

(1) *Netherlands Govt. Rpt. to F.A.O.*, 1951. The figures include self-supplies.

(2) *Organization for European Economic Co-operation, 3rd Rpt.*, 1950.

These values do not agree quantitatively with those in the Netherlands Government Report but they are in the same direction.

The total nutrients per head per day were:

		Protein grams			Fats	Carbohydrate
Average	*Calories*	*Animal*	*Vegetable*	*Total*	*grams*	*grams*
1936–38	2,822 (1)	39·6	41·1	80·7	100·3	379·6
1950	2,901	39·7	39·6	79·3	103·2	394·6

(1) *F.A.O. Food Balance Sheets*, 1949, give as the average for 1934–38, 3,007 calories and 114·7 grams of fat.

There is, however, a change in the details: the 1950 dietary includes less meat and cereals, about 20 per cent less cheese, nearly 50 per cent less eggs than that of pre-war days, but more milk, potatoes, pulses, and fruit, and somewhat more sugar and fat. It is too early to know how far these changes are likely to be permanent; rationing was in force till November 1949, when it was discontinued for everything excepting coffee.

Two important questions arise in connection with Dutch agriculture: should it aim at making Holland self-supporting so as to avoid the present imports of cereals, sugar, and oil seeds; and can the output of exportable food be increased if and when Great Britain is able to buy indefinitely large quantities of its produce? The present production of wheat is less than half the requirements; the yields are already good and doubling the output would necessitate considerably increasing the present area at the expense of other cereals or by ploughing up grassland: either would still further reduce the supply of animal food. On general grounds, also, it would be failing to make the most of the exceptional skill of the Netherlands cultivators if they were simply set to grow additional cereals instead of the high-grade products which they can do so well. Fodder grains are most economically produced in the semi-arid countries. Oil seeds cannot, as yet, be grown in sufficient quantity for climatic reasons; rape is being developed for this purpose but oil seeds are really tropical products, and imports may always be needed to supply Holland's margarine industry.

In so far as it depends on cereals and oil seeds the future of Holland's agricultural output depends considerably on others. But the remarkable success achieved in replacing imported concentrated foods by home-grown foods justifies the expectation that still more can be done in this direction. Potatoes steamed and ensiled directly after harvest are already much used for fattening pigs; varieties are being selected of higher content of starch equivalent and protein so as to improve them for this purpose. The cultivation of fodder beets is being extended. Improved varieties of grass and clover are being sought for the reseeding of poor pasture; ensilage is being developed so as to facilitate the conservation of roughage now wasted: losses at present are sometimes 20 to 30 per cent of the dry matter: they need not exceed 15 per cent. Methods are being investigated for raising the output from grassland by better regulation of the water supply, the grazing, and the management generally. On the other side, the efficiency of the farm animals as transformers of fodder into human food is being improved. All these problems are important in other advanced agricultural countries and solutions worked out in Holland would be helpful to many others also.

The Netherlands have for many years played an honourable part in the advancement of agricultural science. The chief experimental station is the well-known one at Wageningen, but there are some important regional stations deservedly held in high repute.

The remarkable virility of the Dutch was vividly shown by the rapid recovery after the devastating floods when 67 great gaps were torn in the coast defences by the storm and high seas of January 31, 1953. In less than six months they were practically all repaired and the land was well on the way to rehabilitation.

DENMARK

Having no mineral or timber resources and no overseas possessions, Denmark has always exported food to pay for her imports; she and the Netherlands have the distinction of being the only important food exporting countries in north-west Europe.

After the loss of Schlesvig–Holstein in the war with Germany, in 1864, the Danes resolved to make good their losses by greater production from the territories still left to them. Grain was then their chief export and remained so for the next twenty years; then came the flood of wheat from the American prairies in the 1880's with which Danish farmers could not compete. Realizing that this new situation was likely to last for many years they changed their system of agriculture, developed an intensive livestock industry based on large imports of this cheap grain and of the oil seeds which were also becoming available, and aimed at supplying their two big industrial neighbours, Great Britain and Germany. Great Britain was their largest, most lucrative, and most open market, and the Danes very wisely decided to specialize in the Englishman's breakfast dishes: bacon, butter, and eggs, while they sent medium-quality meat to Germany. For various reasons it was decided to develop a system of small freehold farms: this process had already started with the agrarian reforms of 1760 and later years; it was realized that animal husbandry is pre-eminently suited to these conditions. Detailed surveys were carried out to discover the market requirements, and methods of production and marketing were devised that ensured high standards of quality, efficient distribution, and satisfactory prices. Co-operative action was seen to be essential at every stage and the strictest honesty and fairness of dealing between producer, salesman, and customer. The development of co-operative systems has been one of Denmark's greatest contributions to modern rural life.

The capital required for effecting the necessary changes in the first instance was obtained through co-operative land credit associations which had been functioning since 1850, and also through savings banks: these credit arrangements have since been expanded and they now work so well that farmers can generally obtain loans up to two-thirds of the value of their property at 4 or $4\frac{1}{2}$ per cent interest; further loans are obtainable at somewhat higher rates. Indeed, the credit facilities are so good that something of a problem has arisen; the average indebtedness per holding was, in 1951, about £1,300.[1]

Co-operative Societies have, from 1882 onwards, done the processing and marketing of the farmer's products; their inspectors point out to him any defects and advise about remedies. The farmer has only to deliver his milk,

[1] R. Ede, *Advancement of Science*, 1953, Vol. 10, pp. 45–50.

pigs, and eggs to the local factory (Plate 11); the rest is done for him with great efficiency and economy by expert workpeople and salesmen so that he receives the maximum return for his labours. From the outset it was realized that the farmer must be given, not only technical education, but also a good general education, including a knowledge of his own land and people, and, above all, a sound moral education to inculcate high ideals of responsibility to the community as well as to his family and his farm. This was the work of the Folk High Schools, initiated in 1844 but much developed after the disasters of 1864 had stimulated the national consciousness; the great leader was N. F. S. Grundtvig and his aim was to produce honest, God-fearing citizens.[1] It is said, however, that their influence is less now than it was.

On this basis of self-help and co-operation, Danish agriculture has risen to great heights and has given to its people a high standard of life; some of the farm homes, even the small ones, are very attractive. It has become a patriotic duty to farm well, and in going round the country one sees remarkably little bad farming and very few scrub animals. Although the holdings are small there are no peasants: the farmers are specialists, delivering to the food factories, not eating the butter and bacon they produce but having margarine and eggs instead. But the life is very strenuous.

The total area of the country is 10·6 million acres. Its topography was largely determined by the glaciers of the Second Ice Age. Most of it is gently undulating and no more than 100 feet above sea-level: the highest hill, Ejer Bavenhoj, in South-East Jutland, is only 563 feet high and the second, the much frequented Himmelbjerge, in North Jutland, is thirteen feet lower. The rainfall is about 25 to 30 inches in the west, but only 20 to 25 inches in the east; it is fairly well distributed throughout the year, though rather much may come between August and November, and droughts may occur in June and July. The temperatures are moderated by the sea: the average in January is 32° F. and in July is 61° F. Strong westerly winds often cause difficulties. The soils of the islands are heavy loams and clays and are, in general, more fertile than those of Jutland where, especially in the west beyond the moraines of the centre, there is much washed-out sand and blown sand, some of it very light: for long it was simply wild heath.

The land is utilized as follows:

	Million acres	1950
Tillage	6·65	
Permanent grass	1·14	7·79
(including rough grazing	0·21	
Forest	0·96	
Waste and other use	1·85	
Total land area	10·60	

[1] The classical account of the work is given by Harald Faber in *Cooperation in Danish Agriculture*, Longmans, 1931; and by H. Begtrup, H. Lund, and F. Manniche, *The Folk High Schools of Denmark and the Development of a Farming Community*, Oxford University Press, 3rd Ed., 1936. Later accounts are given in Ravnholt, Henning, *The Danish Cooperative Movement*, Copenhagen, Det danske Selskab, 1947, and Skrubbeltrang, Fridlev, *The Danish Folk High School*. Copenhagen, Det danske Selskab, 1947. Information is obtainable from the Danish Council, 136 Oak Tree Lane, Selly Oak, Birmingham.

Nearly three-quarters of the total area is in cultivation and more land is continuously being reclaimed, although, as in other countries, agricultural land is continually being taken for non-agricultural purposes, so that there has been a net loss since 1939.

The area of cultivated land has been:

	1929	1939	1949	1950	*Total land surface*
Million acres	6·87	8·03	7·80	7·79	10·60

The population was 3·5 millions in 1928 and 4·25 millions in 1949, an increase at the rate of 1 per cent per annum. The area of cultivated land is 1·84 acres per head.

The cultivated land is divided up into 208,147 holdings, most of which are under 150 acres; nearly half are under 25 acres; the typical farm is about 60 acres. About 95 per cent of the farmers are freeholders. The ease with which loans can be obtained has enabled the farmer's son to buy out his co-heirs on the death of the father, thus avoiding fragmentation of the farms: in any case, sub-division below 5 acres is now forbidden. Holdings of less than 7½ acres are being enlarged; the number below this size fell by 35 per cent between 1923 and 1949. At the other end of the scale large farms are being divided; the number above 150 acres has fallen. Under the Act of 1948 the Government has power to buy any holding of land value exceeding 35,000 Kr. offered for sale outside of the owner's family: it is then converted into smaller holdings let to tenants on a kind of heritable copyhold tenure, the Government retaining the ownership. There has thus been a shrinkage in number of the very small and of the relatively large holdings and a considerable increase in holdings of intermediate size: between 1923 and 1949 those of 12½ to 25 acres rose by 26 per cent, and those from 25 to 37½ acres by 15 per cent. The present policy is to create more holdings of 20 acres and upwards: some 6,000 new ones have been set up. The units must remain distinct, however; accretion is not allowed. A smallholder cannot become a middle or larger farmer by the simple process of acquiring an adjoining farm and adding it to his own. There are also restrictions on multiple holdings. This procedure has the advantage of keeping the small farms intact but the disadvantage that it makes the path of advancement extremely difficult for a smallholder.

A 20-acre holding can be run by the farmer and his family though it means hard work for all of them including the wife and the young children. For the ordinary 60-acre farm it is usually necessary to engage further assistance, either a young man to live in or a married man who will have a farm cottage. As in other countries the supply of hired workers is falling off: from 478,000 in 1940 the numbers fell to 398,000 in 1950. The difficulty is being met by mechanization and by increasing the number of 20-acre holdings. (Plate 12.)

The old rotation had been little more than an alternation of cereals and grass with some fallow. The modern rotations vary somewhat with the conditions but as a rule have no fallow; half the arable land is in cereals, a quarter in temporary leys and a quarter in roots and fodder crops as in the Norfolk rotation. The ley is, however, usually left for two years so that there are eight courses instead of four; a common sequence is: winter cereal (rye or wheat); roots; barley; roots; cereal undersown; clover and grass two years; oats.

Barley and oats are the chief grain crops, sown either singly or mixed; wheat and rye are the bread grains, the area under wheat, however, has fallen considerably as also have the areas under oats and mixed corn, but there has been an increase in the acreage of barley and of rye (Table XXIX).

TABLE XXIX. *Areas, yields, and production of grain crops 1939 and 1950*

	Barley	Oats	Thousand acres Mixed corn barley and oats	Wheat	Rye	All grain
1939	1,040	929	751	332	338	3,389
1950	1,220	684	660	210	380	3,154

			Yield, cwt. per acre			
Average						
1935–39	24·1	22·0	19·0	24·3	14·1	
1950	26·2	24·1	20·4	28·0	17·1	

			Production, thousand tons			
Average						
1935–39	1,161	1,026	756·5	397·4	255·0	3,596
1950	1,615	834	682·0	297·5	330·5	3,759

(These and other figures in this section are from the *Rpt. of the Danish National F.A.O. Cttee.*, 1951.) Fig. 7 gives the quantities for the intervening years.

The yields per acre of all the grain crops have increased, the result partly of improved varieties, partly of larger applications of fertilizer; also grain tends to be grown by the larger farmers who supply it to the smaller ones. The increased area under roots, and the shrinking area of grass, are distinctive features almost peculiar to Danish agriculture. The Danish farmer is meeting the shortage of imported grain not only by intensifying his grass output but to a much greater extent by growing more roots, different, however, from the old roots in possessing higher feeding value. Mangolds have been largely replaced by fodder beets, and the areas of potatoes and of sugar beet have been greatly increased: swedes still remain, however, the most widely grown. (Table XXX.)

TABLE XXX. *Areas and production of root crops, 1939 and 1950*

	Swedes	Mangolds	Thousand acres Fodder beet	Sugar beet Fodder	Industry	Potatoes
1939	475	351	109	50	100	170
1950	477	94	338	75	180	260

		Yield, tons per acre				
1935–39	23·6	24·7			15·2	6·8
1950	23·6	21·1			14·4	7·0

	Hundred food units (crop units[1]) per acre, 1950					
Roots	22·6	26·3	27·8	29·3		16·0
Tops	2·3	4·8	5·7	6·5		
Total	24·9	31·1	33·5	35·8		16·0
Starch equivalent, cwt. per acre, approximate	36	44	48	50		

[1] See note on p. 109.

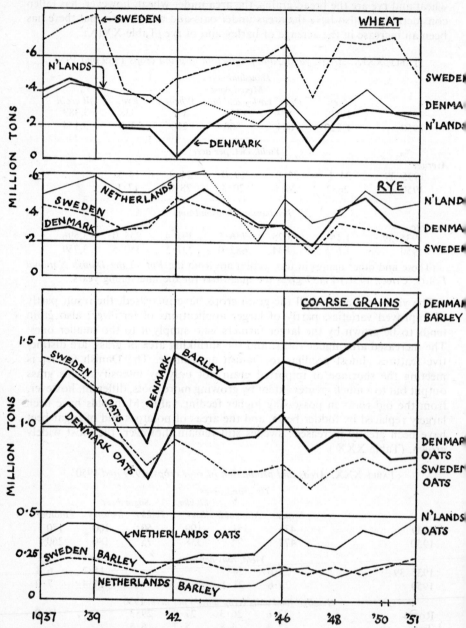

FIG. 7.—Production of bread grains (wheat and rye) and of coarse grains (barley and oats), Netherlands, Denmark and Sweden, 1937 to 1951 (Data from C.E.C. Reports, *Grain Crops*, 1953)

These values compare with 15 crop units or 20 cwt. starch equivalent per acre of grassland and the same from grain crops—including the straw.

The quantity of sugar beet has increased beyond the capacity of the Danish factories and roots have to be sent to Sweden for extraction.

Unlike the grain, the yields per acre of roots and potatoes have not increased. The fodder beets are derived from sugar beet; they were first produced in Denmark in the early 1930's as a cross between Barres and sugar beet. At the same time a strain of sugar beet, Tystofte VII was selected, of high yielding capacity and 22–23 per cent of dry matter.[1] Their high content of dry matter makes these new beets very suitable for pigs; they have replaced a certain proportion of grain in the ration. No other root crop can do this so well. The roots yield on the average 2,800 food units per acre and the leaves 560, a total of 3,360 per acre.

Permanent grass, on the other hand, yields only about 1,400 food units per acre: the reduction in its area is therefore easily understandable. The area under temporary grass, however, has also fallen and though there has been an increase in lucerne and green fodder crops it has been quite insufficient to offset the fall:

		Thousand *acres*		
	Permanent	Clover and		Green fodder
	grass	grass	Lucerne	crops
1939	1,304	1,759	50	20
1950	1,138	1,645	80	27
	—166	—114	+30	+7

Fall (−) or rise (+).

Yields have gone up, but there is not the same intensive management of the grassland as in the specialized districts of Holland. High outputs are, however, obtained: the grazing is well done, the animals being commonly tethered to ensure the fullest utilization of the grass. By September, however, the grazing begins to fall off considerably, especially in the south and south-east, and supplementary feeding with early-lifted roots becomes necessary.

The total numbers of food units produced are given in Table XXXI.

The figures for 1950 are provisional: they differ, however, but little from those for 1949. The root crops give almost twice as many food units per acre as do the other crops, and in spite of the high yields of the grain crops their output of food units per acre does not come up to that of the grass and green fodder crops. About 90 per cent of the total food units corresponding to about 11½ million tons of barley grain are fed to the animals.

Farm and garden seeds, particularly of grasses, sugar beet and barley are produced in considerable quantities and the export is increasing: the quantities have been:

	Thousand tons	
	1935–39	1950
Production	23	35
Net export	12	18·7

[1] Tests in Southern England have given very satisfactory results (M. E. Castle, A. S. Foot, and S. J. Rowland, *Empire Jl. Expt. Agric.*, 1952, Vol. 20, pp. 1–9), Norfolk experience is also favourable.

TABLE XXXI. *Number of food units produced, Denmark*, 1949 *and* 1950

	Million acres		Million food units		Food units per acre	
	1949	1950	1949	1950	1949	1950
Grain			3,880	3,580		
Straw			1,130	950		
Total cereals	3·27	3·15	5,010	4,530	1,532	1,439
Potatoes			400	390		
Roots			3,010	3,280		
Tops			300	330		
Total	1·39	1·44	3,710	4,000	2,667	2,778
Grass and green fodder	2·87	2·89	4,530	4,480	1,578	1,550
Grand total	7·53	7·49	13,250	13,010	1,760	1,737

(*Rpt. of Danish National F.A.O. Cttee.*, 1951.)

As befits a land of small farmers horticulture is increasing in importance. More vegetables and fruit, especially apples, are grown and it is hoped to develop an export trade: till recently apples had to be imported.

The crops are well manured. The farmyard manure is kept in good steadings, the liquid manure is stored in tanks; both are applied to the roots. Fertilizers are used in increasing quantity. The amounts have been, in thousand tons:

	Average, 1935–39	1949	1950	1952/3
N	37	45	60	71
P_2O_5	67	72	79	87
K_2O	37	80	84	150

The nitrogenous fertilizer is chiefly nitrate of lime imported from Norway: the superphosphate is made in Denmark from imported rock phosphate and pyrites.

Crop diseases and pests are not serious. Seed-dressing is widely practised against smut and helminthosporium; rust hardly occurs,[1] and root eel-worms do little harm to root crops, even when grown on the same land for several years in succession. The main troubles are caused by Take-all (*Ophiobolus graminis*), Eye spot (*Cercosporella herpotricoides*), and nematodes affecting cereals, virus yellows of beets, wireworms, and leather-jackets.

Before the war, Denmark had the largest livestock population in relation to the human beings of any country in Europe: there were almost as many cattle and also of pigs, as human beings. During the war the numbers fell heavily and except for pigs they were not in 1952 at their old level owing to the shortage of feeding stuffs; poultry, and especially egg-laying poultry, have been greatly reduced through lack of grain:

[1] Outbreaks of black rust (*P. graminis*) occurred in 1951 and were traced to the presence of *Berberis vulgaris* in the respective neighbourhoods. The plant had been outlawed by an Act of 1903.

Numbers of livestock, July 1939, 1950 and 1952
Millions

	Cattle	Including milch cows	Sheep	Pigs	Poultry	Including egg layers	Total stock units (1)
1939	3·33	1·64	0·147	3·18	33·30	13·94	4·77
1950	3·05	1·58	0·059	3·23	24·55	11·50	4·35
1952	3·1	1·49		3·63	23·4		

(1) One cow is equivalent to 1·4 bullocks, 1·75 heifers, 2·65 calves, 6·25 sheep, 2 sows or boars, 25 sucking pigs, 50 chickens, 1 horse. *Rpt. of Danish National F.A.O. Cttee.*, 1951.

The fall in the numbers of sheep is becoming general in countries where intensive agriculture is practised.

The cattle are of the Red Danish breed, and the general level of quality is among the highest in the world. This has been the result of the wide-spread interest in cattle shows, milk recording, progeny tests, bull tests and, in recent years, artificial insemination, now used for more than 40 per cent of the cows; it was developed in Denmark early in the 1930's and has reached a remarkable pitch of efficiency. One high-class bull at Kollekolle is said to have produced 10,000 daughters in ten years, successfully serving 2,500 cows a year. Several bulls have a much higher performance. Horsens Høg, belonging to the Horsens and District Cattle Breeding Association, made 6,300 cows pregnant in 1951. As a result the scrub bull has been eliminated.

The average milk yield is about 7,500 lb. with 3·85 per cent butter fat: 286 lb. of fat corresponding to 320 lb. of butter, but a reasonably good farmer will reckon to get about 9,000 lb. of milk with 4 per cent fat, giving about 400 lb. of butter; yields up to 13,000 lb. of milk and 4·5 to 5 per cent butter fat are not uncommon.[1] Although the numbers of cattle and of milk cows are less than before the war their efficiency has been improved and the milk output has increased; about half of the milch cows are recorded by Milk Recording Societies.

Most of the milk is used for making butter, but less in 1950 than in 1939 although nearly the same amount of butter was made; a large amount is now sold for consumption as liquid and there is a considerable increase in the quantities condensed and made into cheese:

Utilization. Million tons.

	Total milk produced	As butter	As cheese	As condensed milk	Consumed on farms	Sold for consumption
1939	5·277	4·190	0·202	0·040	0·400	0·445
1950	5·403	3·890	0·413	0·129	0·400	0·571

Denmark is thus following the general tendency to produce more condensed milk and to use more as whole milk rather than to increase output of butter. This change is entirely a question of price, and has been forced on producers by the buyers, chief of which has been the British Ministry of Food. (Fig. 9, p. 117.)

[1] The record up to May 1951, was by No. 294 Stensbygaard: 26,112 lb. of milk with 4·57 per cent fat, i.e. 1,342 lb. butter, in 365 days. During this time she consumed 4·94 tons of concentrates, 8·16 tons of roots, 3·76 tons of silage, 1·38 tons of hay, and some grass; a total of 7,549 feed units.

The skimmed milk resulting from the production of butter goes mainly for the feeding of pigs though some is used for making cheese and casein.

Only little beef is produced; most of the bull calves are killed at the suckling stage.

The cattle have to be housed for the seven months October to April. One stockman and his wife will look after 30 cows and their followers.

The health of the cattle is good. Tuberculosis, formerly very destructive, has been eradicated; all herds were declared free in June 1952, and 91 per cent were free of contagious abortion. Mastitis is still troublesome but great efforts at eradication are being made, while foot-and-mouth disease, generally, gives little trouble;[1] a vaccine is used for protection.

The pigs are Landrace; formerly they were crossed with Yorkshire Large Whites, but now they are commonly used pure: they are kept almost entirely for bacon. Stations have been established for progeny testing in order still further to improve the quality of the bacon. The pigs are killed when about 200 days old: their live weight is about 210 lb. and the dead weight about 155 lb.; the yield of bacon is about 130 lb. The quantity of food consumed per pig, including that given to the mother, averages about 450 food units (p. 109) of which 40 per cent may be bulky foods—potatoes, roots, green fodder, and silage. The proportion of these has increased since the war. Protein is supplied by skim milk, meat and bone meal, dried blood, and fish meal which, however, must be low in oil.

The egg-laying capacity of the poultry has greatly improved since pre-war days. Three-quarters of the birds are Leghorns, about 54 per cent being white and 21 per cent brown. An export trade is being developed in eggs for hatching and in day-old chicks.

The figures for production, export, and home consumption of the principal foods during the period 1935–39 and in 1950 are shown in Table XXXIII. Production of beef, butter, and poultry is now practically at pre-war level. Production of cereals, bacon, and milk has increased by about 3 per cent, of eggs by 10 per cent, of potatoes by 46 per cent, and of sugar by 55 per cent. The achievement is greater than appears at first sight because it has been obtained in spite of a fall in the import of concentrated food: the net import of grain fell by 365,000 tons and of oil cakes by 307,000 tons.

	Thousand tons	
	Net import of grain and grain products (1)	*Net supply of oil cakes and meal* (2)
Average 1935–39	740	848
1950	375	541
Reduction	365	307

(*Rpt. of Danish F.A.O. Cttee.*, 1951. Fig. 8 gives the quantities for the intervening years.)

(1) After deducting exports of 147,000 and 152,000 tons in the two periods respectively.

(2) After deducting exports averaging 88,000 tons a year during the 1935–39 period.

[1] 1952, however, was a bad season.

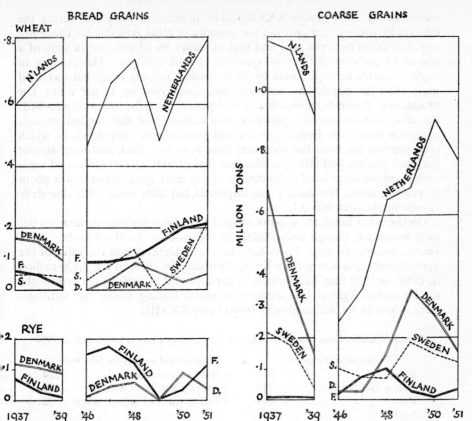

FIG. 8.—Imports of bread grains (wheat and rye) and of coarse grains (barley and oats), Netherlands, Denmark and Sweden, pre-war and post-war (Data from C.E.C. Reports, *Grain Crops*, 1953)

The imported grain goes mostly to the pigs and poultry and the oil cakes to the cattle. The home-grown foods fed to the livestock are the equivalent of some 11½ million tons of grain (p. 101) and the total imported food supplied to them represents about 8 per cent of their total food. The proportion before the war was 13 or 14 per cent but this supplied about 28 per cent of the total protein. The starch equivalent lost through this reduced import has been made good in part by an increased output of roots, especially fodder beets which are rich in dry matter. The shortage of protein, however, is proving more difficult to rectify: peas are the chief source, but their yield is uncertain and beans are but little grown. This problem is not yet solved.

The improvement of the animals to which reference has already been made has resulted in a more economical utilization of the food consumed: more produce is being obtained from fewer animals than before the war.

The output of human food

The pre-war Danish dietary was one of the best in Europe, with a calorie intake of 3,413 per day; it fell considerably during the war and had not fully recovered by 1950 (Table XXXIII). The population increased during the interval by some 15 per cent but the quantity of meat available for consumption had fallen by 7 per cent and that of butter by 27 per cent in spite of a rise of 15 per cent in the total quantity of milk available. The quantity of sugar available increased only by 10 per cent. The only food that increased more than the population was potatoes, which rose by 33 per cent.[1] The production of cereals increased only by 4 per cent and the import diminished; the allocation for animals, however, was reduced and that for human consumption increased. Besides cereals and potatoes the only foods of which consumption per head had increased have been fish, fruit, and beer; that of beef and poultry had fallen, so also had that of butter,[2] margarine and vegetables: on the other hand consumption of pig meat, eggs and milk was about at pre-war level. The dietary has improved but little since 1948: the daily calorie intake then was 3,125.

On the other hand, the exports of food have been not only maintained but even increased, though only slightly in the case of the three leading ones, bacon, butter, and eggs. Prices have risen considerably and the value of the agricultural exports rose from Kr. 1,150 million in 1939, to Kr. 2,830 million in 1950; in 1939 they had formed 72 per cent and in 1950 62 per cent of the total exports. Against this, imports of grain, feeding stuffs, and fertilizers were valued at Kr. 602 million in 1950 (Table XXXII).

TABLE XXXII. *Values in million Kr. of agricultural exports and imports,* 1950

Agricultural exports		Agricultural imports for farm use	
Butter	863	Oil cakes and meal	224
Bacon and pork	748	Fodder grain, bran, etc.	156
Eggs	338	Feeding stuffs of animal origin	32
Cattle	257		—
Cheese	152	Total feeding stuffs	412
Other items	468	Fertilizers	180
		Others	10
			—
Total	2,826		602

In addition, imports of wheat, rye and rice for human consumption were valued at Kr. 64 million.

The total import of grains and feeding stuffs, however, was valued at Kr. 476 million, so that Kr. 64 million worth was used for human food and manufacture.[3]

Of the butter, bacon, and eggs exported about 80 per cent went to Great Britain, the meat and cheese mainly to Germany. If import restrictions are ever abolished in Great Britain the demand for these commodities would certainly increase. Efforts are now being made to broaden the basis of the

[1] Of the total quantities recorded in the table, only about one-third are consumed by human beings, some being fed to stock, some needed for seed, and some are inevitably wasted. A great quantity is used for the manufacture of alcohol, but it is decreasing, as the distillers prefer sugar beet and molasses.

[2] Rationing of butter was in force till November 1950; sugar and coffee are now the only rationed foods.

[3] *Rpt. of Danish National F.A.O. Cttee.,* 1951, p. 9.

export trade by including pedigree seed, malting barley, sugar, and pedigree cattle.

TABLE XXXIII. *Production, export, and home consumption of principal foods, thousand metric tons*

| | Production | | | Export | | Consumption lb. per head per annum | |
	Average 1935–39	1950	1952	Average 1935–39	1950	Average 1935–39	1950
Cereals	3,599	3,784	4,572	−651 (1)	−285 (1)	191	223
Sugar (refined)	205	319	259	13·3	111	113	78·5
Potatoes	1,315	1,849	2,320	31	107	250	282
Beef and veal	164	168	179	57	86	63	41·4
Bacon and pork	340	354	381	217·5	219	72·4	72·4
Poultry meat	26·7	26·0	23	3·1	6·9	14	10
Milk	5,270	5,403	4,998	—	19 (2)	367	370
Butter	182	179	154	149	156	19	10·6
Cheese	30	61	86	9·5	37	12·5	11·4
Eggs	120	132·5	124	89·5	94·5	16·7	18·7
Margarine						47	30

Calories per day		
Vegetable foods	1,906	1,888
Animal food	1,507	1,280
	3,413	3,168
Population millions	3·7	4·3

(*Rpt. of Danish National F.A.O. Cttee.*, 1951.)

(1) Net import. These figures are for grain only, and hence are less than those on p. 104 which include bran.

(2) To Germany for Allied troops, mainly Americans.

Denmark is faced with the double problem: could output be increased to meet an additional demand? Is it possible to produce more food units at home and so reduce the need for imports?

Seventy-four per cent of the total land area of Denmark is already farmed, and although, as in other advanced countries, this area is continuously being eroded for social and other purposes the loss is partly, but not entirely, offset by reclamation of some of the waste land still remaining, particularly the light sands of Jutland. Formerly, some two million acres of moorland were almost unused except for small areas which farmers had managed to bring into cultivation. Systematic reclamation began as one of the many manifestations of the growing national consciousness after the disastrous war of 1864. The pioneer was Enrico M. Dalgas, an officer in the Engineers, who, having had to build roads across the moors, was familiar with their underlying material and was convinced that they could be afforested, or even farmed. In 1866 he founded the Danish Heath Society (*Det danske Hedeselskab*) in the little town of Herning where, at the Hotel Eyde, a small statue of him is set up in accordance with Danish custom; there is a more imposing one at Viborg. The Society receives a Government grant and has by now reclaimed

107

large areas of the heath, some for farm land and some, too light for cultivation, is planted with pine or spruce. Afforestation is the main purpose of the Heath Society; agriculture is the special care of the affiliated Society for Encouraging the Cultivation of Heath Land, established in 1906 and also Government aided. The methods of reclamation vary with the conditions. Where deep tractor ploughing is possible the heather is burned and the land ploughed deeply enough (12 to 24 inches) to break up the underlying hard pan and bring it to the surface mixed with the over-lying white sand and humus; chalky marl is applied at the rate of five or six tons per acre, the land is well harrowed, given a dressing of fertilizer and sown with mixed cereals, later undersown with clover and grass. Water may have to be pumped or brought by canals. Some 10,000 miles of hedges have been planted to protect the soil from the rough westerly winds. Drainage of ponds and bogs has also been carried out on a large scale.

The net result has been that the five million acres of waste heath existing before Dalgas started the Heath Society has now been reduced to 370,000 acres. Before the war reclamation for agriculture was proceeding at the rate of about 10,000 acres a year in addition to the new forest plantings, and it has now become necessary to schedule certain areas as reserves for black grouse: it is proposed, also, to keep the Alheden, an area of 3,000 acres near Viborg, as a National Park so that the memory of the heath may not altogether die out.

The continued cultivation of the heath, once it is reclaimed, is facilitated by the circumstance that the land is fairly level, free from stones and, fortunately, from rabbits also; further, disastrous droughts are rare. Wind erosion has been serious in places where there is inadequate shelter, e.g., near Silkeborg in the moraine country, but it is generally avoided on the agricultural land.[1] The success of the reclamation may be attributed to the skill and energy with which it has been carried out, and, above all, to the circumstance that the work has been done by societies of people interested, many themselves farmers. There has, therefore, been none of the reversion to the wild that has sometimes occurred when the work has been done by Governments without keen local interest.

Yields, both of cereals and of roots, are already high but there are still possibilities of increases. More drastic steps could be taken against weeds, and some of the grassland could be more intensively managed and more silage used. Losses from wireworm can now be curtailed; foot rots in cereals can be avoided or reduced by strict adherence to a suitable rotation. On the other hand it is not clear that mechanization is likely to improve yields, however valuable it may be in overcoming labour shortages.

The country is well supplied with advisers who are appointed by societies and not by the Government. It may happen that a district has two sets of advisers, one appointed by the larger farmers' society, the other by the smaller farmers. The ingenuity shown in overcoming difficulties inspires full confidence that Denmark's farmers will be able to increase food exports as

---

[1] Dalgas gave an interesting account of his work in *Geographiske Billeder fre Heden*, 1867. The choice of *P. Excelsior* and *Montana* was by Fabricius, who planted large areas between 1860 and 1890, and the soil problems were studied by P. E. Müller. A popular account of the work of these societies is given in *Danish Foreign Office Journal*, No. 1, 1951.

the need arises. Equally important, the production by Danish plant breeders of new varieties of crops, especially of fodder beets and of feeding barleys, has been most helpful to the farmers of Great Britain and North-West Europe.

Denmark's most enduring achievement has been to show how, by education and co-operation, the small, poor peasant may become a specialized farmer with a better standard of living and producing considerable surpluses of food to supply the wants of other people.

The problem of establishing a farming ladder for the smallholder still remains. At present, as already stated, his path of advancement is very difficult, and it is fairly true to say that once a smallholder, always a smallholder. The hours are long and the work arduous; the villages offer few amenities, nor would there be time to enjoy them if they were there. Many of the young people are unwilling to face the prospect and are abandoning the life; some go as workers on larger farms where hours and conditions are regulated by law and are, therefore, much easier than on the smallholdings, but many leave the land altogether. The demand for new smallholdings is said not to come from the sons of smallholders but from those of larger farmers who wish to gain experience while waiting to succeed to their fathers' farms. The problem is not confined to Denmark: it arises in other advanced countries and it is one for which a solution is urgently needed.[1]

SWEDEN

Swedish agriculturists have been very successful in dealing with the special problems of food production in cold climates and with the more general ones of raising the efficiency of farm units at present too small for economic use.

[1] For a further discussion see R. Ede, *Advancement of Science*, 1953, Vol. 10, pp. 45–50.

NOTE ON SCANDINAVIAN FOOD UNITS

To facilitate replacement of foods it has long been the custom in Denmark to call 1 kg. (2·2 lb.) of barley one food unit, and to determine the quantities of other foods equivalent to it. The pioneer investigator was N. J. Fjord in the 1880's; his experiments are described in *Forage Crops in Denmark*, Harald Faber (Longmans, 1920); there have been many subsequent workers. The following are the values used:

Quantities equivalent to 1 kg. of barley:

Rye, wheat	1·0	Dry matter of potatoes	1·0
Oats	1·2	Roots	1·1
Hay	2·5	Tops of fodder beet	1·5
Straw	4–5		

One food unit = 2·2 lb. barley, 1,000 food units = 1 ton of barley, and 50 = 1 cwt. of barley. To avoid high numbers 100 food units are called 1 crop unit. There is no simple factor for converting food units into the starch equivalents commonly used in Great Britain owing to the varying food value of the protein in the different kinds of fodder. As a general rule, when the digestible protein content is 10 to 15 per cent, 1·43 food units are about equal to 1 kg. starch equivalent. As the protein increases above this, so the number of food units increase and vice versa: 1 kg. starch equivalent in soya meal equals 1·7 food units, but 1 kg. starch equivalent in mangolds equals 1·36 food units only.

Lars Frederiksen and P. S. Østergaard (*Bull.* 136, Royal Vet. and Agric. Coll., Copenhagen, 1931) give the following formula: kg. S.E. per 100 kg. F.U. = $0·75 \times$ (F.U. per 100 kg. — % digestible true protein $\times 0·655 \times W/100$) where W = Kellner's value number.

Sweden stretches for a length of about 1,000 miles from lat. 55° N. to lat. 69° N. in a narrow strip running roughly north to south. Its southern part for about a third of the way up includes considerable areas of undulating plains; its west is the mountain range separating it from Norway; from this the land falls away in hills and dales to the Gulf of Bothnia in the east. The northern part, 15 per cent of the whole, lies within the Arctic circle.

Thanks to the Gulf Stream the climate is less severe than might have been expected. The average temperature in the south exceeds 50° F for some four and a half months in the year, but in the north for two months only. The high western country is colder than the lower-lying east. Frosts may come as late as June: they are less harmful than formerly, however, since more land has been drained and frost-resistant varieties of crops have been bred. The rainfall is about 25 inches a year in most of the west but about 30 inches in the south-west; it decreases to about 18 inches in the east. The wettest months are usually July and August and the driest May and June; crop yields are often limited by the low June rainfall.

Like other countries of north-west Europe, Sweden formerly produced grain and sheep; then, in the 1880's, cheap wheat from North America made the old system unprofitable and farmers took to livestock, developing a dairy industry. This was greatly stimulated by the separator invented by the Swedish engineer, Gustaf de Laval, which enabled butter to be made in factories far more economically than was possible on the farms. Cultivation extended considerably; methods of reclaiming and managing peat and moorland soils were worked out at Jonköping by von Feilitzen and others (including his son) and became models for use elsewhere. The area under cultivation expanded and reached a maximum about 1923. Thereafter expansion of area ceased and a slow shrinkage set in, but intensification of output began, partly by increasing yields, but chiefly by changing the cropping systems and substituting more leys, higher yielding fodder crops, and, later, oil seeds for the less-remunerative grain. The changes are set out in Table XXXIV.

TABLE XXXIV. *Areas of chief crops under the old and the new systems, Sweden*

Million acres

	Average				
	1876–80	1901–05	1921–25	1936–40	1951
Bread grains	1·07	1·21	1·19	1·22	1·05
Coarse grains	2·44	2·97	3·0	2·58	2·32
Total grain	3·51	4·18	4·19	3·80	3·37
Roots	0·41	0·52	0·71	0·63	0·57
Grass (hay and pasture)	2·02	3·09	3·68	4·22	4·24
Other crops and fallow	1·06	1·02	0·81	0·58	1·03
Total cultivated	7·0	8·81	9·38	9·23	9·21

(*Rpt. of National F.A.O. Cttee.*, 1951.)

Cereals had occupied 50 per cent of the cultivated land in 1910 but only 37 per cent in 1951, while grass ley increased in the same period from 29 per cent to 48 per cent.

In 1950 the land of Sweden was utilized as follows:

110

	Million acres
Cultivated	9·2
Natural grassland	2·3
Forest	55·0
Other uses and waste	34·8
Total	101·3

The population at the end of 1951 was estimated at 7·1 millions; the area of cultivated land per head was, therefore, 1·3 acres. To this, however, a small addition should be made for the natural grassland, but this is unlikely to be equivalent to more than about 0·1 or 0·15 acres per head.

The cultivated land was, in 1944, divided up into 414,400 holdings of which about a quarter were less than 5 acres and about a half were between 5 and 25 acres in extent. The great majority of the occupiers are freeholders, only about a quarter of the cultivated land and one-fifth of the holdings are held by tenants. This minute division of the land has raised problems described later.

The farms are nearly all family affairs. The number of food producers is decreasing and the cost of hired labour has risen considerably. In 1870 about 75 per cent of the population were dependent on agriculture, forestry, and fishing, and 20 per cent on commerce and manufacture. In 1945 only 28 per cent were dependent on agriculture and its allied activities and about 60 per cent on commerce and industry; since then the agricultural proportion has still further declined. It is a great achievement that in spite of this fall the agricultural output has increased, showing an increased efficiency of production per man; it is estimated that this has risen by about 2½ per cent per annum.

The chief agricultural district is in the south; it is divided into the very rich Scania in the far south and the plains somewhat to the north. The cereal-growing period lasts about 120–150 days a year, ample for all the common spring cereals and even for selected winter varieties of wheat and rye. Fodder crops, oil seeds, and roots all do well. Rotations are rather elastic and may vary from four to eight course, in the longer ones two being leys and one fallow. Black-and-white lowland cattle of Friesian type, pigs, and poultry flourish (Plate 13). But this southern region is not everywhere productive. There are areas of light sand subject to wind erosion; on these potatoes are grown, partly for human and animal food, partly for use in farina factories and distilleries.

Farther north the growing season is shorter; at about 61° lat. wheat cultivation ceases to be practicable, though rye, oats, and six-rowed barley can be grown. Grass and clover become more important, particularly *Phleum*, *Poa pratensis*, and *Festuca pratensis*; selected strains of these grow even in the north. Rye grass does not survive north of Stockholm. Red clover and alsike are the common clovers and lucerne in the milder regions. Much of the farming is for subsistence. Dairying is the main activity for cash: the Swedish red cattle predominate on the lower ground, and in the high districts the mountain breed; both tolerate the conditions better than do the black-and-white lowland animals of the far south.

In this north central region a six- to eight-course rotation is common: three

111

years in grass and clover mixture, then three years in tillage. In the third year of the ley much of the clover has died out and been replaced by dandelion and other weeds, then comes one year fallow, followed by two years of cereals. The growing season, however, is only about seventy-five to eighty-five days and although the hours of good daylight are long, only early ripening varieties can be grown. Potatoes and roots are planted separately. Practically half the cultivated land is thus in grass and the long racks on which the hay is hung to dry form one of the most characteristic features of the landscape in summer—though tending to disappear. More and more silage is made, however, as the process can involve less labour, being more easily mechanized.

This north-central region though not the richest is one of the most attractive parts of Sweden. Dalecarlia is particularly pleasing. It is hilly, dominated by the forest of conifers with birch and willow, with undergrowth also of wild berries and many mushrooms; it is studded with lakes, some of them large enough for small steamers. The valleys and level stretches of old river terraces or lake bottoms are intensively cultivated by small freeholders owning some farmland and some forest—at times more forest than farm—dividing their year's work between the two, dwelling comfortably in attractive wooden houses in which one can often see very pleasing furniture and adornments carefully kept, for the country people have a great sense of their past and its cherished arts and crafts.

In the mountains are the summer pastures, clearings in the forest to which the cattle are driven in early June and remain till mid-August so as to allow the farm grass to be conserved for the long winter. But this practice is waning; foresters do not like it because the cattle damage the young trees, and the young people sent in charge of the cattle dislike the isolation of the huts and the absence of the village amenities. The abandoning of the summer pastures has, as yet, caused no local reduction in numbers of cattle.

Farther north, cereals are increasingly difficult to grow though suitable varieties are being sought; grass and clover are the chief crops (Plate 14). Potatoes, however, do well; the long hours of daylight favour continuance of vegetative growth. Vegetables acquire a specially fine flavour.

Table XXXV shows the area and output of the chief crops before and since the war. The fall in acreage and output of grain already noted has continued, but may be reversed by the new price policy of 1951. A remarkable change, however, has occurred in the bread grains. Rye, though still widely used, has fallen greatly in area and output; before the war it had formed 37 per cent of the total output, but in 1949, 28 per cent only; it is being steadily displaced by wheat. For the older generation it had been almost a pious obligation to prefer rye, but the younger people feel less compunction in the matter. Among the coarse grains oats have fallen greatly in area and output; barley also, it now forms only about 10 per cent of the whole. On the other hand, mixed grains have increased in area and output. The total output of coarse grains, however, had by 1949 fallen enough to cause a loss of 268 million food units, while the reduced output of potatoes and roots has resulted in a further loss of 174 million units. But these losses were more than counterbalanced by the greatly increased output of rotation grazing and green fodder which yielded 600 million additional food units. The figures for 1951 are somewhat different but the general result is the same. (Figs. 7 and 8.)

112

TABLE XXXV. *Areas of chief crops and quantities produced: pre-war*, 1949(1) *and* 1951

	Million acres			Million tons		
	Average 1934–38	1949	1951	Average 1934–38	1949	1951
Bread grains						
Wheat	0·718	0·759	0·810	0·696	0·698	0·485
Rye	0·526	0·334	0·241	0·409	0·277	0·176
	1·244	1·093	1·051	1·105	0·975	0·661
Coarse grains						
Oats	1·640	1·235	1·238	1·257	0·840	0·820
Barley and mixed	0·867	0·977	1·077	0·773	0·826	0·939
	2·507	2·212	2·315	2·030	1·666	1·759
Potatoes (2)	0·326	0·332	0·323	1·847	1·720	1·751
Sugar beet	0·129	0·122	0·133	1·888	1·755	1·894
Fodder beets	Nil	0·134	0·115	Nil	1·897	1·526
Rotation grazing and green fodder		0·782	0·582			
Rotation hay		3·212	3·113		4·758	4·233
Oil seeds	(3)	0·352	0·469		0·173	0·270

(1) Yields of wheat and rye were unusually low in 1951, hence the more normal 1949 figures are also included.

(2) Potatoes are less used for the production of alcohol than in other N. European countries, alcohol being made from the sugar present in the sulphite liquor obtained during the manufacture of wood pulp.

(3) Only small acreage.

The total number of food units produced was calculated for the pre-war days and 1949 to be as follows:

	Million food units		
	Average 1936–40	1949	1951
Bread grains	1,017	975	653
Coarse grains	1,755	1,507	1,595
Potatoes and beets	1,335	1,161	1,118
Grazing and fodder crops	1,874	2,542	2,498
Hay and straw	3,012	2,968	2,785
Oil Seeds	—	359	495
Total	8,993	9,512	9,144

No calculation was made for 1951 but the figure would be somewhat lower as there were small reductions in output of grain, fodder beets, and hay to set against an increase in oil seeds.

(*Govt. Rept. to F.A.O.*, 1953, p. 5.)

Two crops have come into greater prominence since pre-war days, both of great promise for the future: fodder beets which originated in Denmark and may find a permanent place in Swedish agriculture; and oil seeds, which had been cultivated only to a small extent till the war cut off the former imports and compelled the Swedes to grow their own in order to keep their margarine industry going. This has been successfully accomplished. As the result of better varieties and of the attractive price fixed by the Government the area under oil seeds rose rapidly to 469,000 acres in 1951, when the production was 270,000 tons of seed (mostly winter rape) containing 93,700 tons of oil. The average yield of winter rape seed has been 7·2 cwt. per acre, containing 320 lb. oil.

Even more striking results are foreshadowed, however. At the Svalof plant-breeding station of the Swedish Seed Association starting from a German variety of rape, Lembkes, a high-yielding winter variety, Matador, has been produced containing up to 40 per cent of oil and yielding 600 or more pounds of oil per acre. Using an X-ray technique a high-yielding variety of winter mustard, Primex, has been obtained. It is impossible to say how far the yield of oil can be finally raised.[1] But as the yield of butter fat per acre under good conditions is only about 50 to 100 lb. one wonders how long production of butter will be able to continue at its present level in view of this increasing competition of margarine.[2]

A considerable development of vegetable growing has taken place, especially in eastern Sweden.

Leaving the oil seeds out of account the total food units produced had, in 1949, increased by 6 per cent over those of pre-war; for 1951 the number was not calculated but would probably be somewhat less. As the population had increased by about 9 per cent it was still outstripping the rate of food production.

Sweden's configuration and position give it an extraordinarily wide range of climatic conditions with no large areas over which they are fairly constant. Varieties of crops suited to these various conditions have been selected and bred with brilliant success at Svalov by Nilsson-Ehle, his successor Å. Åkerman, and their colleagues and successors, and also by the firm of Weibull at Landskrona. Some of the modern wheats yield 30 per cent more than the old land varieties, and oats give 10 to 20 per cent increased output.[3] Among Svalov's triumphs have been Victory and Golden Rain oats which have travelled far out of Sweden, while the Weibull's Atle wheat is doing remarkably well on the English Downlands and elsewhere. (Plate 15, p. 109.)

Crops do not suffer greatly from disease. Rust gave trouble in 1951 and a campaign was organized to destroy the wild barberry as far as possible. Losses are periodically caused by *Cercosporella*, *Fusarium*, *Typhula*, and other fungi, but these are dealt with by breeding resistant sorts. Winter hardiness is a necessary character especially in the south-western region where wheat may be exposed to temperatures of −15° F., or lower.

Fertilizers are increasingly used, largely as the result of the increased cultivation of fodder crops and oil seeds. The quantities have been:

[1] A summary of this work is given by Å. Åkerman in a publication by the National Institute of Agricultural Botany, Cambridge, 1951. The work on wheat has become classical, and that on rye is of special interest as the first practical result of artificially induced tetraploidy of cereals (*Proc. U.N. Sci. Conf. Conservation and Resources*, 1949, Vol. 6, pp. 297–300; U.N. Dept. Econ. Affairs, 1951).

[2] Rape oil yields rather more than its own weight of margarine. In practice other oils are added as well.

[3] The German Probstei varieties were the starting material for the new oats.

Thousand tons of fertilizer

	1938–39	1948–49	1949–50	Percentage increase
N(15·5% N)	172	262	382	120
P(20% P$_2$O$_5$)	283	415	494	75
K(40% K$_2$O)	86	99	131	50

(*Rpt. National F.A.O. Cttee.*, 1951, p. 5.)

The nitrogen fertilizer is mainly Norwegian nitrate of lime and the phosphatic is superphosphate made in North Sweden, but necessitating import of sulphur.

In addition much lime is used as many of the soils in Central and Northern Sweden are podsolic and acid.

The crop yields are good but in view of the excellent advisory work and the improved appliances and varieties available it is surprising that they show little or no tendency to increase. Compared with the pre-war period they have been in recent years:

Per acre Average	Wheat cwt.	Oats cwt.	Rye cwt.	Potatoes tons	Sugar beet tons	Fodder beet tons	Hay cwt.
1934–38	19·2	15·1	15·4	5·6	14·6	—	—
1948	17·2	12·9	16·0	6·2	15·4	13·9	26·0
1949	18·1	13·3	16·4	5·2	14·5	14·2	29·0
1951	12·0	13·2	14·6	5·4	14·2	13·3	27·6

The reduction in amount of labour available may be a contributing factor. There is, as everywhere, a considerable gap between the average farmers on the one hand and the best farmers and experimental farms on the other: in 1948 when ordinary farms in Dalecarlia were getting 12·8 cwt. of oats per acre the demonstration farm was getting 16 cwt.

The numbers of livestock fell considerably during the war and they have not yet recovered. They have been:

Average	Cattle	Millions Sheep	Pigs	Horses
1934–38	2·97	0·402	1·35	0·619
1949	2·58	0·311	1·24 (1)	0·465
1952	2·53	0·257	1·30 (2)	0·386

(1) June.
(2) April.

The numbers of sheep and horses are very unlikely to get back to pre-war levels. Sheep are decreasing in number in many countries where intensive agriculture is practised; unnecessarily in some but with more justification in Sweden where winter pasturage is impossible. But it is sad to see them go; the Landrace are interesting animals and remarkably prolific. Nils Korkman has records of nine ewes that produced 20 or more lambs each: one produced 29 in ten years.[1]

[1] Information supply by Commonwealth Bureau of Animal Breeding and Genetics, Edinburgh. The average number of lambs per ewe in 7 728 recorded ewes in 1951 was 1·95. The Roy. Agric. Soc. *Quart. Rev.* for April 1951 records a Cheviot ewe crossed with a Leicester ram which between 1873 and 1879 produced 32 living lambs.

Pigs are mainly Large Whites and the very similar Landrace. They are the chief producers of meat. The horses are being displaced by tractors at a rate which is causing some anxiety, for while the horse can be maintained on the farm the tractor has to be fed with imported fuel.

The cattle are milk producers: there are very few beef animals; bull calves are commonly slaughtered very early and the only beef produced is from culled cows. The reduction in numbers has not been wholly loss; the numbers fell by 13 per cent in the period quoted but the reduction in milk yield was 5 per cent only.[1]

There are three common breeds, the Lowland, a black-and-white Friesian type, mainly confined to the south; the Red-and-White, a more hardy, dual purpose breed, formed by crossing the Swedish Ayrshires with the older Red Roans but also with some Shorthorn blood: this is the most numerous; and the still hardier polled breeds including the White Mountain breed with black ears and black muzzle of somewhat the size and elegance of a Jersey, and the Red Polled found in the Dalecarlia hill country and the north.

The average milk yield over the whole country is about 5,500 lb. a year but there are considerable differences between the good and the average. For recorded herds the averages have been:

	Lb. milk	Per cent butter fat	Lb. butter fat
Lowland	11,500	3·79	440
Red-and-White	9,500	4·06	385
Polled	7,300	4·35	320

(*The Dairy Industry in Sweden*, S.M.R., Stockholm, 1949.)

Milk Recording Societies are increasingly active. The health of the animals is remarkably good in view of the fact that they have to be indoors for most of the year. Great efforts have been made to eliminate tuberculosis and with much success. By the end of 1950 more than 95 per cent of the herds were free from it and only 0·6 per cent suffered from contagious abortion. Special care is taken to ensure hygienic conditions in the sheds.

Artificial insemination is increasingly practised: it was used for about 200,000 cows in 1951.

Milk is the chief product and it is worked up very efficiently in the factories utilization being almost complete. In 1951 the amount produced was 4,763,000 tons used as follows:[2]

Home consumption and local sales	957
Delivered to factory	3,806

The factory used its milk thus:

			Thousand tons			
Butter making	Sold for consumption	Cream	Cheese making	Dried and condensed	Waste	Total
2,354	747	248	403	40	13	3,806

[1] *Report to F.A.O.*, 1951.
[2] Prof. K. F. Svärdström, Federation Swedish Farmers' Associations.

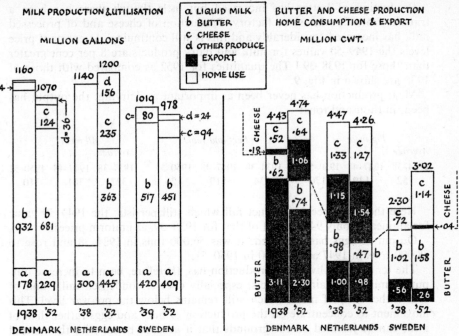

Fig. 9.—Production and disposal of milk, butter and cheese, Netherlands, Denmark and Sweden 1938–1952. (Data from C.E.C. Reports, *Dairy Products*, 1953)

The skim and butter milk left over from the butter are chiefly returned to the producer but some is made into cheese, dried or condensed, or used to produce standardized milk. In 1947, 2,158,000 tons of milk used for the manufacture of butter had given 2,063,000 tons of skim and butter milk which were used as follows:

Returned to producers	Cheese making	Dried and condensed	Standardized milk (1)	Other uses	Total
1,406	391	195	28	43	2,063

(1) Milk sold for adults (but not for children) in the towns is reduced to a uniform fat content of 3 per cent by the addition of skim milk from the creameries.

The output had been, in thousand tons, butter 106, cheese 48, dried milk 10·6, condensed milk 2·2.

The cheese making left 477,000 tons as whey, utilized thus:

Stock feeding	Whey products	Other uses	Not utilized	Total
212	64	10	191	477

(*The Dairy Industry in Sweden*, S.M.R., Stockholm, 1949.)

All that remained unused was part of the whey.

The production of milk and its products has been, in thousand tons:

Milk		Butter		Cheese		Dried and condensed	
Average 1934–38	1951	Average 1934–38	1951	Average 1934–38	1951	Average 1934–38	1951
4,596	4,763	92	106	34	54	2	8

(*F.A.O. Food Balance Sheets*, 1949 *for* 1934–38, Prof. Svärdström for 1951.)

Production of butter has increased but little though there has been a transfer from farmhouse to factory. Production of cheese and of processed milk has increased considerably and this is still continuing. At constant price levels the 1949–50 values for milk and dairy products are 8 per cent greater than those for 1938–39.[1] The quantities for 1952 as compared with those of 1938 are shown in Fig. 9.

Meat production has never been as important as dairying: the output has been, in thousand tons:

Pig meat			Beef and veal			All meat		
Average			*Average*			*Average*		
1934–38	1947–48	1950–51	1934–38	1947–48	1950–51	1934–38	1947–48	1950–51
152	139	170	134	119	126	322	301	310

Here there has been a distinct fall which still persists: the 1949–50 value for all meat is only 94 per cent of that for 1938–39, at uniform prices.

Output of eggs has increased: it was 56,000 tons in 1934–38 and rose to 78,000 tons in 1947 and 83,000 in 1950–51.

The tendency of livestock production has, therefore, been to increase output of milk and dairy products, especially cheese, condensed milk, and of eggs rather than of meat, which still remains below the pre-war level. This movement to concentrate on the production of milk and eggs rather than of meat can be justified on the grounds that it accords better with the natural conditions and is also much more economical of food; both the milch cow and the hen are more efficient converters of animal foodstuffs into human food than is the bullock.

Taking all livestock products together on a basis of values at uniform prices there has been an increase in production of 4 per cent since 1939. This may seem but little: its significance lies in the fact that it has been achieved with considerably less consumption of imported food than before the war.

	Million food units for livestock			
	Average			
	1930–39	1948–49	1949–50	1950–51
Imported	504	347	335	337
Home grown	7222	7189	7426	7522
Total	7,726	7,536	7,761	7,859

(*Rpt. of Swedish National F.A.O. Cttee.*, 1953, p. 6.)

The fact that the total food consumption has increased less than the increased output of animal products is explained by the considerable fall in the number of horses.

PRODUCTION AND CONSUMPTION OF HUMAN FOOD

Before the war, Sweden was almost self-supporting in human food; the deficit was estimated at about 4 per cent. Actually it was greater because the

[1] *Govt. Rpt. to F.A.O.*, 1951.

system necessitated imports of animal feeding stuffs and of fertilizers. Allowing for these the self-sufficiency value was reduced to 79 per cent. In 1951 production on the whole balanced consumption, but with the same proviso: a need—this time a greater need—for imported fertilizers and a need also, but a lessened need, for imported feeding stuffs. After deducting 3 units for imported food and 14 for fertilizers the value becomes 82 per cent. In the future the imports are likely to be greater, as more fertilizers, fuel oil, and machinery will be needed.

There are now surpluses for export of dairy products and of eggs, but against those are deficits of sugar and meat which have to be imported. It is probably not far out to say that on balance the Swedes support themselves on their 1·4 acres of cultivated land per head, and if their developments of oil seeds and fodder crops continue they may diminish their need for imported meat and have further surpluses for export.

The pre-war average dietary was quite good: the quantity of meat per head was less than that of the United Kingdom but those of milk, cream, and cheese were more than double while those of butter and cereals were about the same (Table XXXVI). The dietary was better than that of the Netherlands or Denmark, except that Denmark had more meat. There was a falling off in the war but by 1948 the Swedish dietary was superior in butter and other milk products to the British but about the same in caloric value. The production of margarine had doubled as the result of the increased production of oil seed.

TABLE XXXVI. *Quantities of foods, lb. per head per year pre-war and* 1947–48[1]

Average 1934–38	Meat	Milk and products including cheese (not butter)	Butter	Cereals	Calories per day
Sweden	108	561	24	210	3,122
United Kingdom	135	243	25	207	3,081
1948–49					
Sweden	93	535	31	190	3,070
United Kingdom	91	350	10·3	248	3,030

(*F.A.O. Food Balance Sheets*, 1950 Supplement.)

The dietary has since improved and by 1950 the daily calorie intake per head of population was 6 per cent above the pre-war level although the population had increased by 12 per cent.[2]

This improvement in the dietary began when the war ended and has steadily continued since, except for protein.

Before the war the chief exports were butter, eggs, and pig meat. The quantities fell considerably during and immediately after the war. Dairy produce has already more than recovered in actual tonnage though the products have changed, and not only butter, but cheese and processed milk are now exported:

[1] The Organization for European Economic Co-operation (O.E.E.C.) in their 1951 Report gave the following as the percentage food consumption for 1949–50 (pre-war = 100):

Visible fats	116	Meat	96	Potatoes	96
Sugar	109	Milk	94	Cereals	95

[2] *Rpt. to F.A.O.*, 1951.

Exports of dairy produce, thousand tons

	Average 1936–38	1948	1949	1950	1951
Butter	26	Nil	2	14	27
Cheese	−2 (1)	−3	−1	6	2
Dried and Condensed milk	−1	−1	6	6	4
Net export	23	−4	7	26	33

(1) A minus sign indicates import.

Exports of eggs have increased to an even greater extent. They have been:

Thousand tons

1939	1948	1949	1950	1951
4	−2	5	12	9

On the other hand the export of meat (chiefly pork) has ceased and instead there is now an import. This is partly due to the circumstance that the animal population has not yet fully recovered its numbers but more probably to the circumstance that they are not being fattened as much as before: production of pig meat, however, has greatly increased (p. 118). The changes have been:

Exports and imports of meat, thousand tons

	Average 1937–39	1948	1949	1950	1951
Export	16	Nil	Nil	1	3
Import	7	8	16	28	15
Net export	11	−8	−16	−27	−12

(Bone is included. A minus sign indicates import.)

What are the possibilities of increasing food production in Sweden? At first sight it would appear that more land could be brought into cultivation seeing that only 11 per cent of the total land surface is cultivated. The fact that a shrinkage of some 190,000 acres has occurred since the early 1920's in spite of a rise in population, however, shows that there are serious farming difficulties not yet overcome. Further, the absence of any noticeable increase in yields in spite of the good plant breeding and advisory work, and the increased use of fertilizers and of tractors, suggests some limiting factor not yet controlled.

The explanation lies, partly at any rate, in the uneconomic nature of many of the small badly situated farms. Much benefit may result from the improvement of the farm units now being undertaken. Holdings of less than 5 acres give only part-time occupation, and allow the occupier to take regular and permanent employment, either in the forest or in some local industry. Little difficulty arises in connection with these holdings nor with those of 25 acres or more which give full-time employment. There is, however, considerable difficulty about the holdings ranging from 5 to 25 acres. They are too small to furnish an adequate livelihood and too large to permit a man to take regular work elsewhere. Where a sufficient acreage of forest is attached, or if other casual work is obtainable or market gardening feasible, a satisfactory living is possible. But frequently neither is practicable.

In 1947 the Royal Board of Agriculture was charged with the duty of improving these farms, gradually enlarging them to make them of a workable size. The local administration under the Board was authorized to acquire the necessary land. Credits or grants can be given to enable farmers to clear land, remove boulders, bring in better soil, carry out drainage[1] or other soil improvements, plant hedges or shelter belts for protection against wind or sand-storms, or to make farm roads and reconstruct or recondition farm buildings. A special Institute had earlier been set up for research in farm buildings in view of their great importance in Swedish farm economy.

Sweden has the great advantage of abundant and cheap electrical power: more than 95 per cent of the farms are supplied with it; many of the farm-houses, even the small ones, have such electrical luxuries as hot-plates. Tractors are becoming increasingly common: 80,000 were in use in 1951,[2] about half made in Sweden the rest mainly from Great Britain and the United States. Combines are now so numerous that the question of storage of the grain has already been raised. Co-operation is highly developed: it began in the 1880's and now every important branch of farm production has its appropriate Society which undertakes and controls marketing. The milk is handled by co-operative Dairy Societies federated into a large organization, the Swedish Dairies Association (S.M.R.), which is linked up with the Milk Recording Societies and others such as Meat Marketing and Egg Marketing. These are run by the farmers: there is little direct Government intervention for although Sweden is politically a Socialist country, in practice it is one of the most individualistic in Europe.

Meanwhile the scientific work continues: it is centred at Ultana, near Uppsala where also the educational activities have their headquarters, and there are numerous experimental farms and other institutes also.

FINLAND

The special interest of the agriculture of Finland is that it has solved many of the problems of farming outside the ordinary limits of latitude, and has done this so well that it has enabled the country to achieve a remarkable degree of recovery from the drastic losses of the war.

Finland lies wholly north of lat. 60° N. where its southernmost point begins and it stretches for some 740 miles in a narrow strip as far as lat. 70° N.: it is the only country in the world where agriculture is carried on entirely in such conditions. Over most of the land the mean January temperatures range from 10 and 20° F; only in the south are they somewhat higher, but nowhere do they approach 30° F. The July mean temperatures, however, are, over most of the country, above 60° F and nowhere do they fall below 50° F: this is the result of the mitigating influence of the western air currents. The difference between the summer in the north and in the south lies not so much in its warmth as in its length: in the south the growing season for crops is 210–220 days; in the north it is 120 days or less, a difference of three months. The

---

[1] Before the war it was estimated that about a quarter of the arable land needed drainage or repairs of drains.

[2] Swedish Govt. Rpt. to F.A.O., 1951, p. 17, quoted 75,000 for 1950.

grazing season is even shorter; about 160 days in the south and 100 in the north. Arable cultivation is therefore mainly confined to the south and west, though it is being extended northwards as plant breeders produce varieties of shorter and shorter growing period. Everywhere the long, cold winter necessitates housing the cattle in well-built sheds and saving much winter fodder for them during the summer.

The rainfall is about 20 inches in the north and about 25 inches in the south: half of this falls in the growing season. There is not always sufficient for the grassland and this may suffer from drought in summer.

Some 60 per cent of the land consists of moraine gravels and sands, about 11 per cent is swamp soil and 9 per cent clay and silt: the clays are chiefly in the south and carry about 40 per cent of the cropped area: the swamp soils carry about 30 per cent.

The native vegetation is largely forest and moor; agriculture can be practised only in the clearings and on the drained land, and is at present confined to about 8 per cent of the land. The relations between the agriculture and the environmental conditions have been ably discussed by Otto Valle in *Suomi, a General Handbook of the Geography of Finland*.[1]

The area of the country before the war was 86·1 million acres[2] but of this the Russians have taken 10·6 million so that the present area is 75·5 million acres.[3] The loss was greater than the figures indicate because it was the southern warmer part of the country with much good arable land. Moreover, a heavy indemnity, payable in various commodities, valued at about $570 million[4] was also exacted.

The country was thus faced in 1944 with the problem of resettling the 480,000 people displaced by the Russians, of providing for some 100,000 ex-service men, paying the indemnity, and arranging to feed the population on an agricultural area diminished by more than 10 per cent, which included some of the best land. The problem was thus similar to that set to Denmark in 1864 after their losses of territory to the Germans, but it was both harsher and more difficult. The Finns, however, have tackled it on the same lines as the Danes: by developing systems of livestock husbandry carried out by small farmers banded together in co-operative societies so as to ensure the most efficient handling and marketing of their produce. Fortunately this system had been adopted even before Finland first gained its independence in December 1917; co-operative societies had been started in the 1880's, but systematic development was the result of the propaganda and educational activities of the Pellervo Society, founded in 1899. The co-operative dairies and other agricultural organizations were founded on the Danish and Swiss models; their successful working is ensured by the happy custom of neighbourly co-operation in activities such as harvesting. (Plate 16, p. 109.)

These various efforts have been so successful that a substantial part of the lost area of farmland has been replaced by new reclamations. The areas of cultivated land have been:

[1] Helsinki, 1952. See also W. R. Mead, *Farming in Finland*, Univ. of London, Athlone Press, 1953.

[2] 95·7 in *Ency. Brit.*, 1926.

[3] 83·2 in *Oxford Atlas*, but this includes fresh-water lakes.

[4] The last instalment was delivered in September 1952.

	Million acres				
1938	1940	1943	1944	1949	1950
	(after 1st Russian war)		(after 2nd Russian war)		
6·45	5·79	6·52	5·85	6·07	6·11

1944 loss compared with 1943: 670,000 acres.
1950 gain compared with 1944: 310,000 acres.

The total output of food is now little short of that before the disasters of the war while the general nutrition level seems to be somewhat better. The large displaced population is now settled and the ex-service men are well on the way to settlement also. (Fig. 10.)

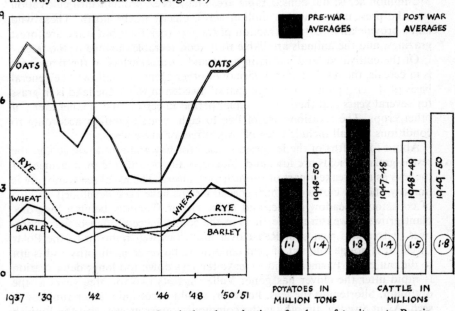

Fig. 10.—Finland's recovery of agricultural production after loss of territory to Russia (1940–45)

In 1950 the area of cultivated land per head of population was 1½ acres. The land utilization is shown in Table XXXVII.

TABLE XXXVII. *Utilization of land in Finland*

	Million acres		
	1938	1949	1950
Cultivated land			
Grass leys	3·30	3·03	3·14
Cereals	2·34	2·27	2·11
Other crops and fallow	0·81	0·77	0·76
	6·45	6·07	6·11
Forest	62·4	53·52	53·55
Natural grass and other use	17·3	16·0	15·8
Total	86·1	75·6	75·5

(Finland Govt. Rpt. to F.A.O., 1951.)

123

About 40 per cent of the population is agricultural; there are some 310,000 holdings, 86 per cent of them less than 37 acres and officially classed as "small," but the 14 per cent of the middle and larger farms have more than 60 per cent of the land. Only 4 per cent of the holdings exceed 62 acres and they have only 21 per cent of the land: their holdings tend to diminish as new farms are made. Practically all the occupiers own their land; many of them have some forest of their own on which they work; 60 per cent of the forest area belongs to the farmers and this allows of smaller farms than would otherwise be possible. (Plate 17, p. 180.)

Wild meadows and pasture lands at the beginning of the century occupied 3·2 million acres, but considerable areas have been brought into cultivation and the present total is 1·8 million acres, chiefly in the north. These wild lands provide an important fraction of the livestock food but some are forest grazings, and the animals are liable to do considerable damage to the trees.

Of the cultivated land half is in grass and three-quarters of the remainder is in cereals, the rest being in a variety of other crops and fallow. The general basis of the cropping is similar to that of Sweden in which the land is in grass for several years and then for an equal period in cereals and smaller areas of other crops. The rotations are of five to eight years' duration according to conditions, but all include a ley of two, three, or more years.

About four-fifths of the ley grass is used for hay and a little silage and the rest is grazed. Yields are low, and, indeed, Valle regards the management of the leys as the weakest part of Finnish agriculture. The usual seeds mixture is timothy and red clover of which special strains have been developed, as also of cocksfoot, meadow fescue, and alsike clover. Timothy being a long-day plant grows as well in the north as in the south, indeed, often better; moreover, it tolerates peat soil. Red clover also does well right up to the Polar Circle; it is not as tolerant of peat conditions, however, as timothy and is apt to die out early. Farmers tend to leave the leys down too long; deterioration is rapid after the clover has gone: Valle suggests two to three years as the optimum. Shortening the leys, however, would necessitate larger supplies of seed. As in Sweden, timothy is the commonest grass grown, and the Finnish plant breeders have selected special strains suited to the conditions: as also they have for meadow fescue, cocksfoot, red and aslike clover. The conditions are too severe for rye grass. Sufficient timothy seed is produced to allow of considerable export, but it is necessary to import some of the other seeds: these come mostly from Denmark.

Of the cereals, oats are by far the most important followed by wheat, rye, and barley (Table XXXVIII). The chief bread grains are rye and wheat. All through the years rye has been the more important; recently, however, it has been displaced by wheat, the acreage of which has doubled since pre-war days, as the result of the successful efforts of the Finnish plant breeders in producing shorter period and hardier varieties of spring wheat using as parent material native and Swedish sorts. Accordingly the wheat area has been pushed farther and farther north (Fig. 11); spring wheat now is grown almost as far north as oats. The expansion has been remarkable:

	Thousand acres		
1930	1935	1939	1949
11·0	114	274	449

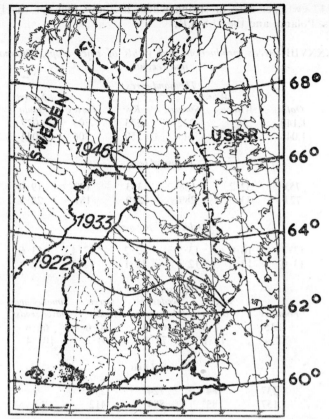

FIG. 11.—Northern extensive of spring wheat cultivation in Finland resulting from the breeding of new varieties and developments in agricultural technique. (O. Valle, in *Suomi, a General Handbook of the Geography of Finland*, Helsinki, 1952)

The gain between 1939 and 1949 was all the more striking in that 47,000 acres of spring wheat were lost when the Russians took Karelia.

Winter wheat is confined to the far south: its area, also, has been pushed northwards; but not as dramatically as happened with spring wheat. Rye is also a winter crop, but it grows up to Southern Lapland. The oats are used almost entirely for animals and very little for human food. Cultivation for grain extends to the Tervola–Kuhmo line (lat. 66° N., south-east to 64° N.), beyond that, oats are grown only for green fodder. Barley is particularly important in the north; four and six-rowed varieties are grown there and two-rowed in the south. After allowing for seed and waste about half the grain is fed to animals, half is used as human food. The mixed grain is usually barley and oats; peas or vetches are not usually added: Valle advises, however, that this should be done.

Yields of all grain crops except wheat have maintained their pre-war level and those of wheat have fallen only slightly in spite of the loss of good land in the south. They are naturally lower than in some of the warmer countries below lat. 60°, but they are higher than might have been expected: the yield

125

of over 12 cwt. per acre of spring wheat is above that for the Danubian countries, Poland, and the U.S.S.R.

TABLE XXXVIII. *Areas, production, and yields of chief crops, Finland, pre-war and recent*

		Wheat				Mixed	Total
Average	*Oats*	*Winter*	*Spring*	*Rye*	*Barley*	*grain*	*grain*
				Thousand acres			
1936–39	1,140	58	222	573	303	027	2,323
1949	1,048	42	449	359	306	044	2,248
				Thousand tons			
Average							
1936–39	753	52·2	158	353	189	19·0	1,525
1949	723	33·5	289	219	181	28·3	1,474
				Yields, cwt. per acre			
Average							
1936–39	13·1	16·0	13·9	12·2	12·4	13·6	
1948–50	13·0	15·6	12·4	12·1	12·3	12·6	

		Sugar	Swedes and	Green	Timothy and	
Average	*Potatoes*	*beet*	*other roots*	*fodder*	*clover seeds*	*Fallow*
			Thousand acres			
1936–39	215	7·6	69·0	40·6	66·6	366·4
1949	214	18·1	77·5	64·2	103·4	264·3
			Thousand tons			
Average						
1936–39	1,337	84	724	239	9	
1949	1,157	183	784	412	13	
			Yield, tons per acre			
Average						
1936–39	6·12	10·9	11·1	5·9 (1)	0·13	
1948–50	6·19	10·0	10·7	6·1	0·13	

(*Finland Govt. Rpt. to F.A.O.*, 1951.)
(1) Fresh weight.

The remaining crops are peas (25,000 acres), Finland's most important leguminous crop next to the clovers, and smaller areas of fibre crops and oil seeds.

Potatoes are chief among the other crops. The long hours of daylight facilitate continued growth and delay the ripening that would put an end to it, while the summer temperatures are adequate. Unlike all other crops potatoes give better yields in Finland than in Sweden, especially in the north, where they are freer from disease than in the south. They provide not only human food but also raw material for the starch and distillery industries.

The area of roots is very small having regard to the number of cattle. They are at present much less grown than in Denmark; but a search for better varieties is being made and the area may increase. A large-leafed turnip, seeds of which were sent to Finland during the war by the American Red Cross, and closely resembling the Green Globe and Norfolk varieties, promises to be a considerable improvement on the sorts now grown in Finland; on the experimental fields at Tikkurila in 1950 it gave up to 36 tons per acre of fresh weight (roots and leaves) containing 3·4 tons per acre of dry matter with 24 per cent of crude protein. No other fodder crop yielded as well.[1] It is frost resistant and grows well on the acid swamp soils so common in North Finland; even there it yields up to 2½ tons dry matter per acre. It is lifted when in full leaf and made into silage. Supplies of seed are now obtained from England and from Holland. Apparently the long days and cool conditions of the Finnish summer cause the great development of leaf; this does not happen in Norfolk. Marrow stem kale is also proving useful. Another promising recent crop is a turnip rape yielding seed rich in oil suitable for Finland's margarine industry. This came from Sweden and has proved suitable not only for southern but also for central Finland. Yields have been obtained of 12–16 cwt. of seed per acre containing 40 per cent of oil (i.e. 5–6½ cwt. oil per acre), the residue after oil extraction constitutes a valuable feeding stuff rich in protein.[2] Both this and the leafy turnip are being actively investigated in Finland. Experience, both there and in Sweden, points to the rape family as a very promising source of food both for human beings and animals in cold climates; it is extremely plastic and the possibilities of breeding new and more productive varieties seem to be considerable. Sugar beet is a comparatively new crop developing after the first sugar factory was set up at Salo in 1919.

Silage is chiefly made by Prof. A. I. Virtanen's method which is adopted also in other countries under the name AIV.

The total number of "food units" produced (see Denmark, p. 109) in 1949 was 3,464 millions, an average of 1,432 per acre. Higher outputs are, however, anticipated.

Fertilizers are not used extensively as they have to be imported and currency is lacking. The quantities of plant foods supplied per acre of the cultivated land have been, in cwt. per acre:

Manure	N	P_2O_5	K_2O
Average			
1936–39	0·08	0·07	0·22
1950	0·11	0·09	0·23
Fertilizer			
Average			
1936–39	0·02	0·10	0·04
1950	0·04	0·18	0·08
Aim	0·08	0·24	0·11

(Otto Valle in *Suomi*, p. 460.)

The fertilizer nitrogen is largely in the form of nitrate of lime, imported from Norway, but the use of ammonium nitrate is increasing. It is proposed to set up a small factory with a capacity of 16,000 tons nitrogen in order to augment the supply. Superphosphate is made in the country but the mineral

---

[1] Otto Valle, *F.A.O. Europe Bull.*, 1950, No. 4, pp. 201–3.
[2] Otto Valle, *Tidskr, Lantm.*, 1951, Vol. 33, pp. 60–3, and 1952, Vol. 34, pp. 69–71 (in Swedish). In Norfolk these varieties do not produce large leaves, probably because the conditions are drier.

phosphate has to be imported. Potash is imported from the U.S.S.R. and from France; the 40 per cent salt is commonly used.

The livestock, except the horses, are the special care of the women: the numbers have been:

	Millions Cattle	*Including Milch*	*Sheep*	*Pigs*	*Poultry*
Average 1934–38	1·895	1·309	1·048	0·501	2·853 (1)
1949	1·542	1·029	1·067	0·409	2·688 (2)

(1) *F.A.O. Food Balance Sheets.*
(2) 1949 Census, *S.Y.B.*

In addition there were some 107,000 reindeer in Lapland, their numbers had fallen during the war but have now more than recovered.

The sheep are Landrace, similar to, but distinct from the Swedish breed; but some of them are staggeringly prolific. Korkman records a ewe that produced 37 lambs in ten years and another that produced 30 lambs in thirteen years.[1]

The cattle are mainly the domestic breed and Ayrshires coming originally from Scotland. Their numbers are high in relation to the population, so high in fact, that grain and oil cakes or seeds have to be imported to feed them. The numbers of animals and output of milk fell during the war but both are now increasing in spite of the loss of much arable land and of the inflation which has greatly restricted imports. Before the war some 82,000 tons of grain were imported for animal feeding in addition to oil seeds; in 1949 the import of grain had been reduced to 30,000 tons and of oil cakes to 67,600 tons.

There are no good figures for the production of milk owing to the difficulty of estimating the farm consumption, which is probably fairly large. Nor is the general average production per cow known.[2] About 22 or 24 per cent of the cows are recorded, and for these the average milk yield was 6,270 lb. with 4·1 per cent fat in 1937–38, 5,600 lb. in the very dry season 1947, and 6,900 lb. in the more normal season 1948–49; the average fat content was 4·1 and 4·2 respectively. The fodder units consumed per cow averaged 2,185 in 1937–38, 2,052 in 1947–48, and 2,433 in 1948–49.

Artificial insemination is increasingly practised though as yet only about 7 per cent of the cows are treated.

The reduction in imports of oil cakes and grains has naturally lowered the production of butter. Before the war this was estimated at 48,000 tons a

[1] Communicated from Commonwealth Bureau of Animal Breeding and Genetics, Edinburgh. For Swedish results see p. 115.
[2] F.A.O. (Food Balance Sheets, 1949) estimate as follows:

	Total milk production million tons	*Average yield lb. per cow*	*Number of cows millions*
Average 1936–38	2·50	4,200	1·321
1947–48	1·70	3,700	1·003

Otto Valle (loc. cit.) estimated the total production of milk before the war at 2,650,000 tons, of which 44 per cent was used as liquid, 51 per cent was made into butter, and 5 per cent into cheese.

9 (*left*) The North East Polder, reclaimed from the Zuyder Sea. (*Courtesy of Royal Netherlands Embassy*) [p. 56

10 (*right*) Intensive horticulture in Westland, the Netherlands. Each block of houses has its furnace and factory chimney. (*Courtesy of Royal Netherlands Embassy*) [p. 88

11 (*left*) Korinth Cooperative butter factory, Funen. (*Courtesy of Danish Embassy*) [p. 97

12 (*right*) Typical Danish farms, Spanager, near Køge, Zealand. (*Courtesy of Danish Embassy*) [p. 98

13 (left) Farm in South Sweden. (Courtesy of Swedish Embassy) [p. 111

14 (right) Drying hay on racks in North Sweden. (Courtesy of Swedish Embassy) [p. 112

15 (left) The Svalov Plant Breeding Station, Sweden: experimental plots of autumn wheat. (Courtesy of Swedish Embassy) [p. 114

16 (right) Neighbours helping with the harvest ("Talkoo work") Finland. (Courtesy of Finnish Legation) [p. 122

year,[1] in 1949–50 at 45,300, and in 1950–51 at 54,000 tons; the figures are not exact because the quantity made in farmhouses is unknown. Before the war there was an export averaging about 14,000 tons annually; this has now practically ceased. Production could be increased by reverting to the pre-war practice of arranging for a good proportion of autumn calves instead of concentrating on spring calving as had been necessary during the war when concentrated feeding stuffs could not be imported and reliance had to be entirely on the spring flush of growth. Storage accommodation is insufficient to hold all the butter that could be produced if calving were mainly in spring, but with wider spread of the calving season this difficulty would be overcome.

As in other countries cheese production has steadily increased and is now greater than in 1938. Production in 1949–50 was 12,500 tons and in 1950–51 15,000 tons; exports have not only been resumed but, by 1950–51, had reached 8,400 tons, thus exceeding the pre-war record of 6,800 tons.

Production of beef and veal has fallen, but that of pork has increased, allowing, in 1949–50, an export of 4,700 tons; but this was not maintained (Table XXXIX).

TABLE XXXIX. *Production of livestock products, thousand tons*

	Production	
	Average 1934–38	1950–51
Butter	48	54
Cheese	14 (1)	15
Meat		
Pork	45	60
Beef and veal	63	40
Other meat	14	6·6
Eggs	19	22

(1) Ten in 1938.

The production figures are subject to the uncertainty about the quantities consumed on the farms. The imports and exports of food are given in Table XL.

TABLE XL. *Imports and exports of food, Finland, thousand tons*

	Net imports				Exports		
	Average				Average		
	1934–38	1947–48	1950–51		1934–38	1947–48	1950–51
Wheat and rye	150	316 (1)	322	Meat	3	—	1·0
Other grains	96	102 (1)	34·6	Eggs	8	—	1·1
Sugar	93	68	113	Cheese	6	—	4·1
Fruit	21	—	21	Butter	14	—	0·6
Vegetable oil	18	12	19				
Butter		3	−0·6				

(*F.A.O. Food Balance Sheets.*)

(1) 1947 was one of Europe's bad years: Finland's production fell from a usual annual level of about 1½ million tons of all grain to 1 million tons only.

Thus the available supplies of grain have been:

[1] *F.A.O. Food Balance Sheets, 1949.*

Thousand tons

	Average 1934–38			1950–51		
	Production	Import	Total	Production	Import	Total
Bread grains						
Wheat and rye	533	150	683	513	322	835
Including wheat	162	103	265	300	237	537
Other grain	937	96	1,033	880	35·4	915
Total grain	1,470	246	1,716	1,393	357	1,750

Of the total grain available 900,000 tons were fed to livestock on the average in the period 1934–38 and 662,000 tons in the year 1950–51.

The proportion of grain imported in 1950–51 was higher than before the war. At the end of the 1930's the country's self-sufficiency in rye, then the principal bread cereal, was 95 per cent and in wheat 85 per cent; imports of these two amounted only to 60,000 tons a year. By 1950–51 imports of all grain had risen to 20 per cent of the total available, and of bread grains to 38·5 per cent; the proportions are less than in 1947–48, however, when they were 30 and 45 per cent respectively.

Nutrition statistics are subject to the usual incompleteness through lack of knowledge of the quantities of food consumed by the farmers and their households. F.A.O. estimates are given in Table XLI.

TABLE XLI. *Quantities of food available, lb. per head per year*

	Average 1934–38	1950–51		Average 1934–38	1950–51
Cereals	282	315	Fruit	40	19
Potatoes	398	282	Sugar	62	73
Meat	72	62	Butter and fats	33	43
Eggs	7	11	Cheese	5	4
Fish	13	23			
Milk	572	534			
			Calories per day	3,000	3,213
			Protein per day, grams		
			Animal	43·7	48
			Vegetable	51·4	52·4
			Total	95·1	100·4

The figures indicate a dietary considerably better than in many other European countries.

The agriculturists of Finland have the double task of making the country more self-sufficing and of increasing exports. Their 1½ acres per head do not provide all the food consumed; the exports are processed products of imported grain and oil seeds. More land is being brought into cultivation and outputs per acre and per animal are to be increased. The first part of the programme is being successfully accomplished. By June 1, 1951, some 4¾ million acres of land had been used for the settlement of ex-service men and displaced persons including about 4 million acres of forest and other land and 586,000 acres of cultivated land for conversion into smallholdings of which there will be 266,000.[1] The element of urgency has necessitated taking

[1] This remarkable Land Settlement Scheme is discussed by K. U. Pihkala in *Bank of Finland Monthly Bull.*, Nos. 3–4, 1952.

land from established holdings, so lessening their size and reducing the possibility of mechanization; the number of horses had, therefore, to be increased. Considerable loss of capital was involved, as the large farm buildings proved unsuitable for the new smallholdings. But the total output of food is expected to increase, though it will cost more in labour. A Drainage Act was passed in 1949 under which 13,580 acres of land were drained forthwith; its operation continues. Under another scheme 100,000 acres were cleared in 1949 and more is to be done.[1] Considerable areas of swamp land in the centre and north could be brought into use.

As yet, however, there is no clear evidence of increasing yields per acre or per cow, but as more fertilizers and better crop varieties become available, crop yields should increase, giving more food for the animals and, therefore, higher outputs of milk, meat, and eggs. Finland possesses a Central Research Station at Tikkurila and two plant breeding stations, the State Station in Jokioinen, and the Co-operative Station in Tammisto. Improvement of the strains of grasses and clovers by further cross breeding and selection may be expected to increase the amount of herbage considerably, and increased production of silage to reduce the need for imported grain. The Finnish experts are fully alive to the possibilities and, now that the war-time difficulties have been largely overcome, further development may be confidently anticipated.

[1] *Rpt. National F.A.O. Cttee. of Finland*, 1950.

131

Chapter 5

FRANCE AND THE PEASANT PRODUCERS OF THE MEDITERRANEAN LANDS

FRANCE

France is of special interest as being the only country in Western Europe where national efforts are made to maintain a peasantry system as distinct from the systems of small commercial farms common elsewhere.

The northern and the southern regions differ widely. Much of the north is an undulating plain with great stretches of deep fertile loess loams and clays; the rainfall ranges from about 30 inches in the west to about 24 inches in the east; the summers are rather warmer and the winters colder than in England, but all Northern France lies within the wheat belt. Over much of its central part the agricultural conditions are good, and the farms large; they may be up to 1,000 acres; perhaps the best section is that included in the Departments Nord, Pas-de-Calais, Eure et Loir, Seine, Oise, Aisne, Somme, where one finds advanced mechanization and all the appurtenances of intensive farming. A usual rotation is wheat, barley or oats, sugar beet; then lucerne which is generally left for two years.

The hill country to the east of Paris, Champagne, Argonne, Haute Marne, has some desperately poor light soil. Favoured districts such as Reims, Epernay, and Soissons produce famous wines; some of the land is in large sheep farms but much is simply rough grazing or planted with conifers; some is simply abandoned. A considerable area is farmed on the unimproved three-course rotation: fallow, two corn crops; the fallow being retained because the sparse population could never provide the labour needed for hoed crops and intensive farming. The Germans during their occupation of this region in 1940–44 tried to abolish the fallow and grow cereals continuously, but they were defeated by the serious weed infestation that followed. The system can be worked economically where mechanization is possible; three men with a tractor and combine harvester can manage a 250 to 400 acre farm growing grain somewhat on Canadian lines but using more man-hours. Sugar beet also can be grown by mechanized methods: the yields are low, but so are the costs.[1]

The western part of Northern France is wetter than the east: it is a land of grass and of livestock, especially dairy cattle and small animals, of apple trees, and cider. In contrast with some of the eastern districts, part of this region, Brittany, Mayenne, Vendée, are relatively densely populated and the farms correspondingly small; in Brittany they are usually less than 25 acres and, being without much mechanical aid, they require about 36 man-days per acre per year.

The southern part of France is dominated by the mountain block that links the Alps and the Pyrenees: this falls away quickly on the east to the

[1] R. Dumont, *Proc. U.N. Sci. Conf. Conservation and Utilization of Resources*, Lake Success, 1949, U.N. Dept. Econ. Affairs, 1951, Vol. 6, pp. 605–9.

Rhone–Saône valleys, and on the west to the wide plain of the Garonne which stretches to the sea. Its north-east part is the so-called *Massif Central*, the poor granitic region of Auvergne and Limousin which produces rye and potatoes, and raises sheep and cattle on an extensive scale. The Larzac sheep give milk for making Roquefort cheese.

The temperatures in the south are higher than in the north and the rainfall lower, especially in summer, except in the higher parts. A great variety of crops is grown: vines, fruits, early vegetables, tobacco, maize, as well as the ordinary cereals and roots. As in the north the western side is moister and more productive than the hotter and drier Rhone–Saône basin in the east, and there are differences in the cropping. In the drier districts olives are grown and also mulberry trees for silk worms, though these are decreasing. In the Rhone valley where irrigation has been developed there is much production of fruit and early vegetables; in La Crau irrigated and warped land gives rich fodder crops, and the recently established rice fields of Camargue are yielding 32 to 40 cwt. of paddy per acre.

The higher districts are largely left as pasture; the animals spend their summers there and come down to the valleys for the winter. The south-east part of the high country from the Cevennes to the Mediterranean was formerly fairly densely populated; its steep slopes had been terraced to conserve the soil. But the cultivation was arduous: manure had to be carried up on the peasant's back, and also, up to the end of the 18th century, any soil that had been washed down; the produce was carried down in the same way. Many of the terraces are so narrow that only hand tillage is possible, and the rural de-population of recent years has thrown much of this terraced land out of cultivation.

South-west of the *massif* there is much thinly populated land difficult to utilize; the hard limestone is overlain by a very thin soil and the rainfall is low and variable. Cultivation is unrewarding; yields of grain are only about 5 to 8 cwt. per acre and there is a considerable risk of erosion. But there is much good land also and some famous products in the valleys of the Garonne tributaries; the Dordogne, the Lot, the Tarn, and others: for this is the land of *fois gras* and of other delicacies made from goose, and of pleasing wines which must be consumed on the spot as they will not travel. Table grapes, peaches, plums, and hybrid maize, are produced in increasing quantities.

The total area of France is 136 million acres; its population at December 31, 1951, was estimated to be 42·4 millions and the density 200 per square mile: sparse in comparison with any of its neighbours. The increase in population is so slight as to be perceptible only over long periods: in 1866 the numbers were 38·1 millions, in 1901 39, in 1931 41·8, at which figure it still stood in 1948, having, in the meantime, fluctuated a little up and down.

The utilization of the land is shown in Table XLII. Before the war 82·8 million acres were in agricultural use, of which 34 per cent was in permanent grass; in 1950 the agricultural area had fallen to 80·2 million acres, and the proportion of grass had risen to 38 per cent. Since 1938 the cropped land has lost 4¼ million acres, of which 1·6 million became pasture, 1·3 million went to "other use," and the remainder reverted to forest and waste. The grassland has for many years been extending at the expense of the arable:

in 1862 its acreage was 12·5 millions only; in 1950 it had risen to 30·4 millions (Table XLII).

The area per head of land in crops and in fruit in 1950 was nearly 1·2 acres; the addition of the pasture raises this to 1·9 acres but much of it is very poor.

Two types of farms must be distinguished: the large intensive commercial farms and the small family holdings of mixed character—the traditional peasant farms of France—producing both for subsistence and for the market. Most of the land is held by peasants, about three-quarters of it is in farms of less than 125 acres; there are about 2½ million farms between 50 and 100 acres and a large number of smaller ones. In the wine districts the holdings may be very small: it is estimated that 4 acres of vines will support a family. Many of these farms, especially in the east, are not in one piece but are scattered in strips of only one acre or less in area. Consolidation—*remembrement*—proceeds only slowly. Of 25 million acres affected only about 1·9 million had been reorganized by 1950; peasants always oppose it. Even after consolidation the farm is still liable to be split up among the heirs on the death of the owner.[1]

About 2½ million of the cultivators are freeholders, cultivating their land with the help of their families, the woman playing a particularly important part. There are some large estates in the west and north on which the farms are leased for nine-year periods, on rentals that fluctuate with prices of the four main products, wheat, beef, barley, pork, and sometimes milk; in addition, certain gifts or *redevances* may be due to the owner, according to ancient custom. In the south and parts of the west—the borders of Brittany and Anjou—forms of share cropping, *metayage*, survive: about 10 per cent of the holdings are on this system but the trend of modern legislation favours their conversion into cash tenancies.[2]

In consequence of the smallness of the farms in the south the number of workers on the land is high; before the war (1931 census) it averaged nearly 11 per 100 acres while in the north, where many of the farms are larger, the average was about six. The total number had fallen by 1½ millions since the 1921 census; on the other hand there had been a steady increase in the number of foreign workers, Spaniards, Italians, and Poles, who came as hired men but often became share tenants and even owners in the south: in 1938 there were over half a million of them.

Agriculture occupies 32 per cent of the total manpower of France as against 35 per cent in industry; 82 per cent of these are self-employed.[3]

The areas and outputs of the various crops in 1938, 1948, and 1950 are given in Table XLIII.

Ley farming is nowhere practised to any extent; leys are sometimes sown but no use is made of selected strains for special uses. There is a rather large, but fluctuating, production of lucerne seed of Provence and Flamand types

[1] Under the Monnet plan (p. 140) 4 million acres had been scheduled for reorganization by 1952. Fragmentation problems are discussed by Sir Bernard O. Binns in *F.A.O. Agric. Studies*, No. 12, 1950.

[2] For the operation of the system before the war, see P. Lamartine Yates, *Food Production in Western Europe*, Longmans Green, 1940.

[3] *Bull. mensuel de Stat.; Suppl. trimestriel* 1950 quoted from *Westminster Bank Review*, Nov. 1953.

TABLE XLII. *Land utilization in France, 1938 and 1948* (1)

	Million acres		
	1938	1948	1950
Cultivated agricultural land	50·15	45·0	45·9
Vines	3·9	3·9	3·9
Pasture	28·85	30·4	30·4
Total agricultural land	82·8	79·3	80·2
Forests	26·6	27·0	27·7
Moor and uncultivated	14·0	14·9	14·0
Other use	12·9	14·8	14·2
Total	136·1	136·1	136·1
Population, millions	41·9	41·8	42·4 (2)

(*F.A.O. Stat. Year Book*, 1951.)

(1) There is a certain amount of bias in French agricultural statistics. The returns are made by the peasants, who tend to report the same figures year after year so long as they are acceptable; during the overproduction period of the 1930's the figures for arable land tended to be inflated so as to cushion the anticipated restrictions, and after 1940 in the "*période de pénurie*" they were deflated to avoid the "*impositions*" on some of the crops (*Le Sol*, September 1947, p. 198). There is therefore some doubt as to the precise extent of the fall in area of cropped land: travellers in France in 1948 could not find the derelict areas which according to the statistics should have existed. The French peasants are extremely adept in making up accounts and returns. The general trend of the figures, however, is correct.

(2) Est. December 31, 1951.

TABLE XLIII. *Areas and output of principal crops, France*

	Areas, million acres			Output, million tons		
				Average		
	1934–48	1948	1950	1934–38	1948	1950
Wheat	12·8	10·4	10·7	8·21	7·63	7·70
Oats	8·0	6·0	5·8	4·57	3·38	3·30
All cereals	25·5	21·1	21·3	15·48	13·70	13·81
Potatoes	3·5	2·6	2·4	16·00	15·68	12·94
Sugar beet	0·78	0·54	0·75	8·78	8·60	10·00
Other crops and fallow	20·6	21·6	22·4			
Vines	3·8	3·9	3·9	{ 8·0 (1) 62·6	6·4 47·4	8·7 (2) 65·1 (3)

(1) 1938.

(2) Grapes.

(3) Wine, million hectolitres.

Consumption having fallen to about 75 per cent that of pre-war this quantity proved too much, and the Government ordered that some of it should be distilled. The problem arose again in 1952 when a similarly large output was obtained.

and of an intermediate called Poitou-Vendée, also of red clover (*trèfle violet*) and a smaller production of sainfoin seed, but for other clovers and grasses home production is often insufficient and imports are necessary.

The reduction in cultivated area recorded in Table XLII fell almost entirely on the cereals which dropped by four million acres during the period, wheat and oats each losing about two million acres. Some of this land was put into grass, and at the other end of the scale poor grassland became derelict or was afforested.

The fall in acreage of wheat had been going on since the 1870's, but the average yield had risen from 8·6 cwt. per acre in the decade 1872–81 to 12·5 cwt. per acre in the period 1934–38, and 14·6 cwt. per acre for the three years 1948 to 1950. This is a usual result of a shrinking acreage, as the least suitable land is, generally, given up first. The average, however, is still low. The yields of wheat in the north are much higher than in the south, 24 cwt. per acre is not uncommon and even 48 cwt. per acre is not unknown, while in the south-west yields of 8 to 10 cwt. per acre are more usual.

Yields of oats have hardly changed; in the period 1948 to 1950 they still averaged about 11 cwt. per acre as before the war. Yields of potatoes show no clear increase: before the war they were 4·5 tons per acre: the average for the five years 1946–50 is 4·8 tons per acre, but this is inflated by an exceptionally heavy yield of 6 tons per acre in 1948, without which the average is 4·5 tons only. After allowing for seed and waste about half the potatoes and all the oats, before the war, fed to the livestock. Yields of sugar beet have gone down: before the war they averaged 11 tons per acre and for the period 1946–50, 10·6 tons; even the record year, 1950, gave only 13 tons per acre. Similarly, the yield of wine per acre has fallen.

The numbers of livestock fell during the war and have only recently recovered: they are, in millions:

	Cattle	Including milch cows	Sheep	Pigs
1938	15·6	8·73	9·9	7·1
1948	15·12	7·70	7·4	5·7
1951	16·16	8·42	7·56	7·22
1952	16·2	8·48	7·1	7·18

(*F.A.O. Year Book of Stat.*, 1951, and C.E.C. Reports, *Meat*, 1953.)

There are some useful breeds of cattle[1]: the big white Charolais produce good beef and the brindled Normandy are dual purpose animals. The animals are fairly well distributed; there is little specialist dairy or poultry farming or fattening of bullocks except on some sugar beet farms in the north. The yields of milk are among the lowest of the recording countries in Europe, averaging about 250 gallons per cow in 1947 and 425 gallons in 1950; this is the result of the feeding and housing associated with peasant conditions, and of the use of some of the cows for work. About a third of the milk in 1946 was consumed as liquid, about a third was made into butter, and the rest went to the animals or was made into cheese or other products. Their variety is amazing: there are said to be 240 different types of cheese.

Sheep are more numerous than in any western country except Great Britain and Spain; they are used for wool, milk, and lamb production, but their numbers steadily decrease. Pigs are important as the chief source of

---

[1] About 16 breeds in all, but the tendency is to reduce their numbers.

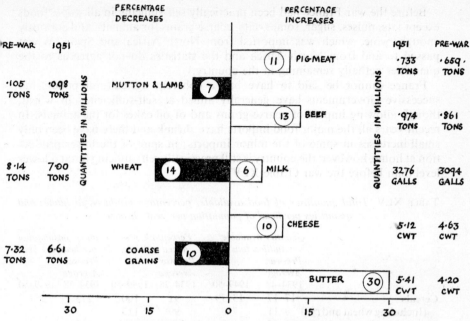

FIG. 12.—Post-war changes in agricultural production: France.
Pre-war values: averages of 1937–39 per grain.
1938 for dairy products and meat.
Post-war values: 1951

It should be noted that 1951 was a bad year for wheat: production in the three years 1948 to 1950 had averaged 7·68 million tons, a reduction of only 2 per cent compared with the 1937–39 average. (Data from C.E.C. Rpts., 1953.)

meat for the peasants. Numbers of small animals: goats, poultry, rabbits, etc., are kept in the *basses cours* of the peasants. Production of meat, poultry, and milk fell off during the war but, according to the statistics, has now fully recovered. The quantities recorded are given in Table XLIV and Fig. 12.

TABLE XLIV. *Livestock products, France, thousand tons*

	Average 1934–38	1948	1950	1952
Pork	670	600	790	850
Beef and veal	885	840	1,011	1,030
Carcass meat	1,660	1,500	1,900	
All meat and poultry	2,219	2,266	2,428	—
Milk	14,200	11,150	15,000	14,200
Condensed and evaporated	24	25	43	—
Cheese	270	180	250	284
Butter	202	160	250	250

(*F.A.O. Year Book of Stat.*, 1951, and C.E.C. Rpts., *Meat, Dairy Products* for 1952 converted here to metric tons.)

The quantity of grain fed to the animals fell from 7·8 million tons a year before the war to 5·4 million tons in 1948/49[1] and the amount of oil cake from 600,000 to 136,000 tons.[2]

[1] *F.A.O. Food Balance Sheets*, 1950.   [2] In 1946 (*Le Sol*, Sept. 1947, p. 199).

*   137

Before the war France had been practically self-sufficing in all staple foods except fats, pulses, sugar, some fruits, coarse grains for animals, and curiously enough, wine, which was imported from North Africa and Spain. Wheat passed to and from North Africa and the statistics do not agree as to the quantities actually remaining in the country.[1]

France cannot be said to have had a coherent agricultural policy, but successive Governments have generally aimed at self-sufficiency in wheat, though allowing import of coarse grains and of oil cakes for the animals. In recent years all the major food imports have shrunk and there have been only small increases in some of the minor imports; in spite of the lower production at home, however, the country is still practically self-sufficing but at a lower level than before the war (Table XLV).

TABLE XLV. *Total quantities of food available, percentage produced at home, and quantities per head of population per year, France*

	Quantity available million tons		Percentage produced at home		Human consumption lb. per head per year	
	Pre-war Average 1934–48	1949–50	Pre-war Average 1934–38	1949–50	Pre-war Average 1934–38	1949–50
Cereals	17·17	13·79	91	100	273	257
(Including wheat and rye)	9·11	7·8	99	112		
Potatoes	15·07	11·74	105	98	315	284
Sugar	1·01	1·00	86	83	53	51
Meat	2·22	2·43	99	102	117	125
Pulses	0·36	0·22	67	58	9	7
Fats and oils	0·84	0·67	39	49	31	24
Milk	14·2	13·3	100	100	330	326
Calories per day per head					2,830	2,680

(1) C.E.C. Rpts., *Dairy Produce*, 1953.

(*F.A.O. Stat. Year Book*, 1951, pp. 164–9.)

The F.A.O. Food Balance Sheets (Supplement 1950) give the following details:

Per head per day	Average 1934–38	1948–49
Calories	2,884	2,740
Animal protein, grams	36·6	38·9
Vegetable protein, grams	51·4	60·0
Total	88·0	98·9
Oils and fats	42·0	81·3

[1] Some of the estimates are:—

	Average net import, 1934–38 thousand metric tons
F.A.O. Food Balance Sheets	232
F.A.O. Trade Year Book	148
U.S. Dept. Agric.	165

The U.S. figure is from their publication *Agric. Production and Food Consumption in W. Europe*, 1951. It agrees fairly well with Commonwealth Econ. Cttee. estimates.

The actual consumption of protein may be higher than these figures indicate. A larger output of food and larger margins for export might certainly have been expected in view of the favourable climatic conditions of France, the absence of long, dry seasons or of very high rainfalls, and the relative large area of agricultural land per head of population. A definite increase over pre-war output might have been expected to result from the advances in agricultural knowledge and technique and greater use of modern appliances. Output of meat and of butter has somewhat increased, but there has been a reduction in output of crops since 1938. This cannot be attributed to war-time devastation for little was done, and the French peasant showed remarkable skill in hoodwinking the Germans who came to collect the requisitioned materials. Wheat growing is admittedly unsuitable to small farmers and might be expected to decrease, but livestock production is eminently suitable.

A possible explanation of the relatively low output is that the peasant system is not as well suited to modern conditions as the system of specialized and highly efficient farming, aided by co-operative societies, that has been so effective in Denmark and Holland. The peasant system certainly has not done all that was expected. It has not induced a high level of production: indeed, the level in France is considerably lower than that in Holland and Denmark, and below that of other Marshall Aid countries except Austria, Portugal, Italy, and Greece. One reason is that France, unlike some of the other countries, did not subsidize fertilizers and, in consequence, they were not as widely used as they might have been; the total quantity used in 1950–51, while greater than in the years before the war, show much smaller increases than in other advanced European countries:

Fertilizer consumption in France, thousand metric tons

	N	P_2O_5	K_2O
Pre-war	218	297	306
1950–51	247	390	410

(*F.A.O. Year Book of Stat.*, 1951.)

Fertilizers are used cheaply in the intensive regions of the north and west, and but little in the south, the centre, or the north-east.

The peasant system has not provided an abundant supply of children, nor has the undoubted attachment to his land developed into a wider patriotism superior to that of other countries, nor has it kept the land entirely in the hands of the French; indeed, in the south at least, there has been some forsaking so that farming has been done by immigrants from other countries. The peasant's instinct to save money has taken the form of hoarding rather than of investment, and a general suspicion of others militates against the co-operation which is so beneficial elsewhere. Only in Normandy is co-operation well developed. As in other countries the peasants are reluctant to change; they know that their methods provide a living, even though it may be meagre, and they cannot afford the risk of changes that may not work so well.

Possibilities of increasing agricultural output are constantly under examination by French experts. Some of them were summarized by René Dumont at a United Nations Conference in 1949.[1] The simplest method would be to crop some of 4 million acres of land now fallowed annually: fodder mixtures of cereals and vetches, or crimson clover, could be grown on two-thirds of this if more power and better harvesting equipment were available. Much of the present waste land could be utilized: 5 million acres could be afforested and more than a million used for agriculture. About a third of the 30 million acres of grassland could be ploughed up and used for ley farming. Much of it was formerly arable land or vineyards but now carries little but brome grass and fescue, yielding only about 8 to 15 cwt. of poor hay per acre as compared with 25 cwt. of good sainfoin hay that might be obtained. But all this would require great expansion of farm equipment and a large increase in the number of tractors: in 1950 France had only 138,700 tractors,[2] one per 377 acres of arable land as against one for 70 acres in Switzerland, and for 55 acres in the United Kingdom.

Dumont estimates that about three-quarters of the grassland is neglected and that more than $2\frac{1}{2}$ million acres could be considerably improved. Admittedly, the management of the grassland is a weak point in French husbandry.

As part of the European recovery programme, fostered by Marshall Aid, the French Government in January 1946, ordered the drawing up of a plan "for the Modernization and Economic Development of the Metropolitan and Overseas Territories"; this was done under the direction of M. Jules Monnet (whose name the plan bears) with a staff of over 1,000 experts; it was published in January 1947.[3] It covered all the national activities: industry, mining, housing, transport, as well as agriculture; out of a total expenditure of 2,251 milliard francs agriculture was to receive 350 milliard. On the agricultural side the aim was to achieve a 25 per cent increase over the agricultural production of 1939 and so raise home consumption by 10 per cent and reduce imports of fats and animal feeding stuffs, or even to eliminate them altogether. As the plan developed it was hoped to export meat, wheat and dairy produce: by 1952 the results were to be:

| | Million tons | Plan for 1952 | |
	Pre-war production	Production	Export
Wheat	8·14	9·50	1·70
Carcass meat	1·70	2·22	·12
Dairy produce (1)	14·6	17·5	1·2

(1) Calculated as liquid milk.

The plan was to be achieved by bringing back into cultivation 3·7 million of the acres that had gone out; by using more tractors (which would necessitate more *remembrement*) so reducing the number of horses and the need for oats: barley would be grown instead; by raising yields through use of

[1] R. Dumont, *Proc. U.N. Sci. Conf. Conservation and Utilization of Resources*, Lake Success, 1949, U.N. Dept. Econ. Affairs, 1951, Vol. 6, pp. 605–9.

[2] *F.A.O. Stat. Year Book*, 1951. Tractors of less than 8 h.p. are excluded. Before the war the total had been 30,000 and at the liberation 25,000 (*Etat des Opérations, vide infra*).

[3] Accounts of the working of the Plan are given in *Etat des opérations du plan de modernisation et d'équipement de l'Union française*, Paris, 1949, and in *Quatre ans de l'exécution du plan*, etc., Paris 1951.

more fertilizers, better weed control and regional seed selection. Wheat yield was to be raised to 16 cwt. per acre and the milk yield per cow to 433 gallons; animals were to be improved and disease combated. By 1952 the plan was still far from fulfilment. The production of wheat had been:

	Pre-war	1947	1948	1949	1950	1952
			Thousand tons			
Production	8,143	3,260	7,634	8,082	7,700	8,380
Export	−96	−487	−1,090	−279	670	−377

A minus sign indicates import.

F.A.O. Stat. Year Book and C.E.C. *Grain Crops* (metric tons).

About seven million tons are required for food, and one million tons for seed: export cannot begin till production exceeds eight million tons. The production of meat has apparently fared better, but more is being consumed at home: a small surplus was available for export in 1950 but whether the plan can be fulfilled remains to be seen. On the other hand, the engineering part of the plan is making progress. The Génissiat scheme on the Upper Rhone is well advanced: it will help both agriculture and industry, for it will not only make possible the irrigation of a large area of land—half a million acres have been suggested—but will provide water for one of the largest hydro-electric plants in the world, which will be a further help to the farmer, whom it can supply with electricity. Already more fertilizers and tractors are being produced.

The Report of the *Commisariat Général* for 1953 complained that agriculture was still a weakness in the French economy. It employed one-third of the occupied population but produced only one-fifth of the national product. The yields were barely one half those of the northern and eastern neighbours and there was still a net import of food.

French agriculture is fortunate in having an excellent research centre at Versailles, for long under the distinguished direction of A. Demolon. There is also the well-known Viticulture Station at Montpellier, besides experimental fields at Grignon and elsewhere. In addition to the official establishment some very good wheat breeding has been done by the Vilmorins, and some of the French varieties have proved valuable in England. France is well provided with competent workers to deal with the scientific problems arising out of the efforts to intensify French agriculture.

But of all countries in the world France is one of the most difficult to assess statistically. No one who has wandered leisurely down the valley of the Loire or the Garonne—or other region of his choice—would be prepared to put a numerical value on the satisfaction he had derived therefrom.

The Monnet Plan is of wide interest because it attempts to improve the peasant system while retaining its essential features. This is the fundamental problem affecting more than half the food producers of the world and the experience gained in France cannot fail to help others engaged in finding a solution.

SPAIN

The agricultural problems of Spain are peculiarly difficult. The population is increasing at the rate of nearly 1 per cent per annum so that the need for food grows steadily. Much of the country is, however, very poor, and as often happens in such conditions, is held in large estates of low productivity. Improvement is physically possible but it necessitates expenditure recoverable only at a high level of food prices; this, however, would lead to serious social unrest, or worse, by reason of the poverty of the great mass of the people. The Government is, therefore, confronted with the highly complex problem of increasing food production and, at the same time, keeping down the cost, especially of wheat, the most important food in Spain, so as to ensure peace at home. In the days of the monarchy the method was to develop an export of the cash crops, oranges, vines, and olives and to import wheat corresponding to about 5 or 10 per cent of the total requirement. The policy, however, is now changed; the aim is to become self-supporting in food, while increasing the exports and to use the revenues derived therefrom for the purchase of manufactured goods. The rather rigid social structure of the country requires a strong and stable Government to carry out the policy and this has been in existence now since early in 1938.

The characteristic physical feature of Spain is the great central rolling region, the Meseta, on the average about 2,000 feet high, almost surrounded by the mountain ranges that cut it off from the narrow coastal belt. Much of it is very poor and rocky, carrying only scrub vegetation of little grazing value, but much, also, is cultivated though giving only low yields. The coastal belt has some better land; the chief towns (except Madrid) are situated there and some good agriculture is found in its hinterland. The climate of this coastal belt is pleasant, especially in the north-east; it is sub-tropical in the south and south-east; in the interior it is more severe: the summers are very hot and dusty and the winters liable to be very cold: Madrid is often said to fare worse than any other capital in Europe: "neuf mois d'hiver, et trois mois d'enfer" is the French judgment. The rainfall is highest in the north-west: it is 66 inches at Santiago, but elsewhere in the north it is about 24 inches and fairly well distributed. It decreases, however, in going southwards to Almeria in the extreme south-east, where it is only 10 inches: a large area in old Castile has less than 12 inches. The gradients are somewhat abrupt; the transition from the wet forest and grass region of the north to the arid scrub of the centre is rather sharp, and there is no important area of good savannah or grass country such as gives rise to fertile arable soils in other lands. Much of the interior is definitely arid. Unfortunately the rivers are not well suited to irrigation, though considerable works have been set up on the Elvo system and on the lower reaches of the Guadalquivir.

The total area of Spain, including the Balearic and Canary Islands, is 125 million acres, of which 107 million acres are classed as productive. The population in 1950 was 28 millions: the density was 144 to the square mile. Of the productive land only 48 million acres (38 per cent of the total area) was actually cultivated (1·7 acres per head), the remaining 59 million acres being pasture, but it is officially considered that much of this could be brought into cultivation though a good deal of it is very poor. Of the 48 million acres of cultivated land rather more than 13 million are devoted to horticultural crops—mainly olives, vines, fruits, and vegetables (including considerable quantities of onions), and the remaining 35 million acres are in farm use, half of this is in cereals, mostly wheat and barley, about a third is fallow, and the rest is in a variety of other crops (Table XLVI). Spain has, indeed, a larger variety of crops than any other country in Europe owing to its wide range of climatic conditions: it is the only European country where sweet potatoes and sugar cane are grown and one of the few countries in the world cultivating both sugar beet and sugar cane. More groundnuts are grown than in any other European country. Spain is a true meeting place of tropical and temperate crops. The high preponderance of wheat, barley, and olives is the result of the arid climate, these tolerating dry conditions better than most other crops; the output of olive oil is the highest in Europe. The dryness also accounts for the considerable proportion of fallow and, in part, for the low yields. About a million tons of oranges a year are grown, mostly in the south; this is the highest output in Europe. Large quantities are exported. France was, in 1950, the chief buyer and the United Kingdom second. A canning industry for peaches and other fruit is being developed and there is a considerable production of nuts. Some of the wine produced is rather alcoholic and goes to France for blending, but the wine from the region round Jerez has an entirely special character and is exported to England where, as the result of English mispronunciation, the name has become altered to "sherry." The production and blending of this wine is a highly skilled occupation.

TABLE XLVI. *Utilization of land, Spain, pre-war and* 1950

	Million acres		Yield, cwt. per acre		Total produce million tons	
	Pre-war	1950	Pre-war	1950	Pre-war	1950
Agriculture						
Wheat	11·3	10·0	7·7	6·7	4·36	3·38
Barley	4·7	3·8	10·0	8·0	2·39	1·50
Oats	1·9	1·5	6·9	6·2	0·40	0·50
Rye	1·5	1·6	7·4	7·0	0·55	0·56
Rice (paddy)	0·12	0·14	50·0	33·0	0·29	0·24
Total cereals	19·5	17·0			8·0	6·18
Beans and chick peas	1·8	1·9			0·53	0·29
Potatoes	1·1	0·9	4·5 (1)	3·2 (1)	4·9	3·0
Vegetables	3·1	3·0				
Fruit	1·25	1·4				
including oranges	0·195	0·198			0·645	·902
Vines	3·9	3·9		{Grapes	2·60	2·20
				{Wine	1·93	1·35
Olives	5·2	5·0		Olives	1·82	1·92 (2)
Sown grasses ⎫	14·1	1·3		Oil	0·353	0·388
Other crops ⎭		1·1				
Fallow		12·5				
Total cultivated	50·0	48·0				

(1) Tons.
(2) 1949. Yield of olives for 1950 not available, but output of oil was down.
(*F.A.O. Stat. Year Book,* 1951, and *Statesman's Year Book,* 1953.)

Spain has the largest population of sheep, goats, asses, and mules in Europe and all (except perhaps the asses) are increasing in numbers; all these indicate poverty conditions, especially the goats; while goats have the merit that they can live where other animals would perish they have the great fault of being very destructive in their grazing habits.

The cattle population is low, and the animals are used mainly for work; they are, however, increasing in number. The pigs commonly graze in herds under the supervision of a herdsman. The numbers have been as follows:

Livestock population, millions

	Cattle	Sheep	Goats	Pigs	Horses	Asses	Mules
1906	2·5	13·5	2·4	2·1	0·44	0·74	0·80
1939	2·7	14·1	4·1	2·9	0·50	0·74	1·05
1950	3·7	16·0	6·9	2·1	0·61	0·75	1·08

(*F.A.O. Stat. Year Book*, 1951, and *Statesman's Year Book*.)

Unlike the more advanced agricultural countries Spain is increasing its number of horses: tractors are as yet but little used.

A considerable amount of honey is produced.

In the north, and in parts of the coastal zone, many of the holdings are small; in places there is a good deal of fragmentation though no more is being permitted. Over large parts of the country, especially the drier interior, much of the land is in large estates of low productivity. Hitherto the owners, while interested in developing them for the sake of the higher revenues, have not been keen to reside thereon, preferring the social life of the towns to the isolation of the country. Moreover, the countryside is not always entirely safe: brigands are still remembered and people are unwilling to live in lonely houses, or even cottages. The country people live in compact villages which come to a sharp end and do not straggle out in the countryside. Travellers crossing Spain see great stretches of apparently uninhabited rolling country with red soils changing to grey, much scrub vegetation, big fields of wheat, barley or beans, and fallow land, no hedges or stone walls, but many olive groves often with cereals growing beneath the trees, and many vineyards. The villages are crowded places of one-storey cottages with white-washed walls and tiled roofs, the streets of cobbles or of earth.

The combination of absentee landlords wishing for higher rents and of workers wishing to avoid hunger tends to pilfering and bribery and is not conducive to the improvement of agriculture. One sees good horses, well-built and active bulls bred for fighting, and good sheep—the famous merinos come from Spain—but otherwise the level of agriculture is low. Taking the statistics at their face value they show a fall in the area of cultivated land of $5\frac{1}{2}$ million acres between 1906 and 1950, including a fall of 2 million acres in cereals but an increase of $1\frac{1}{2}$ million acres in olive groves and of 300,000 acres of vines:

Million acres

	Cultivated land	Pasture land	Cereals	Vines	Olives	Total "productive" land
1906	53·6	59	19 (1)	3·6	3·4	113
1940	50	60	18	3·9	5·2	110
1950	48	59	17	3·9	5·0	107

(1) Including some pulse.

There are, however, signs of a changed attitude towards country life: high prices of food in the towns are showing that it has some advantages.

The food supplies as estimated by F.A.O. are given in Table XLVII.

TABLE XLVII. *Average food supplies in lb. per head per annum*

	Average 1931–35	1948–49	Target 1960		Average 1931–35	1948–49	Target 1960
Cereals	320	277	310	Meats	62	51	55
Starchy roots	240	200	242	Eggs	11	9	15
Pulses	33	31	42	Fish	55	40	42
Sugar	26	20	20	Milk (1)	161	150	172
Fats	33	26	31				
Fruit	110	77	119				
Vegetables	220	253	257				

Per head per day:		
Calories	2,760	2,700
Protein, grams		
Animal	25	23
Vegetable	63	66
Total	88	89

(*F.A.O. Second World Food Survey*, 1952, pp. 46 and 52.)

(1) Including milk products, reckoned as milk.

The average amounts of food available were not, by 1950, back to those of the days before the Civil War (1936–39) nor will this be achieved even if the targets for 1960 are attained. The supplies are, however, better than in the other Mediterranean countries, Portugal, Italy, and Greece; indeed Spain is the only one of them importing less wheat than before the War. (Fig. 13.)

The acreage figures given above show that the general pattern of Spanish agriculture remains as before the war, but the movement of prices has altered the pattern of farm receipts. Before the war wheat accounted for 23 per cent and cereals for 40 per cent of the value of farm production: in 1947 the figures were 12 and 22 per cent respectively, the values of the other products having risen more than those of the cereals.

Agricultural improvements are being carried out in several ways.

Spain has for many years manufactured fertilizers, and both output and consumption have considerably increased since the war:

	Production		Thousand tons	Consumption	
	1938	1950–51		1938	1950–51
N	3·7	6·6		32·0	56·6
P_2O_5	57·6	140·0		60·3	136·0
K_2O	25·5	165·0		28·1	35·0

(*F.A.O. Stat. Year Book*, 1951.)

Output of ordinary crops has not been affected. A Government Department, the Instituto Nacional de Colonización, set up in 1942, is responsible for stimulating improvement of existing estates and for purchasing estates for division into smaller holdings.

A landowner can prepare a plan of improvements such as well-sinking for irrigation, provision of drinking water, setting up manure steadings, tobacco barns or other farm buildings, electrification, drainage, reclamation of salt marshes, planting olive groves or vineyards. This is submitted to the Institute: if it approves it can make grants for the different items, according to a specified scale, varying from 25 to 100 per cent of the cost with the condition that the work is to be done in slack seasons of the year so as to even out employment. Between 1942 and 1953 improvements have been carried out on some 300,000 acres, at a total cost of 870 million pesetos (£8·7 million) of which 410 million were given as grants. The improved estates still remain the property of the owner.

In other cases it has been necessary to break up large estates and make them into smaller farms. At first they were simply handed to the peasants in the hope that unrest would thereby be stilled and prosperity would come to the countryside. But it was soon found that the mere taking of land from its owners to give it to the peasants did not lead to prosperity; the peasants got hopelessly into debt. A new method was then introduced based largely on that used by Mussolini in the Pontine Marshes. It was realized that small farms have little chance of survival unless the water supply is assured, and, therefore, the new schemes are set up only where irrigation is practicable. The Institute acquires the land by voluntary sale if possible, but otherwise by compulsory purchase. In the latter case the price is determined by the amount that has been paid in rates, and those landowners who had astutely succeeded in achieving low assessments now found themselves receiving correspondingly low payment. The area is then laid out as one unit, irrigation is provided and a centre established for machinery, stores, etc. An agricultural expert is in charge. The holdings range from 10 acres in Andalusia in the south where two crops a year are possible,[1] to 18 acres or more in the north where only one crop can be obtained. Good cottages are built, either on the holdings or, more usually, in a new compact village provided with church, school, and other amenities: thirty-two of these had been built by 1953 providing homes for 2,375 families. In some of the earlier schemes the colonists had been selected because they were unemployed; this failed as has often happened elsewhere. The colonists are now nominated by the local agricultural syndicate, they must be local peasants, young, married, and morally, politically, and technically sound. The man is given a course at an agricultural school at the cost of the syndicate, his wife and family, meanwhile, receiving a subsistence grant. He then starts work on his holding and for the first five years is in a state of tutelage, following the instructions of the expert in charge. The Institute supplies seeds, fertilizers, and other appliances, including two working oxen, a milch cow, a pony or mule but no sheep or goats; it also provides family maintenance till his own crops are ready. It takes in payment a specified proportion of the produce so that the colonist becomes virtually a *métayer*. If he is unsatisfactory he can be removed, but if he does well he passes at the end of the five years into the second period, "possession," which lasts for twenty-five years. Here he is more independent—though he must still conform to cropping rules and deliver technical crops, such as sugar beet, to the Institute. He can eat or sell the rest of his produce but must pay to the

[1] In winter: wheat, barley, beans, sugar beet, potatoes. In summer: maize, sweet potatoes, potatoes, tomatoes, and other vegetables.

Institute a cash rent which will refund the expenditure incurred together with 4 per cent interest; he is given a book in which his payments to and receipts from the Institute are entered so that he knows exactly how he stands. If, at the end of the twenty-five years he has cleared his account he becomes the owner of the land.

During this period he can transfer or sell his holding if he obtains permission but not otherwise. He cannot acquire two holdings, even by marriage; if both bride and bridegroom have holdings one must be given up. Nor is division of the holding permitted.

The schemes are costly, and the expenditure may never be recovered; this limits the rate of progress. By July 1952, the area already colonized was 550,000 acres of which 70,000 were irrigated and 480,000 dry; 25,600 families had been settled, with an average of 21·5 acres each. The Institute was developing a further 1·1 million acres, bringing up its total area to 1·65 million acres.

There is a great contrast between the cottage provided in the colonies and those in the old villages, and the Institute has provided a good life for those colonists fortunate enough to be selected; there will ultimately grow up a race of land-owning peasants, which the Latin races are always hoping to achieve.[1]

The extent of development possible is limited physically by the area that can be irrigated and, unfortunately, Spain is not well off in this direction. The lower reaches of the Guadalquivir, stretches of the Ebro, and a few areas along other rivers allow of small canal systems, and in places small dams are set up to hold some of the rain that comes in torrential downpours. But in general the irrigation is from wells, the water being lifted by electric or oil pumps, or by a wheel worked by bullocks or mules. There are no statistics showing how much land is irrigated but the area appears to be about four million acres; the corresponding estimate before the war was about three million acres. More wells are being sunk at depths of 25 to 100 ft.: so far the underground water appears ample in quantity and good for irrigation, though not always for drinking.

Forestry is an integral part of any large scheme for development and it is being expanded for a variety of products and also to protect against erosion: eucalypts are grown in the south for paper making, Mediterranean pines in the north for turpentine and other trees for timber.

Highly centralized scientific services are organized at Madrid under the *Consejo Superior de Investigaciones Cientificas*, which comprises some ninety different institutes. Their work is, to an Englishman's mind, hampered by the low scale of salaries which compels the staff to hold a second, or even a third post, and in consequence prevents that single-minded concentration on the work that is so necessary for full success. In a country where conditions are so varied, as in Spain, close centralization presents serious difficulties, but it is inherent in the Spanish form of government.

---

[1] Fuller information of the colonization work is given in: J. B. Barrachina, "El avance de la tecnica del campo por los trabajos de Colonización," *Estudios*, Vol. 3, No. 17 (1945). J. M. y Garcia de Valdivia, "Modernas orientaciones de la Colonización agraria en España," *ibid.*, Vol. 4, No. 21 (1951). E. G. Ayau, "Actualidad de la política de Colonización," *ibid.*, Vol. 4, No. 23 (1952) (Instituto Nacional de Colonización, Madrid).

Spain makes valuable contributions to the world supply of fruit, particularly oranges,[1] olive oil, and wine, especially sherry. Against this there has in most years, up to and including 1950, been an import of wheat excepting during the Civil War when the need for foreign currency compelled an export. The requirement is about $3\frac{1}{2}$ million tons a year, of which, till recently, about 250,000–350,000 tons had to be imported. But during the years 1951 and 1952 larger quantities were produced so that less importation was necessary—thanks largely to favourable rains. The authorities hope that this will be the permanent position; if so, Spain may become a net exporter of food.

PORTUGAL

Portugal is an attractive country, with very attractive people, and it illustrates well the fact that economic statistics afford only a partial measure of the satisfaction to be got out of life. By all figures it makes a poor showing, and yet there are few countries in Europe in which life can be more pleasant.

It falls into two sharply contrasted parts separated by the Tagus.

The northern part is hilly and in its eastern and central section mountainous; it has a high rainfall, in the west up to 40 inches, in the east rather less.

In the western section the climate is distinctly mild and snow is rare; its most famous product is the very high quality port wine produced in the highly cultivated and closely terraced Douro valley, but nowhere else in Portugal or even in the world. (Plate 18.) The chief farm crop is maize; on good farms this is undersown with Italian rye grass which shoots up after the maize is harvested in September and gives some 3 cwts. of green fodder and a hundredweight of seed before the end of April, so that the two crops are grown within the year; the land is then manured and sown again with maize and rye grass in the following year. The farms are small but the farming is some of the best in Portugal. This is the most densely populated region of the country, carrying more than half of the population.

The north-eastern section has a more severe climate; rye is the chief crop and the farming is inferior to that in the west. The central northern region is mountainous, very wet (up to 80 inches or more of rain), with poor, stoney soil and much forest.

South of the Tagus the land is less hilly and lies lower. The rainfall also is lower, being about 20 to 25 inches in the northern section and decreasing to about 12 inches in the south; it is apt to be irregular and the summers may be very dry and hot. This difficulty is intensified by the fact that there are some $1\frac{1}{2}$ million acres of infertile sand in scrub or forest (some of which goes back to pre-glacial times), these the Government is trying to reclaim. The lightest land is being planted with pines for fuel and turpentine. Grapes are grown, as everywhere in Portugal, but the wine is not particularly good and much of it is distilled for making brandy. The chief farm crop is wheat. On the better soil this may alternate with peas but much of it is grown on poor

---

[1] The export of citrus fruit has much increased:—

	Pre-war	1950	1951
Oranges	220	415	719 thousand tons
Lemons	15	19	55

(C.E.C. Rpts., *Fruit*, 1952.)

soils which, after carrying two or three successive wheat crops, are left derelict to cover themselves with wild herbage and afford a certain amount of very rough grazing. The yields are low and variable, ranging from 4 to 8 cwt. per acre. They are usually reckoned at so many "seeds," i.e. so many times the seeding rate: this is about 0·8 cwt. per acre, so that the ordinary yields range from 5 to 10 "seeds": on a good farm double these yields are obtained. Olives are much grown, as usual in dry Mediterranean regions, and Portugal has a special crop, cork, of which it is by far the chief producer.

The farms in this southern region are large, worked by hired labourers who live in villages and not on the land so that, as in Spain, there is no scattering of houses over the landscape; wages are low: in 1943 they were 10 to 13 escudos per day, i.e. 2s. to 2s. 8d. The children cannot be spared to go to school, so that illiteracy is high.[1] The dietary is very unattractive: potatoes, beans or peas, and cabbage made into a soup; bread, a little pig meat, but very little milk. The workers are given some land on which to grow what they like. The hours are long: in autumn, winter, and spring, from sunrise to sunset, with, however, four hours off for rest. The stockmen sleep with their animals.

In the far south is a sub-tropical region where early fruits and the best oranges are grown.

The area of the country is 34,251 square miles (21·9 million acres); the population in 1940 was 7·2 millions and, in 1950, 8·5 millions; the density then was 248 per square mile. About 60 per cent of the population was engaged in agriculture. The cultivated area in 1939 was 8·9 million acres,[2] this being under 40 per cent of the whole, and allowing just over 1 acre per head. Of the remainder about 6 million acres was forest in 1950. But it is estimated that a further 6·7 million acres of land could be used for agriculture. Of the cultivated area 4·8 million acres were in cereals in 1950, 860,000 in beans, 900,000 acres in vineyards, and about as much in fruit.

As in other European countries, during the unsettled years following 1930 the wheat problem dominated agricultural politics. Portugal needed some 450,000 tons of wheat annually, of which about 60 per cent were produced at home. During the 1930's home production rose to some 400,000 tons—90 per cent of consumption—but at considerably enhanced cost. A high nutrition policy was adopted and consumption has now risen to 800,000 tons of which 550,000 are home produced.[3] (Fig. 13, p. 154.)

The livestock in 1940 included 0·97 million cattle, 3·95 million sheep, 1·25 million pigs, 1·24 million goats, while horses, mules, and asses numbered, respectively, 0·085, 0·122, and 0·245 millions. The low cattle density and the high proportion of goats, mules, and asses, indicates poor conditions as in Spain and elsewhere. The cattle are used largely for work, but at five or ten years they are slaughtered for beef: in spite of this unpromising history some of the beef, notably that from the Barrosad breed in the north, can be surprisingly tender. The sheep are used for wool and milk; much cheese is made, the yield being about double that from cows' milk. The pigs are largely the peasants' animals; one sees many of them in the villages.

---

[1] In 1940, 50 per cent of the population above the age of ten were illiterate.
[2] *F.A.O. Year Book*, 1951. This is the latest figure available.
[3] C.E.C. Rpts., *Grain Crops*, 1953.

The population is continuously increasing but, hitherto, emigration has obviated any pressure problem. This is not likely to continue and it is recognized that more small farms are needed, and that the fragmentation of existing peasant farms must be stopped. Reclamation schemes are, therefore, being put in hand. Some wheat is still imported and a small quantity of maize; sugar comes in from the colonies and for their protection no sugar beet is grown. Against these imports there is a much more valuable export of wine, sardines, and non-food products, particularly cork, resin, and turpentine,[1] so that the agriculture is actually more than sufficient for the needs of the country.

The average dietary as shown by F.A.O. is among the poorest in Europe, but a high target has been set for 1960. (Table XLVIII.)

TABLE XLVIII. *Quantities of foods available lb. per head per year, Portugal*

	Average 1934–38	1948–49	Target 1960		Average 1934–38	1948–49	Target 1960
Cereals	227	264	330	Meat	51	42	46
Starchy roots	167	200	230	Eggs	4·4	4·4	6·6
Pulses	22	22	40	Fish	66	68	70
Sugar	22	26	29	Milk (1)	112	95	117
Fats	29	22	31	Per head			
Fruit	132	90	110	per day			
Vegetables	176	158	185	Calories		2,110	2,730
				Protein:			
				animal		22	21
				vegetable		44	63
				Total		66	84

(*F.A.O. Second World Food Survey,* 1952, p. 46.)
(1) Includes cheese and other products but not butter.
The consumption of fish per head is exceeded only by Iceland.

There is always considerable doubt about the quantities of food eaten by peasant producers and it may well happen that these figures are too low. The peasants do not strike one as badly undernourished.

ITALY

Italy is the most densely populated of all the Mediterranean countries, and has a lower standard of nutrition than any of its northern neighbours, or than Greece or Spain; the calorie supply is higher than that of Portugal. It is especially interesting because of its remarkable land reclamations carried out before the war, its ingenious system of co-operation for agricultural production as distinct from the British and Danish systems of co-operation for credit and trading, and its method of demographic emigration and colonization which, though not entirely new, had some valuable features.

Italy's food problems are of the familiar type: a population growing more rapidly than its food production expands, while exporting capacity does not

[1] Also wolfram.

increase sufficiently to allow enough import of food for maintaining the nutritional standards; these, therefore, are falling.

The most productive region of Italy is the north, the fertile valley of the Po forming a great triangle with its apex west of Milan and its base on the Adriatic, stretching from Trieste to Rimini. This is also the most populous part of the country. It is a region of small farms and tenant farmers on large estates, some paying a cash rent but more being share-croppers (*mezzadri*).

The poorest region is the south: Calabria, Lucania, and Apulia; the spur, heel, and toe of Italy; a region of arid plains and barren hills, mostly treeless, of low rainfall and poor soils but with a teeming population that used to supply many migrants for the Americas. It has always from Roman times been held in large estates, *latifundia*, owned by absentee landlords living in Rome or Naples, and farmed on a low level of productiveness by managers or tenants using casual labour. The agriculture is backward; the main crop is wheat with some peas and beans, there is much fallow and little livestock. Villages and people are wretchedly poor, most of all, perhaps, in the country round the heel.

The great stretch between the fertile north and the poverty-stricken south is dominated by the Apennines with a rather large plain on the Adriatic side in Puglia, and others on the west coast. This is a region of small farms, some of them very small; of villages pleasing in the distance but squalid on nearer acquaintance; of fruits and vines and many valleys, each producing its own special and often very agreeable wine.

The total area of Italy is 72·7 million acres utilized in 1950, as follows:

Crops, fallow and orchard	41·0
Permanent grass	12·8
Forest	14·8
Other use	4·1
Total	72·7

(*F.A.O. Stat. Year Book*, 1951.)

Some 50 million acres are privately owned; about 8 million by 8 million persons and the rest by rather more than one million; 2½ million acres are owned by 500 persons.

The areas of the chief food crops, and the quantities produced are given in Table XLIX. Two periods must be clearly distinguished: the Fascist regime which lasted from October 1922 till near the end of the war; and the Republican regime which began in 1946.

Wheat has long been Italy's staple food. Most of it was always produced in the country itself, but as Italy is on the southern side of the European wheat belt the durum or macaroni wheats are easier to grow and are less liable to rust than the northern bread varieties: hence the prevalence of macaroni and spaghetti in Italy. Prior to the 1914–18 war about 80 to 85 per cent of the total consumed was produced at home and 15 to 20 per cent imported; after the war the rising population necessitated further imports, rising to 35·7 per cent of requirements in the period 1919 to 1922 and 41 per cent during the year 1922–23. Mussolini decided that this must stop, and a wheat campaign was started. It was realized that the acreage could not be greatly increased

TABLE XLIX. *Areas and quantities produced of the chief food crops, Italy*

	Million acres Averages				Yield, cwt. per acre Averages				Million tons produced Averages			
	1923–26	1934–38	1948	1950	1923–26	1934–38	1948	1950	1923–26	1934–38	1948	1950
Wheat	11·7	12·5	11·5	11·7	9·6	11·5	10·6	13·0	5·83	7·25	6·16	7·63
Maize	3·68	3·60	3·07	3·07	13·6	16·5	14·5	12·4	2·61	3·00	2·25	1·92
Rice	0·34	0·35	0·35	0·36	34·4	42·4	34·6	38·1	0·60	0·753	0·619	0·69
Oats	1·19	1·06	1·18	1·17	9·6	10·1	8·2	9·4	0·585	0·539	0·486	0·553
Rye	0·31	0·26	0·25	0·25								
Barley	0·58	0·48	0·62	0·61	8·0	8·8	7·4	9·4	0·233	0·212	0·230	0·291
All cereals	17·80	18·25	16·97	17·16								
					Tons per acre							
Potatoes	1·00	1·00	1·01	0·95	2·4	2·6	3·0	2·5	2·06	2·63	3·01	2·37
Beans some peas	—	2·82	2·58	2·35								
Vines alone	2·22			2·53	Wine, million hecto-litres		45·3				36·8	
Vines in other crops	8·49			7·08								
	10·71			9·61								
Population, millions	38·7	43·0	—	46·7								

(*F.A.O. Statistical Year Book*, 1951.)

TABLE L. *Quantities of food produced and imported: quantities available per head. Million tons*

	Production Average		Net import Average		Available for food, lb. per head per year Average	
	1934–38	1948–49	1934–38	1948–49	1934–38	1949–50
Cereals	11·92	9·64	0·610	2·78	361	339
Including wheat	7·25	6·14	0·492	2·48	277	282
Potatoes	2·80	3·01	−0·046	−0·040	80·5	84
Other vegetables	3·27	4·48	−0·37	−0·35	123	176
Fruit	2·05	2·73	−0·534	−0·556	61	87
Meat	0·796	0·753	0·044	0·018	43	37
Milk and cheese	6·54	6·45	−0·018	0·007	91	110
Oils and fats	0·53	0·31	0·169	0·110	26·4	20·0

A minus sign (−) indicates export.

(*F.A.O. Food Balance Sheets*, 1950.)

but the yields could be raised. Prof. N. Strampelli was encouraged to breed new varieties, and Prof. Todaro of Bologna to select better strains; land improvement and reclamation schemes were also put in hand. Meanwhile, a vigorous propaganda campaign on military lines was carried out for the "Battle for wheat" and a marvellous exhibition—one of the most impressive of its kind that I have ever seen—was staged in Rome in 1927, to show what had already been achieved and to press for more. The results were striking: in the end the area under wheat was increased by well over nine million acres, the yield per acre raised by 40 per cent, and the percentage of self-sufficiency raised from 64·3 to 93·4:

Average for	Million acres	Yield per acre (1), bushels	Million bushels	Consumption, bushels per head	Home production per cent of total
1919–22	11·22	15·0	168		64·3
1922–27	11·63	17·5	204	6·6	70·0
1927–32	12·03	18·9	228	6·6	78·0
1932–37	12·42	21·2	263	6·0	93·4

(Paul de Hevesy, *World Wheat Planning*, Oxford Univ. Press, 1940, p. 535.)

(1) The weight of a bushel varies, but for general comparisons 1 million bushels may be taken to weigh 27·2 metric tons, and one bushel to weigh 60 lb.

There were paeans of praises as the victory was proclaimed and emphasis was laid not only on its economic importance but on its spiritual and political significance as showing what could be achieved under the "infallible guidance" of *il Duce*.

Other cereals did not receive such official encouragement, however; their yield per acre increased but their areas fell. About half the increased acreage of wheat had been at their expense so that the total area under cereals had risen only from 17·8 millions to 18·25 millions. Moreover, the final victory had been won by reducing consumption per head thus automatically raising the level of self-sufficiency.

The increased yield per acre was, however, a solid achievement and persists to this day. But the acreage of wheat has not been maintained; in 1950 it was back to the 1922 level and the need for wheat imports was greater than ever. (Fig. 13, p. 154.)

Next in importance to wheat comes maize: its area had fallen somewhat during the Fascist regime and considerably afterwards, so also did the yield; the 16·5 cwt. per acre averaged over the period 1934–38 was reduced by 1950 to 12·4 cwt. More than half the maize is fed to the animals.

Rice is of special interest: it is grown mainly in the Po valley, and Italy shares with Spain (where, however, the acreage is very much less) the honour of having the highest average yield per acre in the world: production exceeds consumption, and the surplus is exported to Austria and elsewhere.

In spite of all that has happened during the past thirty years the general pattern of Italian agriculture shows very little change and, with few exceptions, the values for 1948 and 1950 would fit comfortably into either of preceding periods.

Fruits, vegetables, nuts, and wine have long been produced in sufficient quantities to allow of considerable export; these are now resumed on their pre-war scale. The quantities have been:

	Thousand tons Average 1934–38	1948–49	1951
Fresh fruit	550	575	Oranges 574
Vegetables	370	355	Lemons 275
Nuts	130	127	

(*F.A.O. Food Balance Sheets*, 1950.)

More than half the fruit is citrus; Italy is the chief European producer of lemons. Against these exports there are some imports: the net figures are shown in Table L. There are smaller exports of potatoes and other vegetables.

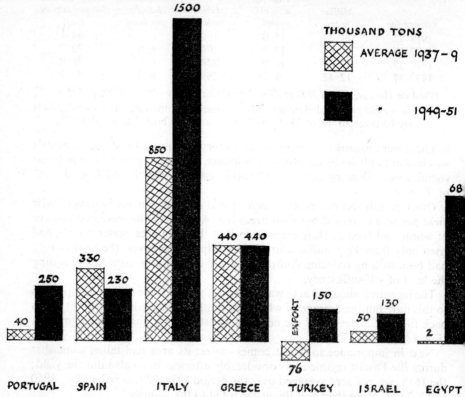

FIG. 13.—Growing needs of Mediterranian countries for wheat; post-war increases in imports: grain and flour. (C.E.C. *Grain Crops*, 1953)

The livestock population has increased as also has the production of meat. The total quantities, however, are not large. The numbers of cattle and of pigs are less than in France or Switzerland in relation to agricultural area or population, but the number of sheep is higher being exceeded on the Continent only by Spain and Yugoslavia. Sheep on the Mediterranean systems of husbandry are a sign of poverty rather than of wealth. The numbers and production have been:

	Numbers, millions			Meat, thousand tons Average		
	1939	1949–50		1934–38	1948	1950
Cattle	7·88	8·33	Beef and veal	320	205	302
Pigs	3·30	4·05	Pig meat and lard	223	209	262
Sheep	9·80	10·30	Mutton and lamb	49	64	48
			Total	592	478	612

(*F.A.O. Stat. Year Book.*)

The 1951 figures for meat are somewhat lower.

154

While production of the staple foods has not increased the human population has gone up steadily and is still increasing at the rate of about 0·7 per cent per annum while the total quantity of food available was falling, at least till 1949,[1] so that the average quantity per head was decreasing. The daily calorie intake for the period 1934–38 averaged 2,510, for 1949 it was 2,343 compared with 2,740 for France, and 3,096 for Switzerland. Consumption of cereals went down, as did that of meat and fats; the only good feature was the increased consumption of vegetables, fruits, and milk.

Among the efforts now being made to increase the output of food is the use of larger quantities of fertilizer which began in the season 1950–51. The quantities have been:

	Thousand metric tons		
	1938	1949–50	1950–51
Nitrogenous (as N)	128·5	119·9	165·0
Phosphatic (as P_2O_5)	262·0	247·6	290·0
Potassic (as K_2O)	17·8	16·0	20·0

(*F.A.O. Stat. Year Book*, 1951.)

All the nitrogenous fertilizer and almost all the phosphatic are produced in Italy, but the potassic salts have to be imported, apart from a small local production.

Italian engineers have a long record of successful land reclamation. Between 1870 and 1926 over 4 million acres had been reclaimed on the Adriatic side of the northern plain, and further large schemes were undertaken in the Fascist times, usually by a "consortium" of the landowners with Government "help." The most notable of these was the reclamation of the Pontine Marshes, the stretch of 200,000 acres of low-lying land between the hills south of Rome and the sea. All through the ages it had been water sodden and malaria infested: it was mostly scrub forest affording a little rough grazing but too unhealthy for men and animals to be of much use. Many attempts at reclamation had been made but without success.[2] A new start was made in 1926: it succeeded because of the greatly increased efficiency of modern engineering appliances and of the enormous advantage possessed by an untrammelled dictatorship in being free from difficulties concerning supplies and conditions of labour or money. Detailed surveys had shown that no drainage scheme by itself would suffice; the water had come from the hills and must be intercepted before it got into the marsh. A system of canals was constructed; the labour was arduous, the men sometimes had to work up to their waists in water and they suffered much from malaria. The canals discharged into the sea: the upper and middle ones by gravity, the lower one by pumping. When the land was dry enough it was laid out according to a comprehensive plan. Four towns were set up, each distinctive, each designed on generous and pleasing lines by a competent architect and possessing from the outset its *piazza* dominated by the church and having, also, a complete

---

[1] The last F.A.O. food balance sheet issued is for 1948–49. In June 1952, it was reported that food production had just surpassed that of the pre-war period, but the amount per head was still less.

[2] These are described in Cesare Longobardi, *Land Reclamation in Italy*, trans. by Olivia Rossetti Agresti, P. S. King and Son, London, 1936.

set of public buildings, the house of the Fascists, school, clinic, cafe-restaurant, etc. A soil survey was made of the whole area and on it was based the plan for agriculture. The farms vary in size from 25 to 62½ acres according to the quality of the soil: each has its house and buildings permanently built at the outset: there was no corrugated iron or shack stage. Properly conducted experiments were made to work out suitable schemes of crop and animal husbandry, the crops being wheat and fodder mixtures for cattle with provision for some pigs and poultry. (Plate 19, p. 180.)

The work was done by large Government-controlled corporations, the *Opera Nazionale per i Combattenti*, named after the ex-service men, being responsible for the laying out and construction of the farms and their general supervision.

When all was ready, houses built, and land ploughed, the colonists were brought in *en masse*. They were mostly peasants from the more crowded parts of Italy, each batch being kept together in a group, and all carefully selected on strict Fascist principles always having in view the fundamental purpose of increasing the number of young Fascists and of binding the peasant to the soil. Once settled in, the peasant was told what to do and shown how to do it, the *Opera* provided the animals, equipment, implements, the first seeds and the first cultivations, the family provided the labour and carried out the farm drainage. The *Opera* took half of the main produce, excluding, however, the small animals, pigs, poultry, milk for home use, garden produce, and certain allotments of wood. The system is thus based on the *métayage* already familiar to many of the peasants, but modified to make it into a hire-purchase system, so that the peasant should ultimately become the owner.

Colonization in Libya was confined to the coastal steppe zone, the Arab population being displaced to the interior. The rainfall is only about 12 to 15 inches a year, and rapidly lessens in passing inland, but fortunately two underground water tables were discovered; one near the surface and not very abundant, the other several hundred metres deep which was not only abundant but under pressure so that it rose to the surface or even jetted out to a height of several feet.

The colonization was on the same lines as for the Pontine Marshes: the plan was based on proper surveys; towns, farms, and roads were constructed, and wells made; when all was ready the colonists were brought in but with a more dramatic touch. The ship on which I travelled to Libya, in March 1939, carried six hundred colonists carefully selected in groups; on disembarking they were marched through the streets with band playing and flags flying, put on to lorries, and each group dispatched to its village. There, each family found a complete farm with barns, implements, and livestock; a house with the heavy furniture, beds, cupboards, tables, chairs all provided and in place, and, most cheering of all, a meal awaiting them. Marshal Balbo, the Governor, visited the village and had the gift of making each colonist feel that he took a special interest in his or her personal welfare.

As in the Pontine the supervision was by a Corporation, in this case the *Ente per la Colonizzazione della Libia*, which also provided seeds, manures, and feeding stuffs; it instructed the peasant what to do, and during the first twelve months paid him a wage sufficient for the maintenance of himself and his family; by the end of that time he had reaped his crops and needed no wages; he then became a *métayer* as in the Pontine. After about five years he was to pay a rent which included interest and sinking fund on the basis of repayment after twenty-five or thirty years. He was given an account book in which were entered all payments and advances made to him and all receipts from him, and when the accounts balanced and repayment was complete the farm became his.[1]

The costs were, of course, high. No attempt was made to justify either reclamation or colonization on economic grounds. The purpose of the reclamation was, in Mussolini's phrase: "to reclaim the land, and with the land the men, and with the men, the race." The Libyan colonization was to have the political purpose of exercising a predominant political influence in North Africa in virtue of its central position there; hence its colonists must be numerous, and must develop a subsistence agriculture but could export to Italy such things as must, in any case, come from outside. Libya was to be regarded as an integral part of Italy—the *Quarta Sponda*, the fourth shore, was its popular name. In Balbo's words the colonization was "una grandiosa opera di colonizzazione, su un territorio che fa parte integrante della Patria, a esclusivo beneficio della Patria, sotto le insegne della Patria fascista."[2] The underlying conception was thus fundamentally different from that of the British colonies, and had more affinity with that of the French but was more explicit.

The first batch of colonists had arrived by October 1938; 20,000 of them from the crowded Po valley came in 17 ships; others kept coming in and early in 1939 2,450 holdings had been set up and more were under construction. Already in March of that year the farms were being put into good shape and it looked as if the sturdy industrious colonists would make a success of the scheme.

Unfortunately, political and economic factors frequently work in antagonistic directions and this was so with Mussolini's empire. It collapsed and Libya is no longer a *parte integrante della Patria*. How the colonists will fare, and what will become of their farms, it is impossible to say. In 1951 Tripolitania still had 45,800 Italians among its 768,600 inhabitants.

Demographic colonization has some interesting possibilities, and it is a tragedy that Mussolini's military adventures put an end to the scheme. It has the advantage of ensuring development of new areas on the sound basis of careful scientific surveys, and of reducing to a minimum the labour and the suffering that the old system had, in many cases, involved. Libya might have become a model for much of Africa, parts of India, and of South America.

The dream of empire has gone and the maps Mussolini had had carved in stone on the Via Imperiale showing its expansion under Fascist rule and the blanks that still remained to be filled have become only political curiosities. Italy is now thrown on her own resources and is developing them quite seriously, so far without the inflation that has so distressed France. The redundant peasant population can no longer be demographically migrated;

[1] For a fuller description of the Pontine Marsh and Libyan Schemes, see E. J. Russell, *Geog. Journ.*, 1939, Vol. 94, pp. 273–92.
[2] Italo Balbo, Coloni in Libia, *Nuova Antologia*, 73 (1938), pp. 3–13.

it is to be absorbed into industries which have been expanded with Marshall Aid. Agriculture also is to be improved—though, at present, it is receiving only a small part of the public and private investments available in 1951 for development, three-quarters going to industry.[1] Prior to all further agricultural improvement, however, comes the question of land reform which has long been a grave political problem in Italy. The Christian Democrats who had promised to deal with it came out as the leading party in the elections of 1948 and in the following year Signor Segni, Minister of Agriculture, put forward a scheme requiring all estates over 250 acres in intensively cultivated regions, and all over 750 acres in mountain regions, to surrender part of their land for the creation of small farms or for large co-operative peasant farms except where, as in the well-managed dairy farms of Lombardy, dismemberment would lower output of food. It was hoped that 3·2 million acres of land would thus ultimately be made available on which two or three hundred thousand poor peasant families would be resettled, thus considerably reducing the number of casual day workers, the *braccianti*, who, being very much under-employed, have long constituted a serious problem, especially in the River Po delta and in Northern Apulia.[2] A start was made in Sila, the central part of Calabria where distress had driven the peasants to rioting and forcible possession of the land in 1949, A Bill was passed in 1950 expropriating 175,000 acres and providing the equivalent of £8·5 million spread over six years for settling in the new peasant proprietors on a hire-purchase system enabling them to become owners in thirty years; and, as smallholdings would not in themselves solve the problem, provision was to be made for more roads, irrigation, afforestation, housing, and general soil improvement.

By May 1953 nearly 1¾ million acres had been expropriated in Italy and Sicily and some 560,000 acres distributed to the peasants. An Act of 1952—the "12 Year Plan"—provided cheap loans for working capital.

In addition more than a million acres were to be improved by their owners who could, however, obtain 38 per cent of the cost from the State. All this is described as but the forerunner of greater schemes. It will be interesting to see the results.

Fortunately, Italy has for many years had its own system of peasant co-operation, different from the Danish in that its aim is production and not only trading. A group of peasants voluntarily unite to form a society which purchases land and arranges for its cultivation. This may be done in either of two ways. The land may be worked collectively as one large unit and the produce pooled; or the land may be divided into smallholdings and let to the members who farm it individually; they must adopt approved methods and include prescribed crops but the produce is entirely their own. The choice depends on the people and on the conditions. Those who have long been smallholders almost always wish to remain so and only under compulsion become collectivists: they value their independence and their social status as peasants even though they are only the Society's tenants. In this they are encouraged by the Catholic Church and so it commonly happens that the

[1] *The Times*, June 18, 1952.

[2] In 1951–52 out of 7·5 million engaged in agriculture, 1·5 million were *braccianti* working on an average only 161 days a year. (Tremelloni Rpt., Aug. 1953: quoted from *The Times*, Aug. 18, 1953.)

individualist societies operate under Catholic auspices. The advantage of co-operation to them is that they thereby become members of the owning body and henceforward are saved from any possibility of rack-renting. Peasants who have always been hired workers, however, find the collective system better; they often lack the knowledge and ability to run a small holding, and they are saved from responsibility, having only to follow instructions. These societies are, in general, run under Socialist or Communist auspices. There is also a distinction according to the conditions. Field crops, such as wheat, sugar beet, and rice are more suited to large collectivist farms than to small ones; on the other hand livestock, vines, and olives are readily producible by individual farmers.

The first society was started in 1886 at Ravenna, in Emilia, a region of large estates worked by paid labour, the *braccianti*, but as the agricultural population increased so did the unemployment. The society set up farms of collective type and the movement spread vigorously; it was, however, suppressed by Mussolini. Since the war it has been restarted and is now making steady progress; already there are more farms of this type than in any other country in Europe except Yugoslavia. The farm is run by a manager appointed by the society; the members work in gangs each under a foreman; the method of payment, however, has not been entirely satisfactorily settled, there being at present little incentive to the individual to do his best. The workers live in the villages; there is insufficient land to give each man his own little holding as in the Russian system.

The individualist societies came only a year later; the first was started in 1887 at Calvenzano, in the Province of Bergamo, Lombardy. This also was a region of large estates but many were cut up into small farms. Frequently the owner—often a public body—leased out the estate to a contractor who found the tenants and fixed the rent; there was much rack-renting. The society lets small farms to its members, but, as there are always more applications than land, allocation is not infrequently by lot and the letting is on short leases only—three to nine years. The amount of land allowed per family depends on its size, so that periodical redistribution is necessary. Fragmentation is not permitted; all heirs under Roman law have equal shares, but the son that succeeds to the farm must buy out his co-heirs.

The fixing of rents is often a contentious matter, but once done it remains unchanged; the tenants are no longer share-croppers as many of them had been under the old system. The rent is commonly paid in kind: a fixed quantity of one of the society's chief products—for the society may run a processing factory. There are none of the supplementary payments or "presents" to the middleman as in the old days.

The collective farms can readily use mechanization, fertilizers, and improved seeds, but so also can the individual farms except that mechanization may be more difficult. The collective farms are not necessarily the more productive, but they can more readily be made to satisfy Socialist and Communist ideas of social justice and *solidarita*. They differ in many details from the Russian farms and fundamentally in that membership is voluntary and that members are free in their spare time to undertake paid work on private farms.

The societies often have difficulty in raising capital. Each of the two groups has its distinctive political colour and the Government in power favours its own supporters.[1] The co-operative farms afford valuable material for the study of this most important problem of organizing small producers in such a way as to ensure maximum efficiency.

ISRAEL

The food production problems of Israel have an importance out of all proportion to the size of the country or the number of its inhabitants. They present, in a compact space and under more uniform conditions than can be found elsewhere, practically all of the more serious difficulties besetting the agriculturist and administrator in the crowded regions of other semi-arid countries, and they are being attacked with a vigour and an earnestness rarely feasible elsewhere. Israel can be regarded as a pilot scheme for the settlement and development of marginal dry lands.

The Palestine of history was a geographical unit. It consisted of a block of hills some 2,000 to 3,000 ft. high in the centre of which stands Jerusalem, fringed north and west by low-lying plains, on the west by the narrow Jordan valley, and stretching southwards into the desert uplands of the Negev and Sinai. The most important of the low-lying areas is the coastal plain of Sharon bordering the Mediterranean and stretching northwards to Mount Carmel where the hills come nearest the sea. The plain north of the hill country is the Emek ("the valley") or Esdraelon: this links on to the Jordan by the valley of Jezreel and the small plain of Beisan.

Much of the country is semi-arid. The rain comes in winter only; it is from the Mediterranean and is caught on the central block of hills; the streams flow down into the surrounding plains, some perennially, some intermittently; some get more or less lost in marshes which are—or were—among the most characteristic features of the plains. The Jordan, however, is fed mainly by the snows and rainfall of Mount Hermon, in Lebanon, and flows continuously. The rainfall is highest in the north-west: there it is about 25 inches a year; it decreases towards the south and east, slowly at first but more rapidly farther on. Esdraelon has about 30 inches, the central part of the coastal plain about 22 inches, Gaza, in the south, about 15 inches, and Beersheba, inland to the east, has 9 inches only. In the Jordan valley Tiberias in the north has 18 inches, Jericho in the centre 6 inches, and the south end of the Dead Sea less than 4 inches. Southward of a line from Gaza to Jericho there is so little rain that the country is practically desert. This includes the Negev and it covers about half of the historical Palestine. Agriculture and settled life have, throughout history, been confined mainly to the region north of this line, though the actual boundary has fluctuated a good deal from time to time.

For many years Jews have been purchasing land from the Arabs and setting up colonies, usually in the plains; they paid good prices for it and not infrequently had to purchase it twice over—once from the cultivator who thought he owned the land, and once from the pascha who, in fact, held the title deeds. For the Jews, however, it was not an ordinary investment but the

[1] See an interesting account by Sir Malcolm Darling in *Co-operative Year Book*, 1952, Horace Plunkett Foundation.

discharge of a sacred duty, and the pioneers who built up the first settlements were inspired by the ideal of making a national home to which all Jews might go as of right, and be free to lead their lives in their own way without the fear and persecution from which they had suffered in so many other lands.[1] From the outset the settlements were planned on generous and permanent lines: there was no haphazard ramshackle stage: some beautiful examples— Rosh Pina, "the head cornerstone" and others—can be seen in the hills of Nazareth and by the Sea of Galilee. The heavy influx of refugees about 1950 involved the rapid construction of temporary "transit villages"—*ma'abaroth* —but these are not expected to continue once the refugees are placed.

When the new State of Israel was founded on May 15, 1948, the Jews were already in possession of most of the coastal and northern plains, and these, together with the arid Negev, constitute most of their territory to-day. The only hill country included is the corridor leading to Jerusalem from the coastal plain, and the tract north of the Acre–Safad Road, which is the southern extension of the Lebanon Hills. The central block of hill country, however, forms part of the new State of Jordan. The country is straggling and very irregular in shape and its boundaries are extraordinarily long and complicated.

The total area of old Palestine had been 6·6 million acres: that of Israel is 5·06 million acres, but a large proportion of this is desert. Israel's share of the old Palestine includes most of the good land; for old Palestine this had been estimated at 777,000 acres and for the new State at 733,440 acres.[2] Some of the poorer land is being brought into use; about 844,000 acres were actually cultivated in 1950–51 and it is intended to raise this to one million acres.

The population in March 1950, was 1·29 millions but fresh immigrants have since come in at the rate of about 200,000 a year. The population at the end of March 1952, was 1·585 millions of whom 1·411 millions were Jews. This compared with a Jewish population of 650,000 in May 1948.

The plains differ somewhat in soil and climatic characteristics, and they are put to different uses in strict accordance therewith. The choicest is the coastal plain. This is of alluvial origin; its soils vary from sand to heavy loams or clays and it is well supplied with numerous streams and also with subsoil water percolating from the hills and reached easily by wells: irrigation is, therefore, practicable over large areas. Fringing the coast, however, is a strip of sand which, unless fixed by grass and trees, is liable to drift inland and bury fertile soils. This has happened in the past: Caesarea, once a flourishing seaport town with a fertile hinterland, is now a tract of sand dunes long approachable only by horses and not by car. Prior to the establishment of the new State fixing of the dunes was in places impeded by the grazing rights of the Arabs.

The sand also blocked some of the streams, especially in parts of the north, and potentially good agricultural land became converted into malarial marsh. Reclamation was for long hampered by ancient Arab grazing rights. These are now extinguished and reclamation has proceeded vigorously. Some remarkable results have been achieved. Between Kakaun and Zichron there

---

[1] The ideals and aims have been set out in a prodigious number of books, one of the more recent being Martin Buber, *Israel and Palestine* (East and West Library, 1952).

[2] E. C. Willatts, *Geog. Journ.*, 1946, Vol. 108, pp. 146–73.

were, twenty-five years ago, some 25,000 acres of malarial swamp land affording only limited grazing to the Bedouin. No good road crossed it; when the writer first visited it in 1929 a guide was needed who knew which of the various tracks led anywhere and which did not; in wet weather it was impassable. Two other pestilential swamps were of considerable size: the Hadera, south of Bingamina, and the Kabarra, of 10,000 acres, to the north. These are now flourishing farm lands.

The climate of this coastal plain is admirably suited for citrus fruits and quantities are grown on the light soils where irrigation is practicable. The heavier soils, unsuited for citrus, are used for irrigated vegetables and fodder crops for dairying.

Where irrigation is impracticable fodder crops are still grown, and in suitable areas, vines and aromatic plants, but cereals become more important, particularly as one goes northwards and less water is available for the crops.

The plain of Esdraelon is entirely different from the coastal plain. Its soils are heavier, it has less water—in 1943 only 8 per cent of its cultivated land was irrigated though this has since been increased by a pipe-line laid from Haifa to Affuleh—and its climatic and other conditions are not suitable for oranges though some grapefruit is grown. It produces the northern fruits, apples and plums, and some grapes, but its main products are cereals, which till recently covered about half the cultivated area, fodder crops, and roots. Fodder crops are now, however, being more extensively grown.

As on the coastal plain there were considerable areas of malarial marsh which, however, the Jewish colonists drained. One of the worst of these, formerly called by the Arabs "The Valley of Death," is now a prosperous colony, Nahalal ("We will praise God"). (Plate 20.) Farther east, the malarial swamp of Dagania was drained and transformed into productive farmland.

The Jezreel Valley has about the same area of irrigated land as Esdraelon; most of it is used for green fodder and vegetables; but the unirrigated land is largely in cereals and fodder crops, with a certain amount of fallow, as in Lower Galilee.

Upper Galilee has more of the intensiveness of the plains; more of its cultivated land is in deciduous fruits, especially apples and grapes, and in vegetables and green fodder, than in Lower Galilee and the northern plains.

Since Israel was established as a State in 1948 there has been a remarkable increase in the area of cultivated land. It was at the outset 412 thousand acres; by 1952 this had been raised to 868,000 acres. (Table LI.)

The details of the field crops are given in Table LII. Winter crops occupy about 70 per cent of the area; wheat was till recently the most important; it is usually sown in October or November and harvested in June or July. Being grown without irrigation its yield is very dependent on the rainfall, especially in spring. In addition it is liable to be badly damaged by the Khamsin, the hot wind of the spring months that shrivels the soft grain before it is ripe, and it suffers from rust and locusts as it did 3,000 years ago when Solomon, dedicating his new temple, prayed for protection against "blasting, mildew, locust," and also caterpillar; nowadays birds could be added to the list. Wheat breeders have long been seeking earlier varieties to escape the Khamsin and the rust, and experiments have shown that nitrogenous and phosphatic fertilizers increase the yields provided the rain has been adequate. Yields are

TABLE LI. *Utilization of land, Israel. Thousand acres*

	1948–49	1950–51	1951–52
Unirrigated field crops and fallows	266·5	637·5	650
Irrigated fodder, etc.	16·25	29·5	31·8
Vegetables and potatoes	17·25	39·25	48·2
Fruit plantations	90	98	102·5
Fish ponds	3·75	6·75	7·5
Miscellaneous (1)	18·25	26·5	28·0
	412·5	837·5	868·0
Irrigated area	72·5	110	—

(*Govt. Year Book*, 1952, p. 340: amended figures from *Stat. News*, Vol. 3, No. 9.)

(1) The "miscellaneous" item includes vegetable and potato areas in the auxiliary farms, which accounts for the apparent discrepancy with Table LII. The unirrigated field crops for 1950–51 include 110,000 acres ploughed in the Negev in readiness for sowing in the season 1951–52; and the figure for 1951–52 includes 75,000 acres ploughed for cropping in 1952–53.

very low but they tend to rise, though only slowly, the average for the period 1934–38 was 3·2 cwt. per acre, for 1940–45, 4 cwt., and, in recent years, 6 cwt. per acre, though some colonists do much better and have had 10 cwt. or more. Much of the wheat is grown in the valleys and in Upper and Lower Galilee: here it occupies about one-third of the winter crop area.

Since 1949 barley has displaced wheat in importance and although on most of the farmed land its yields are no higher it has now become the leading crop. It is fed to milch cows and poultry, and to grow all he needs for this purpose is more attractive to the farmer than to increase his output of wheat for sale in the market where it competes with wheat which, within the limits of the International Wheat Agreement, is supplied from overseas more cheaply than barley would be. Further, in dry conditions as in the Southern Negev, barley gives higher and more stable crops than wheat; even in the old days it was grown in preference to wheat in the drier districts, e.g. at Beersheba, where the rainfall was only about 9 inches. Oats have proved less suitable than barley for livestock and are not much grown.

Weeds are a serious difficulty in the cultivation of cereals but will no doubt be satisfactorily controlled by selective weed killers.

Fodder crops are extremely important and in recent years they have increased in area considerably more than the crops for human consumption in spite of the great gain in human population. A number of them are grown, chiefly in winter for conservation as hay, but some also in summer for silage. Grass occupies only about 17 per cent of the total cropped area; the Jewish farmers had till recently neither pastures nor meadows; but some irrigated lucerne and Rhodes grass pastures have now been set up and experiments on mountain pastures begun.

Much ingenuity has been displayed in devising sequences of crops to cover the whole year, bridging the dry season that causes so much difficulty in semi-arid countries. The problem is simplest where irrigation is possible. Maize sown in April is cut green as wanted from June to October. Berseem, also sown in April, is ready in October or November and lasts till May. The gaps between the maize and the berseem are supplied by pumpkins and vetch hay.

TABLE LII. *Sown areas of chief crops in Israel. Thousand acres*

	Unirrigated				Programme
	1948–49	1949–50	1950–51	1951–52	1951–52
Winter					
Wheat	75·6	92·2	101·9	81·5	145·0
Wheat, thousand tons	21	27	13	(1) 30	20–30
Barley	38·8	124·0	153·0	201·5	225·0
Barley, thousand tons		37	27·5	97 (4)	
Oats and rye	5·0	4·3	7·5	9	12·0
Fodder crops, hay	30·2	55·0	86·2	94	105·0
Fodder crops, others	15·0	27·5	50·4	54	{ 70·0 / 11·5
Total, winter	164·6	302·9	399·1	440	568·5
Summer					
Maize and sorghum	27·5	45·8	28·3	40·4	112·5
Oil crops	10·1	17·3	8·6	11·5	25·0
Tobacco	2·2	6·8	11·5	13·5	12·5
Melons	9·3	14·5	10·0	15·0	12·5
Silage and fodder	6·4	17·4	23·2	18·5	12·5
Summer hay	1·4	2·8	5·2	1·6	
Others	1·2	2·1	2·2	2·7	
Total summer	58·2	106·8	89·0	103·2	175·0
Cultivated fallow	43·5	34·1	39·4	31·5	56·6 (2)
Total unirrigated	266·4	443·8	527·5 (3)	574·5	800·0
of which in Jewish farms	207	303	397	460	
Non-Jewish farms	59	141	131	115	
	Irrigated				
Total area	72·5	87·5	110·0	127·5	
Including fodder, etc.	16·2	20·2	29·5		37·5
Potatoes	6·5	8·8	9·2		
Potatoes, thousand tons		36·0	37·0		
Vegetables (including not irrigated)	20·0	31·4	35·5	48 (5)	
Thousand tons		124	142	225 (5)	
Government forest			121		
Total area of country, million acres	5·06				
Number of workers, thousand	47	59	70	85	

(*Statistical Bull. of Israel*, 1952, Vol. 3, Nos. 1 and 2. The original figures are in dunams; they are converted into acres using for simplicity of reference the factor 1 dunam = 0·25 acres. The true figure is 1 dunam = 0·247 acres, but the difference is within the error of the statistics.

(1) Year of drought.

(2) Including "other crops."

(3) This total omits 110,000 acres ploughed in the Negev and included in the total of 637·5 given on p. 163.

(4) Includes oats.

(5) Includes potatoes.

Where there is no irrigation similar sequences can still be devised, but the gaps are longer and more provision is necessary.

The areas of irrigated field crops were, in 1948–49:

		Thousand acres			
	Coastal		*Upper and*	*Other*	
South	*plain*	*Valleys*	*lower Galilee*	*areas*	*Total*
0·33	7·1	7·5	1·2	0·03	16·2

Of these 8·6 were winter crops, chiefly berseem, and 7·6 summer crops, chiefly maize.

Vegetables have always formed an important part of the Jewish dietary and the acreage rose to nearly 45,000 in 1950–51, producing over 179,000 tons (157,500 from Jewish farms). The variety is considerable: it includes potatoes, onions, tomatoes, cabbage, cauliflowers, carrots, egg plants, cucumbers, radishes, and beetroots; the largest area is on the north coastal plain.

The area under fruit and plantations has increased more slowly than that of field crops: it rose from 90,000 acres in 1948–49 to 110,000 acres in 1951: the chief items being:

	Thousand acres
Citrus	34
Vines	18
Olives	37
Deciduous and others	21

Of all these, citrus fruits (chiefly oranges) are far and away the most important, playing a great part in Israel's economy and accounting for about half of the total exports. The citrus industry is a great triumph of Jewish technical skill and organization, both in production and in marketing. From a steady low area of about 7,000 acres in the pre-mandate days before 1922, the area rose rapidly to nearly 75,000 acres, half Jewish and half Arab, in 1935. Then came a check when the industry was badly hit in the world slump; it also suffered considerably during the war and later; many of the groves were abandoned. Rehabilitation has recently begun, but in 1950–51 the area was only 32,500 acres; this was raised to 34,000 acres in 1951–52. In pre-war Palestine annual production during the years 1934–38 had averaged 400,000 tons; for Israel the figures have been:

		Thousand tons	
	1949–50	1950–51	1951–52
Production	262	311	308
Export	158	149	141

(C.E.C. Rpts., *Fruit*, 1952.)

About half the output is exported and about a third is worked up into by-products. If settled, peaceful conditions could be assured the export demand would certainly increase greatly, and as the necessary capital becomes available considerable further planting can be expected.

Citrus trees have the great merit that they grow best on sandy soils which without irrigation[1] are unsuitable for ordinary agricultural crops except

[1] If irrigated they can produce vegetables, groundnuts, fodder, and other crops plentifully.

melons; in consequence, the soils which in the old days were of small repute have now become the most desired of all those on the plain. The irrigation in the citrus groves was originally entirely of the basin type, the water being pumped from wells, each grower having his own. The spraying method is now, however, widely used. It is much more economical of water and of labour; on the old method one man would water only three-quarters to one acre a day; using modern Californian sprinkler equipment he can water two to two-and-a-half acres.

Deciduous fruits are grown in the northern plains which are not quite suitable for oranges; about 15,000 tons a year are marketed, but production is certainly considerably greater.

The ancient fruits of Palestine were olives, figs, and grapes, but of these only grapes appealed at first to the modern Jewish settlers; the figs and olives are more appropriate to the hills and were grown by the Arabs and the groves are now being rehabilitated, using some ingenious cultural devices. Even grapes were not much cultivated till recently—in spite of the fact that they grow on the heavier soils unsuited for citrus and usually require no irrigation; the area of both dessert and wine grapes has now, however, been extended. Wine is produced in the district round Rishon le Zion, and the associated experimental work is done at the school at Mikveh Israel; the wine is light and pleasant, but produces no great vintages and is not much in demand.

The quantities of non-citrus fruits produced in 1950–51 were, in thousand tons:

Grapes, table	7·1	Bananas	5·7	Deciduous	3·5
Grapes, wine	6·25	Olives	2·7	Others	5·65
	13·35		8·4		9·15 Total 30·9

(*Govt. Year Book*, 1952, p. 335.)

Livestock

The traditional livestock of Palestine were sheep and goats and they remained the chief animals of the Arabs; the goats have considerably hampered reafforestation in the hill country and so have contributed greatly to the erosion of the soil. The Jewish colonists have broken completely with tradition; they have comparatively few sheep and goats and these are mostly in the hill country north of the Haifa–Beisan line. Attempts are being made to increase the numbers of milking goats of improved breeds but grazing goats are to be eliminated. New breeds of sheep including Dorset Horned are being tested. The chief livestock are dairy cows; milk production is one of the most profitable ways of using the heavy soils. The numbers of cattle are increasing: they were, in September 1950 and 1951:

	Thousands	
	1950	1951
Total	47·2	57·4
Milch cows	24·8	29·9

The increase of over 20 per cent was partly the result of importation. Milk production in 1949–50 is estimated to have been about 21 million gallons, and in 1950–51 about 24 million gallons. The general average yield per cow is stated to be about 800 gallons and herd averages of 900 a year are not uncommon; this contrasts with the Arab yield of 150 gallons from their native cows and 440 gallons from Syrian cows. Most of the milk is consumed as liquid: about 13,000 tons of laben[1] and labenia are made, some 6,000 tons of cheese but very little butter (350 lb. only).

As in other Jewish agricultural enterprises the cost of production is high, owing to the scarcity of summer foods in absence of much grass, and to the high cost of rearing calves because so much milk is fed to them. To overcome this difficulty the area of summer fodder crops is being expanded.

There is but little production of meat. Bull calves are not saved but are quickly slaughtered; and as yet but little mutton or goat flesh is produced. The output of meat in 1949–50 was:

		Tons		
Beef	*Veal*	*Sheep and goats*	*Lamb and kid*	*Total*
850	200	100	150	1,300

(*Statistical Bull. of Israel*, 1952, Vol. 3, Nos. 1 and 2.)

Poultry are very popular in spite of difficulties of providing enough barley and maize for them; the numbers were:

	Millions	
	Sept. 1950	*Sept. 1951*
Total	5·06	4·08
Laying hens	2·54	2·53
Chicks	2·37	1·22
Eggs produced in year	330	400

The heavy reduction of numbers in September 1951 suggests considerable slaughter to satisfy the demand for food. Poultry supplied in 1949–50 some 6,850 tons of meat against only 1,300 tons from all other farm animals. Another factor was the drought of the summer of 1950, and the resulting shortage of fodder.

Food supplies

As the area of cultivated land is only a quarter acre per head and the yields are low it is physically impossible to produce sufficient food for the needs of the population. Considerable imports are therefore needed. Before the war it was estimated that the average amount of food available per head in the cities supplied 2,533 calories per day and 80 grams of protein of which 30 were of animal origin.[2] The colonists supplied 15 per cent of the calories, 34 per cent of the animal proteins, about 75 per cent of the vegetables and fresh fruit, and most of the milk, but only a small proportion of the cereals. The pattern of supply was much like that of Great Britain but the proportions imported were even greater. Since then there have been great upheavals and such a flood of immigrants as to cause great disturbances in food supply. To add to the complexity of the food problem the feeding habits of the different groups

---

[1] Coagulated sour milk, an Arab drink. [2] L. Samuel, 1937–39 data.

vary widely according to their origin and degree of orthodoxy. Some are rice eaters; others, on religious grounds, refuse certain kinds of fish, which, however, are perfectly edible and nutritious; and, of course, none of them eat pig meat. The usual diet is bread, cheese, fish, vegetables and salads, and fruit, but practically no meat—except for visitors and guests.

In spite of all these difficulties the official figures suggest that the average nutrient supplies per head of population have been slightly better than they were before the war. The children look very healthy—as, indeed, they always did. A food balance sheet was drawn up for 1949–50 by the Central Bureau of Statistics and Economic Research for Palestine and is summarized in Table LIII.

Average quantities available per head per day	Pre-war (L. Samuel)	1949 (Govt. Year Bk.)	1951–52 (Govt. Year Bk.)
Calories	2,533	2,650	2,500
Protein (grams per day), animal	30	33	27·5
Vegetable	50	50	55·5
Total	80	83	83

In recent years the calorie intake has fluctuated between 2,300 and 2,600 a day; present feeding plans are aiming at an intake of 2,650.

The experience of housekeepers living in Israel, however, showed that these quantities were not always generally available and that recourse was necessary to the flourishing black market—always an accompaniment of rationing in times of scarcity. In September 1951, sugar was selling there at 35s. a kilo, meat at 80s. a kilo, potatoes at 10s. a kilo, and chickens at £5 each. Migrants were pouring into the country, few of them were agriculturists, home production of food was entirely inadequate and foreign currency was lacking to import more food.[1] Israel is practically self-supporting in milk, eggs, fresh vegetables, and fruit, but is far from being so in beef, fish, cereals, potatoes, sugar, pulses, and oil seeds. All these have to be imported at a cost which, in 1950 and in 1951, was practically double the value of all exports.[2] The values were in Israel £ millions:

	1950	1951
Cost of imported food, tobacco, and beverages	23·50	27·91
Total value of exports (omitting re-exports)	12·55	15·98

(*Stat. Bull. of Israel*, 1952, Vol. 3.)

[1] *The Times*, September 6, 1951.
[2] In 1951 the values were:

	£ million (Israel)
Total imports	122·6
Total exports	16·0
Adverse balance	106·6

This is a normal occurrence; the deficit is covered by large aids from the United States (some $293 m., since the new State was founded in 1948, up to 1952) and other Governments, by generous gifts from Jews in other countries, and as soon as they begin from German reparations ($820·4 m. payable over 12 years).

The quantities imported in 1951–52 were in thousand tons:

Wheat	239	Meat	9·8
Rice	6·5	Fish	18
Lentils	8·1	Sugar	30
Potatoes	31		

The import of wheat was 72,000 tons higher than in 1950–51 partly because of the increased population, partly also because the severe drought caused a loss of some 12,000 to 15,000 tons of grain. On the other hand import of meat was less than in 1950–51: for potatoes, fish, and sugar it was about the same.

The poultry consume considerable quantities of barley, much of which has, in the past, been imported. It is hoped that the Negev may be able to supply this in future: in seasons of good rainfall considerable quantities might be produced there.

TABLE LIII. *Quantities of food produced and imported, and amounts available per head of population, Palestine, 1949–50*

Cereals	Home production, thousand tons	Import, thousand tons	Home production as per cent of total supply	Quantity available, lb. per head per year (1)
Wheat	27	167	14	264
All food grains	27	180	15	277
Animal food (barley)	37	37	50	
Meat, excluding poultry	1·3	13·8	9	29
Poultry	6·85	0·75	90	13
Milk and products	123	13	90	212 (liquid milk 170)
Butter, margarine, and vegetable fats	23	5	82	34
Eggs	18	0·67	96	33
Fish	6	17	26	38
Potatoes	36	30	55	102
Other vegetables	124	10	92	238
Pulses, nuts, and oil seeds	6	15	29	19
Fruit	345	−209 (2)		238
Sugar	0·44	29·5	1	38·5

(1) After allowing for seed, waste, and changes in stock.
(2) Export. There is also an import of 11,000 tons chiefly dried fruits.
(*Statistical Bull. of Israel*, 1952, Vol. 3, Nos. 1 and 2.)

Plans for development

Like other countries, Israel has its plan for development—many, indeed: few countries have had more, or more would-be advisers—and, in particular, plans for producing more food at home so as to reduce the need for these heavy importations. The four-year plan issued in 1951 assumes a population of 2 millions in 1955 and aims at producing all the necessary food excepting meat and grain: of these 50 per cent of the requirement is to be produced instead of 9 and 23 per cent respectively, as in 1949–50. The plan necessitates the establishment of 50,000 new farms which would be run by new immigrants.

It is assumed that the population will further increase until it reaches a final limit of 2½ millions. The stream of immigrants is to be deflected into 24 planning regions, 21 of them being rural. Eighty per cent of the total food requirements would be produced, while exports of citrus and other agricultural products would still be continued. An agricultural population of 500,000 is envisaged; this would be 20 per cent of the whole, the same proportion as in Holland and Switzerland, instead of 14 per cent as in 1950 and 1951. Some change in system will be necessary. Land being scarcer than labour the fullest output of food units per acre must be achieved even at the cost of more man-hours of work: preference must, therefore, be given to crops such as potatoes, tomatoes, sugar beet, flax, oil seeds, peas, and lentils which give higher output per acre on unirrigated land than do the wheat and barley at present grown. Output of fish also is to be increased, both the catches from lake and sea, and the produce of culture in ponds, a procedure which the Jews have carried to a high stage of development, limited, however, by the need to import food for the fishes when output is forced too high. The quantities produced have been, in tons:

	1947–8	1950	1951(1)
Fish from pond culture	2,254	2,534	3,117
Lake and sea catches	237	3,897	3,790
Total	2,491	6,431	6,673

(1) Provisional.

The difficulty of forecasting production in Israel even by skilled experts is illustrated by the disparity between the planned and the accomplished acreages for 1951–52 shown in Table LII (p. 164.)

It is improbable that anything like 80 per cent of self-sufficiency could be achieved on the one million acres of cultivated land at present in sight as this allows only 0·5 acres per head. Much reclamation of land at present unused would need to be done, and now that the problem of Arab grazing rights has disappeared the difficulties are, with few exceptions, mainly technical and financial and, therefore, surmountable. The most important exception is the reclamation of Lake Hula and its associated swamps on the Jordan River, above Lake Tiberias and on the Syrian frontier. The total area is 14,300 acres made up as follows:

Water-logged soil	3,200
Swamp	4,200
Swamp with peat deposit	3,700
The lake	3,200
	14,300

Two thousand new farms averaging five acres could be established on the 11,000 acres of land thus gained, and as they would be well provided with water all the year they should be capable of producing large quantities of grain, groundnuts, vegetables, fruit, and livestock, while the lake should supply much fish and the peat would furnish badly needed fuel; finally, the quantity of water saved annually from evaporation would serve to bring into cultivation some 50,000 acres lower down the Jordan valley. The advantages of the scheme are obviously great: the region at present is a malarial swamp dangerous for the neighbouring people and serving no useful purpose whatsoever.

Reclamation began in March 1950 and is still continuing. Unfortunately, however, objection is taken by the Syrian Government on the grounds that they are not satisfied with the boundary, although it was fixed internationally after the 1914–18 war, and also they wish to preserve the marsh for strategic reasons. Happily the United Nations has intervened: it would, indeed, be a tragedy if such a beneficent undertaking had to be curtailed or abandoned.[1]

No such difficulties arise in connection with another great enterprise, the exploitation of the Negev, the desert region of the south that constitutes more than half of Israel. Settlement south of a line joining Beersheba and Rafiah at present seems hopeless, but north of that line it is being achieved, thanks to the devoted labours of a number of Israel's young people who took their courage in their hands and undertook the work: by mid-1951 there were over fifty settlements: twenty-four collectives, the rest smallholdings, and more were being started. In 1952 some 125,000 acres of wheat and barley were harvested there.[2] Water is to be piped to them from the Yarkon River which flows across the coastal plain to Tel Aviv—forming, as usual, a malarial marsh on the way: this, however, will disappear leaving, instead, good agricultural land. The supply will be increased from wells *en route* for the sinking of which powerful mobile drills have been imported from the United States. One of the models can penetrate to a depth of 2,000 ft. In addition, dams are constructed on the hills adjoining the desert to hold as much as possible of the scanty rainfall. Life would become less unpleasant if trees can be established to temper the hot desert winds laden with sand, and underground water can be found. Large numbers of eucalypts and tamarisks have been planted. A settlement has been made and more may follow, even in the southern part of the Negev, the Arabah valley lying between the Dead Sea and the Gulf of Aqaba; water has been found and roads are being made.

A subsidy is paid on land sown with winter crops and considerable construction schemes, especially for piping of water, are going forward. There is even talk of bringing 750,000 acres into cultivation, but this does not mean a correspondingly close settlement. Large areas can be ploughed with great tractors, sown with barley or sorghum and left till harvest, subject to protection from nomadic Bedouin. The cost is relatively small and while the uncertain rainfall brings in serious risks, they are deemed worth taking in view of the urgent need of grain for poultry and other animals.

But however the Negev is developed, the enterprise is one for young people inspired with a great ideal and fired with the enthusiasm that can overcome difficulties before which a calculating economist would quail.[3]

Other districts besides the Negev will benefit from this new water supply:

[1] Control of the Yarmuk River which flows into the Jordan from Syria at the south end of Lake Tiberias would add greatly to the possibilities of irrigation but it necessitates the peaceful co-operation of Syria, Jordan and Israel.

[2] Chiefly barley. The yield was estimated at 5½ cwt. per acre on unfertilized land and about 11 cwt. when fertilizer had been applied. The winter rainfall had been good.

[3] These various developments are discussed by Sir Clarmont Skrine in *Geog. Journ.*, 1951, Vol. 117, pp. 343–48, and in *The Negev*, E. Boyko and E. J. Mayer, WIZO, Tel Aviv.

Jerusalem, for example, is to receive 50 per cent more water than at present. The reliance on the underground water supply has, of course, the risk that the total quantity available, though believed to be large, is not known, so that there can be no certainty as to how long the supplies will last.

Developments are also going on in the hill country. Much of it has been terraced from ancient times and still remains productive; some now waste is being brought into use in the Israel section, though at considerable cost: some 80 to 120 man days may be needed to clear one acre from rock and there is still need for terraces or other protecting works. 60,000 acres are being thus converted into farm land in the barren uplands and the Jerusalem corridor; the work is being done by Yemenite refugees.

During the centuries of neglect prior to 1922 much of the forest that had formerly covered the hills had been destroyed by felling and by grazing of goats with the result that severe erosion had taken place. Striking examples can be seen in travelling from Jerusalem to Jericho. The hill sections in Israel are being replanted wherever necessary; a usual tribute to a person of merit is to plant 100 or more trees in his name. There were, in 1950, 121,000 acres of forest and plantations owned or controlled by the Government, most of it open forest reserve:[1] it is planned to afforest 50,000 acres of the barren uplands in the corridor leading to Jerusalem. Suitable use is made of Eucalyptus, Australia's great gift to warm, semi-arid countries.

Whatever the outcome of these various enterprises they cannot fail to provide information of the greatest value for agricultural experts concerned with the development of arid and semi-arid regions elsewhere. The Jewish colonists will certainly not be deterred by economic troubles, and their efficient scientific organization and deep respect for their university ensures that the best available knowledge will be applied in solving the difficult problems involved.

An even greater contribution to agricultural development in other countries is the information accumulating about methods of organization of small producers. Several have been tried: four have survived on a significant scale and are being carried on side by side under the conditions of a good experimental test. The methods are:

(1) Collective and communal (*Kibbutz* and *Kvutze*). Work is collectively organized, and all property and earnings are collectively owned. The people all live together in a communal establishment; there are no private houses but married couples have their own room. Work is equally shared between men and women, the children are all brought up together in the communal crèche, but parents see their children in the evenings. There is no home life in the Western sense. There are no "labour days" as in the Russian system: if a man does not work satisfactorily he has to go.

(2) Collective but non-communal (*Moshav shitufi*). Work is organized communally and earnings and spendings are added to and drawn from a common pool, as in the *Kibbutz*, but there is more individual life. Each family has its own house, and there is home life as understood in the West with no communal institutions except the school and community centre.

(3) Workers' Co-operative smallholdings settlement (*Moshav ordim*). Farmers work individually but with the maximum of co-operation—credit,

[1] *Israel Govt. Year Book*, 1950.

cultivation, marketing, etc.; as all are to have equal opportunity the farms are all of the same size.

In none of these is there individual ownership of land, nor may any hired labour be engaged.

(4) Individual farmers privately owning their land and property, and organizing their own lives as in Great Britain. Where the holdings are small, they take other work as well.

Every individual is completely free to make his own choice between these systems: no pressure of any sort is exerted. Israel is the only country in the world where collective farming is practised without compulsion and with complete liberty to abandon it for individual farming.

The collectives and co-operatives are linked by great national institutions. These include a large purchasing agency, the Hamashbir, somewhat like our Co-operative Wholesale Society; a large selling agency for agricultural produce, the T'nuva; and another for the citrus, Pardess. A bank organizes overseas marketing and labour has a very powerful organization, the Histadruth.[1]

The relative popularity of these different forms of organization has varied from time to time. The original settlers were individualists. Later comers from Russia and Eastern Europe preferred the collective–communal *Kibbutz*. Between 1936 and 1943 nearly 20,000 new settlers entered these as compared with an increase of only 10,000 in the individual villages, and between 1948 and 1949, sixty new *Kibbutz* settlements were established. Their communism was "idealistic," not political, and the ban on private ownership of the land was based, not on Marx, but on Moses: "The land is mine, saith the Lord, and shall not be sold for ever; and ye are sojourners in it." Then came an influx of Oriental Jews who cherish the family life and they preferred the co-operative and non-communal collective organizations: only seven new *Kibbutz* groups were formed between 1949–50. The numbers of the different settlements have been:[2]

	Communal collective	Non-communal collective	Workers Co-operative	Individual ownership	Total
December 1949	210	20	120	89	439
June 1951	211	26	215		

Half a million immigrants entered Israel between May 1948 and December 1950; practically all were from Eastern Europe, the Middle East, including Yemen and Aden, and North Africa; hardly any were from Western Europe or America. Less than 1 per cent of them were agriculturists; more than half had had no previous training of any sort, another 27 per cent were children

[1] For a full account see Malcolm Darling, *Commonwealth Conf. on Agric. Co-operation*, 1951, pp. 21 *et seq.*

[2] In 1951 the Jewish farms had 98,750 acres under summer field crops distributed as follows among the various types of settlement:

		Thousand acres				
	Smallholdings		Schools and training	Urban	Village and	
Collective	Workers	others	farms	settlements	others	Total
64,800	21,720	1,710	1,310	1,460	7,560	98,570

(*Statistical Bull. of Israel*, 1952, Vol. 3, p. 22.)

under 16, and of the remaining 22 per cent about a quarter were professional and business people; the rest were workers of various sorts. The task of welding these very heterogeneous groups into a single community will be very great, and will not be eased by the circumstance that the old religious bonds which formerly united all Jews seem to be losing their hold on the younger generation. For purposes of settlement in the countryside the collective farms have the great advantage that the newcomer's life and work is completely organized for him and he learns agriculture without risk to himself. As the collective fields are large, mechanization is possible on a scale beyond the reach of the smallholder. Against this is the fact that the individual must subordinate himself to the group, and some of the more intelligent have found this irksome and have transferred after a time to a more individual type of farming. The standard of comfort in the communal farms was before the war lower than in the individual homes.

It is impossible as yet to say which of these various systems will prove the most stable and satisfying to the people concerned. Much turns on the personality of the members and especially on the durability of their enthusiasm. It may be that no method will emerge as an absolute best, but that each will be found to possess some advantages and some disadvantages. But, whatever the outcome, the knowledge and experience gained will be of the greatest value to agricultural administrators in Africa, India, and elsewhere.

EGYPT

No country in the world presents sharper contrasts than Egypt either physically, economically, or socially. 96 per cent of the country is absolute desert but the remaining 4 per cent includes some of the most productive land in Africa; there is very little marginal land. Its chief agricultural products, long- and medium-stapled cottons, command high prices on the world market, and the nation's wealth is concentrated in the hands of a relatively small number of people: the great majority live in dire poverty. It is a country of land owners, yet 0·4 per cent of them own more land than the 94 per cent whose holdings are less than five acres in extent. How long this position can be kept stable remains to be seen.[1]

The area of Egypt is 386,198 square miles—247 million acres—of which only 8·6 million acres are actually settled, 6·2 million of which are for cultivation. This cultivated land falls into two parts: the delta of Lower Egypt which stretches for 100 miles from its apex, near Cairo, to the sea, and has as base the coast line of 150 miles from Alexandria to near Port Said; and the strip of land on either side of the Nile, of a width depending on the height above the river level but rarely exceeding ten miles, and, in any case, extending only so far as the flood water can be made to flow. Only in two places does the cultivated area widen out: in the Fayum, near Cairo, and at Komombo in Upper Egypt.

[1] For a discussion, see Chas. Issawi, *Egypt, an Economic and Social Analysis*, Oxford Univ. Press, 1947. This survey was made under the auspices of the Royal Institute for International Affairs.

A good account of Egyptian agriculture is given by C. H. Brown in *World Crops*, 1952, Vol. 4, pp. 281 *et seq.*

The boundary between the green cultivated strip and the desert is absolutely sharp: there is neither grassland nor savannah; away from the river trees occur only in the few oases.

The reason for this sharp division is that the country is almost entirely rainless excepting on the coast where some 8 to 12 inches a year may fall, but this rapidly decreases on going inland, and Cairo has only about 2 inches a year.

Egypt is thus completely dependent on the Nile—its only river—and it has been able to survive on its present scale only because of the flood that starts with the heavy summer rains in the equatorial regions, reaches Egypt about mid-July, attains its peak in late August or early September, and continues till November.

The fellahin learned early to make good use of this water, and the old traditional methods still remain in use. The area to be flooded may be several hundred acres: it is bounded by earth banks, roads, etc.; the flood water comes in, deposits its silt, saturates the soil, and ultimately drains or seeps away. This is called basin irrigation; it can be used wherever the flood water can go; it has the advantage of requiring no permanent construction works, but the disadvantage that it operates only while the river is in flood and so allows the growth of only one crop a year.

The second method of irrigation is by lifting or pumping the water out of the river, or, much more conveniently, drawing it from an artificial high-level canal taken off from the river higher up its course. Still farther up the river dams have been constructed to make huge storage reservoirs so as to ensure supplies for the canals even after the flood has ceased. Irrigation thus becomes possible at any season: it is called perennial irrigation and allows two or even three crops a year to be grown. The necessary engineering works are both costly and elaborate; they have been developed to a high pitch of engineering perfection by British experts. The land to be watered is divided into small rectangular compartments by low earth banks, it is levelled by dragging over it a flat wooden implement; this is done wholly by eye, and the fellahin have a wonderful capacity for detecting and smoothing out surface inequalities. Wheat and berseem are grown on the flat, but for cotton the land has to be put up into ridges. Some three-quarters of the irrigated land of Egypt is now watered in this way.

The population in 1947 was 19·09 millions: it had risen from 15·93 millions in the preceding ten years, an increase of 2 per cent per annum, one of the most rapid in the world. Of the 1947 population 8·2 millions were in the delta, 7·2 millions in Upper Egypt, and 3·6 millions in Cairo, the other large towns, and the canal zone.

The area of cultivated land per head of population is steadily falling: in 1937 it had been 0·38 acres per head: by 1947 it was down to 0·32 acre per head. Some of this carries two crops a year so that the actual area of crop per head is somewhat, but not much, greater. Small as it is, however, it is not all available for food production: about 20 per cent is in cotton, and some of the rice produced is exported.

Some 60–65 per cent of the population are peasants, mostly very small freeholders. The total number of landowners was, on December 31, 1949, 2·73 millions of whom 72 per cent had less than 1 feddan and 94 per cent had 5 or less,[1] only 0·4 per cent had more than 50. But these few larger owners had more land than all the 94 per cent of small men:

	December 31, 1949				December 31, 1940			
Size of holding acres	Number of owners		Area of land		Number of owners		Area of land held acres	
	Total 1,000's	per cent	Acres 1,000's	per cent	Thousands	per cent	1,000's	per cent
Up to 5·2	2,574	94·3	2,094	35·2	2,336	93·4	1,971	32·4
5·2 to 52	145	5·3	1,942	30·9	149	6·0	1,848	30·7
More than 52	12	0·4	2,150	33·9	12	0·5	2,256	36·9
	2,731	100·0	6,186	100·0	2,497	100·0	6,075	100·0

(*Statesman's Year Books* 1943, 1950.)

Much of the northern part of the delta is in large holdings, and of the southern part is in small ones. During the nine years some 111,000 acres had been added to the cultivated area, the largest holdings had lost 106,000 acres or 4·2 per cent of their land, the medium holdings gained 94,000 acres or 5 per cent, while the small holdings gained 123,000 acres or 6 per cent. The new Government (1952) is continuing this policy.[2]

The problem of providing for the growing population is thus being met, in part, by a slight fining down of the larger holdings and by bringing more land into cultivation.

The large farms are run in rather a special way. The proprietor is interested almost solely in the cotton, and grows it with the labour of his tied tenants, he providing the seed and 2 cwt. per acre nitrate of soda[3] as fertilizer. He may also grow wheat on the same terms giving that also the same fertilizer dressing. These crops are his. He then lets out the land to his tenants who apply farmyard manure and grow maize followed by berseem, both for themselves.

The chief crops are maize, wheat, berseem (Egyptian clover), and cotton, which together occupy about three-quarters of the crop acreage; berseem being of special importance as providing food for the animals (there being no grass) and maintaining soil condition. Rice and millet come next in acreage, then pulses, barley, vegetables, especially onions, and sugar cane with other less-important crops. The areas and quantities produced are given in Table LIV. Maize, wheat, and rice are grown mainly in the delta: maize and rice in summer, wheat in winter. Rice has the special advantage that it tolerates salt better than maize or wheat and hence can be grown on land that is beginning to suffer from salt accumulation. It gives heavier yields per acre than any other cereal. Millet and maize are not grown together; maize is confined to the north and millet to the south; the division comes about 50 or 100 miles south of Cairo. Sugar cane also is a southern crop grown chiefly south of Minya, much of it on the Komombo plain. Vegetables are grown everywhere, but onions largely in the basin lands of Upper Egypt

[1] 5·2 acres: 1 feddan = 1·04 acres.
[2] It is reported that about a million acres from the large estates are to be expropriated and made into smallholdings.
[3] In Upper Egypt this dressing may be doubled.

from Assiyut southwards: they are a valuable export crop, commonly said to be used for making whisky. They are also grown in the Delta, intersown with cotton, but only for local consumption.

TABLE LIV. *Areas and production of chief crops*

	Areas million acres			Yield, cwt. per acre			Production, million tons		
	Average			Average			Average		
	1934–38	1946	1950	1934–38	1946	1950	1934–38	1946	1950
Maize	1·60	1·72	1·51	19·9	16·4	17·1	1·62	1·42	1·31
Wheat	1·46	1·65	1·43	16·1	14·0	14·2	1·18	1·16	1·02
Rice	0·43	0·65	0·73	27·9	28·3	33·8	0·61	0·94	1·24
Millet	0·35	0·57	0·41	24·2		20·6	0·43		0·43
Barley	0·28	0·25	0·12	15·8	14·8	14·9	0·225	0·178	0·091
Beans	0·40	0·39	0·37	14·3		10·6	0·296		0·198
Lentils	0·08		0·08	13·6		12·0	0·056		0·051
Sugar cane (1)	0·062		0·084	32·7	{Cane		2·21		2·53
					{Raw sugar		0·146		0·195
Citrus fruits (3)	0·023	0·028	0·031	(4)			0·235	0·210	0·270
Cotton	1·84	1·29	2·03	8·2		6·8	0·771 (2)		0·701 (2)

(1) Area harvested.
(2) Cotton seed. (3) C.E.C. Rpts. Fruit 1952, (4) 1948
The total acreage of crops exceeds the area of cultivated land because some land carries two crops a year.
(*F.A.O. Stat. Year Book*, 1951.)

Cotton is the great cash crop; the conditions of the delta are eminently suited to the long-stapled varieties of high quality while medium stapled cotton is grown in Upper Egypt. Great improvements were brought about through devoted labours of Lawrence Balls, M. A. Bailey, T. Trought, and later British plant breeders, and a special organization, the "State Domains," has assured supplies of pure seed. The extent to which this great natural asset can be exploited is limited by the need to provide food, and the balance between cotton and food crops shifted considerably during the war. Maize in the north, and millet in the south, are the two crops competing with cotton, because, like cotton, they are grown in summer. Wheat, on the other hand, does not compete, being a winter crop. Before the war the area under cotton was 1·84 million acres, and under the five chief cereals 4·2 million acres. Then, in 1942, there came a great change: at the instance of the Middle East Supply Control the Government reduced the area under cotton by 1·1 million acres to allow more food production and the area under these cereals rose by the same amount to 5·30 million acres, 2·06 million being maize, 1·64 million wheat, and 0·69 million paddy. But this re-grouping lasted only one year; the area under cotton began steadily to increase and that under the cereal grains to diminish. Maize, naturally, suffered most: by 1946 its area had fallen by 0·35 million acres and paddy had lost 44,500 acres, but the areas under wheat and barley changed little. By 1951 the area under cotton had returned to its pre-war level, but the area under food crops, though somewhat higher than before, had not kept pace with the increasing population.

Thanks to adequate irrigation the yields of wheat, maize, and paddy were good before the war with a brilliant peak period for wheat from 1936 to

177

1939: unfortunately, they have since fallen. During the period 1942–46 maize fell from its pre-war level of 19·9 cwt. per acre to an average of 14·5 cwt., wheat from 16·1 cwt. per acre to 13·3 cwt.[1] and paddy from the pre-war 27·9 cwt. to 20·3 cwt.[2] The fall is attributable partly to the change in rotation, partly, also, to the fact that during the war no nitrate of soda could be imported; this is the fertilizer most commonly used. The peace-time system had been a two-year rotation:

	First winter cotton	Summer wheat	Second winter maize	Summer berseem
Nitrate of soda per acre	2 cwt.	2 cwt.	(Farmyard manure)	—

The 1942 order compelled the cultivator to drop out cotton and berseem from some of his land and to grow only wheat and maize, without fertilizer or berseem. Naturally, cultivators elected to sacrifice their poorest land, so that the extension of the wheat area was on to land below the average in quality. There has been some recovery since: paddy was, by 1946, nearly back to its pre-war level of yield, but maize and wheat were still well below.

It is also improbable that the irrigation has been as efficient since 1942 as it was before the war when a number of British experts were in charge, and there is real fear that loss of yields due to faulty irrigation may continue.

The result of these falling yields is that the total production of the two chief foods, maize and wheat, has decreased in spite of an increased acreage; there have been small, but not countervailing, increases in production of millet, but a larger increase in output of rice.

Livestock

The numbers of livestock are small: they have been, in millions:

Average, 1946–47	Cattle	Buffaloes	Sheep	Goats	Camels
	1·32	[1·2] (1)	1·87	1·47	0·20

(1) *F.A.O. Food Balance Sheets*, 1949.
F.A.O. Stat. Year Book, 1951. No later figures are available.

Buffaloes are the working animals, required to draw the ploughs and work the saggias that lift the water; they also supply milk. No wild grazing is available; the animals are fed on berseem with some farm residues; this crop, however, involves no strain on the land as it helps to maintain the supply of soil nitrogen and to restore the soil structure.

The output from the livestock is very low: F.A.O. estimated the average yield of milk per cow at 100 to 130 gallons and per buffalo at 220 gallons per annum, while that of ewes, which, till recently, provided much of Egypt's milk, is about 10 gallons.

[1] This had been about the average yield (25 bushels per acre) for the 40 years prior to 1927, but during the period 1936–39 the yields averaged 31·5 bushels, after which they fell to 27 bushels (P. de Hevesy, *World Wheat Planning*, p. 429). During the 40 years the acreage had varied between 1·20 and 1·25 million, during the latter part of the time the population was about 12 to 14 million; in 1946 the acreage was 1·64 million and the population 19·1 million.

[2] These are the yields of paddy. To convert them into edible rice one-third must be deducted; they then become 18·6 and 13·5 cwt. respectively.

The Food Balance Sheet

The staple foods are either maize, wheat, rice, or millet, in that order, beans, lentils, and vegetables. Meat is eaten only rarely by the mass of the people; many of the peasants are said to have it only about once a year on the occasion of some celebration, and then it may only be old camel so tough that it needs stewing for three or four days before it can be eaten. The average consumption of milk in all forms is less than two pints a week; this is among the lowest on record.

Before the war the production of maize, wheat, and millet was just about equal to the consumption, and there was an export of paddy, onions, some sugar and molasses and a good deal of cotton seed. Since the war the fall in production of maize and wheat and the great increase in population have necessitated considerable imports of wheat from Russia and maize from Yugoslavia,[1] even so the amounts available per head of population have fallen. The additional production of paddy, however, has allowed an increase both in export and in consumption per head. Paddy and onions are now the only direct foods exported; that of sugar and molasses has ceased.

The result of these various changes (Table LV) has been an apparent shift in the cereal dietary; consumption per head of rice and of wheat has increased, that of maize has fallen. So also has consumption per head of pulses and fats; on the other hand consumption of vegetables has increased. By 1949 the various gains had counterbalanced the losses, so the total calorie intake and the daily intake of protein were at about the pre-war level. The quantity of animal protein remains particularly low. The ratio of grams of protein to 100 calories which should be about four is below three.

These average figures conceal great inequalities. The poor in the towns live wretchedly, and the peasants suffer not only from low dietary but also through drinking canal water: bilharzia and ankylosostomatiasis are common and the expectancy of life is said to be about twenty-five years. But the Egyptian fellahin have an almost unlimited capacity for silent suffering, and, in any case, their intake of calories and of protein is better than that of the average Indian peasant. The deterioration of the dietary can probably go a good deal further before anything serious happens.

At first sight it seems wrong to devote so much land to the growth of cotton when there is such a shortage of food, but there is the economic justification that the quality of Egyptian cotton is very high, and an acre of it will buy far more wheat or maize than could be grown on the same land.[2] But it is also true that cotton is the chief source of wealth for those who own their land, and they are naturally anxious to keep the acreage as high as possible. The Government recognize that an adequate amount of wheat must be produced in the country and so they still require, as during the war, that each cultivator shall grow a certain minimum acreage. The small cultivators, however, prefer maize as food, and sell their wheat in order to buy it.

[1] Some confusion arises from the circumstance that in Egypt maize is called *dura shami* (Syrian dura), while millet is *dura aweiga*. The import of wheat in 1951 exceeded one million tons.

[2] C. H. Brown reports that in February 1952, Egypt bartered with Russia 500,000 kantars of cotton (1 k. = 100 lb. ginned cotton) for 200,000 tons of wheat. The cotton had been grown on 100,000 acres of land, but the wheat would have needed three or four times that area (*World Crops*, 1952, Vol. 4, p. 282).

The possibilities of increasing food production

The area under cultivation can still be increased: it was estimated in 1946 that some 1·7 million acres could still be reclaimed, but at the 1940–47 rate of progress, 12,000 acres per annum, this will take a long time. The desert region west of the Nile is underlain by a considerable mass of water derived from rain that fell on the hills of the Western Sudan many thousands of years ago.[1] Some of the saturated beds have become exposed by erosion, forming oases in which plants will grow. By systematic exploitation of this "fossil water," as it has been aptly called, about half a million acres could be got from the Siwa and other oases; it would, of course, be necessary to provide pumps and to control malaria. More land could be used on the coastal strip between Alexandria and Sollum; the average rainfall is only

TABLE LV. *F.A.O. food balance sheets*

	Production, million tons		Net export, thousand tons		Available for consumption, lb. per head per annum	
	1934–39	1948–49	1934–39	1948–49	1934–39	1948–49
Wheat	1·18	1·09	−7	−469	121	130
Maize	1·62	1·41	−2	−332	188	167
Millet	0·43	0·56	3		52	53
Rice (1)	0·615	1·31	144	617	37	55
Barley	0·23	0·17	7	−11	2	3
All cereals	4·08	4·52			400	408
Pulses	0·42	0·43	−38	−8	49	27
Sugar cane	2·20	2·50				
Sugar	0·43	0·41	90	Nil	31	35
Vegetables	0·80	1·67	113	127	84	152
Including onions	0·24	0·25	131	147		
Including potatoes	0·05	0·29	2	−23	6·8	14·3
Fats and oils	0·092	0·143	−8 (1)	−17 (1)	12	8
Milk and products					87	117 (2)
All meat	0·115	0·180			16	40
Calories per day					2450	2475
Fat per day, grams					42·0	39·0
Protein per day, grams						
Animal					9·3	11·0
Vegetable					64·2	60·9
Total					73·5	71·9
Population, millions					15·9	19·8

A minus sign (−) indicates import.

(1) Paddy, 100 parts gives 65 parts consumers' rice.

(2) Owing to a difference in mode of calculation the figures for the two different periods are not comparable.

[1] G. W. Murray. The water beneath the Egyptian western desert. *Geog. Journ.*, 1952, Vol. 118, pp. 443–52.

about 6 inches a year but in favourable seasons Mariut barley, olives, and vines can be grown in the moist hollows.

In the Nile valley provision for more irrigation is being made. A great dam is projected at Owen Falls, Uganda, to regulate the level of Lake Victoria and so control the river at its source. Other great dams have already been erected at Gebel Aulia on the White Nile above Khartoum, and at Aswan, in Upper Egypt, to hold back some of the flood water so as to even out the flow. Barrages have been erected farther down the river at Esna and Nag'Hammadi, while the old Asyut barrage has been remodelled; these will ensure water supply for basin irrigation when the flood is low, and they will enable some of the basin irrigation to be converted into perennial irrigation. In the delta the old barrage below Cairo has been replaced by a larger one about a quarter of a mile lower down the river. All these schemes offer the possibility of increasing output but as they all necessitate raising the level of the river they also involve the risk of flooding the lower-lying land[1] and of translocating salt. The Egyptian peasant is skilful in growing his crops but the modern canal systems require not only skilful, but absolutely honest administration.

The main task now is to raise the yields once more to the 1934–38 level. Above all things it is absolutely essential that the irrigation schemes should be administered with scrupulous honesty and worked with the maximum efficiency, otherwise serious trouble is likely to arise. The danger is that politics may be allowed to enter into what should be purely technical problems and no one can foresee the result. Already the very competent British irrigation experts and the scientist in charge of cotton breeding have been dismissed and replaced by Egyptians and there is no evidence that they can maintain the old levels of efficiency.

[1] W. Lawrence Balls has pointed out that this rising water table has negatived all recent improvements in cultural methods, pest control and new varieties in cotton cultivation. (*The Yield of a Crop*, 1953).

Chapter 6

AFRICA: I. SOUTHERN REGION: THE WHITE MAN'S FARMING

Africa is, of all the continents, the poorest in agricultural resources apart from the lower Nile region and parts of Mauretania. The soils are poor, large areas of those under forest have been drastically leached, and none of the grasslands have formed fertile black soils like those of the Russian black earths, the North American prairies, or the South American pampas. Few of its native plants are susceptible of improvement for human use, only in Ethiopia are a few species of food plants native: wheat, barley, millet, peas, and some others, but these were never developed by the inhabitants. Food for animals is equally sparse: the native grasses are nutritious for only a short period of their growth so that cattle cannot easily become either good workers or good milkers. Almost the whole continent is beset with insects of great variety, often carriers of disease: malaria and sleeping sickness in man; trypanosomiais, East Coast fever, rinderpest, and many others in animals. Horses never spread into most of the country: they could not have withstood the insects; cattle, however, developed some more or less resistant strains.

Over vast areas prolonged droughts are liable to set in, resulting in famine.

No great African civilization ever developed comparable with those of Asia and Europe; the ancient Egyptian and Mediterranean cultures came mainly from outside. There were no important African inventions; neither writing, the arts of town dwelling, or of establishing communications, except of the most rudimentary kind, not even the wheel or the plough, so that all porterage was done by human beings, largely on their heads, and all cultivation by the hoe. Agriculture was primitive and never progressed far.

The modern development of Africa has been rapid. Within living memory large areas were entirely unknown: there was much pestilential waste, many of its people were entirely uncivilized, many even were cannibals. "Darkest Africa" was no figure of speech but a grim reality. The change was brought about by Western European peoples; it has brought many benefits to the Africans. Unfortunately, in the early days there was an intensification of the ancient slave trade and, although this is long since dead, it has left bitter memories that will long persist. For many years now some of the best of the young people of Western Europe, notably the United Kingdom, France, and Belgium, have spent their best years in the difficult and often thankless task of raising the standards of life of the Africans. Working under very trying conditions they have improved the food crops, introduced more efficient methods of cultivation, made roads and transport facilities, introduced hygiene and medical science, and modern education; they are constantly seeking ways of making these measures more effective.[1] Africa has an enormous number of tribes and their response to the impact of European civiliza-

[1] The very difficult problem of education in particular has been much discussed. A good summary is given by A. L. Binns in *Advancement of Science*, 1952, No. 34, pp. 236–44.

tion has varied greatly, some being able to assimilate its spirit, others, as yet, only its form or not even that.

These developments have raised an extremely difficult set of technical problems. The old mode of life kept the population almost stationary, and the peasant system of agriculture could supply sufficient food for a low level of subsistence. But the improved health services, better dietaries and living conditions, and the cessation of tribal warfare have caused the population to multiply so that the old food production systems no longer suffice. The pressure on the land has been greatly intensified, while over considerable areas the productiveness of the soil is decreasing and soil erosion is increasing.

The problem now is to reverse these processes: to stop the erosion and to improve the soils; methods are known, but they are only inadequately applied. They require continuous skilled and resourceful direction such as only Western people are at present able to give, and this has introduced human problems for which, as yet, no general solution has been found. Only two small countries in the whole continent are under exclusively African control: Ethiopia, and the Republic of Liberia which owes its origin, and much of its present well-being, to modern American philanthropy. The rest of the continent is under the control of Arabs or European nations, the British section, however, working towards self-government.

Most of Africa lies 2,000 or more feet above sea level, and the very considerable area south of lat. 8° S. and the part north of this and east of long. 30° E. lie much higher, often 3,000 to 6,000 ft. elevation and even more around the equator and in Abyssinia. West and north of this high country are the great basins of the Congo and the Niger, and the Sahara, Nubian, and other deserts of North Africa, which are much lower; a small part of the northern Sahara is actually below sea-level. The high country is fringed by a coastal belt, widest in the south-east, in the Portuguese colony of Mozambique.

The rainfall of each region depends largely on its position in relation to the equator. A belt round the equator from about lat. 5° S. to lat. 5° N., including the Nigerian Coast, has, over great tracts, some 60 to 80 or more inches of rain annually in the west but less in the east; the rainfall decreases in going both north and south.[1] To the north it decreases so rapidly that above lat. 15° N. it is less than 5 inches a year so that this great stretch of country is practically all desert except for the Nile delta and a coastal belt of higher rainfall in the north-west. Southwards from the equator the rainfall peters out less suddenly; it is still about 40 inches a year at lat. 15° S. in the interior where Southern Rhodesia begins, and farther south a considerable north–south belt, in the eastern part of the Union, has more than 20 inches a year; some of the high districts much more. The western part of the region south of lat. 15° S. is, however, very dry in spite of its proximity to the Atlantic: the current drifting from the Antarctic northward along this coast, is so cold that the winds carry little moisture until near the equator.

Over most of the country the rainfall is seasonal. In the western part of the equatorial belt, on its north side, the wet season may last for ten months, with peaks in May or June and in September; farther inland it may last only five months, the peak coming in August or September. In the drier eastern part

[1] There are exceptions along the west coast up to about lat. 10° N. Sierra Leone has some 150 inches a year.

of the equatorial belt the December–April period is practically rainless, and the March to November wet period is usually broken by a dry spell from May to October, forming two pronounced wet seasons, the "long" one from March to May or June, and the "short" one from mid-October to mid-December, separated by well-marked dry seasons. In the neighbourhood of the great lakes, however, rain may come during the May–October period, making a long wet season, as in the west, but with a peak from March to May.

South of the equator the wet and dry seasons are the reverse of those in the north: practically all the country, except the extreme south, also has its rainfall in summer, i.e., between September and April, especially December to February; the winter period April to September is dry. In the extreme south, however, the rainfall comes in winter and the summer is dry.

Much of the rain is torrential, coming in thunderstorms, and is of little agricultural value except where it can be impounded: the storms often do damage. The rainfall is always uncertain and erratic.

The equatorial region is often regarded as the hottest, but it is not; the high rainfall in the west and the high altitude in the east keep down the temperatures. In the west the temperature ranges from about 60° F to 100° F with an average of 80° F (87° F by day and 73° F by night), temperatures in themselves fairly tolerable, but the high humidity, averaging 80 per cent, makes the climate very enervating. In the drier east the average temperature in the low-lying coastal regions is also about 80° F and a daily range of about 12° to 15°; in the highlands the average temperature falls as the elevation increases but the daily range increases; at about 9,000 ft. the average is about 56° F. but the daily range is 25° to 30° F: Tothill instances a range of 57° from 32·9° to 89·8° F in one day at Narok, in Kenya. The humidity is low and hence Europeans can live in comfort on the highlands of the eastern equatorial region. At 5,000 ft. or more elevation they frequently need fires at night in their houses.

Northwards from the equator the temperatures are higher because of the lower rainfall; they reach a maximum in the desert regions where the bare sand, being devoid of vegetation cover to shield it from the sun's rays, becomes very hot: 136° F. in the shade has been recorded at Azizia, in Tripoli. Still farther north the coastal region has a Mediterranean climate, with pleasant warm winters, dry, except in the north-west, but subject to hot, trying winds in summer.

The native vegetation and, therefore, the agricultural possibilities, are governed primarily by the rainfall, the temperature, and particularly the length of the dry season.

The western equatorial region of high rainfall and no long dry season is in tropical forest;[1] it is utilized for tree crops, cocoa, and palm nut; the necessary food crops are grown on clearings, but the land readily reverts to forest if left untilled. Contrary to common belief these tropical forest soils are not naturally fertile, they have been well leached and they are very liable to water erosion if left without vegetation cover.

Under lower rainfall, about 30 inches to 20 inches, the forest thins out and

---

[1] The vegetation and ecology of the tropical rain forest is described by F. W. Richards, *The Tropical Rain Forest*, 1951.

tall, vigorous coarse grasses cover more and more of the ground as the rainfall decreases and the dry season lengthens; the scattered trees are mainly flat-topped acacias with crooked stems and branches, and thorns that seem to increase with the dryness. This is the savannah type of country; it can be used either for crop production or grazing.

Under still lower rainfall, 20 inches down to 15 or 10 annually, the large trees disappear and are replaced by small ones, shrubs, bushes, and particularly by low-growing grasses. This is the grass country; it can be used for grazing cattle or sheep so long as water is available either from a storage dam, a borehole, or some natural source. Ticks and other insects carrying pathogenic organisms are common and cause much loss. The carrying capacity is generally low and 15 to 30 acres or more may be required per head of cattle.

Soluble salts (often sodium sulphate or chloride) are liable to occur in the soils making the water saline; animals, however, are more tolerant of this than crops. Arable cropping is very risky because of the liability to drought and the great likelihood of wind erosion.

In still drier conditions the liability to salt increases and a special flora develops tolerant of salt and drought; this is the salt-bush country. Some grazing is still possible, but it is mainly restricted to sheep, goats, and camels, and the carrying capacity is very low. There is much land of this kind in North Kenya and Somaliland.

Finally, in the very arid north are the deserts of the Sahara and of Egypt, almost devoid of vegetation except in the oases. The south is less arid and its deserts, the Kalahari and the Karroo, have a characteristic vegetation of their own.

Under irrigation both the grass and the salt-bush country can yield abundant crops. Unfortunately Africa's rivers with the exception of the Nile do not lend themselves to great irrigation schemes, and there are few large riverain plains where tube-well irrigation could be adopted; a few inland deltas, e.g. the middle Niger below Sansanding and the Okavango in Bechuanaland offer possibilities, and there are many areas of marsh that could be drained though at some risk. The three European nations responsible for most of Africa have done much to improve the productiveness of their respective territories and have set up large projects for doing more.

The high country is largely in the British Commonwealth, except Ethiopia in the north-east and the Portuguese Angola in the south-west; most of the lower country north of the Belgian Congo and west of Egypt is in French hands. Certain coastal regions in the north-west: Nigeria, the Gold Coast, and others, are British, and the Sudan has hitherto been a condominion jointly with Egypt and Great Britain but is now acquiring self-government. The areas associated with or administered by the various European powers are:

	Million square miles
France	4·20
Great Britain	3·98
Belgium	0·93
Portugal	0·79
Spain	0·14
Total area	11·46

For agricultural purposes Africa may be divided into four regions:

I. *European Settlement.*—Southern Africa. South of lat. 15° S. with out-posts in the Kenya highlands. Large blocks, however, are reserved exclusively for Africans: the chief are Bechuanaland, Basutoland, and Swaziland under British administration, and Transkei and numerous smaller areas under the South African Government. The European part includes the Union of South Africa, the Rhodesias, and the Portuguese territories Mozambique and Angola; in all this region the Western mode of life prevails although most of the population are Africans.

II. *African Region.*—From about lat. 15° S. to lat. 15° N. The Central part includes the Belgian Congo; the western part of the north is chiefly French, except for the British colonies on the coast; and the eastern part of the north is chiefly the Sudan and Abyssinia.

III. *The Arab desert region* north of lat. 15° N.

IV. *The Arab coastal region* of the north: the Nile delta, Libya, Morocco, Algeria.

THE UNION OF SOUTH AFRICA

(i) *The Regions of European Settlement*

The Union of South Africa is of crucial importance for the study of world food production because it presents within its borders all the difficult problems: the growing population, the low and in some areas declining productiveness of much of the soil, the gradual change from production of surpluses of food for export to a need for imports, and the hampering com-plications resulting from preoccupation with political affairs which tend rather to relegate unspectacular but difficult technical problems to the background.

The Union consists of a great block of high lying land, most of it over 3,000 ft. in elevation, separated from the high land to the north by the Limpopo and Molopo valleys, and fringed on the east, south, and west by a narrow, low-lying coastal strip. It is highest in the east where much of it is about 5,000 ft. altitude; its eastern scarp falls sometimes steeply, sometimes through tumbled foothill country to the low coastal strip; the highest part of the scarp forms the Drakensberg Mountains some 7,000 to 10,000 or more feet high. This High Veld extends westwards almost as far as the railway line from Pretoria to Bloemfontein—long. 28° E. and beyond. Then there is a quick drop to about 4,000 ft. to the Middle Veld, which stretches west-wards to a north–south line about long. 23° E. where there is another drop to about 3,000 ft.; the land continues at about this level to within some forty miles of the Atlantic coast. At its southern end comes the Great Karroo, with its characteristic flat topped hills or kopjes; it stretches southwards and south-westwards for 200 or 300 miles, decreasing in altitude from 4,000 ft. finally to 2,000 ft. It terminates in a smaller plateau, the Little Karroo, of altitude as low in places as 1,000 ft. (Plate 21, p. 181.)

Between the main block of land and the sea in the southern region are some small mountain ranges, the valleys of which have great agricultural importance.

North of the High Veld and at a lower level is the Bush Veld, an extension of the Middle Veld plateau but different in character; on its north-eastern side in a strip running north and south is the unhealthy Low Veld, of only about 1,500 ft. altitude; still farther eastward is the lower coastal plain of Mozambique.

In consequence of this plateau structure the annual mean temperatures vary but little from 60° to 65° F in the different parts of the country except in the highlands of the great escarpment where they are lower. There is, however, greater variation in the temperature ranges; the monthly maxima vary from 80° to 90° F and the minima from about 45° to 55°. The rainfall is highest in the east. On the coast and in the mountains it is 40 inches or more; it is less and less towards the west; on the High Veld it is about 25–35 inches, decreasing to about 20 inches at a line running roughly southwards from Mafeking, finally at the western coast it is 5 or 10 inches. About three-quarters of the country has less than 25 inches a year.

The rainfall is seasonal. Over most of the country some 80 per cent of it falls during the summer months, October to March, and as almost invariably happens when the total fall is low, much of it comes in torrential thunderstorms which do little good and may do much harm. In a narrow strip parallel to the coast west of Cape Town, however, the rain falls in the six winter months, and in a strip along the south coast it comes both in summer and winter, and is non-seasonal.

Evaporation is high and this often reduces the value of the rainfall.[1]

The rivers mostly run away from the agricultural regions rather than through them. Several tributaries of the Limpopo break out from the northern scarp and flow through the Bush and Low Velds; various rivers rise on the eastern scarp and run the short distance through Natal to the sea, but the only important system crossing the Union is that including the Orange River, the Vaal, the Modder, the Caledon, and others, which rising in the high eastern country flow westwards through the arid regions where much of their water is lost. This western arid region contains a number of dry rivers, the beds of which are now filled with sand; sufficient moisture may accumulate below the surface, however, to allow the growth of drought-resistant grasses or even Kaffir corn unless too much salt is present.

The line of 20-inch rainfall—long. 25° E.—is of crucial importance for South Africa. The drier western part is the pastoral sparsely settled Cape Province; the wetter eastern part includes the more fully cultivated and more closely settled Provinces of Natal and most of the Transvaal and the Orange Free State. The areas and populations were at the time of the 1951 Census:

	Cape Province	Population, millions Transvaal	Orange F.S.	Natal	Total
European	0·936	1·205	0·228	0·274	2·643
Non-European	3·481	3·597	0·790	2·134	10·003
	4·417	4·802	1·018	2·408	12·646
Area, million acres	177·3	70·66	31·78	22·58	302·4
Acres per head of population	40	15	31	9	24

Of the total non-European population in 1946, 7·8 million were Bantu, 0·928 million coloured, and 0·285 million Asiatic.

[1] A comprehensive account of the climate is given in the *Official Year Book of the Union of South Africa*, 1940.

In the drier western part, the soils are usually underlain near the surface by rock or by the calcareous layer often occurring in dry regions; the natural vegetation is shallow rooted and treeless; short grass in the east but with more and more desert shrub in going west. The Karroo in the south possesses a highly interesting xerophyllous flora: salt bush, cactus of many sorts, mesembryanthemums, arum lilies, aloes, and many other flowering plants. The rainfall is low, but heavy mists and dews may occur in the lower southern section.

Apart from the southern coastal regions this western part of the Union is largely pastoral; its crop production is at a low level except under irrigation, and this is practicable only along a few sections of the Orange River.

The southern area of winter rainfall stands out in sharp contrast with the region to the north. The actual amount of rain is no greater, but coming in the winter it is less subject to loss by evaporation. It comes at a period very suitable for wheat, fruit, and vines, and as the temperature conditions are also suitable the greatest part of their production is concentrated here.

Eastwards of the 20-inch rainfall line there is much greater range of soils, natural vegetation, and crop production than to the west. The soils are lateritic on the Low Veld in the north, podsolic on the High Veld to the south, and solonetzic and alkaline on an area running southwards from Bloemfontein on the Middle Veld and separating the eastern from the western regions.

The natural vegetation reflects the topographic and rainfall conditions; the Middle Veld about the 20-inch rainfall line has a mixed grass flora; the High Veld to the east with higher rainfall has short but dense grass, the still wetter scarp and foothill regions have tall grass, while the Low Veld to the north has bush and grass, and the east-coastal regions of highest rainfall have bush and subtropical forest.

The agricultural use of the land accords closely with these ecological conditions.

The Middle Veld

The Middle Veld is largely untended pasture, but the eastern part receiving an uncertain 20 to 25 inches of rain has in recent years been increasingly brought into cultivation, especially the sandy soils of the north-west Orange Free State. Neither grazing nor cropping conditions are, however, particularly good and sheep have suffered by the change. Land on which they had been kept with advantage is now ploughed up; the cattle land is less suited to them. The soils are so deficient in phosphate that grazing animals are liable to suffer from phosphate starvation and to develop a morbid craving to devour bones, which may cause serious disease from putrefying material adhering thereto. This can be counteracted by feeding bonemeal, which, however, is not sufficiently done. Gallamsiekte, stywesiekte, anthrax, and other diseases are widespread; methods of control are known but not always practised. Soil erosion is very liable to occur; appropriate preventive measures have been worked out but not fully applied. In absence of surface water boreholes have been made to supply both animals and men; the Geological Survey advises as to the best locations, but the numbers of bores are increasing and it is not known how long the underground water will last.

The farmer's greatest difficulty is the liability to drought; the resulting food shortage may lead to heavy losses of animals.

Crop production is hampered by the poverty of the soils and the erratic rainfall; 8 inches may fall in a week destroying many of the plants, then may come six weeks drought killing some of the survivors, then another torrent doing still more damage.

As usual in dry regions the cropping is almost entirely confined to cereals. Millets and sorghums are best suited to the conditions, but maize is so much more valuable that it is grown in preference. On most of the farms no rotation is adopted; some 80 per cent of the maize is grown continuously till the land is worn out, when it is left to run wild and fresh veld is ploughed up. Little fertilizer is used, and not much kraal manure; there is little green manuring or periodic rest in grass. Yields are low and tend to fall, though in some areas they are rising. The system leads naturally to soil deterioration and erosion, yet it may last surprisingly long; cases are known where maize has been grown continuously on the same land without apparent harm for 40 or 50 years, but of course at low levels of yield.

The High Veld

The High Veld, a region of prairie soils and a rainfall of 25 inches or more, includes some of the most productive farmland in the Union; it has a larger variety of crops, better management, and better yields than elsewhere. The Bethal district in the north-east is perhaps the most notable: it is one of the most important potato-growing districts in the Union besides producing much maize. Further south, where the temperatures are lower, wheat becomes more important; the summer rainfall impedes ripening but favours growth of green leaf which provides grazing for lambing ewes; the subsequent grain yields are low but the crop is still profitable.

TABLE LVI. *Changes in land utilization in passing southwards down the High Veld* [1]

	Transvaal High Veld B1(1)	Northern Free State B2	Central diversified B6	Caledon River B3
Annual rainfall, inches	26·3	25	25	26
Percentage of farmland cultivated	31·5	24	36	42·6
Percentage under maize	73	84	61	35·5
Percentage under wheat	—	0·4	20·7	50·5
Yields: Maize, cwt. per acre	9·0	4·5	5·6	6·2
Wheat, cwt. per acre	—	—	3·7	4·2
Percentage of farm income (all farms):				
Crops	73·4	43	59·4	68
Livestock	26·6	57	40·6	32
Stock units (2) per 100 acres	16·5	14	16	15
Average size of farms, acres	1,360	1,650	1,800	1,530

(1) Survey marks, each denoting a region within which physical and economic conditions are similar.

(2) One stock unit equals one head of cattle or seven sheep or goats.

[1] Compiled from data in the Agro-Economic Survey of the Union published in 1948.

The changes in going from north to south in the High Veld are illustrated by Table LVI; this shows the increasing importance of wheat in going southwards and the diminishing importance of stock as contributors to the farm income.

This table, like the later one, shows the superiority of the Transvaal High Veld both for crop production and for grazing, yet neither in yield per acre of maize nor in carrying capacity of the Veld is it in any way remarkable.

The Northern and Eastern Regions

The Bush Veld north of Pretoria and east of the line of long. 26° E. is about 3,000 ft. in altitude and as already stated is well watered with tributaries of the Limpopo rising in the High Veld; irrigation is practicable in its valleys though only in small-scale enterprises. The largest is the Haartebeest Dam, erected where the Crocodile River breaks out from the escarpment heights near Krugersdorp in its northward course to the Limpopo; this waters several thousand acres as far as Brits. The undulating treeless plateau affords poor grazing, unsuitable for sheep and made risky for cattle by the occurrence of poisonous weeds. The Springbok Flats are now being developed for crop production; much tobacco is grown here.

The Low Veld to the east has never been much inhabited. It is a land of scrubby bush, often about 15 ft. high with thin, crooked stems; there are no timber trees; it was formerly fever ridden and insect infested; a land of mystery much exploited by 19th century writers of romance. It is not yet healthy, but is still subject to malaria, black water, horse sickness, and other diseases of men and animals. Soil and grazing are alike poor; about 15 beasts can be carried per 100 acres. About half of it is occupied by the Kruger National Park.

The valleys running down into the Low Veld from the north-east scarp have, however, been made very productive by irrigation from some of the streams, especially the Crocodile (different from the one already mentioned) and the White Rivers; citrus, pawpaws, and other tropical fruits of good quality are produced.

The eastern scarp of the High Veld is formed by the Drakensberg Mountains, the slopes of which are used chiefly for grazing though there is a small proportion of arable land producing maize, oats, and fodder crops. The soils, however, are poor and little is done to improve them; yields therefore are very low; maize gives only about 4 cwt. per acre and the winter grazing is poor. But the conditions are very healthy and Merino sheep provide the major part of the farm income; they are much more important than cattle. East of this strip comes the Natal foothill country of podsolic soils, also mostly grazing; sheep, however, do not do so well as on the mountain grazings and cattle are more important here. Part of this foothill country is in wattle, grown only in Natal.

The coastal strip was originally tropical forest; but it now produces tropical fruits and other products, including, on one section, sugar cane. The changes in passing eastwards from the arable eastern Middle Veld to the more productive High Veld, then to the Drakensberg grazing lands and on to the foothills, are illustrated by Table LVII, compiled from the same source as Table LVI.

TABLE LVII. *Changes in land utilization in passing eastwards from the Middle Veld to the Natal Foothills*

	Middle Veld Western Transvaal B4 Long. 25–27° E.	High Veld B1 29–30° E.	Drakensburg grazings D1 around 30° E.	Foothills E1 around 31° E.
Annual rainfall, inches	22·4	26·3	30·0	31·2
Percentage of farmland cultivated	27·6	31·5	12·5	10·7
Percentage of cultivated land under:				
Maize	86·4	73·0	51·6	46·7
Kaffir corn	6·8	—	—	0·4
Fodder crops	6	21	38·4	8
Yield of maize, cwt. per acre	6·2	9·0	4·0	4·9

Percentage of farm income:				
Crops	76·0	{92·3 potato farms / 58·8 maize farms}	7·2	
Livestock	24·0	{7·7 potato farms / 41·2 maize farms}	92·8	87·0

Stock units per 100 acres	11	16·5	15	14·5
Average size of farm, acres	1,650	1,360	2,500	2,000

In the Foothills region (E1) 38 per cent of the cultivated land is under wattle.

Winter Rainfall Region

The winter rainfall region consists of two blocks of land, one of about 32 million acres north of Cape Town and one east of it of about 10 million acres; this latter may have rain in any month. The rainfall is only about 17 or 18 inches annually, but 10 to 15 inches of it falls in the winter months April to September, and it was early recognized that these conditions are much more favourable to wheat than to maize. Unlike most parts of the

TABLE LVIII. *Land utilization in winter rainfall districts, S.W. Cape Province, percentage of total area*

	Swartland K1	Rûens K3	Lower Langeburg K4	Western Strandeveld K2
Percentage of farmland				
cultivated	32·6	34·7	24·1	16·9
Old and fallow ..	41·0	30·1	24·5	20·8
Abandoned	3·4	3·5	4·5	4·7
Pasture	23·0	31·7	46·9	57·6
Of 100 acres cultivated land				
Wheat	30·6	33·9	26·3	22·9
Other cereals	12·6	18·5	21·1	20·9
Old and fallow	55·6	46·4	50·4	55·1
Yield of wheat, cwt. per acre	7·2	6·5	6·5	4·6
Rainfall, inches	18·4	17·3	18·7	12·7

Union a crop rotation is common here—wheat, oats or barley, fallow—like the old system of medieval northern Europe except that about half the land here is in fallow. There is also a certain amount of worn-out and abandoned land. Lupines and lucerne are now, however, being included in some of the rotations.

Some 70 to 85 per cent of the farm income is derived from crops, wheat being by far the most important; livestock contributes the rest, sheep (Merinos) being on the whole more important than cattle. Wheat yields are low; the best average is about 7 cwt. per acre in the Swartland district where out of 18·5 inches of annual rainfall 14·5 comes in winter when it is most needed; elsewhere yields fall as low as 4½ cwt. per acre where the summer rainfall is higher. Table LVIII shows how the land is used.

Total Acreage and Production of Crops in the Union

The total area of the Union is 302 million acres utilized as follows:

	Million acres
European farms	213
Native reserves	32
Other uses and waste	57
	—
Total	302

The 32 million acres set aside as native reserves are practically all located on the tall grass savannah land of the eastern side; in the Transkei, in Natal, and the Northern Transvaal; they are all in the belt of 20 inches or more rainfall a year; indeed they are officially stated to be all included in the Union's 100 million acres of productive land.[1] In addition, a certain amount of the farm land, usually in the Transvaal and Free State, about 2 per cent, is set aside for the use of the permanent native workers as part of their wages. These areas and the crops raised thereon are excluded from the data presented here except where otherwise stated.

Apart from the growing of fruit in the Cape Province and of sugar cane in Natal the agriculture of the Union is almost everywhere entirely extensive in type. Less than 18 million out of the 213 million acres of European farm-land are cultivated, and of these less than 13½ million are cropped; 4½ million are fallow and 1 million are in plantations, chiefly wattle in Natal and other trees in the Transvaal. The Orange Free State has the highest percentage of its land in farms and of farmland cultivated, but this latter figure is only 20 per cent; for the Cape it is 3·8, for the Transvaal and Natal 14 and 12 respectively. The proportions actually cropped are even less; they are given in Table LIX.

Over the drier western part of the Union 96 per cent of the land remains as untended veld, as does 80 per cent even in the most highly cropped province, the Free State. Of the small proportions of farm arable land 35 per cent is fallow in the Cape Province, 30 per cent in Natal, and 24 per cent in the Free State and the Transvaal.

As usual in extensive conditions the farms are large. Two-thirds of the

[1] Malcolm Lomberg, *Jour. Roy. Soc. Arts*, 1951, Vol. 99, pp. 813–27.

17 (left) Farm and forest work combined, Finland. (Courtesy of Finnish Legation) [p. 124]

18 (right) Terracing in the Mediterranean region, Vineyard at Pinhão, Douro Valley, Portugal. (Photo: Alvao, Porto) [p. 148]

19 (left) Reclaimed Pontine Marshes, Torre Campanaria. (Photo: ENIT) [p. 156]

20 (right) Planned Settlement in Israel —Nahalal. (Photo: Govt. Press Division, Israel) [p. 162]

21 (left) Wild Veld, S. Africa: 10 to 15 inches rainfall. (Photo: I. B. Pole Evans) [p. 186]

22 (right) A good grass for binding soil and withstanding drought: *Pennisetum clandestinum* (Kikuyu grass). (Photo: I. B. Pole Evans) [p. 207]

23 (left) Virgin bush, near Njoro, Kenya. (Photo: Lady Russell) [p. 259]

24 (right) The same cleared and seeded down, trees left for shelter and protection against erosion: a good European farm. (Photo: Lady Russell) [p. 259]

TABLE LIX. *Land utilization in the four provinces, 1946 Census.*
Million acres

	Total area	European farms	Area culti-vated	Sown to agric. crops	Fruit	Fallow	Percentage of farm land under crops (1)	No. of farms, thousands
Cape	177·3	131·1	4·89	2·93	0·249	1·61	2·4	41·3
Transvaal	70·6	41·1	5·68	3·95	0·063	1·27	9·6	36·8
Orange Free State	31·8	29·8	5·97	4·45	0·016	1·42	15·3	24·8
Natal	22·6	10·8	1·31	0·56	0·023	0·24	5·4	11·1
Total	302·3	212·8	17·86	11·89	0·351	4·54	5·4	114·0
1937			14·87	11·68	0·315	2·00		

(1) Including fruit but excluding plantation.
(*South African Year Book*, 1949, p. 867). In South African statistics the figures
are given as morgen. 1 morgen = 2·12 acres.

farmland in Cape Province is in holdings of 4,000 acres or more; in the
Transvaal and the Orange Free State about 1,500 acres is a usual size; there are
smaller farms, but they are considered uneconomical. In Natal the general
average is about 1,000 acres.

Also as usual in extensive conditions the crops are almost entirely cereals;
these occupy no less than 11 million out of the total 12·9 million acres.
The others are chiefly fodder crops, teff grass, lucerne (often on irrigated
land), oats or barley grown as green feed, and smaller areas of potatoes,
oil seeds, and pulses. With this heavy preponderance of cereals, rotations
are impracticable, and in particular the arable land has no period of recupera-
tion under leguminous crops.

The Crops

The areas of the chief crops grown on the European farms in the Union
are given in Table LX.

TABLE LX. *Area of chief crops, Union of South Africa European farms, 1947–48*

Cereals, million acres		Other crops, thousand acres	
Maize	7·30	Lucerne (321), teff (291), and	
Wheat	2·24	other grasses	679
Oats (0·80), Kaffir corn (0·45),		Groundnuts (327) and sun-	
and others	1·55	flowers (251)	578
	———	Potatoes	158
	11·09	Cowpeas and beans	268
Non-cereals	1·85	Tobacco	58
	———	Others	108
Total crops	12·94 (1)		———
Percentage of cereals	86		1,849

(*Report on Agric. and Pastoral Production*, 1947–48.)
(1) Excluding fruit and plantations.

Maize is grown in most parts of the Union except the winter rainfall
region of the south-west, but chiefly in the Free State and the Transvaal,
especially the area extending from Ermolo in the east to Lichtenburg in the
west and southwards to the Vaal River.

	Million acres
Orange Free State	3·600
Transvaal	2·920
Cape	0·445
Natal	0·329
Total	7·30

The total area rose to 8·0 million acres in 1950.

Yields are highest in the Transvaal High Veld; about 9 cwt. per acre in the good region; outside this and in the Free State they are 4½ to 6 cwt. per acre; the average annual yields for the Union have been, in cwt. per acre.

1927–37	1934–38	1941–44	1947–48	1950
4·7	5·4	5·1	6·0	6·2

(*F.A.O Stat. Year Book* 1951.) C.E.C. Reports, *Grain Crops*, 1953, give the value 7·3 for 1950.

These figures are very low; in the United States about 16 cwt. per acre is usual in spite of the fact that the growing season there is some 4 to 7 weeks shorter than in the Union. The yields, however, are increasing and also the output: the average annual production on European farms in the three-year periods before and after the war have been:

1937–39	1946–48	1949–51
1·77	2·10	2·51 million tons

(C.E.C. Repts., *Grain Crops*, 1953 (long tons).)

In addition, some 380,000 tons of maize were produced annually by Africans on the Reserves or on European farms.

The quantity of maize produced is more than is needed for human consumption, seed supply, etc., but the method of disposing of the surplus has changed. Before the war about 75 per cent of it was exported and 25 per cent fed to stock; in 1947 only 12·5 per cent was exported and 87·5 per cent was fed to stock. The amount available as human food rose by 232,000 tons, but as the population has risen from 9·6 millions to 11·6 millions the quantity available per head fell from 252 lb. to 242 lb.:

	Thousand metric tons Average 1935–39	1947	1948
Net export	508	93	370
Animal feed	183	635	636
Seed, manufacture waste	207	225	195
Human food	1,098	1,275	1,304
Total	1,996	2,228	2,505 (1)
Population, millions	9·6	11·6	11·9
lb. per head of population	252	242	235

(*F.A.O. Food Balance Sheets.*)

Wheat is much more localized in the Union than maize. It is sown in autumn and depends for growth on rainfall during winter; it is chiefly confined to the winter rainfall region of Cape Province and the Orange Free State where, although most of its rain comes in summer, some 15 to 20 per cent of it falls in autumn and winter; here also, as already explained, the young crop may be grazed in spring which commonly reduces the yield considerably. The small area grown in the Transvaal is mostly irrigated, it suffers from bird damage, however, and the yields are low. Tables LVI and LVIII show that the yields of grain average about 6 or 7 cwt. per acre in the Cape Province and about 4 cwt. in the Free State; the production in the different Provinces was, in 1947–48:

		1947–48	
	Thousand acres	*Thousand tons*	*Yield, cwt./acre*
Cape Province	1,174	274·4	4·7
Transvaal	129	36·0	5·6
Orange Free State	935	170·2	3·6
Total	2,238	480·7	4·2

(*Rept. on Agric. and Pastoral Prod.*, 1947–48.)

Before the war (1934–38) the acreage of wheat had been 1·90 millions and the production 448,000 tons; under the stimulus of tariffs the acreage rose in 1942 to 2·74 millions and the production to 566,000 tons, but since 1943 the acreage has fallen. The total output varies considerably from year to year, mainly because the variability of the rainfall in the Free State has caused its production to range from 25,000 to 200,000 tons.

The annual averages have been:

	2 years 1937–38	4 years 1946–49	1950	1951	
Area	1·85	2·41	3·1 (1)		thousand acres
Production	366	447	698	687	thousand tons
Yield	4·0	3·7	4·7		cwt. per acre

(C.E.C. Repts. *Grain Crops*, 1943.)

(1) F.A.O. estimate.

Oats are grown for livestock and mainly in the winter rainfall area of the Cape, but some are in the Free State.

Kaffir corn, *Sorghum vulgare*, was formerly eaten by the Africans, but is now grown chiefly for making native beer. The 450,000 acres of Table LX are on the European farms mainly in the drier western parts of the Transvaal; the production was about 118,000 tons; the Africans, however, grow a further 155,000 tons. The crop suffers from bird damage and aphis attack, but much more of the dwarf hybrid sorghums could probably be grown for stock feed.

These various cereals make up 86 per cent of the crops. The only other important food crop is potatoes, of which there were, in 1948, 158,000 acres, about half in the Transvaal, and the remainder nearly equally divided between the Cape Province and the Free State:

1947–48	Thousand acres	Thousand tons	Yield per acre, tons
Cape Province	39·0	46·6	1·2
Transvaal	71·5	137·6	1·9
Orange Free State	36·7	43·9	1·2
Natal	11·2	20·4	1·8
Total	158·3	248·6	1·6

(*Rpt. on Agric. and Pastoral Production, 1947–48.*)

The yields are extraordinarily low, averaging only 1·9 tons per acre even in the Transvaal which includes the productive Bethal region; they are worst in the Cape Province and the Free State. An important reason is the poor quality of the seed potatoes; efforts are now being made to build up cleaner and better stocks. The production has, however, been increasing; it has averaged:

	Thousand tons		
1922–25	1936–39	1945–48	1950
108	174	281	290

(*F.A.O. Stat. Year Books.*)

The output of groundnuts has greatly increased. The acreage rose from the pre-war 60,000 to 450,000 by 1948–9 and production from about 14,000 to 80,000 tons. Yields, however, did not increase: they varied about 4 cwt. per acre. Groundnuts are chiefly grown on the sandy soils of the western and northern Transvaal and north-western Free State, almost entirely on European farms using mechanized methods. About a quarter of a million acres of sunflower seed are grown in the Transvaal and the Free State; its yield also is very low, only about 3 cwt. per acre. Cowpeas and various beans, grown chiefly in the Transvaal, yield about 5 cwt. per acre or less.

Fruit

Among the early settlers in what is now Cape Province were Huguenot refugees who bought with them the culture of the vine and the arts of making wine and brandy. Some of the southern valley proved very suitable for the purpose and the industry has developed considerably, producing agreeable table wines that have become very popular. Production is still, however, confined almost entirely to the Cape Province. Other Mediterranean fruits also grow well in these valleys, especially pears, apples, peaches, apricots, plums, and also citrus fruits, and more recently pineapples. The other provinces of the Union have not proved so suitable for fruit excepting in a few districts, the most important being some of the irrigated river valleys of the eastern Transvaal, where citrus fruits are more widely grown than in any part of the Union. Natal produces the more tropical fruits: bananas, pawpaws, mangoes, and others.

No recent estimate of areas has been made; the figures given in the 1951 *Year Book for South Africa* relate to 1945–46. They are:

	Thousand acres				
	Cape Province	Transvaal	Orange Free State	Natal	Total
All fruits	251	64	16	23	354
Including citrus	20·4	25·6	0·07	4·7	50·8
Grapes	127·8	0·67	0·11	0·01	128·6

Much of the fruit has long been grown for export, but war-time shipping difficulties compelled a development of the home market; thanks to the rising standard of living this was satisfactorily accomplished. Improved cold-storage facilities have made it possible to retain apples in the Union instead of shipping them directly they were ready. Production has, however, increased so well that exports have not only been maintained but have actually increased. Grapes come first both in area and quantity. The production is almost entirely for wine and spirits, only about 7 per cent are sold as fresh fruit; of these about half are exported. Citrus are the chief fruits sold as such; some 90 per cent are oranges and about half the total production is exported. The total production of deciduous fruits (omitting grapes) is about half that of the citrus, but not more than 10 to 15 per cent has been exported up to the present. This may be increased; a canning industry is being developed for which special varieties of peaches are grown, and there is an export of jams and marmalade made with sugar produced in Natal.

The quantities produced and exported are given in Table LXI.

TABLE LXI. *Production and export of fruit, South Africa. Thousand tons*

	Citrus		Deciduous		Grapes (wine and table)			
					Production		Export	Wine
	Production	Export	Production	Export	Total	Table	(table)	produced
1938	232	93	76	20	280	22	10·0	33
1948	233	120	109	19	420	29	16·5	57
1951	210	142	76	21	460	26	16·7	62

(C.E.C. Rpts., *Fruit*, 1952.)

The fruit production is very well done; there has already been considerable expansion and more is possible, particularly of the output of citrus and pineapple.

Sugar Cane

Sugar cane is confined to a coastal strip in Natal only a few miles wide, extending from Mtubatuba in Zululand to Port Shepstone about 200 miles to the south; the rainfall is about 40 inches a year. The cane yields two harvests at intervals of about 18 months (a little longer in the south and a little less in the north); at the end of the three years it is cleared out. Sunn hemp (*Crotolaria juncea*) is then grown and ploughed in as green manure, and cane is again planted. The land is left bare for as short a time as possible so as to reduce the risk of erosion. The area planted is about 450,000 acres, but only part is harvested each year; in 1947–48, 185,700 acres yielded 4 million tons of cane, about 22 tons per acre harvested; this gave 2½ tons of sugar per acre and a total sugar output of 457,000 tons,[1] the factories recovered 83·65 per cent of the sucrose in 1950–51; the molasses are converted into alcohols. The output of sugar has increased; before the war it was 444,000 tons, in the good seasons of 1944–45 and 1948–49 it rose to nearly 450,000 tons[2] and in 1950 to 612,000 tons. About two-thirds of the production is by farmers and only about one-third by companies.

[1] *S. Africa Year Book*, 1949, p. 856.
[2] *S. Africa Year Book*, 1949. The United Nations Economic Report, however, give the figure as 585,000 tons.

This increase has been largely due to improved varieties of cane, better field practice, and higher mill recoveries. Further developments in these directions are still possible; also the area can be increased; there were in 1950 some 80,000 acres of suitable virgin land available for further planting.

A well-equipped research station at Mount Edgecombe has been at work since 1927 improving the varieties and dealing with other of the growers' problems, and a sugar milling research institute is being started to deal with the millers' problems.[1] Sugar cane has the distinction of being the only crop for which South Africa's yields compare favourably with the world average.

Two other products must be mentioned for their indirect effort on food production by increasing the farmers' financial resources.

Timber Plantations

The timber plantations are chiefly in Natal and the Transvaal; and they are extending. Among the trees grown is *Pinus patula* for pulp and paper making. The areas in 1946 were in thousand acres:

Cape	Transvaal	Orange Free State	Natal	Total
80	395	86	481	1,042

An increase of 160,000 acres since 1937. They are not only a source of profit but provide fuel and assist in soil conservation.

Tobacco

Tobacco is grown on light soils where irrigation is possible, and is a very lucrative crop. One of the chief areas is in the Rustenburg district west of Pretoria; good quality cigarette tobacco is produced here and a special research station has been set up to deal with the problem. After two years of tobacco and one of maize the land goes back to wild grass for a period and is then put into tobacco again. The output in 1938–39 had been 23·9 million lb.; in 1947–48 it was 49·6 million lb.

Fodder Crops

Fodder crops occupy some 700,000 acres, the largest part of the non-cereal land; lucerne and teff grass are the chief. Nearly 90 per cent of the lucerne is grown in the Cape Province, usually under irrigation, though efforts are made to increase the area grown on dry land in association with wheat and other winter cereals. Its average yield as hay is about 30 cwt. per acre, and the total annual production about 400,000–500,000 tons. Teff grass (*Eragrostis tef*), a remarkable cereal found wild in Abyssinia, is grown chiefly in the Transvaal and the Free State as a summer hay crop; the average yield is about 15 cwt. per acre, and the total production about 200,000 tons. It can, however, do much better; it has in good conditions given nearly 2½ tons of hay per acre. The present strains are not drought resistant, but the University of Pretoria is introducing other strains from Abyssinia for

[1] For further accounts see A. C. Barnes, *World Crops*, Oct. 1951.

further trial. In addition there is a small area of about 65,000 acres of other sown grasses, chiefly annual, and about 80,000 acres of wild veld has been resown or replanted with better grasses. About 250,000 tons of wild hay are obtained from the veld; the yield in Natal is about 1 ton per acre, in the other provinces about 12 to 15 cwt. per acre. The total amount of hay of all kinds produced in the Union is less than one million tons per annum.

Livestock

The number of cattle in the Union is about equal to that of the human beings and the number of sheep and goats is about three times as great (Table LXII).

TABLE LXII. *Livestock population of the Union. Millions, 1949*

	Cattle	Sheep	Goats	Pigs
European owned	7·1	27·8	1·8	0·76
Native owned	5·1	4·1	3·7	
Total, 1949	12·2	31·9	5·5	0·76
1939	11·8	38·4	6·1	0·47

The cattle slowly but steadily increased in number till the early 1940's and have since varied little about 12¼–12½ millions. The sheep increased to a maximum of 48·4 millions in 1930; later the wooled sheep decreased rapidly bringing the total number down to 35 millions in 1934 and 27 millions in 1946; they have remained about that figure ever since. Two-thirds of the sheep are in the Cape Province; the Free State comes next in importance. About 22 million are wooled, chiefly Merinos, yielding high quality wool but very inferior mutton; about 1 million are Karakuls. The 5 or 6 million non-wooled sheep include the old Afrikanders and the fat-tailed, black-faced Persians which tolerate drought and disease better than the Merinos and thrive on semi-desert vegetation; they produce good mutton and skins suitable for glove making. They are slowly increasing.

Goats, especially the Angoras, are decreasing; they are mainly in the Cape Province; Natal and the Transvaal have about one million each, but the Free State has very few. The Karroo is the world's chief source of mohair.

Pigs are few but they do well and can easily be increased; they rose in fact from 545,500 in 1948 to 761,500 in 1949.

Sheep are financially the most important of the livestock because of their wool, but the cattle are of special interest because they seem to offer scope for increased output of food.

The chief dairy breeds are Friesians and Jerseys—the latter tolerating the high temperatures apparently because their smooth skins reflect much of the sun's rays. Dairying is restricted by the need for ample supplies of good water, and it is chiefly practised on the good farms. The overall average milk yield per cow is given by F.A.O. as 71 gallons a year without counting milk fed to livestock or wasted, but this includes production from native-owned animals. No general statistics are available for European farms. The good dairy herds do much better; only few are as yet recorded, but the 4,200 registered cows of all dairy breeds gave in 1948–49 an average production of 923 gallons with 3·95 per cent butter fat in 294 days;[1] this compares favourably with results elsewhere. Yields of 3 to 4 gallons per day from good Friesian cows are considered low.

The beef cattle include most of British beef breeds, Shorthorns, South Devons, Herefords, Sussex, and others. There are some good pedigree herds of both beef and dairy cattle, but the beef breeds deteriorate more rapidly than the dairy breeds and so require more frequent importations of new blood. Crossed with Afrikanders they produce good steers which thrive better in the high temperatures of the ranching areas than the pure bred animals.[2]

The draft cattle are mainly Afrikanders, a powerful, hardy breed, inured to ill-treatment and long periods of under-nourishment such as horses could not tolerate. At 5 to 10 years of age they are more or less fattened and sold as beef. Earlier maturing strains are being produced which can be marketed at 3 to 4 years of age.

Unlike dairying, beef production is almost entirely on the veld. The best beef-producing region is the north-eastern part of Cape Province and of the Transvaal with some of its central part; here the stocking may be at the rate of 3 to 5 acres per beast. Further westwards the rainfall is lower; in the Mafeking district about 10 acres per beast are needed; the farms are about 4,000 to 6,000 acres and may carry 500 to 600 head of stock. Further west, in the still drier regions the stocking becomes very light: 30 acres may be required per beast; while in the drier regions of the west and the Karroo, sheep and goats become more important. Where as often happens the veld has been over-grazed about 50 per cent more land is needed. The difficulty everywhere is that the rainfall comes in summer only; the grass is then green and succulent, but in the six dry winter months it becomes parched and brown and can no longer support the animals; even the summer rains are not certain, and droughts are not uncommon. Few farmers practise fodder conservation beyond the making of some hay; ensilage is not common, though a mixture of maize and beans is known to make good silage; many farmers leave their animals on the veld long after the best of the herbage has gone. The result is over-grazing, killing out of the good grasses, in many cases leaving the land bare and subject to erosion when the next torrential downfall sets in. It is generally agreed that the grazing lands are deteriorating.

Livestock diseases are a continual source of trouble though not as bad as they were, thanks in the first instance to the devoted labours of Arnold Theiler. This great veterinarian went from Switzerland to South Africa at the time when the rinderpest plague of 1895 had killed vast numbers of cattle in Africa, and when also the country was devastated by horse sickness, blue tongue of sheep, heart water of cattle, sheep, and goats, as well as other diseases. He spent his whole working life there, discovering causes and remedies and he founded the Veterinary Research Institute at Onderstepoort

---

[1] *Farming in South Africa*, December 1950, p. 447.

[2] This question of adaptability has been studied by Jan C. Bonsma and colleagues at the Mara and Messina Research Stations of the Union. See *Empire Jl. Expt. Agric.*, 1953, Vol. 21, pp. 154–175.

where the work has been continued under the direction of P. J. du Toit and later experts. Dramatic successes have been achieved; rinderpest has disappeared for the past fifty years or more, there is no foot and mouth disease except near the game reserves, pleuro-pneumonia has become only an occasional visitation from the north-west, nagana, carried by tsetse fly is uncommon. There still remain tick-borne diseases; heart water in cattle, sheep, and goats, red water and others, but these are controlled by arsenical dips sometimes fortified with D.D.T. or gammexane. Mastitis and tuberculosis occur among the dairy cattle and some horse sickness remains though it can be prevented by inoculation.

Nutritional diseases are still common on the veld caused by lack of phosphate in the soils and the herbage; fowls may suffer from a lack of manganese.

Total Production and Consumption of Food in South Africa

The average quantities of food produced annually in the pre-war years 1935–39 and for 1947 are given in Table LXIII, together with the quantities consumed in the country as human and animal food seed, manufacture, and wastage. Surpluses were exported and deficits made up by import. Production of all foods had increased excepting of wheat, mutton, vegetable oil, and butter. But consumption increased in even greater proportion, reducing the surpluses and increasing the deficits in all cases, except rice.

The result has been to transform the Union of South Africa from an exporter of food into an importer. The magnitude of the change is seen by a comparison of exports and imports for the two periods (Table LXIII).

TABLE LXIII. *Changes in food supplies, pre-war and 1947*

Thousand tons

	Exports				Imports		
	1935–39	1947	1948		1935–39	1947	1948
Maize	508	93 (1)	370	Wheat	11	26	130
Sugar	187	9	34	Millet, barley,			
Citrus fruits	111	98	102 (3)	oats	2	18	−72 (2)
Deciduous fruits	34	15	74 (4)	Rice	63	14	22
Beef	6	Nil	Nil	Beef	(export)	1	9
Butter	5	Nil	Nil	Other fats	4	30	14

(*F.A.O. Food Balance Sheets*, 1949.)

(1) A bad maize year. The C.E.C. Grain Crops Rpt., 1939, taking different months, gives 94,000 tons as the average export for the three years 1949–51, and 213,000 tons as the average imports of wheat for that period.

(2) Export.

(3) Subsequently, however, the export of citrus fruits increased, and in 1951 amounted to 142,000 tons (Table LXI).

(4) Includes 50,000 tons fresh fruit made into preserves: hence differs from the figure in Table LXI.

The fall in export of maize is particularly unfortunate as the Union had been an important source of supply for other parts of Africa; the alternative source is the Argentine, but this is costly. (Fig. 14.)

The increase in home consumption continues and is likely to do so; for although the dietary of some of the population groups is satisfactory, that

*

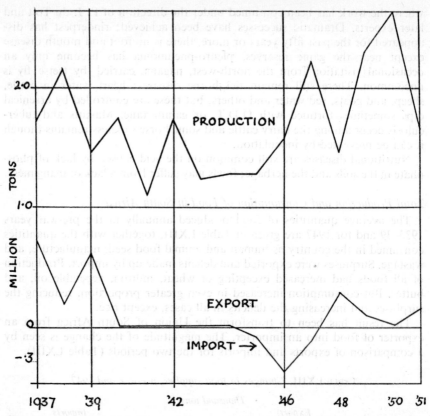

FIG. 14.—Production from European farms and exports of maize, Union of South Africa 1937–51. (Data from C.E.C. Reports, *Grain Crops*, 1953)

of others is not. In 1944 the National Nutritional Council reported much malnutrition, many persons having inadequate supplies of milk, butter, eggs, fruit, and vegetables; four years later F.A.O. stated that "standards of nutrition remain very low as a whole among the native population"—some of the mineworkers excepted.[1]

F. W. Fox[2] in 1947 drew up a statement of food requirements for the whole population giving each of the three main groups a dietary according with its needs and customs. He shows that the supplies then available were nearly sufficient for cereals and meat but woefully short for vegetables and milk. A later estimate made jointly by officers of the Departments of Agriculture, Native Affairs, and Health[3] leads to the same conclusions and gives a measure of the extent to which the quantities actually available in 1949 would have failed to satisfy or alternatively have more than satisfied the dietaries approved by the National Nutrition Council for the different

[1] *F.A.O. World Food Appraisal*, 1949.

[2] F. W. Fox, *Pub. S. African Inst. for Medical Res.*, 1947, pp. 207–34.

[3] A. J. du Plessis, G. van de Wall, and R. J. Smit, *S. African Med. J.*, 1951, Vol. 25, pp. 955–60.

TABLE LXIV. *Annual production and consumption of principal foods, Union of South Africa, pre-war, 1947, and 1948*

Thousand metric tons

	Production Average			Home use (1) Average			Surplus (export) or deficit (import) (−) Average		
	1935–39	1947	1948	1935–39	1947	1948	1935–39	1947	1948
Maize	1,996	2,228	2,868	1,488	2,135	2,135	508	93	370
Wheat	448	416	488	459	442	557	−11	−26	−130
Kaffir corn	126	176	244	128	176	170	−2		74
Rice	—	—	—	63	14	22	−63	−14	−22
All cereals	2,729	2,961	3,873	2,296	2,926	3,156	433	35	292
Sugar (refined)	408	464	552	221	453	502	187	9	34
All vegetables	471	732	698	470	698	682	1	34	—
Including potatoes	172	290	242	171	256	226	1	34	18
Beef	216	349	347	210	350	356	6	−1	−9 (2)
Mutton and goat	107	109	89	107	109	89			
All meat	365	517	489	363	518	498	2	−1	
Milk, whole and condensed (as fresh)	1,142	1,369	1,797	1,143	1,384	1,801	−1	−15	−4
Butter	18	19	30	13	19	30	5		
Fruits:									
Citrus	163	191	198	52	93	96	111	98	102
Deciduous	183	213	256	149	198	182	34	15	74
Dried	12	14	14	5	13	10	7	1	4

Population (millions) 9·59 (3) 11·6 (4) 11·89

(1) "Home use" includes quantities used for seed and fed to stock (chiefly maize and oats). The quantities available for human food are given in Table LXV.

(2) All meat.

(3) 2·00 European; 7·59 non-European.

(4) 2·4 European; 9·2 non-European.

(*F.A.O. Food Balance Sheets.*)

groups of the population; their results are given in Table LXV. So far as comparisons with pre-war years and 1947 are valid the figures indicate an increased consumption per head of all groups of foods, especially in sugar, meat, and fruit and vegetables; but the short-fall for the latter remains considerable as does that for milk and its products.

It seems certain that this rising consumption will continue, and it is equally certain that the Union will be in a position to finance even considerable imports of food so long as prices for the export commodities, gold, uranium, and other metals, diamonds, chemicals, wool, and others, are maintained anywhere near their present level. But it is highly unfortunate for the world market that South Africa should be changing over from the position of supplier to that of purchaser in view of the sparseness of its population and the large areas of undeveloped land.

The most impressive picture of the change is shown by the money values of the imports and exports of agricultural products before the war and after. The figures are, in £ million:

	Exports			Imports	
	Average 1930–34	1946		*Average* 1930–34	1946
Fruit and nuts	2·19	4·91	Food and drink	4·29	27·09
Cereals and products	1·56	0·47	Tobacco and oil	0·98	4·82
Meat and fish	0·63	0·94			
Dairy products	0·58	0·12			
Sugar, wine, tobacco, and others	2·08	5·26			
	7·04	11·71		5·27	31·91

Excess (+) or deficit (−), exports over imports. +1·77 −20·20

TABLE LXV. *Quantities of "available food stuffs" and excess or deficit over the quantities required in 1949 for approved dietary*

	Thousand metric tons							
	F.A.O.			*du Plessis*	*Surplus* (+)			
	Pre-war			*et al.*	*or short-*	*lb. per head per year*		
	1935–39	1947	1948	1949	*fall* (−)	1935–39	1947	1949
Wheat	284	364	463	456				
Maize	1,098	1,275	1,306	1,318				
Other cereals	111	108	109	89				
	1,493	1,747	1,878	1,863	+ 67	343	331	333
Meat, fish, eggs	412	581	—	682	+ 87	95	110	122
Milk and cheese	687	881	996	1,003	−473	158	167	179
Fruit and vegetables	556	801	820	936	−537	128	152	167
Sugar	221	453	503	481	+237	51	86	86
Butter, margarine, and fat	29	39	58	67	− 86	7	9	13
Pulses and oil seeds	21	54	36	38	− 30	5	10	7
Estimated population, millions	9·59	11·60		12·32 (1)				

(1) 2·67 million Europeans (1950).

Approved dietary, intake per day		
	Europeans	*Bantu*
Calories	2,500	2,900
Protein (gram)	66	66
Fat (gram)	70	65

The Possibility of Increasing South Africa's Production of Food

Of all the foods in Table LXV, fruit and sugar are in the most satisfactory position. The management of the orchards, vineyards, and sugar cane plantations is generally good, and there are still possibilities of increasing their areas. Output of deciduous fruit is likely to be improved by the extension of canning, particularly of peaches of which considerable areas of special canning varieties are being planted, and by the improved facilities for cold storage whereby apples can be carried over from one season to the next. There seems good reason to expect that South African fruit growers will be able to supply the increasing internal demand and to maintain if not increase their exports. The sugar producers will probably do the same, though consumption is increasing rapidly.

The position is quite different, however, in regard to the ordinary farm products. In spite of much excellent scientific work at the experimental farms and stations the average yields from the arable land and the veld of the European farms are among the lowest in the civilized world; they are much below the world average yields and also those of countries where the conditions are comparable (Table LXVI).

TABLE LXVI. *Yields in the Union of South Africa compared with those elsewhere*

Cwt. per acre	Union average 1927–37	1947–48	World average	Comparable Average country
Maize	4·7	6·0	10·7	10·6 (S. Rhodesia)
Wheat	4·4	4·2	7·7	6·4 (Australia)
Kaffir corn	4·3	—	—	7·0 (U.S.A.)
Groundnuts (unshelled)	3·6	3·6	13·8	10·7 (S. Rhodesia)
Potatoes	46	24–38	108·7	48·8 (S. Rhodesia)
Sugar cane (tons per acre)	9·9	—	8·0	—

F. W. Fox in *Social Medicine*, E. Cluver, Pretoria, 1951: based on data from G. Van de Wall, except 1947–48.

More than 90 per cent of the farmland of the Union is left as wild veld, and even in the Free State where cropping conditions are better the percentage of wild veld is 80. Much of this is in areas of low rainfall and much also would be liable to erosion if broken up. But it is difficult to believe that so little of the land is cultivable. J. C. Ross[1] estimates the potential cultivable area at 30 million acres, nearly double the area at present in crop and in fallow. (Table LIX, p. 193.)

Control of weeds and the improvement of the soil moisture conditions will probably always necessitate considerable fallowing in preparation for grain crops.[2] The fallow area amounts to about half that of the cropped land in the Cape Province and Natal, and about one-third in the Transvaal and the Free State; improved cultivation technique may reduce the proportion, but Canadian experience does not hold out much hope in this direction.

Some new areas are being opened up for the cultivation of maize in the Springbok Flats of the Crocodile River valley north of Pretoria and elsewhere.

Greater output would be obtained by fuller use of fertilizers, especially superphosphate. Considerable quantities of this are manufactured, but the raw materials have to be imported as there are no important local deposits of calcium phosphate but only of iron and aluminium compounds unsuitable for treatment. Small amounts of good quality guano (9–10 per cent N, 10 per cent P_2O_5) are obtained from Government-owned islands, but nitrogenous fertilizers have to be imported.

The total fertilizer consumption has increased since the war and in 1952 was estimated at about 800,000 tons, chiefly phosphatic; about 60 per cent is used in the maize belt. About half a million tons of kraal manure is used also. Some fertilizer is exported.

[1] *Soil Conservation*, Dept. of Agric., Pretoria, 1947, p. 4.
[2] Spraying with 2–4 D to kill weeds has raised yields of maize by 50–100 per cent. (T. D. Hall.)

But neither mechanization nor better plant protection nor even fertilizer will remedy the prime cause of the persistent lowness of yield; the loss of soil organic matter brought about by continued cropping with maize interspersed with fallow, a loss amounting in J. J. Theron's experiments to about half the initial stock after 25 years. Sooner or later this leads to deterioration of soil structure and loss of surface soil. Dressing of superphosphate for a time may maintain or even increase yields, but after a while over considerable areas in the northern and eastern parts of the summer rainfall district superphosphate has become less effective and even complete fertilizer dressings ceased to act well. Farmyard manure would no doubt restore productiveness, but it is not generally available in adequate quantities. More diversified cropping is essential, and if possible the introduction of leguminous crops. In the High Veld districts of good rainfall near Pretoria, maize while still predominant is alternated with groundnuts, beans, and other legumes; its yield may then be about 10 cwt. per acre, about double the average. Under lower and less certain rainfall, however, this simple method ceases to answer. At the Potchefstroom Experimental Farm further west alternation of maize with cow peas did not increase its yield; the best results were obtained when 10 tons of farmyard manure were applied every three years to the continuous maize. It is unfortunate that no leguminous crop is yet known that will grow well in semi-arid regions and have the same beneficial effects in the farm economy in general and on the soil in particular as clover has in the moister regions; the world's food position would be revolutionized if a group of such crops could be found.

A grass ley affords mechanical protection against erosion and re-forms the soil structure; under humid conditions where clover is a constituent of the ley it also increases the amount of nitrogenous organic matter and humus in the soil. Theron has shown, however, that little or no soil organic matter accumulates under grass in regions of lower rainfall where leguminous plants cannot grow even when superphosphate is applied. But when nitrogenous fertilizer is also given there is formation of soil organic matter and Theron points out this should be taken into account in assessing its value on the farm.[1]

One of the greatest advantages accruing from the more general use of rotations would be closer integration of livestock and arable husbandry than was possible in the old system. The resulting increase in the acreage of lucerne, various fodder crops and above all of cultivated grasses, would not only provide the ample and regular supplies of winter food for stock indispensable for the development of efficient dairy and beef production industries, but even more important, would widely increase the fertility of the soils by re-forming the crumb structure destroyed by long cultivation and by adding much needed nitrogenous organic matter.

Africa is very rich in wild grasses, a number of which are good enough to be worth cultivation. Unfortunately some of the best do not easily set seed when grown on farms though they do so readily enough in the wild state; the reason is not yet clear. Dr. I. B. Pole Evans has been the chief pioneer in studying their possibilities. His first studies were with woolly finger grass,

[1] J. J. Theron, *J. Agric. Sci.*, 1951, Vol. 41, pp. 289–96, and with D. G. Haylett, *Empire Jl. Expt. Agric.*, 1953, Vol. 21, pp. 86–98.

Digitaria stolonifera, a widely distributed drought-resistant plant useful for stopping erosion because its stoloniferous habit enables it speedily to colonize empty spaces. It has also considerable nutritive value: a half-acre paddock at the Dry Land Experiment Station, Groenkloof, kept a cow in good condition for five years without other food. But as it does not set seed easily it must be propagated by runners and has therefore not proved popular. In his well-known botanical expeditions in Africa[1] Pole Evans has found other valuable grasses and brought them to the experimental field near Pretoria where they are grown and studied in detail. One of these, *Acroceras macrum*, an excellent grass from the swamp areas of Nyl Vlei in the Northern Transvaal is unfortunately a poor seed producer. Two other grasses, more useful because they produce abundant seed, are a variety of *Panicum coloratum* which he found near the great Makarikari salt pan of the Kalahari in the 6–10-inch rain belt; and a leafy strain of *Setaria sphacelata* found in the Kazungula marsh on the Zambesi. (Plate 22, p. 181.)

In addition to these grasses found by Pole Evans several local grasses, especially *Eragrostis, Aristida, Themeda triandra, Hyparrhenia spp., Paspalum,* and others, are being used, the wild seed having been collected and multiplied.

The total area of all of these fodder crops and grasses is as yet only about 6 per cent of the total cropped area; an extension seems to hold out considerable hopes for the improvement of South African agriculture. Great results might be expected from more extended selection followed by plant breeding to obtain varieties and strains suitable for the three pressing needs of the Union: the increased productiveness of the good rainfall region, the extension of the cropped area into the marginal dry region, and the prevention of soil erosion.

The Improvement of the Veld

The improvement of the veld offers great possibilities for increasing the output of food from the Union. The main source of trouble has hitherto been overstocking; this has led to the destruction of the palatable herbage leaving bare soil liable to erosion or to colonization by poorer herbage or bushes. The areas ordinarily required for one cow and calf are:

	Acres for one cow and calf	
Annual rainfall, ins.	Average stocking	Overstocking
15–20	30	45
20–25	11	15
25–30	5	10

(I. B. Pole Evans.)

The overgrazing results from the fact that growth of herbage takes place only during the six summer months when rain is falling, it ceases during the remaining six months. Only little provision is made for this dead period; very little silage and less than one million tons of hay are reported for the whole Union's population of 12½ million cattle and 38 million sheep and goats (p. 199); farmers must therefore leave their animals far too long on the veld unless they are able to send them to another farm for the winter.

[1] Some of these are described in Memoirs 21 and 22 of the Botanical Survey of S. Africa, Pretoria, 1948.

Numerous investigations on pasture research in the Union have shown ways of effecting improvement. The animals should not be allowed to roam indiscriminately over the whole veld; fences should be erected to protect vulnerable veld and to allow the systematic resting for appropriate periods during the growing season. Sufficient watering-places should be made to avoid the formation of the deep cattle tracks that result when only one is available; the Geological Survey advises as to the best location of the bore holes. Seeds of good indigenous grasses should be sown on bare land, and the encroachment of bushes—now extending to some 16–20 million acres[1]— should be stopped. Surplus summer grass should be made into hay or silage. Anti-erosion measures should be taken. All these, of course, require capital, and for some of them loans or subsidies are available.

Another cause of serious erosion is the burning of the veld which normally takes place shortly before the summer rains to encourage new growth directly they start; on farms where sheep are to be wintered, however, burning takes place at the end of the summer. This has some good results: dead and worthless vegetation and also ticks are destroyed, but considerable harm may be done, and it would be a great advantage if the burning could be avoided. More mowing machinery is urgently needed.

Fertilizers, especially nitrogen used with phosphate, effect considerable improvement in the good rainfall areas: results by T. D. Hall and his colleagues have been per acre:

	No manure lb.	Nitrogenous and phosphatic fertilizer lb.
Bullocks, live weight increase[2]	60	120 to 200
Gain per lb. N. in fertilizer	—	2·4
Total digestible nutrients	600	1,000 to 1,600
Gain per lb. N. in fertilizer	—	15·3–13·6
Yield of milk[3]		
1949–50, gallons	125	200
1950–51, gallons	120	240

The Possibility of Establishing Livestock industries

The combination of a large cattle population and a great expanse of grazing land, with a farming population of European origin, well-equipped with agricultural and veterinary research institutes, naturally suggests the possibility of establishing a vigorous livestock industry. Good dairy farmers as we have seen obtain satisfactory yields of milk, but it is improbable that output would in our time exceed the local demand. In the period 1935–39 the average production of milk was 1·1 million tons; by 1947 it had risen to 1·3 million tons, but this had not quite kept pace with the growth of population or with the demand, and an import of condensed milk had become

[1] J. C. Ross, Farming in South Africa, Dec. 1950, p. 44.
[2] T. D. Hall, D. Meredith, and R. E. Altona, *Empire Jl. Expt. Agric.*, 1950, Vol. 18, pp. 8–18.
[3] C. J. Rose, *ibid.*, 1952, Vol. 20, pp. 35–42. Done on the veld of Botanical Research Station of the University of Witwatersrand, between Johannesburg and Pretoria. Alt. 5,500 ft., rainfall 31 ins., mostly November to March.

necessary. Production still rose but importation of butter from South West Africa was necessary in 1950.[1] Supplies of winter food for the animals and of good water seem insufficient for the production of permanent surpluses on which any important expert trade could be based.

Beef production, however, is a different matter, and here there seem to be possibilities of development. The great difficulty is the provision of food during the dry months of the year when the veld is ceasing to make new growth. The production of good quality beef requires a continuance of ample supplies of suitable food during the whole life of the animal: long breaks of under-nourishment such as South African cattle normally have to suffer are entirely detrimental. Dairy farmers are already studying this question of winter food supply and ways round the difficulty will no doubt be found; extension of forage crops, of leys, and above all the improvement of the veld would give surpluses of food in summer that could be stored as hay or as silage for the winter. Even the present supplies of veld herbage are not fully utilized; millions of tons of potential hay remain uncut each year; its value is only slowly being realized. Pole Evans has suggested that the large area proposed for irrigation in the north west of Bechuanaland (p. 217) could be linked up with the veld so that it could receive the animals for finishing just when the veld had given them all it could.

Soil Erosion

Soil erosion is an old trouble in South Africa; striking pictures of gullies or *dongas* appear in some of the early numbers of the *South African Journal of Agriculture* in the beginning of this century. But, as in other countries where land is plentiful and water is not, it was not taken very seriously till it began to upset the water supplies. The continued drying up of springs and of streams, the periodical floods, and the deterioration of the veld it brought about, led to the establishment of the Drought Investigation Commission whose report in 1923 was the first comprehensive review of the subject. Action followed, but farmers were not particularly interested and erosion became worse; by 1946 J. C. Ross, head of the Soil Conservation Division, estimated that about a quarter of the original fertility resources of the Union had been lost, and the native lands had suffered worse than the European. Public opinion now became aroused, and in October 1946, the Soil Conservation Act was passed; it is one of the most comprehensive in the world.[2] Soil conservation districts are established as in the United States; in each of these the farmers with expert help draw up plans for rehabilitation of eroded lands and prevention of new damage; when approved the programme is compulsory on all owners of land, but financial help is given when necessary. A National Veld Trust was set up to maintain public interest in the work— the public having to pay for it. By January 1950, no less than 90 million acres had been included in the soil conservation districts. Dr. Ross still had to report, however, that farmers were operating chiefly that part of the programme providing for the mechanical works, contouring, terracing, etc.— these being grant earning—but were less enthusiastic about the other equally

[1] *F.A.O. Food Balance Sheets*; "Farming in S. Africa," December, 1950.
[2] Government of S. Africa White Paper, "Agricultural Policy," 1946. See also Departmental Rpt., "Reconstruction of Agriculture," 1943.

essential part; better farming, especially better veld management; they suffered also from shortage of fencing material. The good so far effected, however, has been offset—and perhaps more than offset—by retrogression elsewhere. Meanwhile the soil conservation officers, however, continue their efforts, and much rehabilitation has been achieved.

Irrigation

Improvements in the water supply would add enormously to the output of South Africa's soils. Unfortunately, as already stated, the South African river systems are not well suited for irrigation, and only a little over one million acres are irrigated, mostly in small schemes; their distribution in 1946 was:

		Thousand Acres		
Cape Province	Transvaal	Orange Free State	Natal	Total
635	352	103	46	1,136

This, however, represents a gain of 170,000 acres, 17 per cent, since 1937 when the irrigated area was only 966,000 acres. Much of the Cape irrigated land is on the lower Orange River and is under lucerne; in the Transvaal some is on the rivers flowing northwards and eastward from the Drakensbergs; in the Free State it is in the Ladybrand–Harrismith region. Fortunately the salt problem is less serious than in some other parts of the world. There are still possibilities of further irrigation, but the most optimistic estimates do not exceed $1-1\frac{1}{2}$ per cent of the total area, i.e. 3–4 million acres; others set the limit at about 2 million acres.[1]

Transport for live animals, properly equipped packing houses, and refrigerator transport of carcasses to the purchasing countries would need to be provided; the undertaking would be costly. It might still be worth doing, for the central parts of Africa also have large possibilities of cattle production which are not as yet adequately developed.[2]

Improvements in South African agriculture are likely to take time; the gap between the methods of the ordinary farmer and the better ones demonstrated at the experiment stations is very considerable.

It is reasonable, however, to hope for the attainment of self-sufficiency in maize, wheat, and dairy produce, for the production of small surpluses of maize and potatoes which could be exported to neighbouring native areas, and for a general export of sugar, fruit, wines, and spirits. If the veld were sufficiently improved and the livestock and arable husbandry properly integrated there could be a considerable output of meat, but this would necessitate a great improvement in the general level of the farming.

THE NATIVE RESERVES AND PROTECTORATES OF THE SOUTHERN PLATEAU

The native reserves in the Union, and the Protectorates of Swaziland, Basutoland, and Bechuanaland, are mainly restricted to African natives, and

[1] E.g. J. C. Ross in *Soil Conservation*, Dept. of Agric., Pretoria, 1947, p. 4.

[2] For a full discussion, see I. B. Pole Evans, "The Possibilities of Beef Production in Southern Africa," *Empire Jl. Expt. Agric.*, 1950, Vol. 18, pp. 81–94. A general account of agriculture in South Africa is given by John Fisher, *Farming, Practical and Scientific* (Juta and Co., Cape Town, 1949).

the tribal organization and native methods of pastoral and agricultural production still in the main continue.[1] Some of the land is held by Europeans, but usually only for ranching, and the general policy is that this should diminish. Livestock is the chief interest of the people partly for economic reasons but largely on social and religious grounds. Only rarely is there sufficient cropping to allow an export of grain, indeed grain not infrequently has to be imported against an export of live animals and wages brought in from the mines. In general, production of food has failed to keep pace with the increases in human and animal population, and this has raised certain problems common to all native areas: control of soil erosion, soil improvement, and improvement of the human dietary.

The Reserves in the Union

These occupy in all about 32 million acres and another 6 million have to be purchased under the Act of 1936. This represents about 30 per cent of the productive area of the Union. The native population is about 3 million.

The Transkei is one of the largest reserves in the Union: it is 8·6 million acres in extent; it has good rainfall and over considerable areas its native vegetation is tall grass. In 1946 it had a population of 1·25 million people compared with 0·94 million in 1921. In 1918 the cattle population had been about half a million; in consequence of the increased human population, additional money earnings, and above all the effective veterinary services, the livestock numbers trebled by 1942 when there were 1·48 million cattle, 2·54 million sheep, and 0·83 million goats. The density of stocking greatly increased: only 3, and in some areas, only 2 acres per livestock unit were available, and heavy overgrazing resulted. The grass formerly good became coarse and was invaded by poor annuals, inedible bush, and other herbage of low value. The sheep have been particularly harmful; the tall grass is unsuited to them and attempts to keep it short have led to erosion. Milk supplies decreased. In spite of the import of maize from the European farms of the Union human malnutrition became rife; plague, typhus, tuberculosis, and syphylis were common; it was estimated that about one-third of the children died before reaching the age of three.[2] Human food production continues to decrease; in the native areas of the Union it is estimated to have fallen by one-third between 1931 and 1951. J. and T. Gillman have described the precarious native dietary especially the lack of milk and resulting deficiency diseases, and J. H. Dugard, Inspector of Schools, reported that 84 per cent of 11,000 schoolchildren observed had only one meal a day.[3]

The Union Government is endeavouring to establish better systems of crop production and to limit the stock to the carrying capacity of the pastures; the reserves also are being replanned to ensure the best utilization of the land.

[1] The present land policy of the Union is formulated in the Native Trust and Land Act, No. 18, of 1936, and there is a later discussion in "The Native Reserves and their Place in the Economy of the Union of South Africa," Rpt. No. 9, Social and Economic Planning Council, Pretoria, 1946.

[2] Rpt. on Soil Erosion and the Conservation of Soil and Water in Swaziland, 1944, Vet. and Agric. Dept. Swaziland, revised edn., 1946. Ignorance on the part of the mothers, and lack of hygiene, were important factors.

[3] J. and T. Gillman, *Nutrition Reviews*, December 1947, J. H. Dugard, *S. African Med. J.*, 1945, Vol. 19, p. 412. Later reports on malnutrition in Transkei children are by Le Riche, *et al.*, *ibid.*, 1953, Vol. 27, p. 103, and J. H. Jackson, *ibid.*, p. 136.

An area is surveyed, and a plan for betterment is drawn up; aid is given in carrying it out. Everything is done to make the natives contour-conscious: they are taught to plough on the contour, to leave grass strips between the various lands, and also to save fodder for winter. But it is discouraging work, for the Bantu are very unco-operative; much education is necessary especially among the chiefs and their councils to arouse interest, to give the necessary technical knowledge, and above all to overcome the native suspicions; there has been some sabotage of the reclamation works. At the same time local industries are to be established to take off superfluous workers from the land;[1] there is always a demand for labour in the mines and on the European farms. If the programme can be carried out it should provide the inhabitants with enough food and perhaps even a surplus of cattle for export to the European farmers in exchange for more maize.

Little more than self-sufficiency can be expected, however, even if it can be attained. In spite of the fact that there are three agricultural schools in the Transkei and one in the Ciskei the farming is very primitive.

THE PROTECTORATES

These are administered under the Commonwealth Relations Office; each has a British High Commissioner, and the three form a co-ordinating committee with the Minister of Native Affairs of the Union.

Basutoland

Basutoland is an enclave in the Union occupying the highest part of the Drakensberg mountains between Natal, the Orange Free State, and Cape Province; its altitude ranges from 5,000 to 11,000 feet above sea level; its climate is mainly cool and healthy; its rainfall is variable but averages about 28 inches a year. Its area is 7·49 million acres. About 6 million acres lie above 6,000 feet and carries mountain grassland vegetation; this is pastoral country, only about 5 per cent is cultivated and it is only sparsely inhabited. The remaining tract of 1½ million acres of lower land, 500 to 600 feet elevation, carries high veld grass; about 25 per cent of it is cultivated and the greater part of people live here.

The cattle population in 1949 was about 431,000 and there was a small export (about 4,000) to the Union for draft and pack purposes, but the conditions are better suited to sheep and goats than to cattle, and they numbered respectively 1·6 million and 0·61 million.[2] The human population more than doubled between the beginning of the century and 1936 when it was 562,300, all but 2,700 being Basutos;[3] they had had to spread up the river valley and on the slopes of the higher ground. Later there came a fall, probably by migration to the Union, and the 1946 census recorded 563,800. There are few trees, cattle dung has to be burnt as fuel, and consequently the soil has deteriorated. There has been a good deal of overgrazing, overcropping, and erosion. During the period of rapid increase of population

[1] Malcolm Lomberg, *Journ. Roy. Soc. Arts.*, 1951, Vol. 99, pp. 813–27. "Rehabilitation of Native Reserves in South Africa."

[2] *South Africa Year Book*, 1949.

[3] *The Basuto*, Hugh Ashton, Oxford Univ. Press, gives a good recent account of those likeable, vigorous, and intelligent people.

the quantities of food produced no longer sufficed. By 1936, when the Colonial Office began its nutrition survey, there was considerable malnutrition in the lowlands; its effects could be seen in every village, physique was deteriorating, pellagra was increasing, and resistance to disease decreasing. Conditions were better in the highlands.

Great changes have since been made. Under the Colonial Development and Welfare Act of 1944, Basutoland received £830,000, in addition to earlier grants, to be spent on development schemes approved by the Home Government; a further £133,000 has since been added. Among other valuable results achieved has been a considerable amount of soil conservation; by September 1951, 715,793 acres had been protected. Much of the work was done by R. W. Thornton and his colleagues and is now being carried on by L. H. Collett. Worn-out veld has been restored by resting, so that the useful grass, *Themeda triandra*, could re-establish itself; this not only affords good grazing, but protects the soil against erosion much better than the bitter karoo bush that had sprung up when it was eaten out. Vulnerable lands have been protected against erosion by large banks and graded drains to divert storm water from arable land, running it safely along grass-protected water ways to existing streams; large modern machinery is used for the purpose.

Better agricultural methods have also been developed; manuring and rotations have been improved and a wider range of other crops including fruit and vegetables is grown. Overstocking has been controlled; since 1947 importations of livestock have been restricted. The number of goats is being greatly reduced but the quality of the survivors has been improved by the use of angora rams. Sheep also have been considerably reduced and native ram lambs castrated, Merino rams have been substituted and consequently the quality of the wool has improved so that it now accounts for a large part—in 1950 about 80 per cent—of the total value of the exports. Cattle numbers also have been lowered, and there were further losses due to drought in 1949.

The quantities of cereals produced normally allow a substantial export to the Union; in 1948 the quantities were:[1]

| | *Thousand tons* | | |
	Produced	*Exported*	*Retained in the country*
Maize, tons	80	3·15	76·85
Wheat, tons	39	8·23	30·77
Sorghum, tons	34	7·90	26·60

Allowing 7½ per cent for seed and wastage this left 500 lb. per head of population per annum of all three grains. Much of the sorghum is converted into native beer which, however, has some nutritive value. In addition to grain and some livestock products a certain amount of fish is available; the rivers contain quantities of trilapia, a good edible fish. In order still further to improve the dietary the growth of fruit and vegetables is being encouraged; quantities of seed of cabbage, carrot, onion, and turnip, and numbers of peach and fig trees and of vines have been issued free.[2]

1 *South Africa Year Book*, 1949.
2 Colonial Reports, Bechuanaland Protectorate, 1949, H.M.S.O.

Production is very variable, depending on the season; 1949 was a year of severe drought and crops were only about 10 per cent of the 1948 quantities; maize had to be imported from the Union. So also in 1945 and 1946. On the other hand, 1950 was a much better year; the production of maize was 210,000 tons, and of wheat and sorghum 49,000 tons each. Basutoland has the advantage of being ethnologically homogeneous; there is only one African tribe and one paramount chief, and if his or her[1] interest can be secured, conditions become more favourable for carrying out agricultural improvements. Much of the work falls on the women for about half the males are at any one time absent at work in the Union; human labour is Basutoland's chief export.

Swaziland

Swaziland lies between the eastern Transvaal, Portuguese East Africa, and Natal. It is divided into three strips of almost equal width running north and south. The one to the west is the High Veld, 3,500 feet or more in altitude; its rainfall averages about 40 inches a year, its temperature is moderate, and it has dense grass vegetation. In the centre is the Middle Veld, savannah country, about 2,000 feet in altitude, with rainfall about 32 inches and its temperature higher than in the west. To the east is the Low Veld, only about 500 to 1,500 feet in altitude; its rainfall averages about 23 inches, but it is well watered by streams flowing eastwards from the higher land; the temperatures are tropical and the vegetation is grass with tall trees.

The population in 1950 was estimated at 194,000. At the census of 1946 it had been 185,000, of whom 181,000 were Bantu; it had been increasing at the rate of 2·2 per cent per annum since the 1921 census; it is unevenly distributed in the country and tends to avoid the Low Veld as this is much more subject to malaria than the higher land.

The total area of the country is 4·3 million acres, only half of which was in 1950 held by the natives; the other half, 2·2 million acres, being in the hands of Europeans who numbered, however, only about 3,200, less than 2 per cent of the total population. The European land is partly in small and not very prosperous farms, partly in large ranches or farms where sheep are brought from the Union to winter; the numbers range from about 100,000 to 250,000 a year, though they are likely to become less as the roads become fenced and travelling flocks can no longer feed indiscriminately as they go to or from their winter quarters. The European farms are much more productive than those of the natives: their yields are about double, and they have accounted for about three-quarters of the country's food production.[2]

Cattle numbered about 434,000 in 1949; they had been only 146,500 in 1921; this great increase had become possible as a result of the successful labours of the Veterinary Departments; in addition there were in 1949 262,000 sheep, goats, and pigs, but about 114,000 sheep were winter boarders from the Union.[3] As the native grazing land was about 1·80 million acres only—some of it very poor—the stocking has become very heavy: one stock

---

[1] The paramount is at present a woman.

[2] Colonial Office Nutrition Report, 1939.

[3] Colonial Rpts., Swaziland, 1949, H.M.S.O. The numbers for 1950 are somewhat lower but the winter-boarding sheep were higher.

unit per 4·3 acres; even under favourable conditions and good management it should be 5. The result is continued deterioration; Pole Evans[1] reports a fall in carrying capacity but points out that the production of beef could be considerably increased by raising animals on the ranches of the Middle Veld and fattening them on irrigated pastures on the Low Veld.

The native arable land is about 200,000 acres, i.e. 1·1 acre per head, which should suffice, but it does not. Yields are low, there is a prejudice against using kraal manure, so that fertility is not maintained; the pernicious witch-weed (*Striga*) is spreading, and general bad farming accentuates the effects of drought. The result is that maize has usually to be imported; often about 2,700 to 3,600 tons, and even twice as much in time of drought. As against this there is an export of cattle to the Union for slaughter; 13,500 went in 1946 and the number rose to 19,700 in 1949. Groundnuts also are exported. Swaziland's most important export, however, is asbestos.

Erosion is a potential danger and the water shortage resulting from the increasing ratio of run-off to rainfall is becoming serious, but the country has not yet suffered greatly. Protective measures include the restoration of a complete grass cover to the grazing areas and division of the cultivated area into alternate grass and arable strips. The officer in charge, H. Hutchinson, has shown that a mulch of cut grass spread on the surface of the arable soil not only protects against erosion, but facilitates the soaking in of the rain; the yield of maize on the experimental plots was raised from 1,400 to 2,000 lb. per acre.

The Colonial Office Nutrition Committee of 1939 found the dietetic conditions better than in Basutoland, children only and not adults showing deficiency symptons, due probably to the adults using as food certain wild plants rich in vitamins. In the 1944 Report[2] the ordinary native consumption per head per annum is put at about 400 lb. of maize with small quantities of beans, sweet potatoes, native spinach, fresh and sour milk, etc.; the consumption of milk, however, was falling off as it was being sent to the creameries for making into butter for export.

Like Basutoland and Bechuanaland, Swaziland is to receive £830,000 out of the Colonial Development and Welfare Fund set up in 1944 in addition to earlier grants for carrying out approved schemes of development. A further £83,000 has been added and an annual grant of £95,000 is made until 1956 for geological surveys. The Colonial Development Corporation has started schemes for afforesting 100,000 acres in the Great Usutu Valley and for developing along the Kumati River an area of about 100,000 acres, of which 30,000 will be watered for the growth of rice.

Like the Basutos also, the Swazis are ethnologically homogeneous and have one paramount chief.

Bechuanaland

Bechuanaland, the largest of the Protectorates, is a sparsely populated native territory of about 275,000 square miles lying between South-West Africa, the Transvaal, and Southern Rhodesia and bordering on Angola;

1 *Empire Jl. Expt. Agric.*, 1950, Vol. 18, pp. 81–94.
2 Report on Soil Erosion and the Conservation of Soil Water in Swaziland, 1944, Vet. and Agric. Dept., Swaziland, revised edn., 1946.

it extends from lat. 18° S. to lat. 26° S. Its eastern and western sections are about 3,000 to 5,000 feet altitude; the central section is about 2,000 to 3,000 feet elevation. The winters are dry and the climate is then delightful, but in other months the temperatures are high. The rainfall comes in summer only, November to April, and is very erratic, much of it coming in thunderstorms; in the north and east it is about 20 to 30 inches a year; it decreases in going southwards and westwards; in the central and western parts—which include most of the country—it is about 10 to 15 inches, and in the Kalahari desert in the south only 5 to 10 inches. More than three-quarters of the country consists of open, featureless plains almost waterless, with short-growing, short-lived grass and scattered thorn bushes; in the moister north and east trees occur and the vegetation is savannah in type; the grass is taller—3 to 6 feet high—but coarse and unpalatable to stock. The Kalahari desert is a region of rolling sand dunes sparsely covered with coarse grass and low shrub, much of it is underlain by a concretionary layer of calcium carbonate, but in places the soil is deep, black, very heavy, and sticky when wet, somewhat like the black cotton soil of the Sudan Gezira.

The population is only about 295,000. In 1946 it included 2,200 Europeans, 1,700 Coloureds and Asiatics, and 290,000 Bantu, mostly living in eight native reserves each under its own chief; there is no paramount chief as in Basutoland and Swaziland. Maize, sorghum, beans, melons, and pumpkins are the chief crops; there is an export of beans, and in good seasons of maize and sorghum. Most of the inhabitants are pastoralists. The cattle include the famous great horned animals and were estimated in 1949 to number 983,000; in addition there were 658,000 sheep and goats; there is some export of live animals (70,400 cattle and 20,600 sheep and goats) to the Union and the Rhodesias, and a small but promising export of dairy produce by European and native farmers. Men and cattle alike are concentrated mainly in the north and eastern sections of higher rainfall; the lack of surface water and shortage of boreholes leaves much of the central part unused.

The Colonial Office Nutrition inquiry of 1936 showed that the normal diet consisted almost entirely of maize and beer made from sorghum. Milk supplies were only intermittent because of the distance of the cattle posts from the villages. In consequence of this unbalanced diet the people were of poor physique with low resistance to malaria, tuberculosis, and other diseases.

Yet Bechuanaland has great possibilities of food production. It is almost surrounded by rivers; the Zambesi in the north, the Nato in the south, and the Okavango and the Chobi in the north-west; all have been suggested as suitable for irrigation. The first proposal to attract wide attention was made in 1920 by E. H. L. Schwarz,[1] as part of his scheme for moistening South Africa's atmosphere and so improving the rainfall; he suggested a dam on the Zambesi fifty miles above the Victoria Falls to divert the waters into some of the dried-up rivers and lakes and also to irrigate half a million acres east of Lake 'Ngami. The scheme was unacceptable to scientific and engineering experts and was not carried out; incidentally it would have reduced the

---

[1] E. H. L. Schwarz, *The Kalahari, or Thirstland Redemption*, Cape Town, 1920. The subject is still discussed in South Africa; for a later summary see D. F. Kokot, *An Investigation into the Evidence Bearing on Recent Climatic Changes over Southern Africa*, Govt. Printer, Pretoria, 1948.

flow of the Zambesi by about half and greatly curtailed the Victoria Falls. The Okavango and the Chobi, however, offer better possibilities. The Okavango rises in Angola in the region of 50 to 60 inches rainfall, after about 640 miles it enters Bechuanaland and flows for a further 160 miles, then breaks up into an inland delta which has become a vast swamp of some 5,000 square miles. Out of this issues another but smaller river, the Botletli, which flows eastwards and then in turn is lost in the large salt Makarikari Pan. The swamp is recent; it was a real lake—Lake 'Ngami, some 270 square miles in area, when Livingstone visited it in 1850, but for at least thirty years it has been in its present state. The Chobi or Kwando also starts in Angola and enters Bechuanaland between the Okavango and the Zambesi and finally floods the Chobe swamp out of which the Linyati flows into the Zambesi.

Many proposals have been put forward for utilizing the waters of these two rivers; all are costly. Utilization of the rivers by ordinary systems of dams and canals seems impracticable. J. H. Wellington[1] has suggested utilizing the waters of the delta. Pole Evans,[2] whose botanical explorations of this region have already been mentioned, points out that these delta swamps and some areas of Mozambique are unique in southern Africa in affording grazing all the year round, and if they were properly levelled and irrigated they could fatten large numbers of animals brought in from drier areas when their supplies of grass were exhausted. Unfortunately mosquitoes and tsetse fly abound and seem to be increasing, but if these could be controlled, and if a proper system of transport were organized, he estimates that some two million animals could be fattened annually. F. Debenham,[3] who has made detailed studies of the region, agrees that the engineering problems of a delta irrigation scheme would not be serious but transport would be difficult.

Active developments are proceeding in several directions aided by substantial grants from the Colonial Development and Welfare Fund.[4] These include drilling for underground water and construction of small stock dams so as to make better use of the large tracts at present only very lightly utilized.

The largest development of all is the proposed establishment by the Colonial Development Corporation of two cattle ranches, one of about 10 million acres on the Chobi Crown lands intended finally to supply about 50,000 head of cattle a year; the other in the dry Molepole Crown lands in the south. An expert commission sent out in 1952 to study the possibilities of cattle ranching reported that some 50 million acres of the western Kalakari seemed distinctly promising.[5] In addition some 500,000 acres in the rain belt of the east are to be cultivated for grain to eliminate the present shortage and to furnish food for the livestock. An abattoir and freezing plant are to be established at Lobatsi capable of dealing with 70,000 head of cattle annually. The expenditure involved is estimated at £2½ million.[6]

[1] *Geog. Journ.*, 1949, Vol. 113, pp. 62–9.

[2] I. B. Pole Evans. "The Possibilities of Beef Production in Southern Africa," *Empire Jl. Expt. Agric.*, 1950, Vol. 18, pp. 81–94.

[3] Colonial Office Report, 1949.

[4] £830,000 (as in the case of Basutoland and Swaziland) to which a further £83,000 has been added; also £95,000 is given annually till 1956 for making geological surveys.

[5] The Commission included L. Van der Post, A. Gaitskell, Tsehedi Khama, and others.

[6] A detailed account of the country and its people is given by A. Sillery, *The Bechuanaland Protectorate*, Oxford University Press, 1952.

SOUTHERN RHODESIA

The importance of Southern Rhodesia in its relation to world food supplies lies in its attempts to develop systems of intensive production on light soils under rather low and variable rainfall and subject to a long, dry season: conditions which are widespread in various parts of the world. The key products are tobacco as the chief source of cash, maize for food, and green leguminous crops ploughed in as manure for the arable land, with beef production on the large uncultivated areas of veld. Interest in Southern Rhodesia is enhanced by the circumstance that its development began within the memory of the present generation, and that already its more advanced farmers have passed out of the pioneer stage and are working out efficient mixed farming systems.

Southern Rhodesia forms part of the southern African plateau, but it is cut off from the Union by the Limpopo River and from Northern Rhodesia by the Zambesi. Its area is 96 million acres; the eastern part, Mashonaland, has about 51 million acres and the western part, Matabeleland, about 45 million. The central watershed traverses the country from the south-west about Bulawayo to the north-east; it carries the railway and from it run streams to the south-east, the north, and the north-west to join these two large rivers and also the Sabi and the Odzi. This high region, the High Veld, is mostly 4,000 feet or more in altitude—4,800 feet at Salisbury—and it occupies about 25 per cent of the land surface of the country. It is surrounded by a wide fringe of Middle Veld of altitudes varying from about 4,000 feet to 3,000 feet traversed by the rivers rising in the High Veld and interspersed here and there with complex ranges of hills and clumps of kopjes; this forms about 33 per cent of the total area of the country. The remaining 40 per cent of the country is the Low Veld and it includes the valleys of the Zambesi, the Limpopo, and the Sabi, which is much the largest; its altitude varies from about 2,000 feet to 1,000 feet.

The rainfall comes in summer during the $4\frac{1}{2}$ to $6\frac{1}{2}$ months October–November to March or April; it is highest in the east and north-east and decreases towards the west and south; it is everywhere variable. In some of the eastern border districts and in the remarkable Bikita area it may range from 40 to 70 inches a year. Rather more than half the country has averages of 25 to 35 inches, which would be admirable for crop production if it were reliable and well distributed; unfortunately it is not. The southern and western part, somewhat less than half the country, has less than 25 inches, also unreliable; the Sabi and Limpopo valleys in the south have only about 15 inches. In general the High Veld has high rainfall and the Low Veld low. Most of the rain, however—65 or 70 per cent—comes during the months of December to February, often in heavy showers or thunderstorms; long droughts may come during the summer causing great losses to farmers. Only about one-third of the country has reasonably good and reliable rainfall. The wet months are succeeded by the dry, cool winter lasting from May to mid-August.

Over about three-quarters or more of the country the soils are light sands generally lacking both fertility and depth. About 15 per cent of the country consists of red and brown clay-loams capable of high production when properly farmed though they readily deteriorate unless organic matter is regularly supplied. In low-lying, ill-drained areas heavy black soils called *vlei* occur, especially in Mashonaland; these become productive when the water conditions are made satisfactory. There are, however, no important areas of productive black earths like those of the Russian steppe or the Canadian prairies. All the soils are very liable to erosion, especially where the slope is steep.[1]

The native vegetation is savannah; the tree and bush growth is thicker on the Low Veld than on the High, and the bushes often tend to increase as closer settlement affords protection against fire and game.

The High Veld is the most suitable region for European settlement and systems of farming. Its climate is very congenial, the temperatures average about 60°–75° F. and rarely exceed 90° or fall below 40°, though frosts may come between May and mid-August; the rainfall is adequate in total amount; there are considerable areas of good soil and where sufficient moisture is available most European and sub-tropical crops can be grown.

The natural herbage of both High and Middle Veld consists mainly of perennial grasses, with no small legumes, though there are leguminous shrubs and trees. The grasses grow abundantly during the months of rainfall; their nutritive value is high at first, but it quickly falls off as they mature, and during the long winter months the veld grazing affords little nourishment for the animals except in the Low Veld and parts of the Middle Veld. In spring the dead vegetation is commonly burned either deliberately or accidentally to give the young shoots a better chance of growth; mowing, however, is recognized as better practice.[2] There are often many trees and bushes on the veld and in its natural state it will seldom maintain more than one head of cattle per 20–30 acres without extra feeding.

The Low Veld is unsuited to arable farming and it is used for ranching. As the rainfall is low and the temperatures sub-tropical the grass is thin, but it is palatable and of good nutritive value, better indeed per unit weight than on the High Veld; it is, however, easily damaged by overgrazing. The Zambesi valley is tropical and has Rhodesia's worst climate; the Limpopo valley is cooled somewhat by sea breezes.

The area of 96·2 million acres has been allocated as follows:

At December 31, 1945	*Million acres*
African reserves	21·13
African purchase area	7·86
European area, alienated	31·75
European area, not yet alienated	16·53
Unassigned	17·78
Forest	1·0
Other land	0·14
Total	96·19

The population is rapidly increasing; the figures have been:

[1] Classification and areas of the soils are given in Rpt. of Commission on Preservation of National Resources, Salisbury, 1939.
[2] R. R. Staples, *Rhod. Agric. Jl.*, Vol. 42, p. 44.

	European	African
1939	64,000	1,374,000
1946	82,386	1,764,000
1951	136,000	2,010,000 (estimated)[1]
1953	158,500	

More Europeans, chiefly British from Great Britain or South Africa, are entering the country as rapidly as the Screening Boards permit them; the limit is temporarily set by the shortage of houses. But the population is still very sparse, only 2·2 persons per 100 acres.

Of the 31·75 million acres of the European area already alienated some 28·6 million are in farms, utilized as follows:

	Thousand acres
Crops	737
Orchards	5·2
Forest, natural	14,695
Forest, planted	74
Pasture, natural	10,221
Other uses	2,860

(1950: Census for F.A.O.)

The farms fall into two great groups. Those on the High Veld are mainly mixed farms of about 1,000 to 6,000 acres—about 70 per cent of all Rhodesia's farms are within these limits, and over 50 per cent between 2,000 and 4,000 acres—while those on the Low Veld are mainly large ranches of 20,000 to 60,000 acres or more. The farms number about 5,500.

The High Veld districts having 32 or more inches of rain can be developed for dairying; a suitable size of farm is 1,500–2,000 acres, about half to one-third of which should be arable. Under lower rainfall (28 inches upwards) tobacco grows well on the high-lying granite sands and maize on the heavier soils; on good farms both are combined with livestock; dairying if labour and transport are available, or alternatively intensive beef production. These conditions occur over about 40 per cent of the country. Where the rainfall averages some 28 to 20 inches a year, but is too uncertain for grain production, it is still possible to grow fodder crops and make hay or silage for semi-intensive beef production with pigs and poultry as side lines; this is the position over about half the country. The remaining 10 per cent of the country has less than 20 inches of rain, too little for arable farming, and can be used only for ranching.

The realization of these various potentialities, however, depends entirely on the possibility of smoothing out the water supply so as to tide crops and animals over the long dry period. This is the crucial problem in Southern Rhodesian agriculture.

The Crops of European Farms

Crop production is almost entirely confined to the summer months, November to April, the usual season of rain; during winter, the rainless period, it is possible only under irrigation or on the most vlei soils, and is

[1] Also 6,000 Coloured and 4,400 Asiatics.

but little practised. Three crops dominate Rhodesian agriculture: tobacco, by far the most valuable commercially; maize, the most widely grown of all crops; and green manures. Cotton, sorghum, and fodder crops are also grown and a variety of others including beans, groundnuts, and tubers, but their aggregate area is as yet only small. (Table LXVII.)

TABLE LXVII. *Areas of chief crops, European farms, 1951–2*

Thousand acres

Winter Crops 1951 Total 5·6		Summer Crops, 1951–2 Total 841			
Wheat	1·0	*Grain*		Potatoes	3·2
Oats	0·9	Maize	361	*Fodder*	
Barley	0·9	Millets and		Peas and beans	41
Potatoes	1·5	Sorghums	12·4	Maize	24
Onions	0·23	*Seed*		Sunnhemp	11
		Peas and beans	27	Sunflower	2
		Sunnhemp	12		
		Sunflower	6·5		
		Green manure Sunn hemp		50	
		Others		52	
		Commercial Tobacco		189	
		Cotton		26	

(*Econ. Stat. Bull. S. Rhod.*, 1953, Vol. 21, No. 3.)

Green manure crops are a characteristic feature of Rhodesian agriculture; no country grows them in larger proportion or uses them to better advantage; they are usually combined with phosphatic dressings. The need for them has long been emphasized by H. G. Mundy who showed that the chief factor governing the productiveness of Rhodesia's light soils was the supply of organic matter, and as kraal manure was poor he experimented with green manures at the Salisbury Experiment Station and the Gwebi demonstration farm. Sunnhemp or a mixture of sunflowers with cowpeas, velvet beans, or dolichos beans manured with superphosphate (150–250 lb. per acre) and then ploughed in proved to be an effective preparation for maize, and by repeating the treatment at regular intervals of two to four years yields of 15 to 25 cwt. per acre of maize or 9 to 15 cwt. per acre of wheat could be maintained more or less indefinitely; also the soils did not become eroded. Without the green manure, on the other hand, the soil speedily lost its organic matter, and after the first few crops the yield of maize fell to 5 or even down to 2 cwt. per acre; erosion was also liable to set in.[1] About one-sixth or one-seventh of all the arable land is put in one or the other of these green manure crops; sunnhemp is by far the commonest and has given excellent results; Mundy instances a yield of 64 cwt. of hybrid maize per acre over 180 acres on an old-established, well-run farm. Green manure crops have the disadvantage, however, of occupying the land for the whole season; the long dry period prevents their growth as catch crops. And so although in some of the experiments maize alternating with a green manure crop gave an average of 26·6 cwt. of grain per acre, two successive maize crops alternating with one of green manure averaged 20 cwt. per acre only, and an alternation with three successive maize crops gave a lower average yield still, the total

[1] H. G. Mundy, *Empire Jl. Expt. Agric.*, 1953, Vol. 21, pp. 123–30.

output per acre over a period of years was very little different for the different treatments because of the seasons when no maize but only the green manure had been grown. It still remains to be been how long this would continue.

Green manuring, however, is not equally successful everywhere. Mundy points out that while it has been very effective in Mashonaland it has not answered so well in the drier conditions of Matabeleland, the western part of Rhodesia; ploughing in the entire leguminous crop proved no better than ploughing in the stubble only. This problem of maintaining the organic matter content of the soil in dry conditions arises in Kenya and elsewhere in Africa and is still unsolved.

Composts containing adequate amounts of animal droppings are also effective and are made as far as practicable, but the labour required is considerable. The organic matter thus added to the soil speedily disappears: 12 to 20 tons per acre of green matter or 7 tons of compost may be ploughed in, but no residue can be detected after about two years. There are no earthworms making good mould, but white ants and other animals which destroy the organic matter completely.

Mundy has made the interesting observation that the leguminous shrubs and trees, of which Rhodesia possesses a considerable number, do not appear to benefit the surrounding grass in spite of copious nodulation, although white clover or subterranean clover growing on irrigated soil are markedly beneficial. Fodder crops, especially leguminous, also enrich the soil in organic matter beside furnishing green food, hay, and silage for the animals. Their acreage is about the same as that of the green manure crops, and is increasing as farming becomes more mixed: in 1941 the area under green manure and fodder crops had been 124,000 acres, it had risen to 215,000 in 1949. The principal leguminous crops are velvet beans, sunnhemp, and cowpeas, the chief non-leguminous crops are maize for silage, which is rapidly spreading, and cultivated grasses, notably elephant grass or Napier fodder.

The production of maize has fluctuated a good deal, but during the last 25 years has shown no steady tendency to increase till quite recently. The acreage has varied between 224,000 in 1944–45 and in 1945–46 and 361,000 in 1951–52, and the output from 79,000 tons in 1946–47 and 223,000 tons in 1951–52; the average yields per acre have ranged from 6·2 cwt. in 1950–51 to 13·3 cwt. in 1935–36 and 1931–32; for the 10 years 1941–51 they have averaged over 10 cwt. per acre and they have shown some tendency to rise.[1] The chief producing districts are on the High Veld and include, as for other crops, Hartley, Lomagundi, Salisbury, and Mazoe. Here yields of 18 to 20 cwt. per acre are obtainable in good seasons by good farmers.

The American hybrid maize recently introduced has so far proved much superior to the old sorts; its acreage is rapidly increasing:

	Hybrid			*Other sorts*		
	1949–50	1950–51	1951–2	1949–50	1950–51	1951–52
Percentage of total acreage under maize	22	58	61	78	42·0	39
Average yield, cwt. per acre	14·3	7·5	14·4	8·2	4·2	8·6

[1] Data since 1919 in *Econ. Stat. Bull. S. Rhod.*, Vol. 20, No. 5, June 1952.

Allowance must be made for the fact that the best farmers would probably be among the first to try the hybrid maize, but the prospects of considerable increase in output as it is more widely adopted seem very good. Millets were until recently grown only by Africans; now, however, they are grown also by European farmers; they have the advantage of being more resistant to drought than maize.

Groundnuts are being increasingly grown but the area in 1951–52 was only 8,400 acres and the production just over 1,500 tons; higher outputs are expected in future.

The chief winter crop is wheat, but its production is declining. Yields are very low; only about 4 to 6 cwt. per acre. As already stated, it is restricted to irrigated or naturally wet areas such as vleis; attempts to grow it in summer have not yet succeeded but are being continued.

Potatoes are grown chiefly as summer but also as winter crops; Salisbury is the most important district for both. Yields are low: only $2\frac{1}{2}$ tons per acre for the summer and 3 tons per acre for the winter crop.

Over considerable areas the conditions seem suitable for fruit and some is already grown in certain districts: citrus fruits at altitudes between 2,500 and 4,000 ft.; deciduous fruits—apples, peaches, and plums—at higher levels; and tropical fruits, mangoes, pawpaws, etc., in the hot, low-lying country. At present only one large organization is growing citrus fruits, mainly irrigated oranges. Part of the crop is sold fresh where transport facilities exist; most of it is processed; the skins yield essential oils and pectin, the juice is concentrated and sold as syrup, and the residue used as cattle cake. The area is not at present increasing, but it seems that more fruit and vegetables could be grown and a canning industry could be developed.

Tobacco is commercially by far the most important of all the crops. Rhodesia's vast stretches of sandy soils suit it admirably and so over large tracts does the climate. The area planted has increased rapidly: in 1946–47 it was 90,700 acres, and by 1950–51 it had risen to 168,000, one-fifth of the whole cultivated area and half the area of maize. No other crop or livestock product has shown anything like so remarkable an increase; it accounts for more than half the value of the agricultural and pastoral output and is by far the largest item of export; it can fairly be called the basis of Southern Rhodesia's prosperity. Practically all the tobacco is grown at altitudes of 4,000 to 5,000 feet or even higher with a rainfall of about 25 to 32 inches, preferably well distributed; most of it is in the north-eastern part of the country. Lomagundi is the chief district, but investigations are proceeding actively to find varieties suited to conditions elsewhere. Most of it is Virginia type flue-cured, but some Turkish is produced, and in the Mazoe district some fire-cured Virginia type. The average yield per acre is about 650 lb.; the highest district average in 1948–49 was 754 lb., but some growers obtain 1,000 lb. or more. The output in 1950 was 105 million lb., a record up to that time. The significance of tobacco for food production is that it grows on light soils not naturally productive, and that it provides considerable sums of money for improving them and making them suitable for general farming as well as for effecting other improvements. It is recognized as the only crop capable of bearing the expense of clearing virgin land and is therefore of prime importance in the development of the country.

223

Livestock

Less than 3 per cent of the European farm land is arable; the remainder is largely wild veld used only for grazing. It is uncertain how much of this could be brought into cultivation; expert estimates of the proportion of the land of the colony suited only for grazing range about 70 to 75 per cent. Livestock are therefore likely to remain an important branch of Rhodesia's agricultural production. The numbers have been:

Thousands

Ownership	Cattle		Sheep		Goats		Pigs	
	1914	1951	1914	1951	1914	1951	1914	1951
European	342	1,155 (1)	67	116	35	15·8	19	49 (2)
African	406	1,810	257	200	639	637	26	62
Total	748	2,965	324	316	674	653	45	111

(1) Including 425,000 cows and heifers in calf, of the native cattle about half were male and half female.
(2) Including 8,000 sows for breeding.

Of the European-owned cattle in 1951, 1·7 per cent (20,000) were pure bred, 40 per cent were grade, and the remainder cross-bred or "common"; 49,500 were cows regularly milked.[1] Of the European-owned, 60 per cent are in Mashonaland, the eastern half of the country; about half are in herds of 500 or less.

Southern Rhodesia is not a good country for sheep. The high rainfall and the cold winter mists of the mountain regions tell against them and everywhere they are liable to internal parasites. Some of the mixed farms, however, keep small flocks of 100 to 150 non-woolled sheep, chiefly Blackheaded Persians crossed with Dorset Horned or Wiltshires, but the numbers are small and show little tendency to increase—in the Native Reserves they have actually fallen.

Cattle have proved to be by far the most suitable livestock and they have increased almost continuously since the records began in 1914: for the ten years 1941–50 the rate was about 4 per cent per annum; the natives now have nearly five times as many as they had at the outset. But the risks are considerable; about 5 to 8 per cent of the European animals are lost each year from disease, lack of food when the veld grazing gives out in the dry season, theft, wild beasts, veld poisoning, and other accidents. Steps are increasingly being taken against disease, and lack of food is being slowly remedied by increased production of fodder crops, maize, silage, etc. But in years of bad drought like 1933 and 1949 the failure of the veld causes heavy losses; in 1949 they exceeded 93,000; more than half perished simply from lack of food.

The cattle usually need four years to mature; the carcass weight ("cold dressed weight") for the European animals averages about 450–500 lb. and for the native animals about 275 lb.; the total production of beef and veal in 1950 was estimated for the F.A.O. Report at 53,800 tons. Hitherto there has been a surplus for export, the better qualities fresh or chilled, the lower

[1] 1951 figures in *Econ. and Stat. Bull. S. Rhod.*, Vol. 20, No. 11, September 1952. The figures are approximate only, as "some farmers and ranchers seem to have difficulty in allocating their cattle under the right headings."

qualities canned or salted for the mining districts of Northern Rhodesia and the Union; against this, however, is some import of live animals. As we shall see later the export is shrinking.

Much of the beef is produced off the veld grass, but at a very low output per acre; the average European yield has been estimated at only 3 lb. of dressed beef per acre, and the native yield even lower, only 1 lb. per acre.[1] There is, however, an increasing amount of more intensive beef production on mixed farms.

Dairy farming is increasing in importance to provide milk for the growing towns. The output of milk in 1951 from the European cows regularly milked was 9·8 million gallons, an increase of 2·8 million gallons since 1942; the average yield per cow had also increased during the same period from 133 gallons to 198 gallons; obviously, however, there is still room for a good deal of improvement. Before the war there used to be a considerable production of butter and even an export, but the recent rush of immigrants has so increased the demand for liquid milk that butter production has considerably fallen off, from 600 tons in 1941 to 400 tons in 1951. A considerable quantity now has to be imported from Australia, and the manufacture of margarine has been started.

The production of cheese after rising to a maximum of 313 tons in 1945 fell to 180 tons in 1950, which also necessitated an import.[2] Southern Rhodesia is well suited to pig keeping, and this is steadily increasing on the mixed farms; production of ham and of bacon is rising and an export of 500 tons began in 1952.

The Native Reserves

The native reserves cover 29 million acres (including 8 million acres of "Native purchase area") mostly on the High and Middle Veld regions of good rainfall. The difficult problem of assessing output has been attacked in 1949 by the method of sample surveys.[3] The results are set out in Table LXVIII. About 85 per cent of the produce is retained for local use and about 15 per cent sold to the European area.[4] The number of cultivators was 280,000 and the area cultivated in 1950 averaged 8·3 acres per head, 4 being in millets

[1] I. H. de la Rue, *Rhodesian Farmer*, April 13, 1949, p. 45. It should be added, however, that R. R. Staples put the native output higher in weight than the European, but adds that the quality is lower and that it is attained at the expense of the land through overgrazing (*E. Africa and Rhodesia*, May 17, 1951).

[2] The details for 1950 and 1951 are:

Thousand lb.

		1950	1951	
Butter	Production	913	933	
	Consumption	2,157	2,622	
Cheese	Production	394	496	60% is Cheddar
	Consumption	706	1,112	30% is Gouda
Bacon and Ham	Production	2,015	2,283	practically all is made in factories.

(*Econ. Stat. Bull. S. Rhod.* 1952, Vol. 20, No. 15; a review of the dairy industry 1942–51.)

[3] Report on the Sample Census of African Agriculture of Southern Rhodesia, Central African Statistical Office, Salisbury, July 1951.

[4] F. L. Engledow, Rpt. to Minister of Agric. and Lands on the Agric. Development of Southern Rhodesia, 1950, Salisbury, 1950.

TABLE LXVIII. *Acreages and output of crops in African reserves, 1948–49 and area:*
for 1950

| | Areas Thousand acres | | Output | |
	1949	1950	Thousand tons	Average yield per acre cwt.
Maize	677	700	117·5	3·2
Millets and sorghums	1,084	1,110	102·1	1·8
Groundnuts (unshelled)	114	120	10·5	1·6
Peas and beans	48	50	5·5	2·0
Mixed crops and others	330	340		
Total	2,253	2,320		

and 2·4 in maize. The cultivated area is thus about four times that on the European farms; for millets and groundnuts the difference is much greater. But all yields per acre are much lower: that of maize is less than a third of the European, so that the total output is less in spite of the much higher acreage; even on the favoured High Veld areas yields were only about 5 cwt. per acre and though in the Limpopo Low Veld they were rather above those shown in the Table, in the Zambesi Low Veld they were much below.

The favourite millet is munga (*Pennisetum purpurem*), closely followed by Kaffir corn (*Sorghum vulgare*) and rapoko (*Eleusine coracana*).

The native production of groundnuts considerably exceeded that of the European, as also did the production of peas and beans, but again the yields per acre were lower; only about one cwt. per acre of unshelled nuts as against 6 or 7 cwt. on the European farms. The officers of the Native Agricultural Development Department have shown that much higher yields can be obtained even on the poor granite sands by proper rotations and manuring, but these better methods are not used.

Livestock did not come into this particular survey, but the estimated numbers are shown in Table LXVII; they considerably exceed those of the European farmers, though the quality is poorer. In the 1948 census, when the cattle numbered 1·3 million, about 30 per cent were cows; some 300,000 were being disposed of annually. Of these, about 162,000 went to Europeans (100,000 for slaughter and about 30,000 for breeding or feeding), some 47,000 died, and 90,000 were slaughtered for African consumption in the native butchers' shops set up in the reserves. The low weight of the animal. makes this business wasteful.[1] Milk yields per cow are estimated at 35 gallons a year only; in 1950 the total milk production was put at 9·5 million gallons.

Amounts of Food Produced

In 1950 a Food Balance Sheet, the first for Southern Rhodesia, was drawn up for F.A.O., it is summarized in Table LXIX. It brings out the disconcerting facts that food production has not kept pace with the growth of population and that Southern Rhodesia, though an agricultural country, now has to import considerable quantities of its food. Before the war Southern Rhodesia exported maize to Northern Rhodesia, Bechuanaland, and elsewhere. But the population has grown so rapidly that the export surplus has disappeared.

[1] *F.A.O. World Food Appraisal*, 1949.

TABLE LXIX. *Production (European and African), import, and utilization of chief foods available for 1950*

Thousand metric tons

	Production	Net import	Fed to stock
Wheat	0·8	38·1	—
Maize	320·3	16·5	44·8
Sorghum and millet	141·0	—	10·3
Rice	6·8	1·8	—
Bran and other cereals	1·7	3·5	3·0
Potatoes and sweet potatoes	14·9	1·3	
Sugar (refined)	0·7	17·9	
Pulses and nuts	29·1	2·4	
Vegetables	92·6	4·2	56·0 (2)
Fruit	12·1	2·5	
Including citrus	9·1	−4·1 (1)	
Meat			
Beef and veal	53·8	−1·6 (1)	
Others	11·2	−0·7 (1)	
Milk	90·0 (3)	3·9	
Cheese	0·2	0·1	
Butter	0·4	0·6	
Vegetable oils	3·2	3·1	

(*Econ. Stat. Bull. S. Rhod.*, 1952, Vol. 20, No. 8.)

(1) Export. (2) Chiefly pumpkins.

(3)European production	9·0 million gallons
African production	9·5 million gallons
Total	18·5 million gallons
At 10·3 lb. per gallon	87,000 tons
Allowing for unrecorded production	90,000 tons

and imports are now necessary; in years of drought 1942, 1949, and 1951, fairly heavy ones. Production of wheat has actually decreased and 98 per cent of the requirements had to be imported in 1950.[1] Butter also was formerly exported; now, however, as already stated, its production has fallen and 60 per cent of the 1950 requirement had to be imported, as also had about one-third of the cheese requirement. The country is self-sufficient for eggs, the millets, such vegetables as sweet potatoes and pumpkins, and it has a surplus of citrus fruits. There is still a surplus of meat for export but it has shrunk. In 1946 the export had been 5,800 tons, about 75 per cent of it carcass meat, in 1950, however, 2,300 tons only, about 66 per cent carcass meat, while the forecast for 1954 based on the numbers of animals in sight when it was made (1949) was a deficit of 20 to 30 per cent.[2] The situation may easily get worse if the population continues to increase rapidly; in any case the Africans are eating more meat and more butter than before. The

[1] The values of imports have been, in thousand £:

	1939	1949	1951
Maize	0·42	510	2,725
Wheat	75	915	1,139

[2] The number required would be 273,000 head: and the probable actual number between 180,000 and 210,000 (Central African Statistical Office, Salisbury, February, 1952).

important question arises: can the production of food be raised so as to make the country self-sufficing, and is there any prospect of a resumption of exports?

It should be said at once that there are some abnormal features in the present situation. The recent influx of immigrants has been very heavy and may not continue at the present rate. Few of them have had any agricultural knowledge and experience and those that took to farming have had a great deal to learn. Even among the older farmers the standards vary considerably, ranging from crude ranching to high-class farming on farms provided with dams and contour ridges, with tobacco and other intensive crops grown under spray irrigation with fertilizer and insecticide dissolved in the spray in the best approved manner. Much educational work remains to be done to raise the general level of performance.

Considerable development of European farming has gone on since the war:

	Europeans actively engaged in farming	Thousand acres Cropped land	Tobacco	Cattle thousands	Africans employed on farms thousands
1939	4,711	483	62·7	756	93·6
1950	6,848	742	156·0	1,149	169·0

The volume of the agricultural output more than doubled between 1938–39 and 1949–50, but the increase was mainly in tobacco, not in maize; dairy products, pigs, and eggs also increased, but not cattle:

Volume of agricultural output in 1949–50
(1938–39 = 100)

Livestock		Crops	
Cattle slaughterings	109	Tobacco	315
Dairying	160	Maize	96
Pig slaughterings	208	Citrus	141
Eggs	250	Potatoes	182
All livestock	138	Wheat	13
		All crops	232

(*Econ. Stat. Bull. S. Rhod.*, May 1952, Vol. 20, No. 3.)

The task now before Rhodesian agriculture is to increase the output of food without lowering that of tobacco.

There are still possibilities of setting up more farms in the European area. Unalienated lands still remain from which the Land Settlement Board allocates new farms of 2,000 to 3,000 acres to include 400 to 600 acres of arable; in the ranching regions larger areas are allotted. These unalienated lands were recorded as nearly 18 million acres in 1948, but H. G. Mundy, former Secretary for Agriculture and Lands, put the figure much lower as the result of better surveying. He estimates that probably only about 150 more farms of 2,000 to 6,000 acres can be got out of the regions of good or marginal rainfall, and another 220 farms in more doubtful districts. Some 18 million acres are "unassigned," but much of this land is in semi-arid or doubtful rainfall zones heavily infested with tsetse fly and without surface water. Some has been set aside for a game reserve; but much has hardly been surveyed and little can be expected from it for the present.

As against this the possibilities of intensifying production on the European farms in the good rainfall areas are considerable. Some of them were discussed by Sir Frank Engledow in his Report on the Agricultural Development of the country; the need for developing mixed farming in the good rainfall districts, for integrating tobacco growing with food production, and for improving the ranches in the low rainfall regions.[1]

Few of the European farms are yet fully developed or producing at their maximum capacity, and much of their land is still uncleared, unfenced, and without water. Improvement would be costly, but fortunately farmers having a good acreage of tobacco are now well furnished with funds to carry them out. Many of the farms, however, are still of the size appropriate to the pioneer stage and are far too large for the more intensive production now necessary.

At present the veld is very unproductive, yielding only about 3 lb. of beef per acre per year (p. 225); in spite of its enormous area its contribution to the food supply is very small. Engledow's estimate of the human food production for 1945–46 in terms of calories is as follows:

Calories in thousand millions: acres in millions

	European land		Native land		Total	
	Calories	acres	Calories	acres	Calories	acres
Arable crops directly consumed by humans	297	0·234	1,120	2·25	1,418	2·5
Livestock from crops grown on arable land	27		11		38	
Livestock on pasture	98	27·2	56	21	154	48
	422	27·4	1,187	23·25	1,610	50·5

Expressed in terms of money value the contribution of the veld to the gross farm output is equally small. For 1949–50 the figures are:

Livestock	£ million	Crops	£ million
Cattle slaughtering	1·884	Tobacco	10·944
Other pastoral and dairy	1·916	Maize	1·999
		Other crops	2·257
	3·800		15·200

(*Econ. Stat. Bull. S. Rhod.*)

The grand total is £19 million of which the veld cannot have been responsible for more than £2 million. Serious efforts are being made to rectify this unsatisfactory position. Investigations are in progress on pasture improvements, and on the possibilities of providing food on the arable land to carry the animals over the dry season.

Rhodesia's greatest need is to conserve the rain water and soil moisture and use it with the maximum efficiency; detailed investigations of methods of doing this are urgently needed.

[1] Sir F. L. Engledow, Rept. to Minister of Agric. and Lands on the Agric. Development of Southern Rhodesia, 1950, Salisbury, 1950.

As in all countries of low and uncertain rainfall soil erosion is liable to set in when the veld is broken up or overgrazed. Vigorous protective measures have been taken by European farmers in co-operation with the Department of Soil Conservation and Extension. During the period 1948–51 some 17,850 miles of contour ridges were set up and 357,000 acres of arable land protected; the work continues as new land is brought into cultivation. At the same time efforts are made to ensure better utilization of the land, which is the surest way of guarding against erosion. The native cultivators have been less co-operative: like most Africans they lack the instinct to conserve soil and they are not born farmers. Some progress has, however, been made and the good example of the European farmers may stimulate further activity. By 1953 practically all arable land on the European farms had been protected. Approved measures are compulsory.

The Natural Resources Board set up in 1941 and working through local committees for the conservation of soil, water, forests, animal and plant life, minerals, etc., has greatly stimulated the construction on farms of dams to conserve rain water and protect against soil erosion, and also to allow of irrigation; during the period 1948–51, 2,374 were constructed providing an aggregate storage of 5,500 million gallons of water, and many others are being set up wherever possible. These not only provide much needed water, but also allow of fish farming, a new enterprise that is making progress, aided by the fish hatcheries and the research work of the Henderson Research Station at Mazoe.

Irrigation has long been practised; by 1946 about 30,000 acres were commanded and some 15,000 acres watered: 12,000 under field crops and 3,000 under fruit. The schemes are mostly small; among the more important are those on the Mazoe and Umshandige Rivers storing 4,900 million and 8,000 million gallons of water and watering 1,800 and 1,500 acres respectively. Irrigation is increasingly practised on mixed farms. The largest earth dam in Africa was completed and filled in the season 1951–52 at Hunyani Poort, some 17 miles from Salisbury; it impounds 55,000 million gallons of water for domestic and industrial use and also for irrigation in the Norton district.

Two other great schemes are now proposed. A dam is planned on the Sabi River near its junction with the Macheke River, with the purpose ultimately of irrigating some 300,000 to 400,000 acres at a cost of £20 million. If this materializes and the land were used for intensive grazing, Pole Evans estimates that it could fatten at least 400,000 bullocks per annum.[1] A pilot scheme has been set up in the first instance to ascertain whether irrigated crop production would be practicable and profitable: the present aim is to grow sufficient grain and vegetables to satisfy all the country's needs and if possible to produce a surplus of vegetables for export to Northern Rhodesia.

Another great dam is to be constructed at the Kariba gorge on the Zambesi: this will not only irrigate a considerable area, but also provide electric power for Northern Rhodesia's mines and for prospective industries in both countries. It is hoped that these dams will benefit not only the areas lying below them, but also the land above them by raising the water level in the soil. One of the most serious difficulties on the African plateau is that the water table is falling and boreholes have to be periodically deepened; this

[1] I. B. Pole Evans, *Empire Jl. Expt. Agric.*, 1950, Vol. 18, pp. 81–94.

necessity would be avoided if the water level should rise sufficiently. The possibilities of increasing output from the European farms are considerable if more water can become available.

Provision is made for the scientific investigation of Southern Rhodesia's many difficult agricultural and soil management problems. An agricultural experiment station has been established on the Rhodes Matopos Estate equipped with some 3,000 head of cattle for animal husbandry investigations, and there is an agricultural college at Gwebi. The country has so many attractions that one can only hope for full realization of its undoubted potentialities.[1]

NORTHERN RHODESIA

Northern Rhodesia forms that part of the southern African plateau constituting the watershed between the Zambesi and the Congo. Much of it is 3,000 to 4,000 feet in altitude rising in places to 5,000 feet. Its rainfall is about 30 to 35 inches and comes mostly in the summer months, October to March, but the distribution is erratic; there is a general resemblance with the rainfall conditions of the wetter parts of Southern Rhodesia. The native vegetation is tropical and subtropical savannah, but with some closed forest.

The area is 194 million acres, and the population in 1950 was estimated to be 1·7 million Africans, 36,000 Europeans, 3,000 Asiatics and others. It is pre-eminently a mining country and is not regarded favourably by Europeans for agricultural settlement; there seem, however, considerable possibilities for food production. Lack of transport facilities has hampered development of arable farming but considerable quantities of maize are grown, also some cotton and steadily increasing amounts of Virginian flue-cured tobacco. The new areas thus opened up for cultivation may in time be used for mixed farming: some enthusiasts have gone there determined to succeed.

There is some cattle ranching which could be considerably developed if the insect diseases were adequately controlled. The tall savannah grasses give place under settlement conditions to nutritious short grasses including some of the valuable digitarias on which cattle could be fattened.[2]

A detailed ecological survey has been made by G. G. Trapnell[3] on the basis of which developments could be planned as they become necessary.

[1] Detailed information is given in the Reports and Bulletins of the Central African Statistical Office, Salisbury.

[2] I. B. Pole Evans, loc. cit.

[3] G. G. Trapnell and J. N. Clothier. The soils vegetation and agricultural systems of North-Western Rhodesia (Report of the Ecological Survey, Lusaka, 1937. G. G. Trapnell: also a corresponding report for North Eastern Rhodesia, Lusaka, 1943).

Chapter 7

AFRICA: II. THE CENTRAL REGIONS: EASTERN GROUP; AFRICAN PEASANT AND EUROPEAN FARMING

Most of this region is a broken plateau from 3,000 to 5,000 feet in elevation; a considerable proportion is savannah with tall hyparrhenia and other grasses, and low trees, combretum and others; under lower rainfall the red grass, *Themeda triandra* becomes more common; under higher rainfall there are more trees, and in the still wetter conditions and higher altitudes the bamboo forests appear; there is, however, little high rainfall forest. The plateau is fringed with a low-lying coastal strip on the east, and it has low-lying areas around the lakes. It is divided up into five territories: Northern Rhodesia, Nyasaland, Tanganyika, Uganda, and Kenya, but the divisions are of political rather than physical significance. In each territory the population, while mainly Africans of many different tribes and races, includes numerous Europeans (mainly British), and Indians.

The old peasant economy was subsistence farming. The procedure was to clear a piece of virgin land, cultivate it as long as it remained productive, then leave it to run wild and break up some new land. An ingenious native method of cropping of unknown but ancient origin gave some protection against erosion. The crops are not grown individually on separate areas, as is done by European farmers following the Mediterranean tradition; instead they are grown together; as each comes ripe it is harvested without damaging the rest and another crop may take its place. At the end of the course the weeds may be grazed, the land once more broken up and sown. The disadvantages are obvious: the probable (though not inevitable) interference of one growing crop with another, the inevitable damage done to a young growing crop in harvesting a ripe one, the difficulty in controlling weeds, and the impossibility of using any better or speedier implements than the hoe. But the method has the great advantage of keeping the land covered with vegetation thus reducing the chances of erosion; and keeping the soil shielded from the sun's rays. It is, of course, extremely troublesome to the statistician for it allows no serviceable estimate of yield or of output per acre. F.A.O. have issued no food balance sheets for Africa excepting only South Africa and Egypt, and the only information available is derived from observation or from limited surveys.

At the same time the insistent demand for better roads and means of transport, for education, health, and other services, and for consumer goods of various kinds, has necessitated the export of commodities sufficiently valuable to pay for all these things. A few of the countries have mineral resources adequate for this purpose: e.g. Northern Rhodesia, and some sections of Tanganyika; but in the main the exports have to be agricultural. This is less difficult than it appears, for the tropical regions have almost a monopoly of the production of vegetable oil, fibres, the alkaloidal beverages tea, coffee, and cocoa. Africa's tropical regions produce in the west nearly 70 per cent of the world's cocoa and palm oil (along with large quantities of groundnuts), and in the east about 75 per cent of the world's sisal and 40 per cent of the world's hard fibres—though only 15 per cent of the coffee and 3·3 per cent of the tea—this last, however, is increasing;[1] also certain desirable fruits, e.g. pineapple, cashew, etc., can be produced more easily than in the cooler regions. Each country of tropical Africa therefore has two groups of agricultural products: the food crops mainly consumed by the growers and their neighbours; and the cash crops, which are sold off the holding and often indeed out of the country. The cash crops in the different regions are:

High rainfall, tropical forest; coastal regions and Congo basin: Palm nut and groundnuts, cocoa in the west, locally rubber, piassava, kola nuts, timber.

Lower rainfall, savannah country; central and eastern highlands: Cotton, groundnuts, sisal, pyrethrum, coffee, tea.

Drier grass country: Livestock products, hides, skins, low-quality meat.

One of the most serious administrative problems in Africa is to strike a proper balance between these two groups, and to integrate the ancient subsistence farming, which is everywhere the basis of the rural economy, with the cash crop farming, which ranges from low-level peasant production to the highly efficient operations of modern plantations. The exported cash crops have to go on to the world market and must therefore satisfy world standards; this necessitates control by Europeans (or Indians) which may be practically complete where close linkage with a factory is necessary as in the case of sugar cane, sisal, tea, and coffee in Kenya and Tanganyika; indirect as with cotton in Uganda; or only slight as in the case of groundnuts and cocoanuts in West Africa. The European enterprises are based on long-period concessions and are worked by hired labour as single-crop plantations; each industry has its research organization and expert technical staff. Where the cash crops are grown by the Africans the scientific help has to come from the Agricultural Departments which are usually very understaffed and charged with other duties also.

The food crops have received less scientific attention than the cash crops —with some striking exceptions such as H. H. Storey's work on cassava (p. 238). The increasing national expenditure in each country has necessitated increasing output of the cash crops, and this seems to have proceeded more rapidly than the increase of food crops; the area under six leading arable cash crops, cotton, groundnuts, sesame, coffee, tea, and tobacco increased from about 13 million acres in 1934 to nearly 17 million acres in 1948—a gain of 27 per cent, while the area under the cereals, maize, wheat, rice, and oats, for home consumption and for sale went up only from 45 million acres to 54 million acres, i.e. about 20 per cent;[2] no data are available for the root crops, cassava, yams, and sweet potatoes, but there is no reason to suppose

[1] Review of Econ. Conditions in Africa: Supplement to *World Economic Review*, 1949–50. United Nations, 1951. The contribution of the British territories is given in "The Products of the Colonial Territories," Col. No. 281, H.M.S.O., 1952.
[2] U.N. Review of Econ. Conditions, 1951. The figures are for all Africa excluding Egypt.

that they have increased more than the cereals. An estimate of the quantities produced annually is given in Table LXX. It is also essential continuously to improve the quality of the cash crops. In general there was less need for the study of food crops because the Africans had already selected varieties and devised methods that, on the whole, produced the necessary food; indeed some of the earlier attempts at improvement by inexperienced officers were not very successful. The chief indigenous foods are the millets and sorghums; the wheat and other cereals indigenous in Abyssinia never spread far till recent times. The Portuguese explorers and the Jesuit fathers from the 16th century onwards introduced from America, maize, sweet potatoes, cassava, and groundnuts, the two last being well suited to poor soils; rice and bananas came from India. Although the Africans in general are very conservative in their habits they gradually adopted these new foods. Sorghums and millets are grown more extensively than any other grains, but much is used for making beer, and the output is decreasing. In East and South Africa they are liable to be severely attacked by a parasite, striga, which may cause considerable loss. Resistant varieties have been found.

TABLE LXX. *Quantities of foods produced annually in Africa. Thousands of metric tons: annual average*

	Millet and and sorghums	Maize	Wheat	Barley	Rice	Cassava (3)	Sweet potatoes	Ground-nuts	Palm oil and kernel(4)
1937–39	9,274	4,584	2,616	2,275	1,561			1,685	570
1947–49	8,982 (1)	6,150 (2)	2,833	3,562	2,132	14,100	9,400	2,182	640
Post-war as percentage of pre-war	97	134	108	157	137			129	112

(1) 1947.
(2) 1949.
(3) 1948 for these last four.
(4) Oil equivalent.

(Review of Economic Conditions in Africa, Supplement to *World Economic Review*, 1949–50, United Nations, Washington, 1951.)

During the ten years the population had probably risen about 15 per cent.

But the Africans have never achieved a satisfactory dietary; almost all those examined are short of fats, vitamins, and mineral substances, and all except those of the pastoral tribes, of protein also. Carbohydrates always preponderate; the dietaries are very unbalanced. These defects are intensified by the various worms that heavily infest the intestines of large numbers of the population and assimilate nutrients that should be nourishing the body. Ignorance and social custom often operate badly; eggs and mutton are taboo for women, especially pregnant women, among some tribes in Uganda; milk is not taken by the men. These dietetic deficiencies lead to lower health, poorer resistance to disease, and low working efficiency; diseases directly resulting from lack of vitamins and proteins are widespread.[1] The subject has long attracted the attention of British experts and administrators responsible for overseas territories. India had been the classical ground for

[1] E.g. pellagra among maize eaters, kwashiorkor (protein deficiency) among children (*F.A.O. Annual Report*, 1950–51).

investigation; Africa came later but much has by now been done. The reports in 1927 by J. C. Gilks and John Boyd Orr (p. 257) on nutrition of natives in Kenya and by E. J. Wright on diseases due to lack of vitamins A and B in Sierre Leone were quickly and widely followed up by studies in all the British parts of Africa. These revealed widespread malnutrition resulting in much ill-health and disease. The whole subject was pulled together in an important report to the League of Nations in 1939 by Drs. Burnet and Aykroyd,[1] which was amplified and discussed in the following September at the full Assembly when Bruce of Australia spoke of the great benefits that would result from "a marriage of health and agriculture." The matter was vigorously taken up in Great Britain by John Boyd Orr, Walter Elliot, and others, and the Colonial Office in April 1936, asked each of the colonies and mandated dependent territories for a survey of the present state of nutrition of their people and of the steps being taken to improve it. In the same year A. D. Hall published his book *The Improvement of Native Agriculture in Relation to Population and Public Health.* The surveys sent to the Colonial Office were examined by a group of experts and their report was published in 1939,[2] by which time a number of reports had been issued from the separate countries showing what was being done to effect improvements.[3] The work goes on unceasingly.

A fundamental difficulty has been that improvements in food production have simply led to increases in population, often at a rate greater than that at which the improvements have taken place. Efforts have been further hampered by the very uneven distribution of the population. The people are anchored to the natural sources of water supply or those opened up by native methods; they are extremely reluctant to move to new areas where water is provided by modern engineering methods; examples from Uganda and Tanganyika are given later. The settled areas become overcrowded, overcropped, and overgrazed, and erosion sets in reducing still further their food-producing capacity.

Matters are made worse by the prevalence of malaria transmitted by anopheles mosquitoes which abound wherever there is sufficient water and the temperatures are not too low; it is a tragedy that the water sources so indispensable to man should also harbour mosquitoes. For although malaria is not usually fatal to adults it is very debilitating, sapping their vitality, lowering their physical capacity for work, and impairing their mental capacity; it is often fatal to children.[4]

This vicious circle, malnutrition and ignorance preventing improvement, and lack of improvement increasing poverty, could never be broken without

[1] Burnet and Aykroyd, *Quarterly Bull. Health Organization,* League of Nations, June 1935, Geneva.

[2] *Nutrition in the Colonial Empire,* 2 vols., Cmd. 6050, H.M.S.O., 1939.

[3] These are summarized in Imperial Bureau Animal Nutrition, Tech. Com. No. 8, Rowett Institute, Aberdeen, January 1937.

[4] The mosquito can be controlled by D.D.T. and the malaria by paludrine. D. Bagster Wilson instances an area in Tanganyika where the average number of children surviving to women who had completed their child-bearing life was only 1·13; assuming equal numbers of boys and girls this would mean that only one woman in two left a surviving female to produce children of her own (Report of the Malaria Unit, Tanga, 1933–34, Govt. Printer, Dar-es-Salaam, 1936).

help from outside. In 1944 the Colonial Office set up the Colonial Development and Welfare Fund to finance essential works that could not be carried out with the local resources, and followed this in 1948 with the Colonial Development Corporation having a capital of £120 million and the purpose of "improving the standard of living of the colonial peoples by increasing their productivity and wealth": it undertakes large-scale operations outside the scope of the local departments. A third body was set up under the Ministry of Food: the Overseas Food Corporation with the intention of producing food for the United Kingdom, but this is more widely known for its failures than its successes.

Another difficulty among many of the tribes in the savannah and grass regions with which we are now dealing is that the crop production is done by the women who are not easily accessible to the agricultural officers; the men are concerned with the cattle which graze on the natural herbage.

The Africans never invented the wheel or the plough. Consequently all burdens had to be carried, usually on the head or the back, and all cultivation had to be done by the hoe. Unlike the plough, the hoe imposes no preference for more or less rectangular fields; it can be used on the most irregularly shaped patches of land. So the African native holdings tend to be in patches. There are various systems of land tenure, but many of them confer on the family the use of a particular piece of land, and this is passed on to the children and remains with them after marriage. The result is that the holdings become subdivided and scattered; a man may have some of his original family holding and, in addition, plots brought in by marriages over several generations. These small, scattered holdings cannot possibly be worked economically, nor can much improvement be effected. Many attempts have been made to consolidate the holdings by exchange of land and to give the whole cultivated area the rectangular layout that would enable modern methods to be used, but in general the natives strenuously object. This is not mere mulish obstinacy; it is the reaction of the peasant everywhere—in Europe as well as Africa—to the suggestion that he should give up a piece of land which has long been in the family and to which he has an attachment incomprehensible to those who have long since lost connection with the soil. Efforts are being made to find some system which satisfies the peasant's desire to keep his land and at the same time allows the use of modern agricultural methods.

Tropical soils are generally poor—in spite of old beliefs to the contrary. Responses are frequently obtained to nitrogenous and phosphatic fertilizers, and to cattle manure, though this is rarely used. Improved varieties are capable of higher yields provided always that the necessary plant nutrients are in the soil or supplied as fertilizers. Better implements would allow of better cultivation, thus facilitating earlier sowing and fuller utilization of available soil moisture. The possibility of introducing mechanized methods has been much studied,[1] but nothing can be done till the holdings are rearranged. In the meantime, as G. B. Masefield has pointed out,[2] much could be done by introducing simple implements of sound design to replace the present

[1] See Rpt. of a survey of problems in mechanization of native agriculture in tropical African Colonies, Colonial Advisory Council Pub., No. 1, H.M.S.O., 1950.
[2] G. B. Masefield, *World Crops*, 1951, Vol. 2, No. 2.

clumsy appliances; they must, however, be light, as the native lacks physical strength; and durable, as he has no feeling for the care of tools.[1]

The livestock are chiefly cattle and they usually outnumber the human beings. They are not used for food, nor for draught purposes as in the ancient Mediterranean and Indian countries; their special purposes are usually to mark a man's social position, and to furnish the bride-price or *lobola* among the Bantu peoples. For these purposes numbers only count, the quality of the animals having no more significance than the condition of a £1 note, so long as it is intact.

Since the cattle tribesmen are from childhood upwards very good herdsmen, it is tempting to think that a considerable livestock industry could be developed in Southern and Central Africa. This may happen, but there are serious difficulties. In the main the native cattle are poor and unthrifty, but a few of the breeds are promising, some for beef production, others for dairying; and they have the advantage of being more resistant to the local conditions and diseases than imported British cattle. Considerable improvement in quality would in any event be absolutely essential, but their present significance for prestige and bride price makes it difficult to effect the necessary culling or controlled breeding. Efforts are made to encourage sales by the establishment of livestock markets under Government supervision to ensure fair dealings. No provision is usually made for the long dry season, however, and in consequence the animals lose condition badly and the land is grazed bare. This indeed is one of the chief causes of erosion.

Lack of refrigeration makes the use of large animals for meat very difficult except in towns; elsewhere the European has to feed on small animals, usually very tough chickens.

There is no link between animal husbandry and crop production; the manure if used at all is for other purposes: fuel, where wood is scarce,[2] plastering the huts, etc., it is not put on the arable land. The grazing areas are burned in time to encourage new growth with the onset of the rains; much harm has already resulted and experts are not yet agreed whether this can be avoided and if so under what conditions.

In spite of a considerable amount of veterinary activity cattle diseases are still widespread. One of the worst is 'Ngana caused by a trypanosome carried by the tsetse fly; another species causes sleeping sickness in human beings. Large areas of bush and forest lying between 10° N. lat. and 15° S. lat., and estimated at one quarter of Africa's land, are so heavily infested with this insect that all domestic animals except poultry are completely excluded: indeed the tsetse fly has been called Africa's best protector against erosion. No other insect is anything like so potent. A vigorous campaign has been in progress for some years against it, by the use of D.D.T., clearance of the bush and in some instances destruction of the game which may constitute a reservoir of the trypanosome. Various chemical compounds have been

---

[1] At Kongwa the groundnut supervisors evolved the aphorism: "Give a native a job and he will finish the tools."

[2] Determinations in the Sudan gave values of 6,050, 6,920, and 6,550 B.T.U. for three samples of dung (T. N. Jewitt and H. W. B. Barlow, *Empire Jl. Expt. Agric.*, 1949, Vol. 17, pp. 1–17).

shown to cure the disease and also to protect against it for some months.[1] Spraying D.D.T. from an aeroplane appears to have eliminated the fly from an infested area of Natal, but this was surrounded by fly-free country; it is less likely to be successful in dense forest regions. In any case, the insecticide may kill beneficial insects and so do indirect harm. Moreover, when the tsetse fly is eliminated and cattle come in they are very liable to cause soil erosion unless adequate steps are taken. In any case the cost is very high.

East coast fever, caused by a piroplasm carried by ticks, results in great loss of cattle, but can be controlled by dipping: it is by far the commonest cattle disease in the tsetse-free areas. Rinderpest is another serious disease: protection is now possible by inoculation with the proper vaccine though the veterinary departments are in some districts too understaffed to treat all the animals.

Diseases and pests are responsible for considerable losses of crop. Locusts occasionally devastate a whole region, birds attack sorghum and millets, insects and fungi attack all crops. Groundnuts and cassava, both of American origin, proved very susceptible to African virus diseases. Fortunately this trouble can now be overcome for cassava; in one of the most impressive studies yet made in the breeding of tropical plants, H. H. Storey succeeded in producing strains combining high yielding capacity with a high degree of resistance to the virus. He did this at the Amani Experiment Station in Tanganyika. The Germans had established this station when they held the country before the first war: there they tested various exotic plants with a view to introduction if successful. Among these was a rubber producer, seara. It proved to be unsuitable and was not further investigated. When the British took over Storey found some of the plants still growing and noticed that, although they belong to the cassava family, they did not take the disease; presumably therefore they possessed the genes carrying resistance. They produced no tubers, and were in themselves useless as food, but Storey was able to cross them with the cultivated cassava. The first generation also formed no tubers, but these appeared after two or three back crosses and ultimately plants were obtained that combined good tuber formation with high resistance to virus. These have been multiplied and are being distributed, their yields are considerably higher than those of the usual susceptible varieties: sometimes double or treble.

The greatest improvement in African agriculture if it were feasible would be a fusion of livestock and arable husbandry such as was effected in Great Britain in the 18th and early 19th centuries. The British farmers in Kenya are working in this direction and will probably find solutions for the practical difficulties. Other difficulties may prove more obdurate. The resulting mixed farming systems require steady continuous work almost all the year round and the native has never been used to this: he is accustomed to long slack

[1] Among the most effective are antrycide, prepared by F. H. S. Curd and D. G. Davey of I.C.I., and phenanthridine. Predecessors included surfen C made in the 1930's by the German firm Bayer, dimidium bromide prepared by Morgan and Walls of the D.S.I.R. Other compounds cure sleeping sickness in human beings, e.g. Bayer's antrypol and the British pentamidine. P. A. Buxton has shown that the human disease has now become relatively unimportant (Colonial Office Rept., November 1948). For fuller details see H. E. Hornby, *Animal Trypanosomiasis in E. Africa* (Colonial Office Publications, 1949), and H. E. Shortt, *British Med. Journ.*, November 11, 1951, pp. 1103–10.

periods. He has no inherent or acquired love of work as such; indeed, both custom and taboo regard it as something degrading or evil, moreover as G. B. Masefield reminds us: "Most natives of the tropics set a much higher value on leisure than do Europeans." Where work is done for wages it has repeatedly happened that no more is done after a certain amount has been earned; increase in wage rates has resulted simply in a corresponding reduction in output. Much heart-breaking educational effort will be required before the necessary change of attitude can be accomplished.

NYASALAND

Nyasaland is the strip of country on the west and south sides of Lake Nyasa; most of it is on the central African plateau but there is lower land to the south; there also are the Shiré Highlands. It is 23·94 million acres in extent, had at the end of 1948 an estimated population of 2·4 million Africans, 3,000 Europeans, and 4,000 Asiatics. The climate is healthy and the high country is not only suitable, but very agreeable for European habitation. The chief cash crop is tobacco which can be produced of good quality; tea, cotton and tung oil are important, and their production is expanding: Nyasaland, indeed, produces more tea than any other country in Africa and its output is increasing, though not as much as that of Kenya:

Production of tea. Thousand tons.

Average pre-war	Nyasaland	Kenya	Mozambique	Uganda	All Africa
1934–38	4·3	3·7	0·5	0·1	9·0
1949	5·7	5·4	2·4	1·5	15·5
1950	6·9	6·6	3·0	1·85	19·6

(*Review of Economic Conditions in Africa*, United Nations, Washington, 1951.) and Internat. Tea Cttee. Bull. of Stat., June 1953.)

These and pulses form the chief exports.

The main food crops are the sorghums of which a number of varieties, mostly of *S. vulgare*, are grown, especially in the drier lower regions. The more common sorts are 9 to 15 feet in height requiring five to seven months for growth, some with sweet, others with bitter grains and stems; others are shorter and require only three or four months for growth; birds, especially finches, do much harm to the close-headed varieties; the open-headed sorts are therefore preferred.[1]

As elsewhere in Africa, maize is displacing the sorghums as food, one reason given being that the maize is more easily ground in the domestic *ntondo*. Where the soil is unsuitable for maize or the rainfall too uncertain, cassava is grown and also sorghum, these being less liable to fail. Some rice is grown (usually as a cash crop) on the low ground where water supply is adequate. It is more dependent on good moisture supply than the millets and is liable to fail if the rains are inadequate: hunger and even famine may then ensue: the sorghums are safer.

A number of wild sorghums occur in Nyasaland, and there seems scope

[1] For an account of some of the African sorghums see S. H. Evelyn, *World Crops*, 1951, Vol. 3, pp. 65–9, and for a genetic study: F. X. Laubscher, *Sci. Bull.* 242, 1945, Govt. Printer, Pretoria. For more on Nyasaland see W. B. Morgan, *Geog. Journ.*, 1953, Vol. 119, 459–469

for some valuable plant breeding work with a view of improving the grain and making it more acceptable to the natives. Its drought-resisting qualities make it specially valuable throughout all parts of Africa where droughts are liable to occur. Where maize displaces the sorghums as food they are still grown but used mostly for making beer.

The people are mainly agricultural: they have very little livestock: cattle in 1948 numbered only 267,000 and were practically all confined to the northern province; goats numbered rather less: there were very few sheep or pigs.

The Colonial Office nutrition enquiry of 1936 showed that the diet of the north supplied a certain amount of animal foods: meat (but only little milk), some game, small rodents, caterpillars, flying ants, locusts and fish; but eggs were taboo in certain cases. Elsewhere there was a considerable range of vegetable relishes both wild and cultivated: beans, peas, groundnuts, edible fungi, tomatoes and onions. One curious result of the great distance from the sea was that the salt was derived from vegetable ash and therefore contained very little sodium; in consequence the dietary was deficient in that element. It was further noted that the increasing adoption of European clothing might lead to a deficiency of Vitamin D which had been synthesized by the sunlight so long as the body was exposed.

The country is now almost self-sufficing in food production, importing only wheat, flour and some sugar, and against this exporting considerable quantities of pulses. These may increase, perhaps also exports of groundnuts, but the most likely export development seems to be more of the present cash crops. Some of the tobacco-growing companies have long had European experts in charge of their land.

Another important export is labour; many of the men seek work elsewhere for part of their time.

TANGANYIKA

Tanganyika has a land area of 217·6 million acres, some of which lies low forming a coastal region narrow in the north, but widening considerably to the south where it joins Mozambique; the greater portion, however, forms part of the central African plateau, here about 4,000 feet high. This is broken by two blocks of higher land: the southern highlands stretching from Iringa in the central plateau to Lake Nyasa, and the northern highlands including Kilimanjaro and other mountains in the Moshi and Arusha districts. The climate in the north resembles that of Kenya; the rainfall is similar in type, the long rains from March to June, when anything from 10 to 30 inches may fall in the agricultural areas; and the short rains in November and December which are quite unreliable. In the southern highlands there is one long wet season from November to May and the total fall may be 30 to 60 inches, the wettest period being January to March. Both highland regions are suitable for European settlement and are so used, but being much smaller in extent than in Kenya the European population is correspondingly less. Nearly half the country (96 million acres) is forest, mostly dry forest, the rest, which receives about 45 inches of rain annually, is largely savannah with the tall *Hyparrhenia* grasses and thickets of *Combretum* and other plants that cover

240

so much of Kenya, Uganda, and Northern Rhodesia. To the north-east there is drier short grass: this is ranching country.

The population in 1948 was 7·4 millions of which 7·33 millions were Africans of more than 100 different tribes each with its own language and customs; there were 60,740 Indians, mostly traders and artisans as in Kenya; and 16,300 Europeans of whom no less than 5,400 were Polish refugees. The population is distributed very unevenly over the land; it is excluded from most of the forest area by the tsetse fly, and from much of the savannah area by lack of water; Clement Gillman pointed out that about five-sixths of the people are concentrated on the one-tenth of the land having sufficient water supply for their needs—areas in the coastal regions, the southern highlands, and districts around Lake Victoria.

As in Kenya there are two groups of crops providing cash and food respectively, but the country is less dependent on cash crops than Kenya, because it has valuable minerals and timber resources now being exploited. Its most serious problems are the control of the tsetse fly and the redistribution of the population which in places is very congested.

Control of the tsetse fly is feasible but very costly; it disappears from settled areas as the bush is cleared. Fortunately only the cattle variety occurs; there is no sleeping sickness among the humans. The fly, however, appears to be spreading, being carried apparently inside the cars or under the mud-guards of the motor lorries that now traverse the country; inspection points have now been set up on the roads. Hitherto the fly has protected the country from erosion by keeping out cattle; it remains to be seen whether other protection can be substituted where the fly is eliminated.

The chief cash crop is sisal of which there are about 250,000 acres grown on deep well drained soils. The plantations are permanent. Many are owned by large British organizations, but some by Indians and Greeks; usually they keep close to the railway for facility of transport. The plants survive the long dry season because they can remain dormant during drought; they are kept in use for six years and are then renewed without any intervening crops. Fertilizers are effective for correcting nutrient deficiencies that have caused physiological diseases, but not usually otherwise. About one-third of the world's supply of sisal comes from Tanganyika and it forms about one-half of the country's exports. The production is well managed. The industry has its own service for recruiting labour, its own welfare schemes; the rations issued to the workers have to satisfy Government requirements. A special experiment station has been established at Ngomeni near Tanga to deal with the various problems involved.

The two other important cash crops are cotton, chiefly grown by the natives, and coffee;[1] there is some production of tea and could be more, also some pyrethrum, tobacco, and sugar, but not enough of the two last to satisfy the home demand so that considerable imports are necessary.

The European settlers in the northern province, and to a smaller extent those in the southern highlands, grow a good deal of wheat.[2] In the north

[1] The Coffee Research Station is financed from the Colonial Department Fund and by a levy on exported coffee. Its first ten years of work is described by the Director, S. M. Gilbert, in *Empire Jl. Expt. Agric.*, 1945, Vol. 13, pp. 113–24.

[2] See N. R. Fuggles-Couchman, *World Crops*, 1951, Vol. 3, pp. 183–7, for descriptions.

there is much mechanized large-scale production, especially between 4,300 and 6,300 feet altitude; as in Kenya, yellow rust becomes troublesome at higher levels and leaf and stem rust at lower levels. In the south, cultivation at higher altitudes is practicable, and there is much African production at 6,000 to 8,000 feet. The areas and quantities marketed are given in Table LXXI.

TABLE LXXI. *Areas of wheat, and quantities marketed in Tanganyika in different years.*

	1939	1945	1947	1948	1950 (1)
Acreage	16,250	96,390	32,225	39,000	30,000
Marketed, tons					
Northern Province					
European	1,293	2,549	1,985	3,326	
African	257	739	274	336	
Northern wheat scheme		6,837	2,267		
Southern highlands					
European	46	110	50	98	
African	100	577	620	420	
Total	1,696	10,812	5,227	4,402	8,000

The acreage in 1930 had been 13,485.

(1) C.E.C. Grain Rpt., 1953. The other figures are from Fuggles-Couchman, *loc. cit.*

The northern wheat scheme was a war-time measure fostered by the Government which brought in 22,000 additional acres, some contiguous to existing wheat land, the rest out in the open grassland of the Oldeani ex-enemy estates. The scheme began in 1944 when it produced 4,000 tons of wheat: it was discontinued in 1948. It had been much criticized, but it proved that Tanganyika could produce considerably more wheat than it had done. The limit is set in the north by the uncertain rainfall and in the south by poverty of much of the soil: a great lack of phosphate and a marked liability to compact on drying; everywhere the serious shortage of transport facilities, as in the case of sisal, keeps production near to the railway.

The average yield on European farms is 9 cwt. per acre, though up to 17 have been obtained on large areas and even 23 cwt. on small areas; African farmers obtain about 5 cwt. per acre. Now that the war-time scheme has been dropped production no longer covers requirements and importation is again necessary.

The chief native food crops are the millets and sorghums with some maize and rice in places. Cassava, sweet potatoes, beans and groundnuts, are widely grown, also bananas and some native vegetables, but the food habits of the different tribes differ widely.

In 1949 cattle numbered 6·4 million, sheep 2·3 million, and goats 3·5 million. There is much export of skins and hides, and a canning industry is being started. The Government propose to lease 300,000 acres in the Northern Province in one or three blocks for livestock ranching.

The nutrition of the natives is on the whole fairly good, though there are usually food shortages of some kind before harvest, and a lack of milk and meat in most dietaries. More and more meat is now being eaten, however. Taboo and tradition forbid the consumption of eggs and milk in some cases; deficiency diseases and malnutrition are recorded, but the Colonial Office Nutrition Report of 1939 was not prepared to state how widely they occurred.

The Colonial Development fund has made a grant of £500,000 to aid in opening up the country. Among other operations is the development of Sukumaland, an interesting example of the work being done by the British in Africa.[1] Sukumaland lies south of Lake Victoria and has an area of 5¼ million acres with a population of about a million people, increasing at the rate of about 1·5 per cent per annum. In places the density of population is 450 per square mile. The rainfall ranges from 30 to 45 inches per annum, and the natural vegetation is thorn bush and open woodland. As this harbours tsetse fly, birds and vermin, it is cleared entirely before cultivation begins. A number of food crops and several cash crops are grown, cotton being by far the most important. The cropped areas are as follows, in thousand acres:

Food crops		Food and cash crops		Cash crops	
Sorghum	346	Groundnuts	25	Cotton	87
Pennisetum	182	Paddy	16		
Cassava	93	Cowpeas	13		
Sweet potatoes	33				
Maize	24				
Others	17				
	695		54		

The area of pasture is 4·9 million acres.

The total area of crops is thus 836,000 for 1 million people, rather more than 0·8 acres per head, or omitting the cash crops about 0·75 acres per head. Average yields per acre cannot be given owing to poverty of data, but in the very dry famine year 1949 sorghum yielded 470 lb. per acre, pennisetum 519, and cassava 4,602: these are probably well below the normal average; it is considered that 800 lb. of pennisetum should be obtainable.

For a family of seven, 2 tons a year of grain and cassava flour are considered a proper ration; this would furnish about 26 ozs. per head per day, giving about 2,600 calories. Some of the grain, however, is used for making beer.

The livestock of the region number about 2 million stock units,[2] and the grazing land is about 4·9 million acres; the area available per stock unit averages therefore about 2½ acres, but in places it is only 1 acre. There has been much overgrazing in places and much erosion; fortunately most of the soils are fertile and deep so that rehabilitation is not difficult, and fortunately also the arable land has not been badly eroded. Hitherto the only cultivating implement has been the hoe, which does not normally bring

[1] N. V. Runce, *Empire Jl. Expt. Agric.*, 1951, Vol. 19, pp. 253–64. For further accounts of agriculture in the Lake, Central, and Western Provinces of Tanganyika, see N. V. Runce, *Agric. of the Cultivated Steppe*, Dept. of Agric., Tanganyika, and Longmans, Green and Co., Capetown, 1949.

[2] 1 stock unit equals 1 head of cattle or 5 sheep or goats, as in Kenya. But note that in the Union of South Africa the equivalent is 7 sheep or goats.

about erosion especially where, as is usual, the main crops are millets inter-planted with others.[1]

Unfortunately improvement necessitates substituting the plough for the hoe, and this may lead to erosion unless the work is done on the contour and ridging and tie-ridging are carried out. It is equally necessary to intro-duce the wheel, so that wheel barrows and wagons may displace the woman's head as means of transport. The use of cattle manure is to be encouraged; it gives remarkable increases—40 to 50 per cent—not only in the year of application but for some five or more years afterwards. Hitherto it has not been used; indeed, there is a prejudice against it—perhaps intelligible as it would have to be carried in baskets on women's heads from the kraal to the field.

Schemes for intensification of cropping are being pushed forward; tractors will be used for breaking up new land, better crop varieties are being sought, more water-holes provided, and devices such as tie ridging for retaining rain water on the land are being developed.

As new areas are opened up, it becomes possible to distribute the popula-tion more evenly over the land. Here, however, serious difficulties arise: the people are very reluctant to move. The Wameru occupy a semi-arid area in the Arusha district which is now overcrowded and quite unsuitable for African methods of cultivation: persistence in them will lead inevitably to soil erosion. The Government proposed to transfer a section of the tribe to better land, some of which had been compulsorily acquired from Euro-peans; £20,000 was spent in putting in water. No objection was raised by the tribesmen when the scheme was announced, but when everything was ready and the time came for moving they refused to go: 2,500 of them organized passive resistance. Yet they had been amply compensated for the land they gave up and all costs of removal were borne by the Government. Their old land, useless for them, could have been advantageously used by Europeans for ranching.[2]

Tanganyika has possibilities of considerable development; it possesses great areas of good soil and considerable forest and mineral wealth. Impor-tant scientific work on tropical agriculture has long been carried out at the Amani Research Station, established by the Germans during their occupation and developed by the British when they took charge of the country. H. H. Storey's work on virus resistant cassava (p. 238) and Geoffrey Milne's studies of tropical soils are among the more notable of the studies.

Some of Tanganyika's enthusiasts think it could become the richest of the three territories. But its development must await better transport facilities, better control of tsetse fly and above all fuller knowledge of the most effective methods of procedure.

Tanganyika will long be remembered as the scene of one of the most spectacular failures in modern times. An attempt was started in 1946 to bring into cultivation 3¼ million acres of tsetse-infested unoccupied land in the southern part of the territory, for the production of groundnuts. The scheme had good technical advisers, almost unlimited money, and a friendly

---

[1] Sorghum is generally grown alone, but pennisetum, which is preferred on the light soils, is mixed with cassava and pulses. Maize mixes well with other crops.
[2] *The Times*, December 4, 1951.

minister, yet the £38 million spent on it by the British taxpayer has gone leaving little trace behind it,[1] except to demonstrate the unsuitability of a remote Government agency for opening up and developing new country. On the other hand the British farmers in Kenya have by their own resources and at no cost to the British taxpayer converted a wilderness that the Africans could never tackle into productive farmland.

The land is now divided up into separate farms worked on more general cropping schemes and under individual management; the indications are that these will prove more successful. The region is typical of vast areas in East Africa at present almost waste; if methods can be devised for making it productive they will greatly help in the development of the country.

MOZAMBIQUE

Mozambique, founded on an ancient Portuguese settlement, is the coastal region lying between Tanganyika and Natal; it is bounded on the east by the high plateau, on which it hardly trenches except in the neighbourhood of the Shiré highlands. The coastal plain is widest in the south: here most of the land is below 500 feet altitude; the rest is below 1,000 feet. It is narrower in the north: most of the land lies mainly between 1,000 and 2,000 feet, but rises higher on the eastern border. There is much tall grass and open woodland on the lower ground, and many palm trees near the coast. The higher land is savannah. The soils of the wide coastal plain are deep alluvials. The annual rainfall is higher in the coastal regions than inland; it is highest in the central coastal region round Quelemane and Beira— about 55 inches; it is lower to the north (35 inches) and the south (25 inches); in the north (Tete) it is about 20 inches except on the high ground near Lake Nyasa (Vila Cabral) where it is 50 inches; in the south it is only about 6 inches at Pafuri where the Limpopo enters the country.[2] The rainfall is seasonal: it comes mostly between September and May with a maximum about March: the winter months June to August or thereabouts are dry; the higher the rainfall the shorter the dry season. What makes the country so rich, however, is its wonderful system of rivers which never run dry but flow gently through the deep alluvial soils of the plains.

The area of the country is 297,731 square miles (190 million acres). It is only sparsely populated: in 1950 the total population was 5·7 millions, including about 28,000 Europeans, and 9,000 or 10,000 Indians—the latter being far fewer than in any of the countries of British East Africa. The Africans are mainly Bantu tribes: they appear to be increasing rapidly; in 1926 they were estimated at 3·48 million: if the figures are correct the average increase during the 24 years had been about 1·4 per cent per annum.

---

[1] Some of the incidental information on costs of production of groundnuts, sorghum, and maize has been summarized by J. F. Cameron, B. W. van Keulen, and others in *Empire Jl. Expt. Agric.*, 1951, Vol. 19, pp. 265–74; and the mechanized land clearing is discussed by J. MacBride, J. E. Capell, A. H. Bunting, and others in *World Crops*, 1951, Vol. 3, pp. 89–94.

For details of the original scheme see White Paper Cmd. 7030, 1947, and for its early progress Cmd. 7314; also A. J. Wakefield, *J. Roy. Soc. Arts*, June 4, 1948.

[2] Anuário Climatológico de Portugal, 1947 (Lisbon, 1951). It is possible that these figures are low, as 1947 was a year of drought in the Union to the south and in Southern Rhodesia to the north.

The higher country is healthy, but there is a good deal of malaria on the coast, and many areas are infested with tsetse fly.

The country is watered with many rivers, which not only mitigate the effects of the dry season, but offer considerable possibilities for improvement of the land by drainage and irrigation. Schemes are now in project on the Limpopo and the Incomati valleys: a large one in the Limpopo valley devised by Col. Balfour was accepted some twenty-five years ago to improve some 50,000 acres of land. The most productive region is in the centre around Quelimane and in the valleys of the great rivers, especially the Zambesi and the Limpopo.

As would be expected from the position of the country, the range of crops is very wide; it includes copra, cashew nuts, cotton seed and sisal grown in its northern neighbour Tanganyika, and sugar cane and maize grown in Natal to the south. (Table LXXII.) The chief export is sugar which goes chiefly to Portugal: in order to assist this industry the Portuguese refrain from producing sugar at home from sugar beet, which they could quite well grow. The output has increased greatly in recent years: in 1926 it had been 51,000 tons; now it is about 90,000 tons. It is grown in the southern section of the coastal plain. Next in importance comes copra, grown throughout the plain, but especially in the central section; the Quelimane district has some of the largest coconut plantations in the world. Maize, cashew nuts and cotton seed are also important exports. Sisal is grown in the north; the conditions are very favourable, but its quality is inferior to that of Tanganyika's product.

The native food crops are as usual cassava and maize, but no dietetic or nutritional investigations appear to have been carried out. Many of the men are away for longer or shorter periods working in the Transvaal mines.

TABLE LXXII. *Estimated production of food crops in the Portuguese overseas territories, 1951. Metric tons*

Crops	Angola (Portuguese W. Africa)	Mozambique (Portuguese E. Africa)	Portuguese Guinea	S. Tomé and Principe Islands	Cape Verde Islands	Portuguese Timor	Portuguese India
Beans	50,000	20,000	—	—	3,000	—	—
Coffee	50,000	—	—	2,000	500	1,500	—
Cocoa	200	—	—	8,000	—	0·09	—
Sesame	800	2,000	—	—	—	—	—
Cotton seeds	10,000	30,000	—	—	—	—	—
Groundnuts	4,000	10,000	40,000	—	—	—	—
Cashew nuts	—	50,000	—	—	—	—	—
Maize	350,000	40,000	—	—	3,000	—	—
Manioc	300,000	10,000	—	—	—	—	—
Rice	20,000	15,000	30,000	—	—	—	42,000
Sugar	55,000	90,000	—	—	—	—	—
Copra	—	45,000	—	4,500	—	2,000	—
Coconut	12,000	—	15,000	4,200	—	—	—
Palm oil	14,000	—	1,200	2,000	—	—	—

(Communicated from Estação Agronomica Nacional Sacavém, Portugal.)

Livestock are very few, as is also to be expected from the general low altitude of the country: the numbers have been in thousands:

	Cattle	Sheep	Goats	Pigs
1940	577	63	244	55
1950	700	70	348	82

(*F.A.O. Stat. Year Book*, 1951.)

Sheep are very few as in Natal: pigs are few but apparently increasing. Cattle predominate: their numbers have steadily increased from 394,000 in 1925 to 700,000 in 1950. They are chiefly in the southern part of the country south of the Zambesi; a great expanse of 97 million acres where abundant grass, good water supply that keeps the grass perennially green, together with proximity to port and rail facilities of Lourenço Marquez makes this region one of the most suitable in Southern Africa for the establishment of a beef industry. Trouble is always liable to arise from tsetse fly and ticks; it is claimed that the latter are so well controlled by dipping that no case of east coast fever has occurred since 1917, but tsetse fly still remains. I. B. Pole Evans, in his recent survey of the possibilities of beef production in Southern Africa, puts this region among the most promising.[1]

KENYA

Most of Kenya lies on the plains about 1,500 to 2,500 feet above sea level spread widely over eastern and southern Africa. Its distinctive feature is a block of higher country about 4,000 to 9,000 feet altitude in its western part, stretching between lat. 1° N. and lat. 1° S., running north-westerly from Nairobi with the snow-clad Mount Kenya as its eastern outpost and ending with Mount Elgon in the north-west, with the Aberdare Mountains, the Rift Valley, the Cherangani hills and the impressive Elgeyo escarpment in between. As a result of this wide range of altitudes there is considerable variation in the climatic conditions. The great plains in the north and centre, which form about three-quarters of Kenya, have some 10 to 15 inches of rain coming in two seasons, March or April to June, and October or November to December; evaporation is high and there are long periods of drought. In the highlands the rainfall is greater, increasing with increasing altitude to about 90 inches per annum; also the dry periods decrease in length. Temperatures at the lower altitudes are high both day and night; with increasing altitudes the night temperatures fall quite low; fires are needed in the evenings and blankets at night. Lake Victoria further modifies the climate by causing rain in the June to October gap, thus making one long wet season from March to December with heaviest rainfall in July and August.

The vegetation follows closely these climatic variations. The arid plains carry desert grass and low shrub, drought-dormant for most of the year; with the increasing rainfall and shorter drought periods of the higher altitudes larger grasses and trees come in; at about 25 inches the grass is largely *Themeda triandra*, one of the commonest grasses in Africa, and the trees mainly flat topped thorny acacias sparsely distributed: this makes the best ranching country; at about 35 to 60 inches of rain larger leaved trees, *Combretum* and others, come in along with taller grasses such as *Hyparrhenia* —this region stretches into Uganda and Tanganyika; in still higher and wetter regions (6,500 to 10,000 feet) high land forest predominates.

[1] *Empire Jl. Expt. Agric.*, 1950, Vol. 18, pp. 81–94.

This high country has profoundly affected Kenya's development, because although it is on the equator it is climatically suitable for European settlement, and being almost uninhabited at the beginning of this century it was marked out for the settlement of soldiers, first after the South African War and later after the wars of 1914–18 and of 1939–45; they were joined by other enterprising spirits who wished to share in the adventure of developing a new country. It was not an easy task, the bush and trees were difficult to clear; tsetse fly and mosquitoes abounded; water was often scarce; lions, leopards and other animals took heavy toll of the farm animals. The economic disasters of the 1930's hit the settlers very hard, but they pulled through: they converted the waste and often pestilential bush into productive farms, made some very attractive homes, the best of them recalling the spacious life of the old English country houses. Roads were made and gradually a highly organized and prosperous community developed. Settlement is still continuing under the auspices of the European Settlement Board; the total area of land available is limited, but as the agriculture has improved some of the earlier settlers have found it convenient to sell part of their holdings for the establishment of new farms.

The land was utilized as follows in 1950:

	Million acres
Native areas	33·28
Alienated or available for Europeans	7·87
Crown forests[1]	3·03
Townships and reserves	0·18
Other Government reserves	0·18
Utilized	44·54
Northern areas	73·86
Unclassified	22·16
Total	140·56

The British and European settlers occupy only a small part of the total area—less than 8 million out of 140 million acres; the rest is reserved for the various native tribes, Bantu, Nilotic, and others and cannot be alienated. Some of these tribes, notably the Masai, are cattle men; others including the Kikuyu are cultivators: in general their land is better than that of the white farmers, but only a fraction of it is cultivated.

The population in 1948 was:

	Thousands
European	29·66
Indians and Goans	97·69
Arabs (24·17) and others	27·67
African natives (estimated)	5,218·0
Total	5,373·0

[1] The total gazetted forest reserves are 3·66 million acres, of which 93 per cent are in the highlands. About a quarter of the forest area (876,800 acres) is scheduled for protection of soil and water supplies.

The Arabs are mainly in the coastal region.

The native population was estimated at about 2·5 million in 1904 and at about the same figure in 1924; since then it has increased at the rate of about 2 per cent per annum. The figures are only approximate, but they show how much the land has benefited from the presence of the British farmers. Of the 41 million acres of native and European land 4 million are estimated to be cultivated and 30 used for grazing.

The British and other European farmers

6·81 million of the 7·87 million acres available for British and other European farmers had been surveyed and alienated by December 1947. About 2 million were classed by Colin Mayer as good. Plantation crops occupied 310,000 acres and arable crops 520,000, the rest was used for grazing or other purposes or was undeveloped. The arable land has since increased considerably.

Plantation crops

The part played by the British cultivators is out of all proportion to their numbers. There are two groups: planters and farmers. The planters grow sisal, tea and coffee; they are specialists; each confines himself to one product and does it very thoroughly. Usually the plantations are owned by British companies and are run by highly skilled British managers and supervisors. The area under tea is to be raised from its present level of 18,000 acres to some 60,000 acres in view of a possible fall in output from Ceylon. Each crop has its special requirement of soils and climate and is therefore very localized and its possible area is strictly limited: unfortunately this has not always been adequately recognized and soils well suited to coffee have been used for housing, though other land was available. Each crop has its own research station: for tea at Kericho, for sisal at Thika, for coffee at Ruiru; the two former are under the growers' organizations—probably the best arrangement when the growers are big enough in mind and outlook—the latter is under the Department of Agriculture. These plantation crops form Kenya's chief exports and furnish a considerable part of the national income. Tea, coffee and sisal are permanent crops: tea and coffee bushes last a considerable number of years—it is not yet known how many; some of the coffee bushes are fifty years old and still bearing well. Sisal is renewed by offsets but always on the same land; as yet there has been no necessity for change. Another export crop, Pyrethrum, is grown by farmers: it stands for several years; then two or three crops of wheat may be taken before the land is replanted.

None of these crops directly affect food production. Their indirect effect, however, is considerable in that they necessitate high standards of cultivation, and effective measures against insect pests and diseases; all these call for modern appliances and adequate distributing and servicing organizations.

Farm crops

The wide range of climatic conditions permits the growth of an extra-ordinary variety of plants. Kenya's gardens show some amazing combinations: daffodils and roses, primroses and chrysanthemums, all flowering together; strawberries and pineapples, oranges and plums fruiting side by side; blossom and fruit at the same time and on the same tree. The climate can be selected at will by choosing a higher or a lower altitude.

The European farms are mainly on the high land where rainfall and temperature permit growth of all English crops, others are in the ranching areas. The former are usually about 1,500 to 3,000 acres, the latter are much larger and may be 20,000 acres or more. The areas of the chief crops are given in Table LXXIII.

TABLE LXXIII. *Areas and production of chief crops, 1950*

| | Farm crops | | | Plantation crops (1948) | |
	Thousand acres	Thousand tons	Yield, cwt. per acre		Thousand acres
Wheat (1)	264	129	9·7	Sisal	226
Barley (1)	20	9	9·0	Coffee	64
Oats (1)	15	6	8·0	Tea	18
Maize (2)	1,130	574	10·2	Sugar cane	17
Millet and sorghum (3)	25		6·0		
Cassava	35				
Groundnuts (4)	14		4·0		
Cotton	57				
Pyrethrum (4)	24				

(*F.A.O. Stat. Year Book*, 1951.)

(1) European farms only.
(2) 1948. The 1949 area was 880,000 acres, but the production is not given by F.A.O. On the European farms the area in 1950 had been 145,000 acres and in 1951, 154,000 acres (C.E.C. Grain Rpt., 1953).
(3) African farms.
(4) 1948.

Other crops include beans, groundnuts, sesame, potatoes, essential oils, cotton; and in the tropical coastal regions tropical fruits, cashew nuts, coconuts.

Livestock owned by Europeans include 612,000 cattle, 290,000 sheep, and 56,000 pigs (1950). The dairy and meat industries are expanding and there are good prospects of the development of a pig meat industry now that the danger of swine fever appears to have been averted.

In addition to the agricultural and plantation crops there are some 90,000 acres of planted timber trees, about half of which are soft wood and considerable areas of wattle.

Wheat and maize are by far the most important crops. Wheat is sown in April and harvested in November; it grows best at altitudes between 6,000 and 9,000 feet. Rusts are common: black stem rust occurs everywhere, the yellow (*P. glumarum*) above 7,500 feet; and the brown and orange stem at lower levels. Wheat breeding was started privately by one of the great pioneers, Lord Delamere;[1] it was put on to a systematic basis as a Government enterprise as the result of a visit by R. H. Biffen in 1926, and is now

[1] For the story of his activities see *White Man's Country, Lord Delamere*, and *The Making of Kenya*, 2 vols., Elspeth Huxley, London, 1935.

centred at the Plant Breeding Station, Njoro, under H. C. Thorpe. He and his colleagues are confronted with the usual difficulty that the rust occurs in a number of different physiological strains, and new ones periodically appear; varieties of wheat bred for resistance to all known forms may succumb to a new one appearing later.

Much of the wheat is concentrated in the north-west of the highlands in the Eldoret, Kinangop, and Uasin Gishu districts, which have long wet seasons. Yields of 22 cwt. per acre are often obtained on good farms; 33 cwt. per acre have been obtained on the slopes of Mount Elgon. The general average yield, however, is much lower; only about 9 or 10 cwt. per acre.[1]

Production exceeds local consumption, and there is a considerable export. The grain is apt to be variable in quality; it is usually weak and not of high baking value.

Maize grows better than wheat at low altitudes, and it has a longer growing season—the seven to nine months from April or May to December or January. Much of it is grown in the Trans-Nzoia district. The common sorts yield about 10 cwt. per acre; selected seed gives about 20–30 cwt. per acre; in Mount Elgon district 36 cwt. per acre have been obtained on commercial farms and even 55 cwt. per acre have been recorded.

Under the stimulus of a special bounty cereal cultivation is highly mechanized. Weeds are troublesome, especially some that have unfortunately been introduced: Mexican marigold, lantana, charlock, and couch. Herbicides are now being used against them.

The so-called European farms are not entirely in British hands; a section of the country around Eldoret is largely held by Afrikanders who began coming in 1908 invited by the then Governor for the purpose of colonizing the empty lands. Some are good farmers managing their land well, but others have followed the usual South African method of continuous cropping with wheat and maize, doing nothing to maintain soil productiveness; in consequence yields have fallen from 22 cwt. or more per acre of maize often obtained on virgin land to 7 or 9 cwt. per acre; wheat is correspondingly down. Already dust storms are beginning: forewarning of serious soil erosion.[2] The officers of the Soil Conservation Service now have power to intervene, and the danger of serious loss may be averted.

The British farmers vary in standard as is inevitable in a new country, and many of them tempted by the present high prices are growing cereals too frequently on the same land. But a considerable number are sound agriculturists and realize the need for conserving their soil, maintaining its structure and its fertility, and making the best use of the available water; but their cash returns being much less than that of the planters they have less choice of methods. No standardized practice is as yet evolved: farmers are feeling their way to good rotations and systems of mixed farming, but they are hampered by the present lack of suitable leguminous crops—the crying need for the dry parts of Africa at present; lucerne, so useful elsewhere,

[1] Barley averages about 10 cwt, oats only 8 or 9 cwt., per acre, as they do not fill out well except at high altitudes.

[2] Instances are known, however, in these dry regions where cropping without manure has been practised for as many as 40 years without serious consequences so long as soil erosion did not set in.

cannot survive the long dry seasons. There are some clovers in the Highlands, which could serve as a starting point for research, and some of the wild dolichos and crotolarias seem promising.

Some of the wheat farmers are trying an eight-year rotation: four years of grass grazed by cattle; then four of cereals, three being wheat and one maize; during this year the foot-rot fungus of wheat dies. Under this method wheat yields about 12½ to 14 cwt. per acre and maize about 16 to 18 cwt. per acre. Molasses grass (*Melinis minutiflora*) is then sown. Others at lower elevations are substituting fodder crops for one of the cereal courses: two years of maize, one of wheat and barley, then one of silage maize and oat hay; yields of maize may be 21 cwt. or more. Rhodes grass (*Chloris gayana*) can then be sown for three or four years. Numbers of other grasses and fodder crops are being tested and some promising ones have been found. Star grass (*Cynodon dactylon*) and Kikuyu grass (*Pennisetum clandestinum*) are already well known,[1] but there is considerable difficulty in multiplication and distribution owing to the absence of a competent and completely trustworthy seed trade.

Peas and beans are also grown and in sufficient quantity to allow a considerable export. Fertilizers are being tested and experience is being gained with organic manures; the disposal of straw and the maize stalks often presents unsolved difficulties: in the dry season they will not decompose when ploughed in. There are few earthworms in the soil, but prodigious numbers of termites, which completely devour the vegetable matter without forming humus.

Mulching and shielding the soil from the sun's rays are both beneficial.

Many of the good arable farmers are developing a dairy industry producing butter fat for the creameries. Friesians, Ayrshires, Guernseys and Jerseys are all popular, especially the first two. Cotton seed from Uganda is available as concentrated food. Milk yields per cow on well-managed farms are about 2 gallons daily—about 600 gallons a year: but may be up to 50 per cent higher where grading has been going on for some time. It is usual to introduce some zebu blood into the animals to confer greater resistance to disease; Sahiwal bulls have been imported from India and their crosses with British breeds retain their native fat contents of about 6 per cent. Some of the local breeds are promising: the graceful Nandis under good European management yield about 350 gallons a year and their advocates consider that this could be raised to 500 gallons by proper selection. Success depends on the provision of sufficient food to carry over the dry periods: more and more silage is being made for this purpose.

Few of the farms even in the cereal areas are as yet fully developed. About 25 to 50 per cent of the farm may be arable, the rest is left wild. Many of the British farmers are using the present high prices to effect improvements. Few farms are more than twenty-five years old, and clearance of the wild vegetation is far from complete: money was not available in the bad times of the 1930's and most of the farmers were away during the war years; appliances were not obtainable when they returned. But clearance is going on with tractors and in places bulldozers; modern insecticides are

[1] For accounts of these grasses see D. C. Edwards, *E. African Agric. Journ.*, January 1940, and A. E. Haarer, *World Crops*, 1951, Vol. 3, pp. 8–10.

used against tsetse fly and mosquitoes. The Mau Mau disturbances of 1953 and 1954 slowed down these developments.

The grazing farms in the drier regions may be 15,000 or more acres in extent: 10 to 20 acres or more may be needed per beast. They are being improved. Better watering facilities are being provided. Dams are made by mechanical excavators for holding the rain water—and incidentally stopping erosion. Boreholes are sunk to tap underground water; this, however, is usually present in limited quantities only and periodical deepening is necessary.[1] Great interest is now being taken in pasture improvement which is being brought about in two ways: by introducing grasses better than the existing sorts, and by changing the management and the conditions so as to develop a new and more nutritive type of herbage.

The British farmers naturally introduced British beef cattle, just as they introduced British dairy stock. Red Polled have proved very useful especially where there is much wild land on the farm. Some of the native cattle especially Boranis and Gallas are very promising, and they are being improved. On a good ranch, cattle can be finished at about five years of age giving a dead weight of 700–750 lb.

The sheep are mainly Merinos for wool in the drier regions, and Corriedales and Romney Marsh for wool and meat in moister regions. Large White pigs do well, and an export of bacon to the United Kingdom might possibly be developed. Swine fever is endemic among the wild pigs, but complete segregation of the domestic animals is now assured.

In spite of much work by the Veterinary Department, cattle diseases are widespread, but active measures are taken against them. East coast fever which causes the greatest losses is controlled by dipping; breeding diseases are being avoided by artificial insemination; 'Ngana by eradicating the tsetse fly with D.D.T. where this is possible, otherwise by treatment with antrycide; and rindepest by immunizing with the appropriate vaccine.

The marked progress in selection and breeding of animals is demonstrated each year at the Kenya Agricultural Show, and if conditions allow of full development of the European farms there is every prospect of expanding considerably the meat and dairy industries. The local demand for meat is steadily increasing, but a permanent surplus is envisaged and refrigerating plant is to be installed to promote its export. Far more fodder crops could be produced, especially when a wider range of leguminous crops becomes available.

Most of the cultivated land is liable to erosion; Colin Maher estimates that protection is needed for some 500,000 to 600,000 acres of the 830,000 acres under arable and plantation crops.[2] The Soil Conservation Service is doing good work, but is sadly understaffed, and in 1951 was protecting only some 25,000 acres a year. European farmers are, however very conscious of the need and are becoming increasingly familiar with the technique, so that they are able to carry out many of the operations themselves.

The manual labour on the European farms is done by Africans. They can work moderately well under close supervision, but in general are ineffective

[1] The levels of the lakes are also falling. The tribesmen say this has happened before, but the water comes back again.

[2] Colin Maher, *Empire Jl. Expt. Agric.*, 1950, Vol. 18, pp. 137–49 and 233–48. Also *World Crops*, 1951, Vol. 3, pp. 215–18 and 258–61.

and get through only about one quarter of what would be done by an English farm worker. As in South Africa most of them have land and dwellings as part of their wages, and also help in growing their crops; the rest of the wages is in cash. They are cheerful and good humoured, managed without difficulty once they can be made to laugh—preferably by a coarse joke. Many qualify each year for the long service medals awarded by the Kenya Royal Agricultural Society. During the last war many of the British were away and left their wives to manage their farms and native workers which they did very successfully with no other help than one or two Italian prisoners of war for each farm. But agitators have since been busy and there is some fear, which may be groundless, that such loyalty on the part of the African workers might not be shown in the event of another war. They are protected by law against "bang" (hashish) and spirits, which would otherwise cause much trouble, but they are subject to mass hysteria and can easily be worked up to a great pitch of excitement.

The high standards of the best of the British farmers call for corresponding high standards in the technical and scientific services. Excellent work is being done on plant breeding at Njoro, on control of diseases and pests and on soils at the Scott laboratories in Nairobi, and on pasture management and veterinary subjects, while the large new East African Agricultural and Forestry Research Organization with laboratories at Muguga near Nairobi is able to tackle the big fundamental problems for which busy departmental staffs have neither time nor facilities. Other regional research organizations are contemplated; all are to be kept in touch through a scientific council covering all Africa south of the Sudan with its headquarters at Yangambi in the Belgian Congo.

The African farms

The native areas of 33·3 million acres—8·3 acres per head—include some of the best land in the country, particularly the valley lands. The old system of management was the usual shifting cultivation with mixed crops, the work being done by the women with the hoe as the sole implement. The main crop was millet interplanted with various pulses; the system protected the soil from erosion and was permanent so long as the arable land could be changed sufficiently frequently. That has long ceased to be practicable. For the last twenty-five years the human population has been increasing at the rate of about 2 per cent per annum; as the people are anchored to the old water sources and are loth to move, some areas have become very congested, with more than 1,000 and in the Maragoli area about 1,400 persons per square mile. There has been some movement of agricultural tribes into drier grazing regions —a reversal of the ancient order when the pressure was by the pastoralists on the agriculturists—but the cultivation methods were not modified to suit the new conditions and consequently soil deterioration and erosion set in.

There is plenty of unused land, and in 1947 an Agricultural Settlement Land Utilization Board was set up to map the under-populated areas and to arrange for resettlement. At Makueni in the Machakos region (rainfall about 20 inches) half a million acres of land uninhabited because of the tsetse fly and rhinoceros have been cleared and divided into holdings of 15 to 18 acres grouped into larger units of about 2,000 acres each, the poorer land being left as communal grazing. To ensure the most economical and efficient farming the whole scheme is under the direction of a competent and sympathetic British officer; but settlement is very slow. Another scheme has been started at Konza near the Tanganyika frontier to encourage the Masai to settle and learn the cultivation of crops; a third is proposed on the Luo plains where irrigated rice will be grown; in the Nyanza Province another tract is to be irrigated from the Kanu river.

Maize is the chief food crop, millet is still widely grown but nowadays is used mainly for making beer; finger millet, Wimbi, is the most popular; it needs, however, more regular water supply than some of the others. The replacement of millet by maize as the chief food has not been wholly good, for maize contains less protein and mineral substances than the millets, but peasants everywhere prefer it. Like the millets of old the maize is inter-planted with beans, pigeon peas, sweet potatoes, etc.; the produce is gathered in by hand and more maize may be dibbled into blank spaces or millet may be sown. Bananas are grown in regions of higher rainfall, also cassava; both are treated as permanent crops and grown on patches of land near the hut. Cassava and sweet potatoes are valuable insurance crops; they tolerate drought better than maize; being tubers they are safe from locust attack, and they can be left in the soil till wanted.

Yields are extremely difficult to assess; 5 to 9 cwt. per acre is the usual estimate for maize—only about one-half or one-quarter of the European yields. In some cases, e.g. Machakos district, two crops a year may be obtained which reduces the disparity if the second crop is good, but it is often very poor.[1] No farmyard manure is used, indeed there is often a prejudice against it: in any case it is frequently needed for fuel or as plaster in making the huts.

The cash value of the subsistence crops for all the 5 million natives in Kenya was put in 1950 at £16·5 million, 26 per cent of the value of the total agricultural product.[2] The Agricultural Officers are satisfied that much higher output could be obtained if their instructions were carried out; but custom requires that men only should receive the instructions, and these are not passed on to the women who do the work.

Considerable increases in food supply would be obtained by more extensive use of cassava, yams and groundnuts, and their growth is being encouraged.

Cassava may yield 5 to 7 tons per acre, still more if Storey's virus resistant varieties are chosen. Yams are not much grown, but they produce large quantities of carbohydrates; they are easy to grow, and, like cassava and sweet potatoes, are out of reach of locusts which periodically devour the crops of maize, millets, and beans. Their culture is being strongly advocated.

In addition to the cultivated crops some of the tribes use certain wild plants known by the women to have dietetic value.

The Kikuyu are among the best cultivators. Those living near Nairobi pro-duce most of the vegetables consumed there; it would be practicable for them

---

[1] Sampling methods are being used in connection with the new F.A.O. census, and these will give much better data. Some preliminary samplings in the Kisumu district gave yields much higher than expected: 22 to 30 cwt. per acre for maize and 9 to 15 cwt. per acre for millets. Agricultural officers in other districts do not expect such high results.

[2] *Review of Econ. Conditions in Africa*, 1949–50, United Nations, Washington, 1951.

to develop a considerable canning industry, and during the war the Government actually set up a factory at Fort Hall which brought much prosperity to the district. Unfortunately African political agitators succeeded in getting it closed.

Livestock, particularly cattle, are the special care of the men and boys who tend them on the wild grazings by day and at night bring them into the *bomas*, enclosures where they can better be guarded against hyaenas, leopards, and in some districts lions. Two of the most typical sights in East Africa are a group of boys with spears or long sticks watching their cattle, and a woman hoeing the shamba,[1] or trudging along the road bearing a heavy burden of firewood on her back or a can of water on her head, with perhaps a baby slung at her side, and yet cheerful, while her husband walks empty-handed in front—but often looking very dour. Livestock are practically confined to the savannah and grass regions; even here insect-borne diseases especially east coast fever (carried by ticks) cause considerable loss, while the tsetse fly completely excludes them from the wetter regions of dense bush and forest.

Severe erosion has been brought about by widespread overgrazing, by the felling of trees on the hill sides for fuel without replanting, and by goats eating the new shoots and young trees and preventing the establishment of a new vegetation cover. This has led to the drying up of wells and springs. One of the most striking sights I saw in Kenya was the contrast shown on a hill face where a well managed English holding adjoins Wakamba land which had been allowed to erode. The English part retained its trees and its grass; the Wakamba land was bare and looked like a red scar: it had been overgrazed; the cattle had been allowed to multiply so that only 3 or 4 acres per head were available, instead of more appropriate 7 or 8. Some of this eroded land has been reclaimed to show what can be done. It has been fenced to exclude grazing animals, the steeper slopes were stabilized by making narrow terraces and gully erosion checked by pegged brushwood wash-stops. The erosion crust on the surface of the soil was broken and grass established by sowing, planting, or natural regeneration; rotational grazing was adopted to ensure the permanence of the reclamation.[2] The manual work was done by communal labour groups, consisting largely of women. It is an interesting sidelight that European supervision halved the time spent per acre and by ensuring more thorough planting, greatly increased the survival rate of the planted grasses.

In various parts of this denuded hill country the Forestry Department is now actively planting trees and already the wells and springs are refilling. Some chiefs co-operate with the agricultural staff in anti-erosion measures, controlled grazing, terracing and other conservation works.[3] Others, however,

---

[1] When one of the men was told that a man with a plough could do more and better work than a woman with a hoe, he simply replied: "a woman is cheaper and she needs no spare parts."

[2] H. C. Pereira and V. R. S. Beckley, *Empire Jl. Expt. Agric.*, 1953, Vol. 21, pp. 1–14.

[3] Erosion control and grazing improvements done by the natives in the reserves during their considerable spare time in the dry season have at times been greatly hampered by the lack of appliances: in the Machakos district in 1950 a dam of 4 million gallons capacity was being constructed by 1,200 people, but only 25 of them had any vessels in which to carry away the earth; the others simply had to transport it in their hands. On erosion control see Colin Maher, *loc. cit.*, who did much good work on this subject.

do not, and there have even been cases of sabotage instigated by political agitators.

Overcrowding and overgrazing of the pastures are inevitable so long as the cattle serve chiefly as marks of social distinction and for the securing of brides; numbers only are required for these purposes and neither quality nor condition count.[1] The Government is setting up cattle markets in the hope of reducing the numbers and improving the quality of the animals; this not only reduces the risk of erosion, but by encouraging trade between the pastoral and the agricultural tribes it is leading to a larger consumption of meat and a better distribution of food stuffs. At present much of the meat is bought for the mine workers in the south; its quality is low—the animals may have had seven years of austere life before they are slaughtered—but it could be much improved.

Milk yields are very low: they may be only one bottle (one-sixth gallon) per day.

The staple food is maize with some millet supplemented by cassava and sweet potatoes, which are dried, pounded with the grain and made into a porridge; this is eaten either as such or dried. This, and beer made from millet constitutes most of the diet: vegetables are but little used. Meat is rarely eaten in the native areas except on ceremonial occasions such as funerals and weddings: some British farmers, however, issue it as part of their workers' rations. A few tribes drink milk, and the Masai drink blood also, tapped by shooting an arrow into the jugular vein then stopping the bleeding when enough has been drawn. One of the first of the dietic studies made in Kenya was the demonstration by J. Boyd Orr and J. L. Gilks of the improvement this effected in the diet compared with that of the almost vegetarian Kikuyu.[2] Children may be breast fed till they are about three in the belief that another conception cannot occur so long as lactation continues. In the Colonial Office nutrition report of 1939 the available food supplies were described as sufficient in total quantity, any deficiencies being the result of maldistribution, poverty or ignorance; there were, however, and still are, the usual shortages of protein and mineral substances. The war-time medical inspections showed widespread lack of some of the B vitamins.[3] The rapid deterioration as the young men grow older is not necessarily due to dietic deficiencies: there is much non-nutritional disease, malaria, syphilis, etc.

The present-day diet of some of the tribes seems to be inferior to that of twenty years ago, some of the food crops have been displaced by cash crops. This presents little difficulty where the cash crops are annuals such as vegetables which can be eaten if prices fall too low; troubles may arise,

[1] In some districts, e.g. the Machakos, the bride price has recently been increasing, somewhat to the discomfiture of the young men, who complained to the elders: the women, however, objected to being devalued.

[2] J. Boyd Orr and J. L. Gilks, *Physique and Health of Two African Tribes*, Med. Res. Coun. Spec. Rpt. Series No. 155, 1931, 82, amplified later by J. L. Gilks, *East African Med. J.*, 1933, Vol. 10, pp. 254–65.

[3] A casual observer could easily miss this; even some of the nurses with whom I spoke had never observed deficiency diseases. The relation of nutrition and efficiency is discussed in African Labour Efficiency Survey, ed. C. H. Northcott, 1947 (Col. Res. Pub. No. 3, H.M.S.O., 1949), where details of dietaries are given.

however, with perennials like sisal, tea and coffee, the cultivation of which is being taken up although it has not yet been successfully integrated with the production of food crops. Vigorous efforts are being made by the agricultural officers to improve the position. Experimental holdings at Bukuru, North Kavirondo and at Nyeri, showed that a holding of six acres, three in arable crops and three in grass should suffice for a family of six. Unfortunately the cropping scheme there worked out was not taken up by the natives.

There is abundant evidence that about 0·5 to 0·7 acres per head should suffice for food crops, and to this something could be added for cash crops. On the native portion of a large British holding in the Machakos district 600 acres of terraced arable land support a population of 1,350 people of all ages, an area of 0·44 acres per head. This suffices normally, but in years of drought it is inadequate and grain has to be supplied from the adjacent British farm to meet about one-third of the total needs.[1]

Rather more land was required in the Kikuyu holdings in South Nyeri studied by N. Humphrey. The average size was 6·5 acres of which 2·5 acres were food crops, 2·8 acres grazing, 0·6 acres fallow and 0·4 acres wattle for sale. The food crops were:—

	Acres
Maize and millet	1·0
Beans	0·3
Sweet potatoes	0·45
European	0·10
Yams, vegetables, etc.	0·4
Bananas	0·25
	2·5

The maize, millet and beans may give two crops a year.

The average family was 5·7 persons so that the total area per head was 1·1 acres and the area actually under food crops just under 0·5 acres per head. The holding produced not only the family food but a saleable surplus realizing about £18 to £20.[2] The Kikuyu, however, have a considerable love of money and perhaps devote more of their land to cash crops than would some of the other tribes who would therefore have more for food crops: on the other hand their yields might be lower.

It is essential that the people should co-operate wholeheartedly with the departmental officers who are trying to stop further deterioration of the land and enhance its productiveness. This would be greatly facilitated by consolidating the holdings and regrouping them into rectangular areas which could be cultivated by modern implements and improved by manures and fertilizers. Co-operative or group farming on these lines is being tried, but it has met with considerable scepticism and suspicion. Even greater advances might result if educated Africans would settle on the land showing how the shambas could be improved and made to give an attractive life. On the British farms it is not uncommon to see young men and women from good

[1] H. C. Pereira and V. R. S. Beckley, *Empire Jl. Expt. Agric.*, 1953, Vol. 21, pp. 1–14.
[2] N. Humphrey (Senior Agric. Officer), *The Kikuyu lands.* (i) *Relationship of population to the land in South Nyeri. The Liguru and the Land*, 1947 (Nairobi).

public schools driving tractors and helping with the harvest: the Egerton School of Agriculture is full of young men wanting to farm. But the African who has had some education wants a Government job: the agricultural class at the Makerere College is small; none of the students to whom I spoke wanted to farm. So long as Africans have this attitude to agriculture progress on the native holdings is bound to be slow. The presence of an active progressive body of European farmers, however, ensures the continued development of better methods besides providing the major part of the revenue whereby the country can be run.

The lower-lying northern part of Kenya—about three-quarters of the whole country—is as yet undeveloped. The rainfall averages about 15 inches downwards; the vegetation ranges from short grass in the moister areas to desert shrub in the arid areas. There is some grazing of cattle and sheep on the grassland and of camels and goats on the desert shrub, but only on a very low level of production. Men who were in the country during the war found that it was healthy for stock, with good water obtainable by sinking wells; it is, in fact, the home of some excellent breeds of cattle. The River Tana flows through it, but at present is unused.

Kenya's human problems are further complicated by the presence of large numbers of Indians, mostly from Gujerat, but with many Sikhs and Goans. There had long been trade between East Africa and India, but the main settlement began when Indian labourers were brought over to build the railway from 1896 onwards to 1903 when it was finished. Many of them took to trading and now have most of the retail and middleman's business of the country besides much of the banking in their hands. They are very prosperous and own considerable property. They have undoubtedly rendered valuable service, but they are not altogether popular: the Europeans think that they do not contribute their proper share of the taxes, and the Africans accuse them of paying too little and charging too much.

Prodigious efforts have been made to develop Kenya. The farmers have put large sums of money and much labour into making their farms, and the Government is spending £4½ million in African resettlement, soil conservation, and other activities. (Pl. 23–26, pp. 181, 316.)

Kenya is undoubtedly capable of considerably more development, but only the British farmers can produce the wealth out of which the necessary expenditure must be found, and only the British scientific and technical staffs can solve the many difficult problems involved: no African personnel is in sight competent to undertake this work. The country has suffered much from politicians who have tried to foster political ambitions, but have failed to recognize that continuous technological and economic developments are absolutely essential in a modern State. In particular, serious mischief has been done by giving the impression that the white farmers are interlopers who have deprived the black man of his land. This is entirely false. None of the tribes at present in Kenya have been there long. Many of them came in from the Nile and other regions—the Bantu came from the south, others, including the Hamitic group from the north; but they never occupied more than a small part of Kenya. The white settlers' title to their land is that they have reclaimed it out of the waste; their title is at least as good as that of the North American farmers to the prairie regions.

A Royal Commission (the Carter Commission) was appointed in 1932 to report on the needs and further requirements of the native population in respect of land; it published a valuable report in 1933. In 1952 Sir Philip Mitchell, retiring after a most successful Governorship, recommended that the whole question of economic development in relation to land and population in East Africa, particularly Kenya, should be studied by another Royal Commission. The recommendation was accepted, but the unfortunate Mau Mau disturbances of 1953 delayed its execution.

Literature

Matheson, J. K., and Bovill, E. W., *East African Agriculture:* a short survey of Agriculture of Kenya, Uganda, Tanganyika and Zanzibar, and its principal products, 1950.

Masefield, G. B., *Handbook of Tropical Agriculture*, 1949.

Masefield, G. B., *Short History of Agriculture in the British Colonies*, 1950.

Jex Blake, A. J., *Gardening in East Africa*, 1950.

THE SOMALI LANDS

Kenya's low-lying northern part ends at the highlands of Abyssinia and on its eastern side joins the low coastal Somalia now under Italian trusteeship. Somalia has two good rivers, the Juba and the Webi Shibeli which rise in Abyssinia and come down in flood twice a year carrying much heavy red silt. A little irrigation has been practised by Italian settlers, but in the main the water is unused: the Juba runs straight out to sea, but much of the Shibeli runs to waste in a great marsh. The rainfall is low and unreliable; the chief food crop is therefore millet, but some maize is grown along the rivers; the seed, however, is poor. The possibilities of development seem to be considerable, especially in the region between the rivers.

Further north but at higher elevation is British Somaliland, an arid treeless region of desert grass and shrub, with a nomadic population tending camels, sheep and goats, and, in the west, growing some millet. Frankincense and myrrh are found in the east; this is, indeed, the world's chief source of supply. One or two streams run during the rains but at other times are dry; it is not a land of promise.

UGANDA

Uganda, the Ganda country, takes its name from the Baganda, the Ganda people; it has been longer associated with Great Britain than any other part of East Africa. It is the north-west bastion of the great African plateau, and is surrounded by the low-lying regions of the Belgian Congo on the west, of the Sudan on the north and of the northern desert of Kenya on the north-east. Its rainfall ranges round 45 inches and is fairly well distributed over the year, but there are two minima: December–January: and June–July. Its natural vegetation is largely the tall grass and thickets—*Hyparrhenia* and *Combretum* that form so much of Kenya and Tanganyika. Tropical jungle occurs only at the edge of swamps or of streams.

The land area is 51 million acres, of which about 7 million are cultivated, and the population in 1948 was 5 million, practically all African: only 37,517 were Indian and 3,448 Europeans, none of whom are agricultural settlers: Uganda is unique in East Africa in this respect. The Indians are increasing in number. As in Kenya they are the artisans and the traders; they have a very firm hold, Africans having apparently little business aptitude. The dominant African tribe is the Baganda, who numbered approximately 1·3 millions—about a quarter of the whole; even before the advent of the British they were the most advanced, and they have long worked as teachers and clerks in Uganda, the Sudan and elsewhere.

The land is held almost entirely by Africans: a few companions are working on leases that have not yet expired but are unlikely to be renewed. No land can now be alienated. The farms are small, usually 3 to 12 acres, though some go up to 300 acres. The chief cash crop is cotton of which in 1949 there were 1·5 million acres yielding 380,000 bales. Where modern sorts are grown yields are rising; elsewhere they are said to have fallen although there are no good data to prove it. The Empire Cotton Growing Association has established an important Research Station at Namulonge under the direction of J. B. Hutchinson. Trouble arises periodically as in 1949 because the ginneries are owned by Indians, who it is alleged grossly underpay the cultivators for their cotton. The obvious solution of establishing growers' co-operative ginneries is restricted by the circumstance that the funds are liable to embezzlement by the officers. Cotton accounts for about half the value of the total exports. Next in importance comes coffee[1]—*robusta* not *arabica* as in Kenya—followed by tobacco, sugar, and tea. Some of the sugar is grown on large estates, the two chief of which are Indian owned.[2] The areas and production of the chief crops are given in Table LXXIV.

TABLE LXXIV. *Areas and production of chief crops, Uganda,* 1950

	Thousand acres	Thousand tons	Yield cwt. per acre
Millet and sorghum	1,670		
Yams and sweet potatoes	505	2,250	90
Cassava	500		
Beans	465	108	4·6
Maize	320	114	9
Groundnuts	350	129	8
Sesame (1)	250	32·5	
Coffee	—	35·6	
Cotton	1,510		

In addition there are considerable areas of bananas and of coffee. The total area cultivated is given as 7 million acres.

(*F.A.O. Year Book,* 1951.)

(1) 1949.

Uganda's food crops differ from those of Kenya and Tanganyika. Bananas have long been the most important wherever the rainfall is adequate for their growth; they are eaten fresh, roasted, boiled or steamed to make porridge; other varieties are used for making beer; in some localities near

[1] For an account of the cultivation of Robusta coffee in Uganda, see A. S. Thomas, *Empire Jl. Expt. Agric.,* 1947, Vol. 15, pp. 65–81.

[2] The one I visited was yielding 28 to 30 tons of cane per acre, producing 2½ tons of "plantation white" sugar.

Estimated numbers of livestock, 1949
Millions

Cattle	2·5
Sheep	1·0
Goats	2·3
Pigs	0·018

The estimates differ but little from those for 1939.

the lake the beer is traded for fish with the folk living on the lake. They are grown as perennials just outside the hut for protection against theft; they receive the household wastes as manure and are mulched and tended by the women, not as well, however, as was done by their mothers, and the yields are said to be going down. Over sixty varieties have been recorded.[1] Now, however, they are being increasingly displaced in Uganda by sweet potatoes and in Kenya by maize. Where the rainfall is insufficient for bananas a millet, generally eleusine, becomes the chief food; only little maize is used. Hardly any leguminous crops are grown, and no manure is given to the other food crops. It is not clear that yields are falling; those of cassava are going up with the spread of Storey's virus resistant strains.

The cattle are zebu; they are of various types and colours, the sizes varying from 3 feet high upwards: all are able to live on shrivelled grass in the dry season. Studies of the Bukedi types at the Serere farm[2] showed that the average live weight of the males is about 800 lb. and of the females 600 lb.: the milk yield ranges about 200 gallons.

The food supply for the animals has been improved by sowing *Chloris gayana;* but the native *Cynodon plectostachyum* readily invades the sown pastures as a good bottom grass.

The Colonial Office nutrition enquiry of 1936–39 showed some deficiency diseases: Vitamin A was lacking; some of the best protective foods were excluded by taboos. Important investigations have been made in Uganda by Drs. Trowell and Davies on the effects of the well-marked protein deficiency in the native diet: they have shown this to be the main cause of a serious disease in children, kwashiorkor (formerly attributed to congenital syphilis), and of other disturbances.[3] While admitting that definite evidence is difficult to obtain competent observers think that the native diet is less varied than it was a generation ago. The number of items used to be about twenty, five or six being staples and the rest supplements. Now the staples are reduced to two or three and there are fewer supplements. People are beginning to purchase food rather than grow it all themselves. There is some evidence that cattle also suffer from protein deficiency in their food.

There are considerable areas of papyrus and other swamp in Uganda, but it cannot be assumed that if drained they would yield fertile soils as happens in England. Frequently the reclaimed soil has proved to be an unfertile sand or clay, and it has happened that the drainage has interfered with the water

[1] R. E. D. Baker and N. W. Simmonds, *Empire Jl. Expt. Agric.*, 1951, Vol. 19, pp. 283–90, and 1952, Vol. 20, pp. 66–76. About 50 were in Kenya, Uganda, and Bukoba, and 30 in the regions nearer the coast—Moshi and Amani in Tanganyika, and Zanzibar. They are not native to Africa but came from Asia probably some centuries ago.

[2] E. Williams and V. A. Bunge, *Empire Jl. Expt. Agric.*, 1952, Vol. 20, pp. 142–60.

[3] R. F. A. Dean, *E. African Med. J.*, 1952, Vol. 29, pp. 1–4.

supply of the lower lying land. This subject greatly needs further examination. Meanwhile the better treatment appears to be partial draining and partial damming to control the water more effectively.

Considerable erosion has taken place, some of gully type but more often the less obvious, but in the end equally destructive sheet erosion. Control and rehabilitation measures are now being adopted.

The simplest method of effecting agricultural improvement is by introducing better varieties of crops as this involves no disturbance of the native methods, but they cannot produce their best effects unless the soil supplies sufficient nutrients. Fertilizers unfortunately often appear to have little action, probably because of the high capacity for fixing phosphate possessed by many of the soils. Uganda possesses considerable phosphate deposits at Tororo which would be very useful if this difficulty could be overcome. Farmyard manure on the other hand often has considerable and persisting effects, but unless wheeled vehicles are available it cannot be transported; in any case, as elsewhere, there is often prejudice against its use on the land and it is frequently wanted as fuel. Well-made compost is also very effective.

The greatest of all improvements if it could be effected would be to regroup the present scattered and fragmented holdings in such a way that improved tillage and proper rotations could be adopted. Pilot schemes for the development of Uganda agriculture were drawn up by E. B. Worthington in 1946,[1] but difficulties of execution have proved very great. The natives strongly object to rearrangement of their old settled areas, though the economic advantages seem manifest, and they are reluctant to quit an ancestral area, even if overcrowded, for a new settlement however neatly planned on Western lines. The Kigezi valley affords a good example. It is very overcrowded, and new areas were laid out at considerable expense. Yet in the seven years 1944 to 1951 only about 16,000 Bakiga have moved and some 400,000 still remain in the old areas.[2]

Regimentation is impossible under British administration, but economic suasion is being tried. The Kawanda Experiment Station possesses a mechanized unit which can be hired out, but not for less than ten acres on any hill, or less than one acre on any holding.

A great dam has been erected at the Owen Falls near Jinja for ensuring better control of the Nile waters for Egypt. It will also generate large quantities of electricity which can be used for the establishment of industries. What economic, social and political changes may thereby be brought about no man can foretell, but they are likely to be very far reaching.

THE SUDAN

The Sudan affords striking examples of what science and sound administration can do for Africa. When Kitchener first took the English troops there in 1898 it seemed a hopeless waste of barren sand where a sparse population grew patches of millet if and when the rains were favourable. Gordon, who knew it well, had said that the Sudan would never have any commercial value, while Stevens in his book, *With Kitchener to Khartoum*, in

[1] E. B. Worthington, *A Development Plan for Uganda*, Govt. Printer Entebee, 1946.
[2] *The Times*, December 4, 1951.

1900 wrote, "The Sudan is a desert . . . it was always poor, and it always must be . . . it is not a country . . . it is a God accursed wilderness, an empty limbo of torment for ever and ever," and few quarrelled with the description.

The Sudan covers a million square miles of the Upper Nile region; its northern part is a rainless sandy desert, but there is an increasing amount of rain in going southwards; at Khartoum it is about 5 inches a year and little except a few acacias grow: further south beyond the Maquar-Kosti railway line it is about 15 inches and certain drought-resisting grasses are found: still further south the rainfall is heavier and more and more trees occur. Finally, in the far south it is about 55 or 60 inches. The rainfall is seasonal, but the season is longer in the south than in the north. In the south it extends from March to November: in Gezira it does not begin till early July and it ends in mid-August, neither the early rains nor late rains reaching so far.

In the far south the Nile forms a great swamp, the Sudd, where the characteristic vegetation is papyrus, but on the firmer ground trees grow or did till they were cut down as fuel for the steamers. Much of the country is a wind-swept plain, almost level, but broken by occasional extrusions of igneous rock known as Gebels which are useful landmarks in the desert. In the west are the Nuba mountains and in the east the hills of Eritrea and around Tokar; in both regions the rainfall is heavier than on the plains in the same latitude.

The southern part is well watered and at first sight looks as if it should be good cattle country. Unfortunately it is badly infested with insects, particularly mosquitoes and tsetse fly, and large areas are impossible for cattle and unwholesome for men. Vegetation is so abundant that insecticides cannot be used on any large scale and all that can be done at present is to leave the insects in possession till some effective means of control can be devised. This insect population has been an important factor in preserving the human population. The Arabs could never penetrate into the south; their horses perished. Even slave raiders could not get very far into the country. In consequence a sharp line separates northern and southern Sudan, and the two parts have little in common: in the north the native population is dominated by Arab culture and the Moslem religion: in the south the people are predominantly pagan (but with many Christians) and the tribes are much more primitive, some are cattle men, others, where the tsetse fly rules, have no cattle but grow crops instead.

Two sharply different types of agriculture are practised, irrigation and rain-fed. The irrigated land is fixed by the water supply and is cropped year after year; it yields well and may give two crops a year: but this intensity of cropping often leads to accumulations of disease organisms. The rain-fed land, on the other hand, is not necessarily fixed; much of the land is ownerless and sometimes one area, sometimes another, is sown, depending on the rain Frequently a bund[1] is built round an area in a slight depression so as to hold as much of the rain water as possible; the seed is sown and left till harvest time: it is safe from pilfering though stray animals may do damage. In the

[1] A ridge about 1 or 2 ft. high. For a description of some of these shifting cultivations see an article by J. K. Jackson and M. K. Shawki, *Sudan Notes and Records*, Dec. 1950, Vol. 31, pp. 216–22.

south where the rainfall is higher the grass covering the land has to be burnt: this is called "Fire Cultivation" ("Harig").

Fortunately, the Sudan possesses in the Gezira an area of about a million acres that can be irrigated without detriment to Egypt, and will then produce the very valuable long-stapled Sakellerides cotton. This has provided money whereby other parts of the Sudan could be developed, and the country now has a prosperous population and exports cotton, gum and surpluses of food.

Kitchener had great faith in what science could do for the Sudan: he set up Agricultural and Educational Departments and laid out Khartoum on generous lines. In 1898 the Gordon College was founded there, immediately after the reconquest of the Sudan. From the outset the Sudan was served by a very good type of man: it was administered by the Foreign Office and the conditions of appointments were more attractive than those of the Colonial Office.

The possibility of irrigation in the Gezira was foreshadowed in 1899 by Sir William Garstin.[1] The Gezira lies between the Blue and the White Niles, and seen from Khartoum where the two rivers meet it looks like an island, hence its name.[2] It is almost level and slopes away from the Blue to the White Nile. The soil is black, heavy and difficult to cultivate, but experiments showed that it could grow the long-staple cotton much in demand by spinners. A pumping station was erected at Tayiba on the Blue Nile and pilot schemes were put into operation there and at Barakat to study the practical problems which the small scale trials cannot reveal: meanwhile a dam was erected at Maquar, 180 miles above Khartoum, which was called the Sennar dam to commemorate the ancient kingdom of that name; it was opened January 1, 1926.[3] This dam is used for storage as well as for diversion. Cotton is the chief crop: it is sown in August[4] and picked from early January till mid-May or earlier: watering begins soon after sowing: some fourteen waterings may be given at fortnightly intervals. Both Niles are in flood from July to September (about eighty days) and the water supply is so abundant that as much can be taken as is desired; indeed a system of escape channels had to be constructed along with the canals to take off surplus water. From January to July, however, the water supply is much less and rigid restrictions are imposed on its use.

From the outset a very ingenious system of land tenure was adopted. The Government took the land on perpetual lease from the landowners, paying them a rental rather better than what they had been receiving. It built the dam and negotiated water conventions with Egypt: it made also the main canal. It then (1910) gave a concession to the Sudan Plantations Syndicate, a public company, to develop the land for a period of forty years. The Syndicate was to lay out the land, make the distributing system from the main canals to the holdings, find the tenants, see the agricultural system properly carried out, in particular to supervise closely the production of cotton, doing the major cultivations at the charge of the tenant, collecting

[1] *Nile Control*, Sir Murdoch MacDonald, Cairo Government Press, 1920.
[2] Gezira is the Arabic word for island.
[3] It came into use for the 1925–26 crop.
[4] Usually August 10-31st, with some resowing in September. The rain may come from July 1st to August 15th.

the cotton from specified points, ginning and marketing it. The net proceeds after deduction of expenses were divided: 40 per cent each to the Government and the tenants, and 20 per cent to the Syndicate. Although nearly level, some parts of the area are a little too high to be watered from the canals, and so were left out of the scheme. The remainder was divided into forty blocks in five groups, each adequately provided with irrigation canals and channels, and these were cut up into rectangular holdings usually of 40 feddans, approximately 40 acres.[1]

By 1950 there were some 841,500 acres in cultivation (210,000 in cotton) and over 20,000 tenants, their yields ranged from less than one to more than eleven kantars per feddan. A further 100,000 feddans were being brought into the scheme. There were never enough Sudanese to work the scheme and many of the tenants and workers are West African Moslems, called Fellata in the Sudan, who are on their pilgrimage to Mecca and earning the necessary money on the way. These West Africans are good cultivators, their villages are very neat and tidy, they are cheerful people fond of their native music and their women have a livelier sense of colour than the Sudanese women possess.

The Syndicate worked through British inspectors which, while the supply was available, were mostly of the Old Public School type; they got on well with the tenants who, indeed, admired their skill both at work and at sport —horsemanship in particular appealed to the Arabs; after the wars the net had to be cast wider. Each large block of holdings has three inspectors as has also each pair of small blocks, each inspector has charge of about 800 to 10,000 feddans of land, including 2,000 to 2,500 feddans of cotton; there are rather more than 100 in all. Their business is to see that all agricultural operations are carried out by the tenants properly and to time, to watch for pests and diseases and take necessary steps against them; generally to do everything possible to ensure good crops. It is hard work and necessitates being out a great deal in the grilling hot sun; from March onwards the temperatures even in the shade are often up to 110° F or more, and the perspiration and dust become extremely trying. Men cannot usually remain for long, and it has usually been necessary to take in 200 men every twelve years in order to keep 100 in the field.[2]

The high cost of the scheme necessitated a large output of cotton, but the need for a rotation was early realized. The system finally worked is to have half the land (20 feddans) in fallow each year, whiie of the other 20, 10 feddans are in cotton, 5 feddans in durra and the rest in lubia or other green crops so far as water permits.

Two groups of difficulties might easily have wrecked the scheme. The soil is of the black cotton soil type, extremely heavy—often containing 55 to 60 per cent of clay,[3] and readily becoming impervious to water when wet. It contains a fair amount of soluble salts—mainly sodium sulphate: also, fortunately, much calcium sulphate. It was from the outset poor in organic

---

[1] 1 feddan = 1·038 acres. 1 kantar of cotton = 315 lb. of seed cotton or about 100 lb. of lint. 1 bale = 400 lb. lint.

[2] Fuller details are given in the Report of the Select Committee of the Legislative Assembly on the Future Administration of the Gezira Scheme, Khartoum, March 1950.

[3] Particles below 0·002 mm. diameter.

Cropping in the Gezira: thousand feddans

Cotton	210
Durra	105
Lubia	54
Groundnuts	3
Vegetables	1·5
Fallow	468
	841

In addition, about 10 per cent of the area is occupied by roads and canals. A further 100,000 feddans are now being brought into the scheme.

matter and could easily have become unworkable. Instead of that it has, if anything, improved in condition although its organic matter content is still as low as ever,[1] and it is remarkable that the organic matter has not fallen lower and that the soil has retained any sort of texture. Only highly efficient management and constant watchfulness could have produced this result.

The second set of difficulties is concerned with diseases and pests. Whenever any considerable area is devoted to one crop pests and diseases are certain to appear. Within five years of the first cotton crop a rain-borne bacterial disease, black arm, and a virus disease, leaf curl, appeared (1923–24), and during the five years (1929 to 1934) did a great deal of damage, reducing the crop from nearly 5 kantars per feddan to less than half—only 1·4 in 1930–31. The scientific staff took up the problems vigorously. The botanist, R. E. Massey, devised methods of field hygiene which greatly mitigated the severity of the attack: when picking finished, the stalks were pulled out and burned, and the dead leaves and any volunteer plants carefully swept up and also burned. But this was laborious and costly; and the preventive measure of sowing late to miss the rains lowered the "grade" of the cotton. The plant breeders therefore set about producing new varieties having the same spinning quality and yield capacity but resistant to these two diseases: this is a long slow business, but in the end is the most effective way of dealing with diseases and pests. Yields rose again to 4 or 4½ kantars per feddan, but meanwhile in 1929 another pest came in, the jassid, a sucking insect. This can be controlled by spraying with D.D.T., but the plants can be effectively protected by giving their leaves hairs long enough to prevent the insect getting down to the surface. This was done by R. H. Knight, who produced varieties resistant to all three troubles, and at the same time of at least the same commercial value as the old sorts. A serious weed pest, seidgrass, later caused much trouble but was controlled by extra ploughing. Undoubtedly new troubles will appear, and a highly efficient scientific staff will always be needed to diagnose them and find a way of overcoming them. The need for fertilizer is now recognized and more than half the cotton area of the Gezira receives it: the cost is about £250,000 annually.

Excepting during the bad period 1930 to 1934 the shares of the Government and of the tenants have each averaged £E1 million after deduction

[1] 0·3 per cent of carbon and 0·03 per cent of nitrogen have long been usual figures. A. F. Joseph in the early 1930's gave the figure as 0·015 per cent of nitrogen.

of expenses: and since 1946 much more: £E4·7 in 1947–48 and far higher in 1950–51. Cotton and cotton seed accounted in 1948 for nearly three-quarters of the Sudan exports and in 1949 the Gezira receipts were more than one-third of the Central Government revenue. Against this the cost of the research work has been about £75,000 per annum. But it is owing to the high quality of the men that such good results have been obtained.

The Syndicate's Concession terminated on June 30, 1950, and its place is taken by a Sudan Board. The division of the proceeds remains as before, but the Board must use two out of its twenty shares on social welfare of the tenants and must foster self-management by the tenants. The British inspectors are to be replaced by Sudanese: five were appointed in 1949. Fifteen were to be appointed in 1950 but could not be found: half the inspectorate is proposed to be Sudanese by 1956. This gives no satisfaction to the West African cultivator who has no wish to lose an efficient unbribable English inspector: how far the Sudanese cultivator will welcome the change remains to be seen. The last year of the present régime—the cropping season 1950–51 gave the highest yield and far and away the highest financial returns in the whole history of the enterprise.

Smaller cotton schemes are in the Eastern Sudan on the deltas of the rivers Barakat and Gash which flow from the Eritrean hills in the rainy season for about eighty days[1] only, starting from mid-June to mid-July. The cotton is sown directly the flood subsides and the plants never directly receive any water during all their lives: as the water level sinks in the sandy soil so the roots follow it, and they are so well provided that even at midday on a hot day (95° F or more) they show no sign of wilting. The quality is equal to that in the Gezira. In 1946–47 the Barakat scheme covered 52,620 acres on the Tokar plain and the Gash 27,448 acres in the Kassala region. There are a number of small irrigation schemes along the Nile banks, but they are under strict control during the critical period January to July.

A considerable amount of cotton is grown without large irrigation, much of it receiving rain water only. This is short-stapled American type, and while less valuable than the high grade long-stapled Sakel cotton of the Gezira it nevertheless adds considerably to the gross income of the Sudan.

The total area of cotton in the Sudan was in 1950–51 519,000 feddans, of which 208,000 were in the Gezira, and 135,000 were carrying rain-grown American varieties: this area increased to 191,000 feddans in 1951–52. The total production was 2·03 million kantars of seed cotton, of which the Gezira contributed 1·43 million.

The maintenance of a large output of cotton, especially high grade cotton, is vital to the Sudan to provide revenue for maintaining the machinery of the State and for giving the cultivators a reasonable standard of life. Ambitious development schemes had by March 1950 been put forward by the various Government departments totalling £E20 million: the Development Account Fund stood at £E3½ millions only. It is by no means certain that the balance can come from outside the Sudan.

So long as the Gezira scheme is worked properly, however, the Sudan will always have a reasonable national income for running the State.

---

[1] The range has been 70 to 110.

The food situation is secure. For some years past there has been a surplus of grain and of meat for export. The most important food crops are the millets, especially durra (*Sorghum Vulgare*): in the drier parts finger millet (eleusine) is safer. In the early days long-stalked varieties of durra were grown in the Gezira; the grain was used as human food, the leaves were fed to the animals, and the stalks used by building the native huts or *tukls* —usually a pair for each cultivator, one for each wife or one for the man and one for his wife. The *tukls* were then on the individual holdings. Now, however, the cultivators live in mud huts in villages where they have the convenience of shops, schools, a midwife or native substitute. The tall-stalked varieties have been replaced by others with shorter stalks which can be entirely eaten by the cattle and giving higher yield of grain. So far only little has been done on the millets by the scientific workers, but investigations are projected at the new experimental station at Kangatu in Equatoria. The cultivators themselves, however, have done much seed selection and some of the villages are famous for their strains.

Cultivators' yields are about 14 cwt. grain per acre (4 ardebs per feddan) in the irrigated parts of the Gezira: at the Wad Medani Experiment Station they have ranged from 9 to 54 cwt. per acre; in the heavily cropped rain areas immediately south of the Gezira yields of 4 cwt. are common; some measured by Jefferson were only 260–300 lb. per acre; experimental farm yields have varied from 3 to over 8 cwt. per acre. On less exhausted areas with a rainfall of 20–30 inches, 10 cwt. is usual. The more penetrable soils of Gedaref and Fung with more rain at times yield up to 20 cwt. per acre.

Schemes have recently been started for growing large areas of durra in rain districts using mechanized methods. Government machinery does the main cultivation, sowing and threshing while the cultivator does the light weeding, thinning and harvesting. The resulting crop is divided equally between the Government and the tenant. In addition the Government has provided roads and water supplies to open up the areas. As usual in rain districts the yields are very variable: at Ghadambaliya (Gedaref) 6,459 feddans of durra had yielded 7 cwt. per acre in 1948–49 but only $2\frac{1}{2}$ cwt. per acre in 1949–50.

Birds take a tremendous toll of the grain, and explosives have had to be used against the nesting places of the migratory weaver bird, perhaps the worst pest, and the ruffs, who run them fairly close. Otherwise durra is fairly free from diseases and pests, and those that occur have been studied by the scientific staff. A black smut responsible for some damage is now controlled by treating the seed with copper carbonate.

In parts of the south, e.g. among the Zande, cassava is increasingly replacing millet: it is not, however, so good a food being deficient in protein and in fat.[1] Other food crops are grown but in smaller quantities than durra. Groundnuts are an important source of protein in the south; beans and lubia seeds in the north: sesame provides oil, while lubia leaves, okra[2] (lady's fingers), and others are eaten as vegetables.

[1] A dietary survey among the Zande of the South-Western Sudan. (Mrs.) G. M. Culwick, Agric. Publications Cttee., Khartoum, 1950.
[2] Forbidden in the Gezira as it harbours a small white fly harmful to long-staple cotton. It does not seriously affect American cotton.

Livestock are fairly numerous except in the tsetse fly areas: their numbers depend on the water supply. In the hills of the West (Kordofan) cattle supplies are so good that Liebig's are erecting a factory at Kosti where they will prepare canned meat and meat products for export to Egypt and other countries. In the south there is more water, but also more insects and epidemic diseases are common, notably cattle plague, bovine pleuro-pneumonia and trypanosomiasis, so that the numbers of animals are less than might be expected and their condition poorer.

The yield of milk of the native breeds kept under good conditions at the experimental farms is about 350 to 500 gallons per lactation, but selected animals may give as much as 800 gallons. Cows' milk is preferred to others, being regarded as more nutritious.

Scientific Services

The Sudan has always been exceptionally fortunate in its scientific staff: the conditions generally were more favourable than in the Colonial Service. The expenditure in 1949–50 was £150,000, half being on Gezira account. The chief stations are at Shambat, Khartoum, and, for the Gezira, Wad Medani. The Sudanization of the scientific staff is intended, but no term has been set, nor are suitably qualified men in sight. Merely labelling a man B.Sc. or Ph.D. does not necessarily mean that he can keep the close watch necessary or devise the methods of coping with trouble quickly and effectively. The Sudanese students at the Gordon College readily take up medicine, a few do science, but hardly any take agriculture. There is, however, a great demand for education for the children: the schools cannot take all, and it is not unknown for parents to bribe the school master to admit their children.

Chapter 8

AFRICA: III. THE CENTRAL REGIONS: WESTERN GROUP; AFRICAN FARMING

ANGOLA

Angola has been a Portuguese possession since the 15th century. It occupies the north-west of the Southern African Plateau: a low-lying coastal belt, varying from 30 to 100 miles in width, separates it from the Atlantic; beyond its northern and eastern frontiers lie the valleys of the Congo and the Zambesi; to the south are the deserts of South-West Africa. Most of the country consists of rolling savannah plains, about 4,000 to 6,000 feet altitude, with a central block of higher country, around which rise a number of streams mostly flowing into the Congo and Zambesi rivers, but the chief among them, the Okovango, becomes lost in Bechuanaland.

The rainfall is about 50 to 60 inches a year on the plateau but much less on the low coastal plain; it there varies from about 8 to 16 inches. There is everywhere a dry season: from May or June to August in the wet districts, and June to November in the dry ones. The plateau is very healthy for Europeans; the coastal plain, however, is not.

The area is 481,351 square miles (307·8 million acres): the population in 1950 was 4·1 millions of whom only about 44,000 were Europeans.

A wide range of crops, including tropical and Mediterranean fruits and vegetables can be grown. Wheat can be grown on the north-eastern section of the plateau, other cereals on the south-eastern section (Bié), maize on the northern part of the broken land dropping from the plateau to the sea (Benguela). Groundnuts are also grown. The chief cash crops are coffee, maize, palm oil and kernels, copra, groundnuts, sugar and cotton. The commonest food crops are cassava, maize and bananas; these are grown almost everywhere by the natives: no detailed enquiries appear to have been made, however, in regard to native dietaries. Maize occupies about 1½ million acres; the present output is about 350,000 tons, an average of 4 or 5 cwt. per acre. About 42,000 acres of rice were grown in 1942,[1] producing 20,000 tons of paddy, the same as at present. Coffee occupied 110,000 acres and produced about 30,000 tons—5½ cwt. per acre—the output has now risen to 50,000 tons. Some 15,000 to 17,000 acres of sugar cane produced about 440,000 tons of cane—nearly 30 tons per acre. Palm and coconut are grown chiefly in the north. Later details of acreage and yields are not available; the estimated outputs for 1951 are given in Table LXXII (p. 246).

Quantities of all crops, including maize and groundnuts are exported chiefly to Portugal, though considerable amounts of coffee go to the United States. On the other hand, some of the foods for the Europeans are imported. Although much grazing is available the numbers of livestock are not high. Around 1949 there were about 1·3 million cattle, 140,000 sheep, 430,000 goats, and 20,000 pigs.

[1] F.A.O. Statistics: these are the latest figures available.

The high rainfall and the broken nature of some of the country has led to a considerable amount of erosion, but this has been recognized and protective measures are to be taken.[1] The problems have been studied by the Junta de Exportação dos Cereais das Colonias in collaboration with the chief Portuguese research station at Sacavem in Portugal, and the workers have the advantage of proximity to the Belgian Congo where much international work on the subject is proceeding. The possibilities of increased crop production are considerable and the Portuguese Government is taking steps to develop them. Research and advisory services are being extended, and irrigation schemes are planned in the valleys of the Kwango and Bengo rivers and also in those of the Matola and Kunene rivers. With its wide range of crops and great scope for improvement Angola offers good prospects of much further development.

THE BELGIAN CONGO

The Belgians are energetically tackling in the Congo region some of tropical Africa's most difficult problems. The conservation of soil productiveness in high rainfall conditions is being effected by first systematizing and then replacing the old shifting cultivation by better methods. An extremely interesting attempt is being made to develop a social system in which African and European can live together in peace. The mode of progression has been to concentrate attention on improving the farming and standards of living of the natives, leaving them meanwhile under their own system of government, stripped, however, of its barbarities. Ideas about Western political systems which they do not understand can come later when general education and better standards of living are sufficiently advanced.[2] The Europeans maintain their own system of life and government. But an African who has attained the necessary cultural level can step out from the African system and "matriculate" into the European system after which he suffers from no disability or colour bar.[3]

The Belgian Congo is in the centre of Africa; it is roughly rectangular with a narrow extension to the south-east and a still narrower corridor to the sea: its shape is not unlike the head of a pharaoh's queen looking westwards—the corridor being the long nose. It is low country lying west and north of the high African plateau and comprising all the southern part of the Congo river system; the northern part, however, is shared with French Equatorial Africa, the boundary being the Ubangi, one of the largest of the Congo affluents. Some of the high plateau is included both to the south and east; here many of the tributaries rise. This southern sector, including the Katanga province, is some 3,000 to 5,000 feet high. The eastern highland border is much narrower but far more mountainous; much of it is 6,500 feet elevation and it has some of the finest scenery in the country, including part

[1] Descriptions and photographs are given by J. Botelho da Costa, *Aspectos do problema da erosão do solo em África* (Lisbon, 1950).

[2] The Belgians have sent very few Congolese to Belgium for higher education in sharp contrast with the British who have sent large numbers of West Africans to universities in the United Kingdom and elsewhere.

[3] *"Immatriculation"* is the expression used.

of the Rift Valley, Lake Tanganyika, numerous extinct volcanoes and peaks of the Ruwenzori range culminating in the Pic Marguerite, 16,500 feet high. Below these high borderlands is a considerable area of rolling plains 1,500 to 3,000 feet in elevation through which flow the rivers rising in the higher ground; the lowest part is the "cuvette centrale" between 650 and 1,600 feet elevation.

The rainfall is determined by proximity to the equator which runs through the northern half of the country. A belt stretching from 2° N. to 2° S. has a rainfall of 60 inches to more than 90 inches and no dry season; it includes much of the low-lying central basin; its mean temperature is about 77° F.: 86° by day and 68° by night; humidity is very high and the climate is very unpleasant. This is the region of equatorial rain forest; dense, with great variety of trees closely set and often very tall, made almost impenetrable by the tangled mass of undergrowth and the profusion of long streamers of epiphytes. Sunlight rarely penetrates.

South of this belt are zones of successively lower rainfall decreasing finally to about 48 inches. A dry season now appears, increasing in length as the rainfall is less and less: in the driest regions in the south it lasts for about seven months,[1] and over much of the country it extends from July to October.

The temperatures in the equatorial belt range about 80° F to 90° F by day, and 45° F to 60° F by night. Further south they are higher during the wet season, being about 104° F by day but not more than 77° F by night; humidity is lower than in the central belt, but the climate is still disagreeable. During the dry season, however, the temperatures are much lower and may fall to 37° or 40° F at night.

South of the high rainfall forest belt the country is savannah, the trees becoming fewer as the rainfall decreases or where fires or human activities have destroyed them, and there are large areas of grassland.

Roughly speaking about half the country is forest and half is more or less wooded savannah. The region of lowest rainfall and longest dry season is in the south-east, Katanga, and this, and the eastern uplands, constitute the pleasantest parts for the Europeans. But as in all relatively dry parts of Africa, the rainfall is very variable and uncertain so that cropping becomes difficult.

The soils are mainly lateritic, and mostly poor both in organic matter and in plant nutrients; there are some richer volcanic soils in Kivu in the east, and some rich alluvial deposits in places along the rivers; on the other hand some very poor soils occur on the sandy plateau in the south-west— the Kwango district. The soils under the rain forest are as usual distinctly poor in spite of the exuberant growth they carry. All soils when broken up for cultivation rapidly lose their organic matter.[2]

The Crops

Soon after the Belgian Government took over the management of the Belgian Congo in 1908 a number of experiment stations were set up mainly to study economic problems; in 1923 these were grouped into one organization by Edmund Leplae, the distinguished professor of Louvain University.

[1] The dry months are defined as those having less than two inches of rain.
[2] The soils are described by P. J. Livens, 1st Commonwealth Conf. Tropical Soils, 1948, Commonwealth Bur. Soil Sci. Tech. Comm. No. 46, 1949.

Later it appeared that more definite scientific studies were needed and in 1933, following the visit of the then Crown Prince, an organization, the *Institut National pour l'étude agronomique du Congo Belge* (always called I.N.E.A.C. for short) was established with a central experimental station at Yanganbi and twenty-six sub-stations in different parts of the country Agricultural development has been planned on an ecological basis.

The population is relatively small; it expands at the rate of rather more than 1 per cent per annum; the white population, however, grows more rapidly:

Millions	1940	1949
Africans	10·35	11·33
Non-native	0·030	0·059
Total	10·38	11·39
Including Belgian	0·021	0·044

Most of the Europeans live in the high country of Katanga, Orientale and Kivu; a considerable number live in Leopoldville. The Africans are spread more evenly; Leopoldville, Orientale and Kasai have, however, larger populations than the other provinces. The African population is chiefly Bantu and Sudanese. The Asiatic population is only small (1,227).

The total area is 579 million acres; about half is in forest, of the remainder about 6–7 million acres are cultivated (Table LXXV), one-third being in cash

TABLE LXXV. *Land utilization in Belgian Congo*

Non-forest area about 300 million acres. Cultivated area about 6–7 million acres

1949	Thousand acres
Cash crops	
European	727
African	1,360
Principal food crops	
European	18
African	3,840
	5,945

Cash Crops

	European			African (2)	
	Thousand acres	Thousand acres		Thousand acres	Thousand acres
	1949	1959		1949	1950
Oil, palm (1)	366	396	Cotton	777	815
Hevea	140	145	Paddy	371	378
Coffee	137	140	Palm	119	129
Cacao (4)	40	45	Hevea	50	47
Quinine	13	15	Urena lobata (3)	49	55
Others	30	25			
	726	766		1,366	1,423

(1) Including 50·4 of wild trees.
(2) Only those enumerated.
(3) A fibre like jute.
(4) Cacao is the tree, cocoa the product.

crops and the rest in food crops. About 12 per cent of the cropped area is in European hands.

Food crops entering into commerce, 1949

	European		African	
	Thousand acres	Thousand tons (1)	Thousand acres	Thousand tons (1)
Roots				
Cassava	11·4	32·7	1,604	5,472
Sweet potato	3·5	7·0	155	375
European potato	0·4	0·77	6	66
Grains				
Maize	1·7	3·5	825	300
Paddy	0·5	0·18	373	159
Sorghum			161	55
Millet			161	
Groundnuts	1·1	0·25	554	145·4
Sum	18·6		3,839	

(1) Crops consumed by the growers are not included.

(*Statistiques, Congo Belge*, 1951.)

The Cash Crops: Oil palm

The forest region north of Lat. 4° S. is ideal for the oil palm, *Elaeis guineaensis*, and this constitutes the country's chief product. It is a native plant, but is being improved by selection at the Yanganbi experiment station. It requires a well distributed and abundant rainfall, not less than about 60 inches a year, but preferably double; and temperatures ranging about 75° F, but not less than 68° F. It will not tolerate permanent water-logged conditions, though it is not injured by temporary flooding as in the river islands. It does not grow above 3,000 feet: its optimal conditions occur in the areas below 2,000 feet altitude and it is here that the best plantations are found.

Three methods of production are used: European plantations, native plantations, and tended wild trees. The respective areas in 1949 and 1950 were:

	1949 Thousand acres	1950 Thousand acres
European		
Plantations in bearing	187	200
Young trees	66	71
Tended wild trees	112	125
Native		
Plantations	119	128

(*Statistiques, Congo Belge*, 1951.)

In the plantations the young trees are raised from seed; they begin to bear when four years old and come into full production in ten to twelve years, continuing for many years. After a time, however, they grow so tall that harvesting becomes impracticable as the nuts and foliage form a great tuft at the top of the trunk. Attempts are being made to evade this difficulty

275

by using dwarf varieties obtained either by selection from *E. guineensis* or by crossing with the slower growing *E. Melanococca.*

The trees are planted in twin rows 33 feet apart and 20 to 25 feet distance in the rows: about sixty to the acre: an adult tree may yield annually about 1 cwt. of nuts containing 25 to 39 per cent of oil. The yield of oil per acre even in a good plantation is of course less than corresponds with these figures being about $6\frac{1}{2}$ to 8 cwt. per acre, but some of the varieties bred at Yanganbi—*E. tenera X dura* and *E. dura X pisifera*—are yielding on experimental plots up to 20 cwt. per acre.

Some of the nuts are exported, but large quantities are worked up in the country itself; the oil is extracted from the kernels and the pulped flesh by centrifuging, and some 90 per cent is recovered.

The output is steadily increasing; during the five-year period 1945 to 1949 the figures have been:

	Wild trees tended Thousand acres	Plantations, thousand acres European	Native	Total area Thousand acres	Production (1) Thousand tons Oil	Nuts
1945	62·0	232	101·5	395·0	113·4	64·4
1949	111·8	254	118·8	484·6	169·9	98·7
Increase per cent	80·0	9·5	17·0	22·7	50·0	53·0

(1) Local consumption not included.
(*Statistiques, Congo Belge*, 1951.)

Next in importance to oil palm in the equatorial wet forest region comes coffee which is grown chiefly by Europeans. *C. Robusta* is the most suitable variety; it requires temperatures of about 72° to 80° F., and is therefore not usually grown at elevations greater than 3,300 feet. A common yield is about $6\frac{1}{2}$ cwt. per acre, but this can be raised to 16 cwt. per acre by using improved methods. *C. Arabica* is much less grown; it is less tolerant of high temperatures and high rainfall and is confined to the higher savannah country.

Cacao has proved to be well adapted to the wet forest zone; it requires at least 60 inches of well distributed rainfall per annum, and temperatures of 75° to 80° F not falling below 68° F; a short dry period is necessary for ripening. The culture is at present almost entirely in the hands of Europeans; the total acreage in 1950 was 45,000, only 15,000 of which, however, had come into bearing, the remaining 30,000 being young trees. The export at present is about 2,000 tons annually; it has varied but little during the past five years. In view of the critical state of cocoa production in the Gold Coast there may be scope for considerable expansion.

Tea of good quality can be produced in the eastern highlands, but elsewhere the general conditions are not very suitable, though considerable yields of poor quality could be obtained for sale on a manipulated market. The possibilities are being investigated.

All these crops supply food to the world market, and in view of the urgent need for them great efforts are being made to increase their output. The European plantations are expanding, and it is hoped from 1951 onwards to increase the African plantations at annual rate of 15,000 acres of oil palms, 6,500 acres of cacao and 600 acres of coffee.[1]

[1] *Discours du Gouverneur Général*, E. Jungers, Conseil du Gouvernement, Congo Belge, 1951, p. 18.

Some of the other crops do not directly supply food, but are indirectly of great importance by providing money needed for the development of the country. One of the chief of these is the rubber tree, hevea, which has been successfully cultivated in recent years, and in 1952 covered 214,000 acres, 144,000 of which are European and 70,000 native; of the European acreage about half was in young trees. The quantity of rubber exported has varied a good deal: in 1950 it was 8,200 tons; there has been no steady increase since 1943. The acreage was about 40 per cent that of the oil palms, but the value of the rubber was only 187 million francs—less than 10 per cent of that of the oil.

Another of these crops is *Urena lobata* which produces a fibre used as a substitute for jute; this is almost entirely grown by the Africans, chiefly in the province of Leopoldville. Other fibres are being cultivated in the forest regions.[1]

In the drier savannah regions cotton is the chief cash crop; it is a recent introduction and has become important only since 1921. It requires only about 24 to 32 inches of rain for growth, and a dry season of several months for the proper ripening of the bols. In places the fringes of the forest zone have these conditions, and some cotton is grown there. It brings in almost as much money as the oil palm, and as it is grown almost entirely by the Africans it makes a substantial contribution to their resources.[2] It is grown in rotation with food crops. The area in 1950 was 815,000 acres, this being far greater than that under any other crop excepting cassava. Most of it is grown in Orientale and Kasai; Katanga and Equatoria also have considerable areas.

Cotton cannot, however, be grown everywhere in the savannah regions. Surplus food crops may then be sold to provide cash; in some districts clay vessels can be made; elsewhere small animals are a form of currency.

The Food Crops

These are short term crops and are not quite as happy in the wet forest region as the perennials just described; after two or three years the soil has to revert to a bush fallow for some eight or ten years.

Cassava tubers (manioc) and in places plantains are by far the most important native foods in the wet forest and also in the bordering savannah regions. Cassava is grown alone or mixed with other crops. It is propagated by cuttings which can be planted during any month having sufficient rainfall; although a high rainfall crop it can tolerate a fairly long dry season. It takes twelve to eighteen months to complete its growth, and up to twenty-four months in high regions.

The total acreage in 1950 was 1·6 million. Good African cultivators obtain 8 to 10 tons per acre in the wet equatorial regions and 4 tons in the drier savannah, but at the Yanganbi Experiment Station selected sorts adequately treated have given up to 26 tons of fresh roots per acre. The roots contain 20 to 30 per cent of edible dry matter: some varieties are liable to contain

[1] For an account of these fibres, see A. E. Haarer, *Jute Substitute Fibres*, Wheatland Journals, 1952.

[2] G. Tondeur (Bull. Agric. du Congo Belge, 1947, Vol. 38, pp. 3–58) describes promising attempts to prepare human food from cotton-seed meal.

a cyano-genetic glucoside and the roots have to be steeped before use; the so-called sweet varieties, however, are free from harmful substances.

At higher altitudes, sweet potatoes are much cultivated; about 160,000 acres are grown by the Africans and a small area—some 4,000 acres—by Europeans. Common yields are 2 to 4 tons per acre, but at the experimental station more than 8 tons are obtained.

Potatoes are grown to a much less extent. Yams were important as food before cassava was introduced, but they are no longer widely grown though they do very well in suitable conditions.

In the drier savannah regions, maize is the chief food crop, having largely displaced millet, the indigenous grain. Some 825,000 acres of maize were grown by Africans in 1949 yielding 300,000 tons, an average of 7·2 cwt. per acre. Europeans grew much less, but their average yields are higher; up to 36 cwt. per acre.

Groundnuts come next in importance to maize in the savannah regions wherever the rainfall exceeds 20 inches; they are also grown in the wet forest regions but less successfully. They are largely consumed locally—only about 25 per cent of the 1949 crop was put into commerce—but there is an increasing possibility of an export trade and the cultivation is being expanded: in 1948 the area had been 490,000 acres and the output 112,000 tons; in 1949 the area had risen to 551,000 acres and the output to 145,600 tons— an average yield of 5·3 cwt. per acre. The crop is almost entirely grown by Africans; only a small area is cultivated by Europeans, but they are able to obtain yields of 12 to 20 cwt. per acre.

Three other cereals beside maize are grown, but are nothing like so widely distributed. Rice is the chief of these; only the hill sorts are grown, however, not the irrigated varieties, the cost of irrigation installation at present being too high. The area in 1949 was 378,000 acres, mostly in Orientale and Equatoria, but a good deal also in Kasai and Kivu; the output was 160,000 tons, an average of 8½ cwt. per acre. In good conditions, using selected seed, 12 cwt. per acre are obtained, and European farmers obtain considerably more. Should it become practicable to grow irrigated rice, high yields might be more commonly obtained.

Sorghum (*S. vulgare*) is the truly indigenous grain crop in the Belgian Congo and it has much to recommend it, but, as elsewhere in Africa, it has gone out of favour as direct food being displaced by maize; it is still grown, however, for the preparation of beer, and for general use in regions too dry or too infertile for maize. It requires a higher temperature than maize. The acreage is about 160,000 and the output about 55,000 tons; the average yield is 7 cwt. per acre, but with proper cultivation up to 24 cwt. per acre can be obtained.

Millet (*Pennisetum typhoideum*) tolerates poorer conditions than sorghum and it is usually grown where sorghum is unlikely to succeed; the yield is generally about 4 or 5 cwt. per acre, though double these quantities are not infrequently obtained.

Serious efforts have been made to grow wheat to supply the needs of the European population, but the usual African trouble of rust has not yet been overcome. Wheat cannot tolerate the heat and high rainfall of the low-lying regions, but is grown at altitudes of 6,000 feet or more in the eastern part of the colony.

278

Shifting cultivation is adopted in the forest region, but an attempt is being made to reduce its wastefulness. East-west strips or "corridors" 100 metres wide are cleared for a length depending on the topography and density of population; they are separated by strips of undisturbed forest of the same width. The cleared land is cropped for a rotation of about four years and then allowed to revert to secondary forest for a period, which may be ten or twelve years; meanwhile land in the adjacent strip is cleared and cropped; so the alternation of crop and secondary forest continues. The purpose of the east-west direction is to give the crops the maximum of sun—light being a limiting factor on the equator—and the comparative narrowness of the strip enables the forest to re-establish itself quickly after cultivation ceases. The crops are generally grown in admixture; this ensures a longer period of vegetation cover for the soil, thus guarding against erosion and shading from the sun. Each family is allotted about 20 to 40 acres of land according to its productiveness.

Soil erosion occurs in the broken hill country of the east and in the lower Congo and Ituri regions. It is brought about mainly by rain water on land that has been injudiciously deforested, over-burned, or cultivated too long without rest in wild vegetation. The usual protective measures are adopted: terracing if the slope exceeds 10°; or, on lesser slopes, strip cultivation or planting along the contours protective lines of plants such as *Pennisetum* or perfume plants which have value in themselves and can prevent the little streams of water from joining up to form bigger ones. Visitors who have seen the work testify that it is well done.

Livestock

Compared with the southern and central African plateau the numbers of livestock are very small; in 1950 they were as follows:

Thousands	Cattle	Sheep and goats	Pigs
European	270·7	33·3	30·1
Native	393·0	1,610·7	145·8
Total	663·7	1,644	175·9

The high rainfall regions are entirely unsuited to farm animals because of the large numbers of tsetse fly which can only very inadequately be controlled. The European cattle, sheep, and pigs are mainly concentrated in the high savannah regions of the south, Katanga and Kasai, and the African's animals in the high north-eastern country of Orientale; there are also numbers in the Kivu highlands of the south-east, but very few in the low-lying forest regions of Equatoria or Leopoldville.

The Africans have far more sheep and goats than of any other animals, while the Europeans have chiefly cattle: there is some tendency for their numbers to increase. The average live weight of the European cattle at slaughtering is 7 to 10 cwt. and of the native cattle 5 to 8 cwt., the higher weights in each case being the result of selection. The European farmers produced 1·8 million gallons of milk, 401 tons of butter, and 163 tons of cheese; the native cattle produce 0·9 million gallons of milk, 48·6 tons of butter, and 9·6 tons of cheese.[1]

[1] *Statistiques, Congo Belge*, 1951, p. liii.

Small animals, poultry, Barbary ducks, sheep and goats are the usual native livestock; they are commonly sold to Europeans for cooking, and as they are neither well bred nor well nourished they possess the usual African characteristics of great toughness and low quality.

The native diet

As elsewhere in Africa, hunger and famine were common before organization began under European direction. The position in the Congo was described at a Congress held at Brussels in 1920: Father Legrand declared that in Mid-Congo and Kwango regions famine was an annual visitation, and hunger conditions prevailed for three or four months a year.[1] There were serious famines in 1926 and 1932, and it was quickly realized that "la politique alimentaire"—the full belly policy—was by far the best colonial policy.

The important *communiqué* issued in April 1925 by M. Daladier, then French Minister of the Colonies, to the staffs of the French African territories, instructing them to study the native dietaries with a view to improvement, had a profound influence on policy in the Belgian Congo. Enquiries were set on foot and the results assembled in 1934 by E. de Wildeman.[2] These showed that the basic diet in each of the major regions was very restricted in kind; it was, however, supplemented by a considerable variety of foods both animal and vegetable collected in the forest or savannah, ranging from antelope to rats, caterpillars and insects, and including wild leguminous plants, many kinds of leaves, fruits especially mangoes, mushrooms and in places certain earths.

In the forest region the basic foods are plantains and cassava. After steeping to get rid of the glucoside it is dried, made into a paste, rolled into a ball, dropped into a casserole containing some "accompaniment" in the form of a *purée* or stew, and then eaten. This constitutes the main meal; it is taken in the evening when the day's work is done. The midday meal is a scrappy affair taken at work by the women in the fields, and by the men while they are hunting or occupied about the village or the house or on a European plantation; it consists of maize or groundnuts eaten raw or after being roasted, or sweet potatoes or cassava cooked in the ashes of the fire. The morning meal is also cassava flour, made either into a porridge or a ball but without the accompaniments of the evening meal. The drink is palm wine, the fermented sap of the oil palm.[3]

In the savannah regions maize is the chief food, followed by rice; cassava is grown but is regarded as a reserve. The maize is made into a porridge or a kind of pancake. Groundnuts are also much eaten. Under arid conditions sorghum replaces maize as the basic food but it is not popular, and is given up as soon as possible. Bananas also are grown.

The drink is commonly beer made from millet, maize, bananas or other fermentable materials. Very little animal food is eaten. The Africans are

---

[1] Quoted in E. de Wildeman, *Documents pour l'étude de l'Alimentation Végétale de l'indigène au Congo Belge*, Brussels, 1934.

[2] Loc. cit. Tribute is paid to the great influence of a book by G. Hardy and Ch. Richet fils, *L'alimentation indigène dans les colonies françaises*, Paris, 1933.

[3] The palm wines of the Kwango are described by E. L. Adriaens in *Bull. Inst. Royal Colonial Belge*, 1951, Vol. 22, pp. 334–50, and by P. Simonart and H. Laudelout, pp. 383–401.

reluctant to kill their animals except on special festive occasions, such as circumcision; sheep and pigs are currency in some districts. Milk, butter and cheese are available in quantities too small to make any important contribution to the dietary. Unfortunately the numerous rivers are not well stocked with fish: 18,000 tons of fish were taken in 1948, 25,000 tons in 1949, and 30,000 tons in 1950. Efforts are being made to develop still further a sound fishing industry,[1] but transport is difficult and curing facilities are inadequate; native methods of smoking are very primitive.

The diet is recognized as being sometimes insufficient in quantity and usually deficient in protein, especially animal protein and in fats; a number of the foods gathered wild by the women contain vitamins, so that the diet is better in this respect than might be expected. A detailed survey of the diet and mode of village life in the Kwango region of the southwest has been made by E. L. Adriaens.[2] Cassava was the chief food and an adult would commonly eat about 1 kgm. of the "luku" (paste) per meal, i.e. 2–3 kgm. (4½–6½ lb.) per day. This corresponded to about 800–1,200 grams of the dry farina or about 3·2–4·8 kg. of fresh root: about 1¼–2 tons a year. Assuming an average yield of 4 tons per acre, two to three adults could thus be provided from 1 acre of land; children consumed about one quarter to half these quantities. No estimate on a calorie basis was made, but assuming the same value as for other starchy foods of comparable composition (100 calories per oz.) the daily calorie supply per adult from this source would be 2,860–4,300.[3] For comparison with dietaries elsewhere it is necessary to reduce these to *per capita* values by deducting 20 to 25 per cent: they then become 2,150–3,200 calories per day, which if correct would be very satisfactory. The quantity of protein thus supplied, however, is small: the percentage varies between 2 and 3, so that the daily intake is about 26 to 36 grams per adult, or 12 to 27 grams per head of population. Shelled groundnuts are much richer, containing 25 per cent of protein and 44 or 45 per cent of oil, while soy beans contain still more protein—about 40 per cent, though only about 18 per cent of oil. Some of the accompaniments are rich in protein: smoked termites supply 36 per cent and 44 per cent of fat, and dried caterpillars over 50 per cent of protein and 13–18 per cent of fat.[4] In the general absence of meat and fish from the dietary the intake of animal protein is low; the annual production of animal protein is estimated at 18,500 tons only, an average of less than 5 grams per head per day.[5] Green cassava leaves prepared as a *purée* supply vegetable protein.

Many of the accompaniments contain various vitamins and mineral

---

[1] Described by C. Halain, *Bull. Instit. Royal Colonial Belge*, 1951, Vol. 22, pp. 363–82. Both malaria and bilharzia may, however, be increased, J. Schwetz, ibid., pp. 414–19.

[2] E. L. Adriaens, "Rechèrches sur l'alimentation des populations au Kwango," *Bull. Agricole du Congo Belge*, 1951, Vol. 42, pp. 227–70. Other observers consider this estimate of the amount of cassava eaten is too high.

[3] The percentage composition of the farina is:

Moisture	Fat	Protein	Carbohydrate	Cellulose	Ash
13–14	0·02–0·3	2–3	80–82	0·5–1·0	2–2·5

L. Tihon, *Bull. Agric. Congo Belge*, 1946, Vol. 37, pp. 829–68.

[4] L. Tihon, loc. cit.

[5] The ten-year plan, quoted by C. Halain, *loc. cit.*

substances. It is not possible to say how far the diets are generally satisfactory from this point of view as there is little information in regard to the prevalence of deficiency diseases.

About 10 per cent of the African males are employed in European enterprises and receive rations prescribed by the Government; these are physiologically satisfactory.[1] The European-owned plantations arrange for production of the food needed by their workers.

The Belgian Congo and World Food Supplies

The Belgian Congo has the enormous natural advantage of ample water supply over most of the country; it does not suffer from the recurrent droughts that cause such great losses on the plateau regions to the south and east. The conditions are eminently suitable for vegetable oil, one of the most precious of all agricultural products; this is likely to remain the chief food export. The steady increase in output seems likely to continue, and may even be accelerated as the research work at Yanganbi develops. Palm oil is the most important, but the output of groundnuts could probably be considerably increased. Soy bean, sunflower and sesame can all be grown.

Output of coffee also has steadily increased but that of cocoa has not; yet it appears that more could be grown if the West African supplies begin to fail. Tea of acceptable quality is unlikely to be produced in any great quantity. Beyond these no important quantities of food can be expected.

The perfect suitability of the conditions over most of the country to the tsetse fly make it improbable that any important livestock industry could ever be developed; poultry are a possible exception, but our unfortunate experiences in Gambia show what great difficulties are likely to be met. The paucity of livestock means of course that little animal manure is available, often none at all; this is specially unfortunate in view of the rapidity with which organic matter decomposes in the soil. The present method of supplying it is to abandon the soil for ten or twelve years to a bush fallow; sufficient organic matter then accumulates to allow two or three annual crops to be grown before another fallow becomes necessary. Fortunately this trouble does not arise with the perennial crops, oil palm, coffee and hevea. The fallow is worked on the corridor system, and if this proves permanently acceptable to the native cultivators it will be a great improvement on the old wasteful shifting cultivation. But it is extravagant of land. At present ample land is available. but I.N.E.A.C. is seeking some quicker method of restoring the soil productiveness: among others a period under grass treated with fertilizers which would raise soil fertility and also permit the production of much-needed animal protein. Little use is made as yet of fertilizers; they would probably give considerable crop increases.

At present food has to be imported for the European population, especially wheat, meat, fish and vegetables; probably all these could be produced in the country if it were necessary. Against the import of wheat can be set a nearly equivalent export of maize and cassava flour, but no

[1] An example is quoted by Wildeman (p. 33): 15 kg. bananas or sweet potatoes, 500 grams meat or dried fish, 400 grams oil; 100 grams salt, 5 kg. dried food (maize, cassava, beans, bananas). The law requires that 33 to 50 per cent of the protein must be of animal origin (G. Tondeur, loc. cit., p. 7).

other food is exported. In view of the world shortage of grains for livestock and the fermentation and other industries there might be possibilities of growing for export some of the modern hybrid sorghums in the savannah regions and selected or cross-bred prolific strains of dioscorea, sweet potato or cassava in the forest regions. Irrigated rice also may be a possibility. Where so much has already been done, but so much remains to be done, it is difficult to see which of the various possibilities will in the end prove the most practicable.

NIGERIA

Nigeria's agricultural problems centre round the intensification of output from soils naturally poor and under conditions ranging from wet tropical forest to dry savannah steppe, but where high output of cash crops is necessitated by the paucity of mineral resources and where improvements are made difficult by the prevalence of tsetse fly over large areas, thereby excluding cattle and preventing the development of mixed farming and the use of grass leys and farmyard manure. The problems have some similarities with those of the Belgian Congo, but they are being attacked in a different way.

The great limb of Africa projecting westwards into the Atlantic and forming the northern shore of the Gulf of Guinea is divided mainly between the United Kingdom and France, the United Kingdom having most of the east-west coast with its hinterland, and France most of the north-south and much of the west Mediterranean coasts, and by far the greater part of the interior including the Sahara desert.

All the West African countries have in common a low lying coastal zone of high rainfall forest, and a higher hinterland of savannah becoming drier and drier the further one goes inland till finally the desert is reached. But there is no smooth gradation: widely separated places may have similar total rainfalls. The distribution of the rainfall is more important than its actual amount for determining the agricultural and vegetation characteristics. Over considerable areas of the southern region, both in Nigeria and in the Gold Coast, the wet season lasts for some ten months and has two peak periods, one in May or June, the other in September, while farther inland the curve changes to a single peak in August or September; the total amount of rain lessens, but the wet season also shortens so that the intensity of the rainfall may be greater. Thus Zaria in the north of Nigeria and Ibadan in the south-west both have about 46 inches of rain a year, but while at Ibadan this is spread over ten months, at Zaria it all comes within five months, and August or September may have 15 inches with resulting flooding.

Nigeria is the largest and most important of all the West African countries. Its area is 372,674 square miles (238·5 million acres), including the part of the Cameroons—about 22 million acres—which is under British trusteeship. The population at the census in 1931 was just under 20 millions; the results of the 1952–53 census are not yet available; meanwhile the present estimate is about 32–33 millions, which if correct would indicate an increase of over 2 per cent per annum.

The coastal belt is a low-lying and narrow mangrove swamp only 10 to

60 miles wide; much of it is taken up by the delta of the Niger and has innumerable streams and creeks with but little solid land and no agriculture; its people live by fishing and trading. The rainfall is about 150 inches a year and the wet season is very long; the temperature is not very high and at Lagos does not usually exceed 90° F. The humidity, however, is high.

North of this comes the belt of tropical rain forest about 50 to 100 miles in width. The rainfall is still two-peaked and high—some 50 to 115 inches in the western province—though less than on the coast, and the dry season is longer but the temperatures are higher. Much of the original forest has been cleared by centuries of shifting cultivation and the present forest is largely secondary,[1] but great areas contain valuable timber and are kept as reserves under the control of the Forests Department which also protects other trees of economic value. This forest belt produces much of the wealth of Nigeria: the oil palm products, cocoa and kola.

These two belts between them form about a third of Nigeria, they comprise most of the Eastern and Western Regions,[2] and have about half the entire population of the country. The Eastern Region is especially populous: about a quarter of the entire population are there, not because the soils are rich, for in fact they are poor, but because of the virility of the chief people, the Ibo. Pressure on the land is considerable, and in places there has been a certain amount of gully erosion on the upland slopes, part of which, however, is geological rather than man-made.[3]

North of this is a belt about 300 miles wide, now mainly savannah. Its southern part was formerly forest, mostly dry deciduous, the rainfall 60 to 80 inches a year with a four or five months dry period being insufficient for tropical rain forest. Much clearing and burning for cultivation has converted it into a man-made or "derived" savannah with a fire-climax vegetation of tall annual grass and stunted fire-resistant trees and shrubs: the so-called guinea savannah. The crops are yams, maize, sorghum, and cassava: some of the trees also supply food: the shea nut (*Butyrospermum parkii*) provides a vegetable butter and the locust bean (*Parkii olivieri*) is used in soups, and being leguminous enriches the ground, improving the crops grown in its shade. These trees also protect the surface soil and enrich it by drawing nutrients from the subsoil. The problem of maintaining soil fertility in this high rainfall region has been studied at Ibadan. One year of green manuring benefits the succeeding crop, but does not increase the stock of humus or of soil nitrogen: apparently this is achieved only when dense vegetation covers the ground for longer periods. Mixtures of leguminous plants and grasses are to be tested as substitutes for the spontaneous vegetation of the ordinary fallow.[4]

Farther north comes the lower rainfall tract of native or Sudan savannah, the Middle Belt, largely level or gently undulating plains about 1,000 to

[1] R. W. J. Keay, *An Outline of Nigerian Vegetation*, Lagos, 1949.

[2] Formerly called Provinces, but the name was changed in the 1951 Constitution because exception was taken to it.

[3] A. T. Grove, "Soil Erosion and Population Problems in S.E. Nigeria," *Geog. Journ.*, 1951, Vol. 117, pp. 291–306.

[4] H. Vine, *Empire Jl. Expt. Agric.*, 1953, Vol. 21, pp. 65–85. The author has also made a provisional soil map of Nigeria.

2,000 feet in elevation, with little surface water but sufficient bush and trees to harbour tsetse fly. These two factors have hitherto hampered human settlement, and in consequence the population is only sparse. The rainfall is about 45 to 55 inches a year; the wet season has two peaks, and, as elsewhere in West Africa, the effects of the dry season are intensified by the dry north-easterly wind, the *harmattan* from the desert, which may blow for spells of several days at a time carrying much fine dust with it. A wide range of crops is grown including rice in the food plains of the Niger; they are mostly food crops and surpluses are exported to other parts of Nigeria. Benniseed has a certain local importance as a cash crop.

Still farther north is a belt including the Bauchi plateau some 3,000 to 4,000 feet in altitude though parts are much higher; where though the soils and farming are alike poor, conditions are healthier and the population more dense, centring around the pleasantly habitable little town of Jos. Mining and overgrazing by the cattle-owning Fulani have caused some soil erosion. The temperate conditions allow the growth of European vegetables.

Farther north again—beyond about lat. 11° N.—the living conditions are better and the well populated districts of Zaria, Kano, Katsina, and Sokoto are among the best in Nigeria for field crops; a zone of about thirty miles round Kano is one of the most intensively farmed areas in the country. Much of the cultivation is permanent and not shifting, and the land is manured. This is the grain belt, and the chief source of cotton and ground-nuts; much of it has 30 inches or more rain a year, but there is a long, dry season.

Still farther north the rainfall decreases, and at Sokoto and Maiduguri in the far north it is only about 25 inches a year; the diurnal range of temperatures is greater and the maxima are higher, exceeding 110° F at Maiduguri. Here the country is too dry for anything more than subsistence farming, and livestock become the mainstay of the people. This is the land of the cattle-owning Fulanis. The extreme north is desert.

The Cameroon country on the eastern border is quite different: it is a narrow strip including the high Adamawa Massif; it possesses a good climate, ample rainfall and rich volcanic soils. The Germans had grown a wide range of crops: oil palm, rubber, bananas, coffee and cocoa; in the portion which we administer we are developing cocoa and bananas. There is much good grazing and many of the Fulani have settled here.

Nigeria includes many tribes of widely different origin and culture most conveniently grouped linguistically. The predominant type is that known as the West Coast negro, purest and commonest in the south-east forest country, but elsewhere greatly mixed. In the south are the Ibo of the east and the Yorubas of the west; in the centre and the north are the animistic peoples and the Moslem Hausas. All these are settled, but the Hausas are considerable travellers and traders. The Moslem Fulani of the far north, however, are cattlemen who came from the east and conquered and dis-possessed the local people; they tend to be more attached to their cattle than to the land and to seek grazing wherever it can be found.

Intertribal wars had furnished many slaves in the old days, and much of the slave trade was centred in Nigeria; it was abolished in the British possessions in 1807 but continued elsewhere right up to our own time. Slave raiding by some of the emirs was not finally suppressed till the entire region had been taken over early in this century; the difficult task of organizing it into a coherent whole was carried out by Lord Lugard.[1] Since then Nigeria has developed amazingly.

The Crops[2]

(a) *Cash Crops.*—The chief cash crops are palm oil and kernels, ground-nuts, cocoa, rubber, cotton and bananas; also as usual in Africa there is an export of hides and skins. These commodities, together with timber and tin from the Bauchi plateau, provide most of Nigeria's external income.

Palm products are by far the most important. Two species of palm are grown: the oil palm, *Elaeis guineensis*, which supplies oil and kernels, and the raffia palm, *Raphia hookeri*, confined to swamps and not cultivated; its sap is fermented to produce an alcoholic "wine" and the leaves yield raffia; it yields no oil. Production is practically all by Africans; only a very small area of plantation is held on lease by non-African companies, and there are no European settlers on the land. Almost invariably the palm trees are wild; they are left standing when other vegetation is cleared for cultivation of food crops. The total production of oil is not known precisely as large quantities are consumed by the people themselves.[3] The quantities of oil and of kernels exported are, however, known; they have been steadily increasing:

Thousand tons

	1945	1946	1947	1948	1949	1950	1951
Palm oil	114·2	100·9	126·0	139·2	160	163	175
Palm kernels	292·6	277·2	316·3	327·1	376	416	

The value in 1950 was £28·2 m.; £11·3 m. for the oil and £16·9 m. for the kernels. The two products are very different; the chief fatty acid in palm oil is palmitic, while in kernel oil it is lauric.

These quantities are considerably greater than those sent out from any other country, but they do not represent anything like the possible limit. A usual African yield of oil is about 3 cwt. per acre. The United Africa Company obtains from its plantations about 12 cwt. of oil per acre, and with their steadily improving strains and technique are well on the way to get more. The difference is partly due to difference in yield per tree, and partly to the efficiency of extraction. Much of the factory production is in the Cameroons on good fertile soil, while in the important eastern regions of African production the soils are much poorer: some, indeed, are exceptionally poor. Also the plantations include trees of the Lisombe variety which produces more oil but less kernel than the wild trees. In any case

[1] See his *Dual Mandate in Tropical Africa*, Blackwood, 1922.

[2] For accounts of Nigerian agriculture before the war see O. T. Faulkner and J. R. Mackie, *West African Agriculture*, Cambridge Univ. Press, 1933; and Leverhulme Trust, West Africa Comm., 1938–39, Tech. Rpts. Crop Production, and Soil Fertility Problems, H. C. Sampson and E. M. Crowther.

[3] In the district east of Onitsha studied by Grove (loc. cit.) a peasant may own about 20 trees, 7 or 8 of which would provide oil and wine for the family, only the kernels being sold, but the whole of the produce of the other trees would be sold.

outputs per acre are not comparable because the land in the native compounds carries not only palm trees but food crops as well, so that its total output is not measurable by the quantity of oil produced: in some places the land is supporting one to two thousand people per square mile. The department is encouraging the planting of improved varieties and higher yields may be expected.

The African methods obtain only about 50 to 60 per cent of the oil and its quality is poor; while the European methods recover about 93 per cent and the quality is better. The native methods, however, leave the kernel with sufficient oil to constitute a valuable feeding stuff which is exported to the United Kingdom and brings in more money than the oil itself. The more efficient extraction of the European plantation leaves a residue of much less value. The pericarp contains a lipolytic enzyme which decomposes the oil forming free fatty acids that greatly lower its value; this often happens in the ordinary native procedure. Better quality is obtained by speedy extraction and sterilization after harvesting so as to put the enzyme out of action. To help in achieving this, hand presses have been introduced for individual use and a new power mill, the "Pioneer," for co-operative African use;[1] it extracts 85 per cent of the oil.

Before the war Indonesia was a serious competitor and there were grounds for anxiety about Africa's hold on the market. That fear has now gone. At present all the oil produced sells at high prices. But other countries are increasing their output and there may later be competition from the Belgian Congo and Malaya; possibly even from Indonesia. A palm oil research station has been set up at Benin where pedigree seed for high yield is selected, new varieties are bred, and fertilizer and other experiments conducted. The programme of work necessarily has much in common with that at Yanganbi in the Belgian Congo. The possibilities of increasing output are by no means exhausted: for the plantation yield of 12 cwt. of oil per acre is far exceeded in Malaya where yields of 30 cwt. per acre are obtained.

Next in importance to the oil palm comes cacao, also a tree crop, and like the oil palm, confined to the rain forest belt because of its dependence on shade and on a moist atmosphere. Unlike the oil palm it does not spring up of its own accord but has to be sown. It is not a native of Africa but of South America; it was introduced by the Portuguese probably from Pará or other part of Brazil; they are said to have planted it in 1822 on the island of St. Thomé and there apparently cacao cultivation in West Africa began, but it was not on any significant scale till about 1870. A Nigerian chief, Squiss Banego, saw it growing on the island of Fernando Po in 1874 and brought it home; he started a cocoa farm in the Bonny district on the coast: by 1887–89 the Royal Niger and other European companies had established a few plantations.[2]

Nigeria is more fortunate than the Gold Coast in that although the destructive virus disease swollen shoot is in the country it has not yet become serious. Export of cocoa, unlike that of palm oil, does not seem to be increasing, but remains fairly steady at about 100,000 tons a year:

---

[1] It is expected that 300 will be set up at an estimated cost of over £1·5 million.
[2] F. N. Howes, *African Affairs*, July 1946.

Thousand tons

1945	1946	1947	1948	1949	1950
77·0	100·2	110·8	91·4	103·6	100·0

(Nigeria Trade Summary, 1951.)

The value of the export in 1950 was nearly £20 m.

The improvement has been in quality rather than in quantity. Ninety-nine per cent of the cocoa bought by the Cocoa Marketing Board in 1950–51 was Grade I, and the Board no longer buys Grade III and IV produce.

Two other forest cash crops are important sources of revenue: rubber, and mahogany and other timbers.

In the drier savannah regions of the north the chief cash crops are cotton and groundnuts. Unlike palm and cacao these are only annuals, and must therefore take their place in the rotation with food crops. And the food crops being the more important naturally have precedence in sowing and in receiving any manure that may be available; the cash crops may therefore be sown later than is desirable, also they receive no manure, and so are apt to give lower yields than could be obtained if they had the priority.

Cotton is being encouraged by the Empire Cotton Growing Corporation which issues seed to distributing centres, operates ginneries in the Zaria, Katsina and East Sokoto districts, and takes measures for continuous improvement of yield and quality. In 1951–52 over 100,000 bales of 400 lb. were exported in addition to what was used by local weavers; this was a record up to that time. It is commonly the first crop when the land is broken up after the fallow; and has the advantage that its cultivation does not interfere with that of the food crops as it is both sown and harvested later than they normally are,[1] with some overlap at harvest. About ½ to 1½ acres may be grown on a holding and the yield is probably 200–250 lb. of seed cotton per acre; better results, however, can be achieved; about 450 lb. per acre are obtained on the Government farms.[2]

Groundnuts, like palm oil, are also used locally as food, and only the surplus purchased for export is known. These quantities are variable, in recent years they have been:

Thousand tons

1945	1946	1947	1948	1949	1950
176·2	285·7	255·9	245·1	378·3	311·2

(Nigeria Trade Summary, 1951.)

The value for 1950 was £15 m.; the reduced quantity compared with 1949 was due to drought.

Groundnuts grow well in the light soil, and it is not uncommon for a peasant having a 4 or 5 acre holding to devote 1 acre to them. The average yield is about 5 cwt. per acre, but this could be considerably increased. A dressing of 50 lb. per acre of superphosphate placed near the seed has been found to raise a customary yield of 700 lb. per acre of kernels to 900 lb.

[1] The optimum date of planting is in the first half of July, but planting may have to be deferred: it is still feasible up to near the end of August.

[2] R. Turner, *Empire Jl. Expt. Agric.*, 1948, Vol. 16, pp. 178–86.

per acre. Both the sulphate and the phosphate present in the fertilizer have proved beneficial.[1] The yields may suffer when preoccupation with food crops causes the groundnuts to be planted late: a delay of fourteen days in planting has reduced the yield by as much as 40 per cent. Also the rate of seeding is often too low, because the seed has been eaten or sold by thriftless farmers. A spacing distance of not more than 9 inches is best, yet 24 inches is not uncommon. This shortage of seed at sowing time has the incidental advantage of facilitating the distribution of improved seed.

The demand for groundnuts in Western Europe and Great Britain is enormous, but there would be no point in increasing the production in Nigeria until transport has been improved. Already each year great pyramids lie for months at Kano and other rail points awaiting transport to the ships, and not infrequently the next crop begins to come in before the old one is cleared. The deterioration is less serious than might be feared, but already a Trogoderma beetle that had hitherto lived on cereal grains has adapted itself to groundnuts, and its larvae are very destructive and difficult to kill. The poor crop of 1950 allowed the earlier accumulation to be cleared, and efforts are being made to avoid similar difficulties in future.

Groundnut plants being leguminous obtain their nitrogen from the air and have greater power of extracting plant food from the soil than most of the ordinary native crops; in consequence they are generally grown at the end of the rotation and without manure. But this very facility is fraught with great danger. Greenwood[2] has pointed out that Nigeria's normal annual export of 300,000 tons of groundnuts involves an annual loss of phosphates from Northern Nigeria's soils equal to that contained in 17,000 tons of superphosphate—and this is one of the elements of plant food most lacking in the country's soils. It would have been courting disaster to expand production without at the same time arranging for supplies of phosphatic fertilizer, and a Fertilizer Distribution Scheme has been set up and financed by the Groundnut Board.

Attempts are being made to extend the cultivation of the fibre crops, *Hibiscus cannabinus*, *Urena lobata* (much studied in the Belgian Congo), and *Clappertonia ficifolia* (bolobolo): which can grow in fresh water swamps. It has been proposed to erect at Onitsha a bag factory for working up the fibre, and also a cotton spinning mill.

Bananas are exported from the Cameroons which indeed are rapidly becoming our chief source of supply: the export has risen remarkably since the war and has now exceeded the pre-war quantity:

	Million stems
1947	1·28
1950	4·68
1951	7 (provisional)

The 1950 export was only about 10 per cent less than that of 1939.

Other crops produced for export, but on a smaller scale, are benniseed (*Sesamum indicum*), chiefly from the Benue area, shea nuts, chillies, ginger,

[1] M. Greenwood, *Empire Jl. Expt. Agric.*, 1951, Vol. 19, pp. 225–242.
[2] Loc. cit.

and soy beans. Tobacco is increasingly grown, mostly in the Zaria district, but for local use only; there is no export.

Small growers are liable to serious difficulties in marketing their produce: the fluctuations in market price may cause them great inconvenience and they may be badly exploited by middlemen. To avoid these troubles the Government, while exercising general control through its Marketing and Export Department, has set up for each commodity a Marketing Board which does all the buying for export, fixing the price at the beginning of the season and retaining any profit as a fund for smoothing out price fluctuations that may occur during the selling period. The Board fixes standards and has been able to raise considerably the quality of the produce, thus assuring for the grower a much better price than he would otherwise have got; it is also able to assist any enterprise likely to benefit the industry.[1]

(b) *The Food Crops.*—The very large number of agricultural holdings, and their irregular shape, make it extremely difficult to estimate the total area of cropped land, and the crops are so intermingled that no good estimate of their acreage is possible. The Department of Statistics, in response to the request of F.A.O. for data for their 1951 World Census of Agriculture, has carried out a Sample Survey,[2] but even this could not cover the whole country as some of the tribes refused to co-operate. The Report gives a good general outline of Nigerian agriculture with estimates of areas, yields and outputs: these are put forward very tentatively and they are the only ones available (Table LXXVI).

TABLE LXXVI. *Tentative data from Sample Census, 1950–51*

| | Area, thousand acres | | Production, thousand tons | | |
	Northern Region	Eastern Region	Northern Region	Eastern Region	All Nigeria
Rice	305	45	156	22	244
Maize	354	402	149	198	744
Millet	3,169	—	927	—	940
Guinea corn	4,175	—	1,776	—	1,833
Cassava	347	1,491	1,308	6,190	10,581
Yams (1)	511	1,446	2,077	5,486	9,340
Cocoyams (2)	13	465	13	638	965
Cowpeas	1,051		177	7	475
Groundnuts	1,036	13	287	3	299
All crops	12,459	4,557			
Population roughly, millions	12	6			26

(1) *Dioscorea spp.*

(2) *Colocasia spp.*

The Western Region is omitted as the Oyo people refused to co-operate, hence no totals for that area can be given. The last column is based on estimates.

[1] In 1950 the Cocoa Board provided £1 million for the endowment of the Faculty of Agriculture at Ibadan Univ. College, and £500,000 for financing a five-year plan to combat swollen shoot disease.

[2] Rpt. on the Sample Census of Agriculture, 1950–51, Dept. of Statistics, Nigeria Survey Dept. Lagos, 1952.

The area surveyed in Nigeria was 210 million acres out of a total of 216 million. About 10 per cent of this total—20·5 million acres—was estimated to be in farm crops, about 1 per cent in tree crops, and 13 per cent in fallow; forest reserves were about 10 per cent and the remaining two-thirds of the land mostly unused and, except for some grazing, left till wanted for shifting cultivation. The area per cultivator varied in different districts from about 2 to about 9 acres, but is usually round about 3 acres: the average area per head of population is about 0·8 acres.

The Cameroons had something under a million acres of cropped land.

The authors insist that the figures "cannot be regarded as accurate statements of the agricultural position in Nigeria": they show, however, the relative importance of the different crops, and they represent the results of much strenuous labour honestly performed under trying conditions.

The food crops vary in different parts of the country, having by long experience been selected by the peasants as acceptable and suitable to the local conditions. In the wet regions root crops are grown, especially the shade crops, coco yams[1] and cassava; the former are inter-planted with other staple foods, maize, cowpeas, beans, and with supplementary food crops such as pumpkins and rosella, a hibiscus (*H. sabdariffa*) grown for its seed and its fleshy calices, used either fresh or dried in soups. Upland rice is grown in the west around Abeokuta, and swamp rice in the east in Ogoja province. The two-peak rain season permits the growth of two crops of maize a year on good soils in the west, the earlier being used as fresh cobs and the later as dried grain. Cassava is growing in popularity and replacing yams in some areas; it tolerates poor soils and can be used to end the rotation since its roots can be lifted after cultivation has ceased. The sequences vary a good deal.

After a period of cropping the land is allowed to revert to bush for a time. In the eastern sections where the soils are very poor the period in bush fallow has to be long in order to recover any important degree of productiveness, but the population is so dense (one to two thousand per square mile) that the land can ill be spared. Efforts have been made to speed up the fallowing process: the growth of *Acioa Barteri*, a deep-rooted shrub, seems the most promising, coupled with applications of fertilizers. No method of obviating the fallow or greatly reducing its extent has been found; this is one of the most difficult soil problems in West Africa.

The Middle Belt, also of high rainfall, is one of the most productive regions of Nigeria: yams are important but cassava seems to be ousting them. Maize and guinea corn are grown in quantity.

The northern savannah country has too long a dry season to suit yams: the typical crops are millets and sorghums, groundnuts and cotton. Cassava, however, is increasingly grown; it has considerable ability to survive the long dry season. Maize is grown where the moisture suffices, but the animistic tribes of the plateau grow as their main crop acha (*Digitaria exilis*), a small-grained cereal that thrives in poor conditions and ripens early.

As the rain season is only short, and has only one peak period, the cereal crops are liable to fail and resowing may be necessary. A common

---

[1] Both roots and leaves are eaten.

practice[1] is to grow cotton as the first crop, then millet sown on or before the first rain; later on sorghum is sown through it and then cowpeas and cassava; the rotation may end with groundnuts. The land around the hut receives household wastes as manure and so keeps up its productiveness; it is used for vegetables, tobacco and other luxury crops. Any household waste not wanted on the compound goes to the cereals, and in some districts land receives a certain quantity of animal excretions from Fulani cattle kraaled on it during the dry season to feed on the residues of cereal crops. Few farmers, however, have cattle of their own and consequently little farmyard manure is available. In urban areas composts prepared by the Medical Department from night soil and town refuse are used: the value of organic manure is well appreciated in built-up areas like Kano.

The cereals respond remarkably to manurial treatment: even 1 ton per acre of pen manure has given astonishing increases in the Zaria province. The effect, however, is due rather to the phosphate present than to the organic matter, and similar results have been obtained with 50 lb. superphosphate per acre,[2] yet many farmers use neither.

About half a million tons of fresh sugar cane are produced annually mostly in the Zaria province, but also in the Katsina and Kano provinces. The cane is grown on the swamp soils or "fadamas"; before the war it was used for chewing only, but during the war the juice was extracted in presses worked by horses; it was made into gur which is becoming increasingly popular.

Livestock

Large tracts of Nigeria are infested with tsetse fly and therefore uninhabitable for cattle: in consequence the numbers are far lower in relation to the human population than in South or East Africa. They live chiefly in the northern savannah regions of low rainfall where they are reasonably safe from the fly, but are still liable to rinderpest and periodically to great losses caused through droughts, as in 1950. The Fulani are the chief cattle tribe; their ancient custom was to trek the animals to the wetter southern part of the savannah during the dry season and back again to the north when the rains began. So long as there was plenty of space this hurt no one, but with closer settlement crops are liable to suffer. The cattle are roughly estimated at more than 5 million[3] of which about 1 million are

[1] Cotton is the main crop only in the Sokoto and Zaria districts: elsewhere in this region the millets and sorghums are the chief crops, along with groundnuts and beans; and cotton is subordinate.

[2] K. T. Hartley and M. Greenwood, *Empire Jl. Expt. Agric.*, 1933, Vol. 1, p. 112. K. T. Hartley, ibid., 1937, Vol. 5, 254–63. The 1949–50 Agricultural Report gives the following results in lb. per acre:

	No manure	Compost 4–5 tons per acre
Sorghum	270	673
Millet	427	725

60 lb. superphosphate per acre gave increases in the first year of 200–400 lb. of groundnuts and of grain, and showed residual effects for the next four years.

[3] Estimates vary: Livestock Mission of 1948 (Col. Office Rpt. No. 266): 5·25 million in Nigeria, more than 0·5 million in the Cameroons. Sample Census based on annual count for taxation but recognized as too low: 3·7 million: F.A.O. 5 million.

slaughtered annually; there are also some 3 million sheep and 6 million goats. A considerable trade in hides and skins has developed, including the red Sokoto goat skins called "Morocco leather" because they used to be exported by camel via the Sahara to Mediterranean ports.

Prices of fat cattle are high and tend to rise. Milk production is not much developed; the native breeds of zebu type are not heavy yielders; at the experiment station the herd average for the White Fulani has been about 250 gallons and for the Sokoto breed 284 gallons.[1] The fat content is high, however, commonly 5 to 7 per cent; the solids-not-fat are 8 to 10 per cent. Improvement seems possible, individual cows of the Shuwa breed have yielded up to 700 gallons a year at Maiduguri. Farmers generally recognize the need for fodder conservation and they make wild hay and even silage. There are numbers of cattle in the Bamenda highlands of the Southern Cameroons; the grazing is good, water is available all the year and there is no tsetse fly.

The prevalence of tsetse fly over large areas of Nigeria greatly limits many activities dependent on cattle: there are no bullock wagons that effect so much transport so cheaply in India, no development of mixed or ley farming that would more than anything else raise the productiveness of the soil, and little prospect of greatly expanding the production of meat and of milk. A breed of humpless cattle, the Ndama, has been found in French Guinea which is resistant to tsetse fly. It is smaller than the zebu types (which are not resistant), but it is a good beef animal. Experiments are in hand to see if its resistance amounts to immunity: if so it will be the only immune breed known. Other experiments are to discover whether the resistance is transmissible to the zebu animals; if so, considerable developments might become possible.

The economic position of the natives has been studied in detail by Daryll Forde and Richarda Scott.[2] Four groups are recognized producing respectively:

(a) *Southern forest region:* root crops for subsistence, tree crops for exchange.

(b) *Northern savannah region:* Sorghum and millets for food, field crops for exchange.

(c) *Plateau areas:* Lower level farming, exchange not well developed.

(d) *Far northern pastoral regions:* farming for subsistence only, livestock for exchange.

Employment of some of the men in mines and other occupations improves the economic conditions, but parts of the south have more than 1,000 persons per square mile with resultant soil exhaustion and decline in quantity and quality of available food supplies.

Nigeria was one of the first of the African territories to study the problems of native nutrition. Dr. McCulloch's investigations began in 1927. In the

[1] Nigeria Agricultural Rpt., 1949–50.
[2] *Native Economics of Nigeria.* An inquiry under the auspices of Nuffield College, Faber, 1946.

Colonial Office inquiry of 1939,[1] nutrition was found to be reasonably satisfactory: in general the town dwellers appeared to be better fed than the peasants and in the north there were hunger periods during the long dry season; also the cattle-owning Fulani had better physique than the settled Hausa. There were some poverty diseases and leprosy in the central part of the south,[2] and an overcrowded region of small farms and poor physique among the forest mountain people of the Cameroons, who lived largely on bananas. But apart from these local black spots there were in general no marked deficiency diseases. As usual in Africa the protein was insufficient and it was suggested that this should be remedied in the north by the development of mixed farming, and in the south by the fuller utilization of fish. Both courses have been adopted, but progress has been slowed down by the war.

No recent systematic dietary surveys have been made, but a general description of the food in the forest area has been given recently by J. A. Packman.[3] It is very similar to that in the Belgian Congo. Three meals daily are taken, the chief is in the evening. The yams or cassava roots are peeled, boiled and pounded to a paste: this forms the "fufu," the basis of the meal. Some others of a wide variety of other foods, green vegetables (grown by the women near the dwelling), beans, peas, onions, edible leaves of trees or wild plants, okra, red peppers, meat or other animal food from the forest, dried fish are worked up with palm or ground nut oil and cooked together—the toughest ingredients being put into the pot first and given longest time for cooking: this forms the "ofe," the supplement. Pieces of the "fufu" are broken off, dipped into the "ofe" to suck up as much of the rich oily sauce as possible, and eaten. The drink is palm juice—which may be fermented. In the north the dietary is broadly similar, but the paste is made of millet or maize and the accompaniment differs in detail. Beer is made from millet or sorghum.

The possibilities of increasing the output of food

The method most immediately effective, and involving the least disturbance of customary methods would be to use more fertilizer, especially more phosphate and in places lime and nitrogen. An extensive campaign was started in 1949 in the good farming districts of Bornu, Zaria and Sokoto as well as in the eastern regions. The plan is to distribute in each of the five years 1950–54 1,000 tons of superphosphate in 56 lb. lots to 40,000 farmers,[4] then to make further quantities available for purchase by those who found it effective. It is hoped that sufficient will be taken up to offset the drain of phosphate resulting from the export of groundnuts and the sale of grain off the farm.

[1] W. E. McCulloch, *Effect of Dietary on Health of the Hausa and Fulani Tribes*, 1929–30. *Nutrition in the Colonial Empire*, 2 vols., H.M.S.O., 1939.

[2] Leprosy still occurs in the eastern districts and to a less extent in other parts of the country. The Colonial Office Report on Nigeria for 1950 (p. 60) states that 26 new villages had been established for segregation purposes; more than 12,000 patients were on sulphone treatment with promising results; other treatments were under investigation.

[3] J. A. Packman, *Food from the Commonwealth and Empire*, Gawthorne, 1951 (with a large number of illustrations).

[4] In 1951 about 70,000 farmers received free samples of fertilizer and scoops for application (*Samaru Conf.*, Jan. 1952, p. 14).

There are small deposits of rock phosphate near Abeokuta, but, like those in East Africa, they mostly contain too much iron and alumina to make good superphosphate; either the finished fertilizer must be imported or it must be made locally from imported raw materials. Nitrogen fertilizers would probably be very beneficial in the eastern provinces; sulphate of ammonia has given good results with yams. Local manufacture may become possible if the great Volta scheme of electrification materializes.

The rock phosphate proved ineffective as direct fertilizer in the northern provinces—incidentally delaying the recognition of phosphate deficiency in those soils, although this had been established by analysis of soil and crop.

Improved varieties of oil palm, cotton and groundnuts have been produced and distributed with good effect. Food crops have been less fortunate, and there is little to show for years of work by plant breeders excepting varieties of cassava resistant to virus. This is not peculiar to Nigeria: it happens also in India and other peasant countries; partly because through a long-continued process of trial and error the peasants have already found suitable varieties—though not necessarily the best—but chiefly because of the innate conservatism of mankind in matters of food. Hybrid maize and dwarf sorghums have not yet been adopted.

O. T. Faulkner in 1922 initiated the efforts still being continued to replace shifting cultivation by a more permanent and productive system of mixed farming; this involves drastic changes. Under the old system all cultivation was done by hand; the hoe was the only tool; there were no ploughs, and no idea of traction by bullocks. The new system required ploughs. They had to be devised and made, the bullocks had to be trained to work quietly, and the cultivators taught the difficult job of handling both animals and plough efficiently. The wooden ploughs which the village craftsman could make were unfortunately ineffective and iron ploughs had to be used, but of course they were more costly. The bullocks had to be protected against tsetse fly and provided with food and water during the dry season. By the beginning of 1952 some 9,000 mixed farms had been set up: 2,300 of them in 1951. In general the plan is that they shall be 30 acres in size, 12 being cropped, 12 fallow, and 6 for the compound; those first established, however, were smaller and dependent on communal grazing. But there have been difficulties in acquiring enough cattle as the Fulani are loath to sell breeding stock; also the new farmers have needed more supervision than the small departmental staff could supply once the numbers of mixed farms began to increase (Pl. 27, 28, p. 316).

The alternative to bullock power would obviously be some form of mechanized cultivation and the possibilities are being studied.[1]

Opening up new land

As already stated, much land in the Middle Belt is unused: in the old days this was partly through fear of attack by other tribes, but now the chief reasons are the lack of water and the prevalence of tsetse fly, carrying

[1] *Native Agriculture in Tropical African Colonies.* Rpt. of a survey of problems in mechanization, Col. Office Advisory Council of Agric., etc., Pub. No. 1, 1950.

the trypanosome of sleeping sickness in human beings[1] and of 'Ngana in animals. Vigorous efforts are being made to eradicate the fly and as these succeed they will enable more land to be brought into use. At Anchau a corridor 70 miles long and 10 miles wide was cleared of the riverine species (chiefly *Glossina tachinoides*) and 60,000 people were settled in a new hygienic tsetse-free town.[2] There came an anxious time when the woodland or savannah species (*G. morsitans*) which had hitherto been absent, advanced eastwards from Central Zaria and invaded the corridor; should it succeed in establishing itself in the forest reserves on the borders of the corridor it might do much harm: an eastwards spread into Kano and Bauchi would be particularly serious. The Department of Medical Services took active steps, spraying the clearings with D.D.T. from TIFA machines, and having a D.D.T.-sprayed herd of 200 cattle patrol the Banki hills; the danger seems to have been averted. In any case closer settlement by destroying the bush effectively controls the *Morsitans* species just as depopulation favours it.[3] Elsewhere an area of 150 square miles has been cleared for mixed farming.[4]

Systematic development in this hitherto sparsely populated region would become possible by a combination of tsetse fly control, mixed farming, and mechanized cultivation. Some interesting experiments in group farming are being made.[5] An area of about 11,000 acres at Kontagora (east of the Niger just about 10° Lat. N.) is being divided into 15 settlements each of 20 farms of about 35 acres, half of which will be in fallow and the other half will carry sorghum and groundnuts; some land is reserved for grazing. The farms are being allotted to Kamberi, a pagan tribe, good farmers, experienced and conscientious.

A more ambitious scheme has been started at Mokwa in the same region but more to the south. Some 65,000 acres of almost unoccupied land selected by the Oil Seeds Mission are being developed by the Niger Agricultural Project Ltd., financed partly by the Colonial Development Corporation and partly by the Nigerian Government. The first part of the scheme is to set up an experimental farm and 10 self-supporting settlements each with 80 farms of 48 acres, to be cultivated on a four-course rotation, including four consecutive years of grass ley. Tractors are being used for cultivation.

Should this succeed a further one million acres in the same area is available for similar development.[6] By the end of 1950, 5,000 acres of bush land had already been cleared and 2,000 were under experimental cropping.

Farther to the east in the Bida emirate 2,000 acres of low-lying swamp land are to be irrigated for rice cultivation, and a survey has been made

---

[1] In 1950 over 300,000 persons were examined and 3,000 new cases diagnosed and treated (Col. Office Rpt. on Nigeria, 1950, p. 61). T. H. Davey in 1948 estimated that tsetse fly causes a direct loss of at least £1 million yearly through death of cattle (Trypanosomiasis in British West Africa, Col. Office Rpt., 1948).

[2] T. A. M. Nash, Progress Rpt., Col. Office, November 1948.

[3] In Nigeria *G. Morsitans* transmits only cattle disease and not human; in East Africa it transmits both.

[4] Col. Office Rpt. on Nigeria, 1950, p. 61.

[5] A group farming groundnut scheme is described in *World Crops*, March 1950. See also the proposals put forward in the Report of the West African Oil Seeds Mission in 1945 (H.M.S.O., 1948).

[6] Colonial Office Rpt. on Nigeria, 1950, p. 41. Later, however, (May, 1954) the Mokwa scheme was abandoned because of its expense.

for the purpose of opening up a further 20,000 acres, also for rice. In the Sokoto and Rimi valleys of the far north-west there are considerable areas of land flooded during the wet season—the so-called fadama lands—which are too difficult to be cultivated by hand but need heavy implements; they are being used for growing rice. Some considerable yields are already reported in the Sokoto district; elsewhere 12 sample plots in the Pategi Lafiagi emirate averaged 2,000 lb. of paddy per acre, and in a controlled flooding experiment at Maigana more than 4,000 lb. per acre were obtained.[1] The Rice Commission of 1948 took a very optimistic view of the possibilities and estimated that 1·6 million acres could be grown in Nigeria if the necessary irrigation could be provided. Steps, of course, would have to be taken to avoid the spread of malaria.

Nigeria has an impressive Ten Year Development Plan approved by the Legislative Council in 1946 and subsequently revised. It was originally estimated to cost £55 m., of which £23 m. comes from the United Kingdom Colonial Development and Welfare Fund. Much of the money is being spent on improving education, health, water supply, transport, etc.

The Cameroons Development Corporation was set up by the Nigerian Government to take over 250,000 acres of plantations formerly owned by the Germans in the territory now under British Trusteeship. Part of the profits are to be ploughed back into the estates, the rest which would ordinarily rank as dividend is passed on to the Governor of Nigeria for the improvement of the life of the people: during the five years 1948–52 some £186 000 has thus been handed over and nearly £1·1 million devoted to capital developments.[2] Bananas are the main products, but palm oil, palm kernels and rubber are also produced. The acreage under bananas is being greatly increased. The crop suffered considerable damage from tornados in 1951 and 1952, but so far is free from the Panama disease which is causing so much loss in Jamaica.

Nigeria's prosperity depends on palm oil, kernels, groundnuts and cocoa, none of which is likely to be super-abundant in any foreseeable future and all of which are more likely to be scarce. Steps are being taken to improve the quality so as to ensure high prices. Export of most of the commodities has expanded considerably since pre-war days (Table LXXVII).

TABLE LXXVII. *Exports of agricultural products, 1939 and 1950, Nigeria*

	Thousand tons		Value £ million
	1939	1950	1950
Palm oil	126	173	11·29
Palm kernels	300	416	16·94
Groundnuts	147	311	14·99
Cocoa	113·8	100	18·98
Bananas (million lb.)	140	128	1·75
Benniseed	16·2	14·4	0·70
Hides and skins	7·8	13·7	4·14
Cotton	4·4	12·6	2·98
Rubber (million lb.)	6·2	29·4	2·49

[1] Agric. Rpt., 1949–50. The Sample Census suggests that the average yield is about 10 cwt. per acre.
[2] Fifth Rpt. Cameroons Development Commission, 1952.

The striking increases in export of palm oil and kernels and also of ground-nuts justify the hope that still higher outputs may be achieved as production becomes more efficient. On the other hand there is no steady increase in output of cocoa, although the quality has improved so that the position is better than the figures indicate. Cocoa requires good soil with good power of supplying water, and it is possible that the most suitable land has already been taken up. Export of bananas is profoundly affected by restrictions by importing countries. Citrus fruit production could be extended in the Abeokuta and Ibadan districts, as could the production of onions and other vegetables in the southern sector of the northern region.[1]

The export of the non-food cash crops, hides and skins, cotton and rubber has considerably increased, so broadening the basis of Nigeria's prosperity. Experiments are being made with *Hibiscus cannabinus* as a substitute for jute.

The semi-arid north presents some special problems: the purpose is to develop a system in which water, livestock, agriculture, and forestry shall form an integrated whole. Water and dipping tanks would need to be provided, grazing regulated and de-stocking arranged; game also would need to be regulated. There is some soil erosion: fortunately less than in certain other parts of Africa; protective measures are being taken, though with the general handicap that many of the holdings are fragmented, and the special handicap that some of the plateau land of the pagans may not be touched for reasons of their ju-ju. One tribe indeed may not sow grass. The African only slowly realizes the need for soil conservation.

The possibilities of improvement are considerable, but so are the difficulties. The necessary appliances cannot be produced in the country and must be imported, the higher technical and scientific guidance must for a long time ahead be brought in from outside.

A University College associated with London University has been established at Ibadan under the Principalship of Dr. Kenneth Mellanby. The Staff of the Agricultural Department though not large includes always some well-known experts on tropical agriculture. African students, however, appear to take more readily to law, politics and medicine than to science and technology. The development of Nigeria's natural resources requires full co-operation based on mutual confidence between its people and the white people possessing the necessary equipment, and its leaders should seek to ensure this.

THE GOLD COAST

The Gold Coast is of special importance as being the first of the British African territories to achieve full self-government. It has considerable natural resources, but they can be developed only by capital, appliances, and technical guidance supplied from other countries. Working solutions can no doubt be found for the various technical problems involved. Much more difficult problems may arise out of the need for securing Western co-operation if development is to succeed. It would be of supreme value to Africa if these more intangible problems could be satisfactorily solved.

[1] Agric. Rpt., 1949–50. Diagrams and a population map are given by A. T. Grove, *Geog. Journ.*, 1951, Vol. 117, p. 292.

The climatic conditions resemble in general those of Nigeria, except that the coastal region has a comparatively dry strip extending 10 to 20 miles inland in which the mean annual rainfall is only about 33 inches: the result of a peculiarity of the local topography.[1] Its vegetation is dry scrub and grassland, and it has little agricultural importance at present. North of this the rainfall is higher and the forest begins, first a belt of 40 to 50 inches rain with poorly grown trees but well suited to crop production, Nye calls this the Southern Fringing Forest; then comes the forest region proper, with 50 to 95 inches of rain falling in two well marked seasons with monthly maxima in June and October, and dry seasons from December to March and again in August. Humidity is high except when the Harmattan wind blows from the Sahara. This forest belt is the region of highest rainfall; the trees are mixed deciduous but now much replaced by secondary bush as the result of shifting cultivation; much also has been cleared to permit of permanent tree crops. The forest belt rises gradually from the coastal plain to the escarpment formed at the junction of the crystalline rocks of the Voltaian and the Akwapimian sedimentary rocks overlooking the Volta Valley where it ends.

North of the forest come the drier savannah region of stunted trees in a large expanse of grass covering North Ashanti, the northern territories, and Togoland.[2] The rainfall is highest in the south—about 58 inches—it decreases to the north and in the far north-east is only 39 inches. More important for vegetation, the dry season increases both in length and in severity; in the north it lasts from mid-October to mid-April and the humidity is very low. This savannah country extends to the frontier with French West Africa: none of the arid north is included in the Gold Coast as it is Nigeria. The areas of these different regions are approximately as follows:

	Million acres
Coastal savannah	6
Closed forest	17
Northern savannah	36

The Cash Crops

As in Nigeria both oil palm and cacao grow in the forest belt, but as the rainfall is lower than in Nigeria the oil palm is much less important than the cacao. It has long been known that cacao would flourish there and trees are said to have been growing in the grounds of the Basel Mission at Akropong in 1868,[3] and a native of Mapong in Akwapim brought seed from the island of Fernando Po in 1879 and planted it on his farm. Its cultivation was encouraged by the Governor, Sir William Griffith; by 1891 the first lot of cocoa beans was exported: the weight was 80 lb. and the price obtained

[1] This has been studied at the Achimota College. Geographical details are shown in *Atlas of the Gold Coast*, Survey Dept., Accra, and Edward Stanford, London.

[2] The soils and agriculture of these various regions are described by P. H. Nye in *Empire Jl. Expt. Agric.*, 1951, Vol. 19, pp. 217–23, 275–82, and Vol. 20, pp. 47–55, and the forest and savannah regions of Ashanti, by M. Fortes, R. W. Steel, and P. Ady in *Geog. Journ.*, 1947, Vol. 110, pp. 149–79. See also *Text Book of West African Agriculture*, F. R. Irvine, 2nd Ed. Oxford Univ. Press, 1953.

[3] F. N. Howes, *African Affairs*, July 1946 (Kew Gardens). Cacao is the name given to the tree, cocoa to the product, but there is a good deal of indiscriminate use.

£4. In 1892 Sir William started a Botanic Garden and experiment station at Aburi to which cacao was introduced from St. Thomé and the West Indies. Development at first was slow: the West Indies were the chief suppliers and world consumption was not yet large. Chocolate had not come into fashion and cocoa was not a very popular beverage: it got somehow associated with political and religious dissent; moreover many people found the oil indigestible, and in one well-known brand (Epps's "Grateful and Comforting") the effects were mitigated by admixture with arrowroot. The Dutch firm of Van Houten removed the fat and so opened the way to our present brands and to the large scale manufacture of chocolate. Enormous development has since taken place and the world consumption of cocoa now is well over 700,000 tons a year. But nowhere has the crop thrived as it does in the Gold Coast. From this small beginning of 80 lb. the export rose rapidly till in 1926 it amounted to 228,537 tons, around which figure it has since fluctuated according to the price rising to a maximum of 311,000 tons in 1936 and falling to 124,000 in 1942; it then rose to 243,512 tons in 1950, and this, with Nigeria's 100,000 tons, brought up the contribution of these two countries to about 50 per cent of the total world supply.[1] The number of cacao trees in the Gold Coast was in 1948 estimated at about 400 million.

This rapid development is all the more remarkable in that from the outset production was entirely by small native growers, usually with less than five-acre holdings, and not by European planters. British capital provided storage and transport facilities and also loans to the growers. All the necessary conditions for the cacao tree occur in this forest belt: suitable shade and the optimum temperature, humidity and water supply; the yields obtained are higher than in any other country. In good districts, e.g. the Birrim Valley and Anyinam districts, they range about 900 to 1,400 lb. dry cocoa per acre; in the drier northern parts of the forest, however, e.g. about Kumasi, they are only about 500 lb. per acre. The effects of fertilizers have not yet been adequately studied in different parts of the cacao belt. The cultivation is entirely suited to the native psychology: it is the man's contribution to the household; the labour is very light and once the seeds are sown and the plantlets thinned out there is little to be done except to wait for the harvest. The whole family help to gather in the beans and to prepare them for sale.

The marketing of the crop is controlled by the Cocoa Marketing Board which has now considerable reserves in its stabilization fund and cushions the effects of varying prices.

For long the crop did not suffer unduly from insect or fungus pests, but after a time, as elsewhere with newly introduced crops, pests, diseases and other troubles began to multiply. Yields are now often lower than formerly: newly planted farms have taken longer to come into bearing, and replanting of old farms has not infrequently been unsuccessful through attacks of the insect *Sahlbergella* and other causes.[2]

[1] The present world consumption is about 750,000 tons a year and is rising. It is estimated that damage by capsid bugs and swollen shoot causes in the aggregate a loss of 200,000 tons a year, but the estimate is necessarily very rough.

[2] H. B. Waters, "Agriculture in the Gold Coast," *Empire Jl. Expt. Agric.*, 1944, Vol. 12, pp. 83–102.

Of all these troubles by far the greatest is the virus disease, swollen shoot, first observed in 1936 though it was then already widespread and was traced back at least to 1922. Up till 1939 trees were dying at the rate of about 1 million a year; between 1939 and 1945 the rate rose to 5 million annually, and from then to 1948 to 15 million: it was estimated that 50 million trees were infected by the end of 1948, and if the ravages continued unchecked the industry would virtually disappear within twenty years.[1] The most heavily infected area is in the Eastern Province between Akwadum and Nankese, north of Accra; this province used to be the most intensive cacao district in the world, but its production fell from 116,000 tons in 1936–37 to 64,000 tons in 1945–46, mainly though not entirely due to the disease.[2]

Swollen shoot occurs also in Nigeria and the Ivory Coast, but it is not known outside West Africa and there was no previous knowledge or experience to go upon; the only treatment that could be suggested was to cut out and burn infected trees immediately they were discovered. This was for a time made compulsory and compensation was paid, but a sense of grievance developed and was fostered by political agitators—who are always looking for such opportunities in Africa—and after some rioting in February 1948, compulsory action was discontinued. Meanwhile, a non-British group of experts was invited to study the problem and they confirmed that destruction of infected trees was the only practicable course of action.[3] The present position is that the Government, which is now entirely in the hands of the people themselves, withdrew the compulsory provisions and left it optional whether infected trees should be destroyed or left, but pays compensation if trees are destroyed and replaced. Up to December 1952, 12,000 acres of devastated land had been cleared and replanted. Meanwhile the disease continued to spread: the 1951–52 crop of 207,000 tons was 51,560 tons below that for 1950–51, representing at current prices, a loss of £12·75 m.[4] The crop for 1952–53 was 244,000 tons, the level of 1950.

A Cocoa Research Station was set up about 1940 and reorganized in 1944 at Tafo, 67 miles north of Accra and in the cacao belt.[5] The ideal solution would be to find or breed a resistant strain, and this should be quite possible as many varieties and strains of cacao occur in the ancestral home in South America; so far only certain types from the Amazon region of Ecuador have been found consistently resistant to infection.[6] But the search is necessarily slow and the cross-breeding even more so, for the trees take five or six years to come into bearing, and even after a resistant strain acceptable to the grower and the market is found, it still has to be multiplied up to the large numbers required by growers. The work is continuing: new strains are being sought of greater vigour, earlier maturity and other desirable qualities.[7]

Meanwhile it was found that the disease was transmitted by slow-moving

[1] Lord Rennell of Rodd, in House of Lords, September 15, 1948.

[2] A. F. Posnette, *Ann. App. Biol.*, 1947, Vol. 34, p. 388.

[3] Rpt. Commission of Enquiry into Swollen Shoot Disease of Cacao in the Gold Coast, Colonial No. 236, H.M.S.O., 1948.

[4] *The Times*, December 19, 1952.

[5] Its work is described by O. J. Voelcker, *Empire Jl. Expt. Agric.*, 1948, Vol. 16, pp. 241–8.

[6] A. F. Posnette and J. McA. Todd, *Ann. App. Biol.*, 1951, Vol. 38, pp. 785–800.

[7] See A. F. Posnette, *Empire Jl. Expt. Agric.*, 1951, Vol. 19, pp. 242–52.

mealybugs (*Pseudococcus spp.*), which feed on the sap of the tree and if this happens to be infected, can carry the virus to another tree. They are transported by ants which feed on the honey dew they secrete and protect them against predators, even building small tents of waste vegetable matter over them.[1] The mealybugs might be destroyed by spraying despite the ant's protective tents, but this is impracticable in a forest. Modern systemic insecticides offer much better prospect of success. The insecticide is applied to the soil, it is absorbed by the plant roots, and transmitted to the leaves and shoots where it destroys any of the insects feeding upon them. The insecticide does not cure a diseased plant, nor will any other method do so, but it should prevent the spread of the virus to healthy plants. So far as present knowledge goes the insecticide has no adverse effect on the cocoa bean.

The treatment is being carried out by a scientifically directed organization, Pest Control Ltd., and the results are being watched with the deepest interest.

If the disease can be brought under control the cultivation of cacao can be extended. Most of the best cacao soils are already taken up, but improvements in varieties and in management should enable other soils to be used. Cacao grows best in moist shade,[2] and the forest, therefore, must be preserved; at present it occupies less than 20 per cent of the forest area. The Gold Coast and Nigeria already produce half the world's cocoa and could produce more.

Meanwhile in case the worst should happen in West Africa cocoa cultivation is being investigated in other countries: Malaya, Borneo, Zanzibar, the Solomon Islands, etc.,[3] while French Africa, Brazil and Mexico are expanding their production.

In consequence of the amazing spread of cacao culture the oil palm has almost faded into insignificance; many of the trees indeed have been cut down in tapping for palm wine. There are, however, numerous trees grown in and around cocoa farms and they are plentiful in the northern and southern fringes of the forest. The Agricultural Department is encouraging their development and also that of other forest products, coconut for copra on the narrow sandy shore line of the drier coastal belt (where alone they grow), and rubber in the wetter forest areas. Other possibilities include kola nut, which is not only saleable on the market, but has special ceremonial significance in West Africa and is an important item in its internal trade.

The food crops in the forest area include coco yams, cassava, plaintains and maize all interplanted and harvested as ready; after a few years (the time depending on the productiveness) the land is allowed to revert to forest and a fresh clearance is made. The amount of food produced hardly suffices for the local needs, and supplies have to be imported.

Some of this comes from the southern fringing forest, cocoa there being less important than the food crops. The system of cultivation is much the same as in the forest proper. A clearing is made, maize is grown in each of the two seasons of the first year; and also in the first season of the second year; cassava is either interplanted or grown in the second season: it matures

[1] For a description see R. A. E. Galley, *World Crops*, 1950 (May), Vol. 2, pp. 189–93.
[2] In Nigeria much of it is grown in the open.
[3] C. G. Eastwood, *Journ. Roy. Soc. Arts*, 1952, Vol. 100, pp. 226–36.

in the third year. The land then reverts to bush for two to five years. This sequence is typical, but not invariable.

The southern part of the savannah has good rainfall and produces many food crops, especially yams, maize, groundnuts and rice (4,500 tons in 1948) for export to the forest towns and villages. As elsewhere, shifting cultivation is practised; yams are commonly grown as the first crop, followed by rice or maize[1] according to the available water supply, then in the third year may come cassava, groundnuts or bambarra beans.[2] After that the land is rested from two to twenty-five years according to the density of the population.

Tobacco is also grown, but only for local consumption.

The field crops are fairly free from diseases and pests, but cassava suffers from virus disease, and maize is periodically severely attacked by rust: 1950 was a bad year for yams and most of the crops of the southern savannah. Sorghum, millet and groundnuts or beans are the main crops usually grown in some sequence, though continuous cropping with cereals or with groundnuts is also practised. The compounds are scattered: around each is a 5 to 15 acre farm continuously cropped and receiving excreta from humans and animals; outside this, shifting cultivation is practised, the land being rested for short periods.

The Northern Territories contain most of the livestock; in 1947 the numbers were estimated at 300,000 cattle, 455,000 sheep and goats, and 1,500 pigs. Rinderpest and contagious bovine pleuro-pneumonia were formerly destructive but can now be controlled. An animal health station has been set up at Pong-Tamale for the preparation of the appropriate sera and vaccines; the numbers of cattle have subsequently considerably increased.

The relatively low rainfall and the long dry season often result in a shortage of water. The habit of burning the grass annually has caused a good deal of sheet erosion very severe in some places. The burning is now partially controlled but fires are still liable to sweep over the savannah. There is as yet no serious overstocking, but in some of the more densely populated areas of the far north there is not enough grazing land.

The ability to keep livestock in these northern territories means that mixed farming is practicable involving the use of farmyard manure and cultivation by bullock power. Already a beginning has been made, and considerable increases in output of food may result. To the south, cattle are restricted by tsetse fly, though some local breeds are fairly resistant to trypanosomiasis in the savannah, but good dairy cattle succumb more readily and so milk production is difficult except in the north. Good quality meat can, however, be produced. In the forest area cattle are completely excluded by tsetse fly though the villages swarm with sheep, goats, and poultry. The usual type of mixed farming seems ruled out here, but a system might be worked out using the small animals. The dry coastal belt is not free from tsetse fly, but if water could be provided it would be practicable to keep cattle there and to use the manure in mixed farming.

[1] The maize is sown at the end of April and harvested at the end of July. The yams have a wider time range, and can be planted from December to April and harvested from July to November.

[2] *Voandzeia subterranea,* somewhat similar to ordinary groundnuts.

The Colonial Office nutrition enquiry of 1939 showed the usual deficiencies of fats, animal proteins, vitamins and minerals in the native diets. As in Nigeria the customary diet consisted of a staple starchy food, root or grain, with a mixed supplement including groundnuts and their oil, shea butter, pepper, etc. To this was added in the forest zone palm oil, rice, raw sugar cane and many wild leaves; other forest products, smoked antelope, monkey, hippopotamus and elephant[1] were popular where they were available, and, on the coast, fish was eaten. In the savannah the additions were tomatoes and onions; neither milk nor eggs were used, and meat was of poor quality. The northern district sometimes suffered from scarcity of food in drought periods especially in crowded areas such as North Mamprussi,[2] though at the same time the usual export of food to the mining areas and the forest was continuing.

The position was but little changed by 1944 when H. B. Waters published his revised survey of the Gold Coast agriculture.[3] Famine was almost unknown and the high prices obtained for the cocoa export tended to encourage imports of foods including live animals, meat, wheat and flour, sugar, rice, vegetables, pulses, edible oils, milk and butter, most of which excepting wheat could have been produced in the country; in 1939 these had been valued at £1·37 million—about one-fifth of the value of all imports. The war, however, caused restrictions both on export of cocoa and on imports of food.

In 1950 the values of the chief exports were: cocoa £49·98 million, gold £8·72 million, manganese £5·00 million, timber £3·86 million, diamonds £1·84 million.

Future developments

The forest products, cocoa, palm oil, rubber and timber with subsidiaries such as kola seem likely to remain the chief source of wealth of the Gold Coast, and in consequence the forest will always need to be conserved and with it presumably the tsetse fly. So long as this happens neither bullock power nor farmyard manure will be available and ordinary mixed farming is therefore ruled out, leaving shifting cultivation as the most practicable way of growing the food crops, unless indeed methods of utilizing sheep, goats, and poultry can be devised or fertilizers can be used. The Belgian corridor system (p. 279) would probably give larger production of food crops in the forest belt but it is impracticable because of the small size of the holdings. Superphosphate increases crop yields both in the forest proper and in the southern fringing forest, but nitrogenous fertilizers do not: the phosphate response is probably economical in the closely farmed areas of the fringing forest, but not in the forest where more land is available and longer rest possible.[4]

The savannah regions afford greater possibilities as the tsetse fly trouble becomes better controlled and as fertilizer investigations give fuller knowledge

[1] Neither elephant nor hippopotami survive now in any number.

[2] C. W. Lynn, *Bull.* 34, Dept. of Agric., Gold Coast, 1937, has described the agriculture of this district as it was then. It has changed but little since.

[3] H. B. Waters, *Empire Jl. Expt. Agric.*, 1944, Vol. 12, pp. 83–102.

[4] P. H. Nye, loc. cit. Some of the soils are deficient in sulphur, and part of the beneficial effect of superphosphate is due to the calcium sulphate it contains.

of fertilizer responses. A long grass fallow does not enrich the soil in available nitrogen compounds when it is broken up.[1] On the contrary, Nye has found a definite shortage of available nitrogen, persisting into the third year and possibly later. Sulphate of ammonia gave marked increases in yield frequently greater than on land cropped more frequently. The fallowing, however, seems to increase the amount of available phosphate in the soil.

Mulching was moderately beneficial, but not lime or potash. In some trials in the Northern Territories kraal manure gave good results due apparently to its phosphatic material.[2] Further development of certain crops may become possible, including limes (which, however, suffer from "die back")[3] and other citrus fruits, bananas, etc., in the Central Provinces. A factory for working up limes has been established by a well-known British firm at Asebu, 15 miles north of Cape Coast.

Some large reclamation projects are planned. The most impressive is to dam the River Volta in the gorge near Ajena and raise its level by some 200 ft. submerging a savannah tract at present unused and making an artificial lake of about 2,000 square miles—the largest of its kind in the world. Hydro-electric plant will generate 550,000 kW. for the production of aluminium from the local bauxite, and some 400,000 acres of good soil under low rainfall can be irrigated for the cultivation of rice, cotton and grass. The scheme is estimated to cost £144 million and is to be undertaken jointly by the Governments of the United Kingdom and the Gold Coast, the British Aluminium Company and Aluminium Limited, of Montreal.[4] The United Kingdom share is not to exceed £56·8 million.

The Gonja Development Scheme covers a district in the north-west, at present sparsely populated but with a rainfall of about 40 inches per annum. The original purpose was the mechanized production of groundnuts on about 12,000 acres, with small blocks of sorghum and fibre crops, Hibiscus and Urena. Later this was changed and the emphasis was on the land settlement and social aspect of the scheme: general food crops were to be produced.[5]

Various other developments are in progress. The Gold Coast Industrial Corporation was established in May 1948 with an authorized capital of £100,000 increased in April 1950 to £350,000 to establish industries based on the natural resources of the country and to help in other ways in its development. Finally, and most significant of all, the Gold Coast now possesses its own University College, associated for the purpose of awarding degrees with the University of London. It has long had the well-known Achimota College opened in January 1927 with the purpose of giving a liberal education preserving the best in the African culture and adding to it whatever is appropriate from western culture. By its constitution the Principal is European and the Vice-Principal African.

---

[1] See also p. 206.

[2] P. H. Nye, *Empire Jl. Expt. Agric.*, 1952, Vol. 20, pp. 227–33.

[3] A. F. Posnette, *World Crops*, 1952 (Feb.), Vol. 4, pp. 64–6.

[4] The report of the experts, Sir William Halcrow and partners, on the scheme was published in 1952. The reserves of bauxite are estimated at 225 million tons, and it is estimated that 1·15 million tons can be processed annually producing 210,000 tons of aluminium.

[5] The original scheme is described by W. V. Blewett in *Journ. Roy. Soc. Arts*, Aug. 1950, No. 4827.

An account of the agriculture of the Gold Coast and its climatic and soil conditions is given by P. H. Nye in *Studies on the Fertility of Gold Coast Soils, Report to the Director of Agriculture,* Gold Coast, 1950.

SIERRA LEONE

Sierra Leone is made up partly of the low coastal belt of West Africa, partly of its plateau; the dividing line starts at its eastern frontier with Liberia about 50 miles from the coast and runs parallel with the coast to French Guinea; south and west of this the country is low lying except for a ridge in the Colony peninsular; to the north it is high, ranging from 900 to 3,000 ft. altitude.

Sierra Leone has the distinction of having the highest rainfall in West Africa. It is as usual seasonal: it comes from April to November and has a well marked maximum from July to September; the period December to March is dry and sometimes even arid when the Harmattan wind is blowing from the Sahara. The rainfall is highest near the coast. It is very variable; at a hill station in the Colony peninsular it has been as much as 300 inches in the year, with 120 inches in one month; but 110 to 150 inches is the normal range in the coastal belt. Inland the rainfall decreases, but nowhere is it usually less than about 80 inches a year. The country does not stretch into the desert. The temperatures are not unduly high; on the coast the mean annual minimum is 72° and mean maximum 88° F, and the shade temperature rarely exceeds 95° F. Sierra Leone used to be riddled with fever on account of its swamps and mosquitoes and was truly called "the White Man's Grave," but British engineers and medical authorities have ameliorated the conditions and made it comparatively safe to live in.

The wet low-lying area is in the rain forest zone; the higher country is naturally deep forest or bush savannah but there has been so much shifting cultivation that much of it now is secondary bush. The total area is 27,925 square miles (17·8 million acres) roughly half being high and half low lying.

The population is about two million and is very mixed.[1] The colony was originally founded in 1787 by Wilberforce and the Evangelicals for redeemed slaves and other homeless Africans. Slave raiding and slavery continued in the hinterland and was not put down till the French and ourselves agreed on boundaries and proceeded to clean up the regions for which we had made ourselves responsible. The last vestiges of domestic slavery were not abolished till 1928.

The crops are the same as elsewhere in wet West Africa. The forest zone produces as cash crops palm kernels and oil, by far the most valuable, benniseed (*Sesamum indicum*), cocoa, piassava,[2] ginger, groundnuts and kola nuts roughly in that order of importance; coffee and copra are also produced. Most of the farming, however, is shifting cultivation for subsistence; the export trade is not large and the cash income averages only about £8 per head.[3] The areas and outputs of the chief food crops were in 1950:

[1] The interesting Mende tribe, formerly brave warriors and now rice farmers but retaining their love of secret societies, has been described by K. L. Little, *The Mende of Sierra Leone,* London, Routledge, 1951.

[2] The stiff bristle-like fibres used for making brushes and brooms, obtained from the petioles of *Raphia vinifera,* a wine palm: a swamp tree, wild and uncultivated.

[3] *Soil Conservation and Land Use in Sierra Leone,* Freetown, 1951.

	Thousand acres	Thousand tons		Thousand acres	Thousand tons
Uplands			Swamp		
Paddy	700	216 (1)	Paddy (tidal)	40	30 (1)
Cassava	33	95	Paddy (inland)	40	25 (1)
Sweet potatoes	5	6	Cassava (inland)		
Fundi (3) (*Digitaria*			(dry season)	1	2·5
exilis)	15	4·5	Sweet potatoes	3	3
Groundnuts	20	7·5 (2)			
Ginger	3	1·5			

Soil Conservation and Land Use in Sierra Leone, Freetown, 1951.

(1) As paddy. Deduct ⅓ to convert to rice.

(2) Undecorticated.

(3) Called acha in Nigeria.

Rice is far and away the most important food crop. The rainfall everywhere suits it; all farming is subordinated to it and it is grown even if the yield is only 400 lb. per acre.[1] It is all used locally, there is no export.

In the uplands a patch of forest or bush is cut, burned carefully and sown with rice and subsidiary crops, cassava, pigeon pea, etc., mixed; a hut is built and vegetables sown around it: these are tended by the women. Long season varieties of paddy are preferred, harvested in October or November; yields may be anything from 400 to 1,200 lb. per acre. Cassava may remain for eighteen months and pigeon peas two or three years. The land is abandoned after one year of cropping in the wetter districts, two, or three in the drier; the cultivator moves on to another patch which he has cleared and does not return to the original area until he has used all the land available to him. If the interval has been sufficiently long the bush has become re-established; the time nowadays does not suffice for the forest to come back, nor is this wanted. Eight or ten years is usually satisfactory, and when this is practicable and a good growth of bush results the system is considered to be the most effective for conserving the soil and maintaining its productiveness. With improved transport, groundnuts for export are being increasingly grown especially in the north but spreading to the south. They follow rice and may be accompanied by fundi or cassava. The yield of groundnuts may vary from 200 to 1,000 lb. per acre; the average is about 750 lb., but over-farmed lands may give only about 200 to 300 lb. per acre.

With increasing population the period of fallow has had to be shortened, so that the bush has insufficient time to re-establish itself; only grass has come in, especially in the relatively drier northern districts. The grass is burnt annually and in consequence grass fallow is less satisfactory than a bush fallow; yields have decreased, fertility and soil structure both tend to deteriorate and erosion sets in. The conditions eventually become unsuitable for rice, and cassava takes its place as the local food crop; the soil is exposed for a long period during the wet season thus further increasing the danger of erosion.

The cultivators are advised to safeguard the bush fallow, and to protect the grass from fire; the experts' task is to find some treatment that will be as

[1] For details see *Soil Conservation and Land Use in Sierra Leone*, pp. 19, *et. seq.*, and K. L. Little, *The Mende Upland Rice Farmer*, Freetown.

effective as bush fallow, but will not require eight or ten years for its operation —but this is Africa's perennial problem.

Elephant grass (*Pennisetum purpureum*) is said to give as good a fallow as bush.

Near the towns vegetables and other garden crops are grown by women to supplement rice in the dietary.

Very little manuring is done: not much farmyard manure is available, compost is not made and fertilizers are not used.

Swamp areas are fairly extensive in Sierra Leone: in the littoral tract they cover some 500,000 acres including flooded grasslands. The mangrove swamps are considered the best for paddy; about 137,000 acres appear to be suitable for cultivation, but only about 10,000 acres are used as yet. Some 63,000 acres of adjoining flooded grass lands could be cropped if the flooding was controlled, but only about 3,000 or 4,000 acres are actually used. There are also perennial swamps, fresh water swamps and empoldered lands in these southern regions;[1] the total area cultivated is about 45,000 acres of which some 40,000 acres are in paddy. In addition there are considerable but unknown areas of inland swamps where also about 40,000 acres of paddy are grown, but the yields are lower than in the coastal region.

Swamp farming has increased, and it has added considerably to the output of rice, but it is not particularly popular: upland rice is preferred to swamp rice as an article of diet. Nevertheless swamp farming must be further developed, if only to save the uplands from being overcropped.

Livestock are few in number. In 1948 and 1949 they were:

	Cattle	Sheep	Goats	Pigs	Poultry
Thousands	57·7	9·5	21·0	3·0	About 500

The sheep and particularly the goats were certainly underestimated. The cattle are fairly resistant to trypanosomiasis (tsetse fly) but liable to contagious pleuro-pneumonia; the chief difficulties in keeping them are the lack of grazing and of water in the dry season. The milk yields are very poor. In the first year after it was assembled (1944) the herd on the Government farm gave an average of 39 gallons only; after four years of selection, better feeding and management, this was raised to 122·5, and the weight of calves at birth rose in the same period from 30·3 lb. to 38·1 lb. It is estimated that not more than 3 per cent of the cattle are sold for slaughter annually, with the result that some ten to fifteen thousand animals are imported annually from French Guinea to supply Sierra Leone with meat.

In consequence of this shortage of cattle there is very little ploughing: cultivation is almost entirely with the hoe; also there is little prospect of introducing mixed farming as is now being done in Nigeria, and of course little farmyard manure can be used.

Native Diet

The Colonial Office Nutritive enquiry of 1939 revealed deficiencies of

[1] Difficulties have arisen on some of these empoldered lands because of the presence of toxic iron compounds and acids in the soil. (J. M. Dent, *Empire Jl. Expt. Agric.*, 1947, Vol. 15, pp. 206–12.) Similar conditions have been reported in Holland.

animal protein and of A. and B. vitamins[1] in the dietary and also some troubles due to unwholesome rice; it was also pointed out that the natives themselves would not increase production of the supplementary foods excepting under supervision. The position seems to have improved since then, for the 1951 Soil Conservation and Utilization Report states that the natives are generally well fed, eating larger and more regular meals than their fathers did especially since the increase in area under swamp rice; they are also eating more peas and beans. There is, however, still a deficiency of protein; owing to the small numbers of livestock the chief source is fish and where, as commonly happens, that is not available the only supply is from wild game and is very erratic: perhaps once in two months some meat may be eaten.

Palm wine is drunk, except by Muslims, and it supplies some Vitamin B.

The staple food is rice; it is mixed with palm or groundnut oil and hot red peppers; the various accompaniments include green vegetables, leaves of cassava, sweet potatoes, "krin krin" (*Corchorus olitorus*) and others with occasional dried fish or meat.

Reserve foods include maize which is ready for harvesting before the rice and may therefore close a gap between one year's supply and the next; fundi serves the same purpose in drier districts, and yams in the savannah. Near the towns sweet potatoes are grown. Where rice is not available, cassava becomes the chief food; it is eaten raw, boiled, dried or as farina with the usual accompaniments.

Future Developments

Much of the land is sparsely populated and the physical possibilities of development, especially of the swamp areas and valley bottoms, seem considerable, but the essential preliminary, the improvement and education of the human material, seems likely to present great difficulty. The expansion of the oil palm industry forms part of the Plan for Economic Development, but the major problem is likely to be the search for a substitute for bush fallow and for ways of tiding the cattle over the dry season so that some kind of mixed farming can be introduced. A rice research centre was established in 1948 with grants from the United Kingdom Colonial Development and Welfare Fund: among its problems are the maintenance of fertility and the removal of salt and other toxic substances from the wetland soils.

GAMBIA

Gambia is the smallest and most northerly of the British West African territories. It is a narrow strip of low-lying country about 200 miles long through which flows the river Gambia; it runs due east and west and is nowhere more than about 500 feet in altitude. The rainfall is about 50 inches a year with a range of about 15 inches each way: it is seasonal, coming mostly in July to October, while the period December to May is dry; and the period December to March is liable to the Harmattan wind from the desert. The area is 4,100 square miles (2·6 m. acres) and the population

[1] Diseases in Sierra Leone due to A and B avitaminosis had already been described by E. J. Wright in 1927.

about 250,000; the natives are said to be of good type, industrious and efficient. The river is navigable and affords the best mode of transport.

The native vegetation is mainly forest and bush. The chief crop is groundnuts planted in June after the early rains and harvested in October or November: these have long been the main export accounting in 1950 for £2·11 million out of a total of £2·29 million for all exports; palm oil and kernels come a long way behind. The large numbers of bees caused the early development of a trade in wax, but West African honey makes no appeal to the British housewife. A small export of hides and skins completes the trading list.

The staple foods are millets and rice, but the latter is not produced in sufficient quantity and some has to be imported, as also have sugar, vegetable oils, tobacco and kola. Crop production has been hampered by the depredations of large numbers of baboons, monkeys and wild pigs, and a scheme has been put forward for their destruction, a price being paid for every tail brought in. In the first season some 30,000 baboons and 12,000 monkeys were destroyed.

Gambia has recently come into prominence through the large poultry scheme started by the Colonial Development Corporation in 1948 with the expressed purpose of maintaining a flock of 200,000 high-class poultry producing up to 20 million eggs and 1 million lb. dressed poultry a year, mainly for export to Britain. The capital approved was £820,000; over 10,000 acres of land were cleared to grow sorghum as poultry food. No sufficiently critical pilot trials had, however, been carried out, and unforeseen difficulties proved so costly that the scheme was profoundly modified and much of the money spent on it was written off.[1]

The intention behind the scheme had been unexceptionable: Great Britain wanted poultry and eggs and Gambia needed some other export product besides groundnuts. The result shows the impossibility of rushing development plans in Africa: no scheme, however attractive, should be attempted until the basic knowledge has been acquired by properly conducted experiments.

FRENCH TROPICAL AFRICA

French Africa comprises most of the country west of the Nile Valley and north of the Belgian Congo with the exception of those areas of coast and hinterland within the British Commonwealth or held by Spain or Portugal. The tropical section is divided into two great divisions. French West Africa (A.O.F., Afrique Orientale Française) and Equatorial Africa (A.E.F.), the areas and populations of which are, in million acres:

	Land area million acres	Cultivated	Grazing land	Forest	Population millions	
					1939	1950
West Africa	1,156	25·0	62	420	14·9	16·7
Equatorial Africa	620	7·5	130	340 (1)	3·9	4·4
	1,775	32·5			18·8	21·1

(1) Including savannah.

(*F.A.O. Year Book of Stat.*, 1951.)

[1] Secretary of State for the Colonies, February 28, 1951. Thirty thousand of the birds had died of fowl cholera in the summer of 1950, and it had not been possible to grow enough food for the birds so that quantities had to be imported.

To these should be added the trustee territories, the Cameroons and Togoland, bringing up the total area of French Africa to 1,900 million acres. Maurice Guillaume[1] tentatively divides it up as follows:

		Million acres
Desert and other waste		500
Utilized for shifting cultivation	175	
Additional for nomadic grazing	75 (1)	250
Not utilized		1,150
		1,900

(1) The nomadic grazing is estimated to occupy 120 million acres, but 45 million overlap with the shifting cultivation.

Thus about 17 per cent of the land potentially cultivable is utilized.

West Africa is by far the more important and the more developed.

The political and economic organization of French Africa differs entirely from that of the British Commonwealth countries. The French territories are regarded as an extension of France—*la métropole*. Once adopted as equals—*assimilées*—their citizens rank equal with those of France, they send to the National Assembly in Paris deputies who are on the same footing as those from the communes of France and like them can attain ministerial rank:[2] they do not even form a Colonial *bloc*. Once a man has achieved a certain level of culture he becomes socially and politically a full citizen of France, without colour bar, at least in principle.

For long Senegal has been the most important of the West African territories. It is on the northern edge of the tropics; only its southern part, the Casamance strip that separates Gambia from Portuguese Guinea, is in the region of tropical rain forest, and its people are not entirely negro, but have much Moorish, Berber, and other foreign blood in them. It was the first of the French tropical possessions to be developed. It is naturally a poor country, but as early as 1840 the discovery was made that it could produce groundnuts and in due course it became the second largest producer in the world, India being the first. Groundnuts still remain Senegal's chief product, but the United States has become the second largest producer, and Senegal now has the third place.

The other important crop is millet with some sorghum; this with cassava is the staple food of the people. A smaller area of maize is grown, and in the wetter Casamance region some rice, but insufficient for the requirements so that some has to be imported.

The Ivory Coast is richer. It has been considerably developed in recent

[1] Adding in the Cameroons and Togoland. *United Nations Sci. Cong. Conservation and Utilisation of Resources, Lake Success* 1949 (U.N. Dept. Econ. Affairs, 1951), Vol. 6, pp. 570–85.

[2] In the 1930's the deputy for Senegal became Minister of Agriculture for France. In introducing me to him the Minister for Overseas France expatiated on the superiority of the French system, under which an African native could rise to so high a rank in the Empire, over the British system, under which he could not. I had to explain that he could if he became a Member of Parliament for a United Kingdom constituency, and there was no bar to prevent him doing this.

years; coffee, cocoa, and bananas, all rich cultures, have been introduced, and the production of palm kernels expanded. As the result of these developments the exports now exceed in value those of Senegal; the two together account for about 80 per cent of the total from French West Africa.

Of the remaining territories Dahomey exports palm kernels and oil, and also cotton: Guinea, with its wide variety of conditions, produces both forest and savannah crops: oil palm, hevea, coffee, bananas and other fruits in the forest districts; groundnuts and millets in the savannah and rice in the wet lands, while the Fouta Djalon district has many cattle. It has also deposits of bauxite and considerable potential water power.

These productive regions occupy in all only about a quarter of French West Africa, three-quarters are taken up by the French Sudan, Niger and Mauretania, all approximately of the same size. Mauretania is a pastoral country very dry and sparsely populated, its chief products are cattle, hides and gum, and an output of dates. The Sudan produces all the main crops and exports some groundnuts; it has half the total cattle population of French West Africa and more than half the population of sheep and goats. The Niger, while sandy and desolate, has some well-wooded country in the centre and south; it produces all the main crops and exports groundnuts. It has about a quarter of the total livestock population; the red Maradi goat furnishes skins for glove making. All three countries owe their relatively large animal population to their dryness: crop production in West Africa tends to stop at the zone of 18 to 20 inch rainfall, but livestock can be kept in the belt stretching down to about 10 inches, subject always to the risk of erosion unless the grazing is well controlled. On the other hand, the wet forest regions are unsuitable because of the risk of trypanosomiasis. The numbers of animals in West Africa are estimated by F.A.O. as follows:

	Millions	
	1938–39	1949–50
Cattle	3·8	6·3
Sheep and goats	12·0	18·5

(*F.A.O. Year Book of Statistics*, 1951.)

The French early turned their attention to the study of nutrition of the natives. M. Deladier's dispatch of April 4, 1925, when he was Minister for the Colonies, has already been mentioned; there were some useful studies in the early 1930's.[1] The foods are as in other parts of West Africa: millet and cassava in the drier regions; yams, maize and rice in the wetter, with groundnuts, bananas, beans and wild foods collected in the forest, in addition to some meat and fish. Statistics of native food crops are notoriously difficult to obtain and unreliable when collected, but such as they are they do not indicate any increased production since pre-war days in spite of the increase in population. Consumption of groundnuts, however, has increased, leaving less surplus for export. (Table LXXVIII.).

The total cereal production apparently fell from 3·5 to 3·1 million tons and production of roots rose only from 2·07 to 2·14 million tons. The

---

[1] Among them G. Hardy and Ch. Richet fils: *L'alimentation indigène dans les colonies françaises*, Paris, Vigot frères, 1933, pp. 388.

TABLE LXXVIII. *Area and production of food crops, French West Africa*

	Area million acres		Average yield cwt. per acre	Production, thousand metric tons	
	Pre-war Average 1934–38	1950	General range	Pre-war average 1934–38	1950
Millet	12·20	12·00	3 to 4	2,561	2,300
Rice	1·43	2·05	5 to 5·5	405	531
Maize	1·63	1·06	5 to 6	532	262
Total cereals	15·26	15·10		3,498	3,093
Sweet potatoes and yams	0·73	0·52	30 to 40	1,170	1,020
Cassava	0·57 (1)	0·62	30 to 35	900	1,124
Total roots	1·3	1·14		2,070	2,144
Groundnuts	3·18	2·80	4·5—5·5	713	704
Population millions	14·9	16·7			

(1) In 1948.

(*F.A.O. Year Book of Statistics*, 1951.)

small fall in production of groundnuts may be exceptional: the crops in 1948 and in 1949 had been 836,000 and 850,000 tons respectively. These quantities do not represent the whole of the food available: some rice, wheat and sugar are imported into Senegal.

The chief export is still groundnuts, but compared with pre-war times the quantity is falling off and a larger proportion is exported as oil leaving the cake which could serve either as food or manure.[1] Export of palm oil, however, has not increased: it has indeed fallen; but export of palm kernels remains substantially unchanged. There has been a great increase in export of coffee and a smaller one of cocoa, both from the Ivory Coast, and a smaller increase in export of bananas chiefly from Guinea, but also from the Ivory Coast. (Table LXXIX.)

TABLE LXXIX. *Food Exports from French West Africa. Thousand metric tons*

	1937	1948	1950	Sources (1950)
Groundnuts	528·7	243	201·5	Senegal (173) Sudan, Niger (about 13 each).
Groundnut oil		49·2	71·4	Senegal.
Palm kernels	81·8	63·3	84·4	Dahomey (46), Guinea (25·4), Ivory Coast (10).
Palm oil	30·1	10·8	11·7	Dahomey.
Oil cake			83·3	Senegal.
Coffee	10·4	56·2	57·7	Ivory Coast (54), Guinea (2·8).
Cocoa	48·1	41·2	61·7	Ivory Coast.
Bananas	55·4	48·2	68·7	Guinea (45·7), Ivory Coast (23).

An important agricultural research station has been established at Bambey, Senegal, under the direction of Dr. F. Bouffil, for the study of the problems involved in the development of the country.

(*Statesman's Year Books*, 1943, 1949, 1952.)

[1] Actually it is eaten only as a last resort and is not used by Africans as manure.

The population increases only slowly and is very unevenly distributed. Attempts to improve the shape and size of the holdings met as in the British territories with difficulties about established rights and usages, reluctance to move and other troubles. As elsewhere in West Africa, large areas of land suitable for cultivation had been left unoccupied; on these systematic reclamation and colonization are being carried out, there being little or no complication due to established usages.

Much irrigation has been done and more is intended. The flood areas also are being better utilized. The Senegal river usually floods about 1·7 million acres of land in the wet months: on this it is proposed to grow rice. The difficulty is that during the dry season the sea flows up the valley and the salt makes the soil unusable; it has not, however, spoiled the texture and would easily be washed out by the rain; if the sea were prevented from returning the land could be brought into use. The scheme presents no insuperable engineering difficulty, but would be costly. Other river basins present similar possibilities and are being studied in detail. Barrages have been erected on some of the rivers for purposes of irrigation, many of them small.

The most impressive of these schemes is in the Sudan territory on the Niger river. The Niger is the largest of the group of rivers rising in the mountain block of Fouta Djalon—*père des fleuves*, as the French call it—in French Guinea about 150 miles inland from the sea. Instead of flowing seawards, however, it strikes inland in a north-easterly direction, then turns east, then south-west through Nigeria to the sea at Lagos making a course like an inverted V, 2,500 miles long. The first part of its course is through the plateau country between 2,000 and 1,000 feet altitude, but near Ségou it drops to the lower level of the French Sudan. Here it has several times changed its bed so that it follows a deltaic merging into a lacustrine course through a region of long grass, shrubs and trees to Timbuktu some 300 miles away. The rains come from June to October; the rest of the year is dry except for a short spell in February. The river is in full flood in October when most of the delta is under water excepting the islets of elevated ground on which the villages are built. The old native cultivation had long been millet and cotton sown as the flood recedes; as along the Nile; rice also was grown where irrigation was possible. There was no rotation and no manuring, and the soils were very impoverished. The growing shortage of cotton for the French mills after the First World War led to the study of this region as a possible source of supply, and a project was submitted to the Ministry of the Colonies in which some 4¼ million acres were to be irrigated. Further studies showed that this was impracticable. An amended project was put forward in 1929 for the irrigation of 2·4 million acres in the delta region on the left bank of the main river, 1·3 million to be in cotton and 1·1 million in rice; 300,000 immigrants were to be brought in from the crowded districts and ultimately the population was expected to rise to 800,000. This plan was accepted: an organization *L'Office du Niger* was set up in 1932 with headquarters at Ségou and the scheme was incorporated in the global grant of 1,500 million francs. A barrage 884 yards long was erected above Sansanding at the beginning of the delta with the necessary levees upstream; this diverted the water along a large canal which after five miles forks, one branch, the Sahel, striking off north-easterly to command land in the "delta morte"; this after seven miles was to be joined on to a rediscovered old river bed which after clearing would become a serviceable feeder; the other branch, the Macina, went eastwards and after fourteen miles was to join another rediscovered old river bed, which was likewise to be cleared and brought into the system (Pl. 29 and 30, p. 317).

The agricultural programme, however, proved entirely unrealizable. Instead of 2·4 million acres only 50,000 had been irrigated by 1951; and instead of cotton, rice has been the main product:

	Spitz 1948	*Harrison Church* 1951
By the Sahel Canal	16,500	21,000
By the Macina Canal	24,000	29,000
	40,500	50,000

Sansanding, les Irrigations du Niger, Georges Spitz, Paris, 1949. "Irrigation of the Inland Niger Delta of the French Sudan," R. J. Harrison Church, *Geog. Journ.*, 1951, Vol. 117, pp. 218–20. The five-year plan (1952–56) is for 42,000 acres of paddy and 11,000 acres of cotton, 53,000 acres in all. Anticipated yield of paddy: 16 cwt. per acre. (Office du Niger, December 1952.)

About one-fifth of the area is in cotton and four-fifths in rice.

The disparity between expectation and achievement reminds us of our own groundnut scheme in Tanganyika and the poultry scheme in Gambia. There are certain common difficulties: lack of basic knowledge due to inadequate surveys beforehand; excessive overhead charges due to proliferation of European staff; and difficulties with the African natives, who, as elsewhere, were reluctant to move from their old villages, however crowded, to the new sites; reluctant also to do the steady continuous work required by the new agriculture necessary under irrigation. They had been intended to assist in clearing and levelling the soil, but they could not and the work had to be done for them by large implements. Also they proved incompetent to maintain the irrigation and drainage works: this too had to be done for them. They lacked the proper cultivation implements, and these could not be obtained in sufficient quantity.

Africa is no exception to the general rule that planning easily outruns achievement in agriculture.

FRENCH EQUATORIAL AFRICA

This lies to the east of French West Africa and Nigeria, and extends from Libya to the Belgian Congo. Much of it is about 1,000 feet to 3,000 feet above sea level, but in the north there is a low-lying tract, which includes the Bodelé depression and the Lake Chad system. The coastal region also lies low.

The area is only about half that of French West Africa and the population little more than a quarter; only a fraction of the land is utilized as yet. In its southern part it has about 170 million acres of tropical forest containing much valuable timber. But as elsewhere in warm climates subject to violent rainfall the soils are liable to denudation and degradation once the forest is cleared; they need long periods of rest in bush fallow before they can again be cultivated and they are best reserved for tree crops: palm nut, coconut, bananas, coffee, cocoa, hevea and others. The prospective demand for these products is not considered to justify much active development at present.

The savannah regions are at present only sparsely inhabited:[1] they could carry a considerably larger population and produce the usual crops, cotton, groundnuts, sisal, shea butter (also called karité), soya bean, fibres, and in the river valleys rice. Two experiment stations have been set up to study the possibilities of development: one at Loudima in the south near the Belgian Congo, the other at Inoni for the Batéké plateau.

Further development of French Africa, especially of West Africa, may be expected. Oil seeds are the special charge of the *Compagnie Générale des oleagineux tropicaux,* and fibres of the *Compagnie des Textiles.* Although much of the country is unsuitable for cattle the high Fouta Djalon region in French Guinea is well adapted to them, and being well watered could probably be made to carry good pastures for fattening animals bred in the marginal regions between the cultivable savannah and the desert. A meat industry would become possible, but it would necessitate abattoirs and refrigerator transport which present conditions could hardly justify.

It is not intended to develop French Africa on plantation lines: that method, it is feared, would lead to the growth of an "agricultural proletariat." The basis is to be settlements of peasants working on mixed farming systems planned to avoid soil deterioration and erosion. One peasant with a hoe can cultivate about an acre; with plough and animal power about 5 to 7 acres; and with some mechanization about 12 to 20 acres: this compares with the 50 to 60 acres per man on a fully mechanized plantation. On the average an acre provides for 1 to $1\frac{1}{2}$ persons where there is a long dry season and for $2\frac{1}{4}$ to $3\frac{1}{2}$ persons where there is not. For the dead periods of the year handicrafts and temporary migrations of the men folk are proposed.[2]

[1] A lack of reproductive power has been noted here, and in parts of the Belgian Congo.
[2] The possibilities of expansion are discussed by Maurice Guillaume in *Proc. United Nations Sci. Cong. on Conservation and Utilisation of Resources,* 1949, Vol. 6, pp. 570–85.

Chapter 9

ASIA: I. INDIA AND PAKISTAN

THE UNION OF INDIA—BHARAT

The Union of India exemplifies all the food problems of Asia, and also shows the way to their solution. The difficulty begins with the statistics. These have been collected for many years, but P. C. Mahalanobis has recently criticized them drastically. During the winter of 1950–51 he directed a National Sample Survey on a sound statistical basis and found a discrepancy of some 20 to 25 per cent between the actual quantity of grain consumed and the supply as estimated from the agricultural statistics. His survey gave the following results:[1]

	Million tons	
Total consumption of food grains	63·2	
Total imports	3·0	
	——	
Home production	60·2	
Official estimate	48	cereals and gram
	44	cereals alone

A discrepancy of 12 to 16 tons, i.e. 20 to 25 per cent, according as gram is counted in or not.

This uncertainty applies to all Asian statistics; but India has been the first country to face up to it. The official statistics are used throughout this section because there are no others: the trends are probably fairly correct, and it is to bring these out that the figures will be used.

The population of the Union of India—Bharat—in 1951 was 362 millions,[2] an increase of some 40 million over that of 1941 Census, a gain of about 12·5 per cent compared with 15 per cent during the decade 1931–41. The high rate of increase largely results from the work of the British agricultural and medical staffs in mitigating the effects of the diseases and periodical famines that used to keep down numbers.

Soil and Water Resources

The gross land area is 1·14 million square miles or 729 million acres. Of this, however, only 528·3 million acres are classified: this part is commonly called the net area and the statistics have reference to it alone. The utilization in 1950 was as follows:

		Union of India.	Million acres		
			Land area sown		Cultivable
Gross	Classified	Cultivable	sown	Irrigated	but not sown
781	536	370	236	49	134
729 (1)	528	366	234	48	133

(1) Omitting Kashmir and Jammu.

(*Report of the Planning Commission*, New Delhi, 1950.)

[1] P. C. Mahalanobis. General Rpt. No. 1 on the First Round of the National Sample Survey, Dept. of Econ. Affairs Govt. of India, 1952.

[2] This includes 4·37 million (estimated) in Kashmir and Jammu which are still a subject of dispute with Pakistan.

The area "cultivable but not sown" includes about 35 million acres of fallow and the area not cultivable includes some 54 million acres of forest. The average area of sown land per head of population is 0·60 acres. There is some double sowing and the area of crops is 282 million acres, but 20 million acres are in non-food crops. The actual area of food crops is 262 million acres. The area per head, however, is constantly diminishing; in 1911 it had been 0·9 acres; since that date the area of cultivated land has somewhat increased, but not enough to keep pace with the growth of population. Meanwhile large areas of land are lost annually by erosion, waterlogging and other causes discussed later. There is no evidence that yields per acre have increased.

The sown land is very unevenly distributed: 80 per cent of it is included in nine states which between them comprise only 58 per cent of the gross area. The statistics for these states are given in Table LXXX.

TABLE LXXX. *Land utilization of the chief food-producing States of the Union of India. Million acres, 1950.*

State	Sown area	Cultivable area	Sown as per cent of cultivable	Irrigated area	Irrigated as per cent of sown
(a) Uttar Pradesh	38·1	50·8	75	12·6	33
Madras	31·6	52·1	61	9·9	31
Bombay	28·2	34·7	81	1·4	5
(b) Madhya Pradesh	24·2	42·4	57	1·7	7
Bihar	17·6	31·3	56	5·3	30
E. Punjab	11·9	16·1	74	6·0	51
W. Bengal	11·2	14·1	80	1·8	16
Orissa	6·5	11·0	59	1·3	21
Assam	5·2	24·1	22	1·0	21
Total "A" States	174·7	276·7	63	41·2	22
Hyderabad	22·5	38·5	58	1·4	6
Mysore	6·2	10·3	60	1·1	18
Union of India	235·8	369·7	64	49·3	21

(a) Formerly United Provinces.

(b) Formerly Central Province and Berar.

As often happens in hot countries, the soils are poor, their content of organic matter and plant food, especially nitrogen and phosphate, being very low; the nitrogen content is often only about 0·05 per cent or less as compared with 0·12 to 0·16 or more in England. This poverty arises partly from the rapid destruction of the soil organic matter by termites and other insects and by micro-organisms under the influence of the prevailing high temperature, but largely from the inability of the peasants to grow such restorative crops as clover, lucerne, or grasses, owing to the over-riding necessity of producing cereals. This low level of plant nutrients results in low levels of productiveness except where it can be overcome by the use of nitrogenous and phosphatic fertilizers or organic manure. In all these materials India's resources are low.

Over most of India water supply is the chief factor limiting crop production: water is more precious than land and is indeed in some districts a potent motive for crime. The peasants have learned by long experience much more about conserving water than about conserving soil.

Of all India's water resources the monsoon is by far the most important. Eighty per cent of India's cropped land is entirely dependent on it and over a large part of the country it is unreliable. It is traditionally reckoned that the monsoon fails in one year in five, but forecasting is not yet possible in spite of much good work by Gilbert Walker and others. Fortunately the failure is frequently only local; hungry areas may be supplied from those more fortunate if transport is available, but this has become more difficult since partition.

The rainfall is highest in the north-eastern regions, especially in parts of Bengal and Assam where it reaches 200 or more inches a year; the Assam hills hold the world's record for measured rainfall—905 inches in the year 1861: of this 366 inches fell in July. Throughout these north-eastern regions floods are liable to occur, often doing great damage.

Going westwards along the northern plain the rainfall rapidly decreases till in Sind it is only 5 inches a year, and in Baluchistan, Rajput and Makran there are great deserts. But much of this plain is so well watered by the rivers rising in the Himalayas, and it has such stores of subsoil water that irrigation can take the place of rain. Going south through the plateau region of the peninsula the rainfall also decreases, but not so much as in the north: in the eastern part it may be 30 inches or more; in the west it is less excepting on the coastal region. In the south the delectable state of Mysore and the happy land of Travancore have fairly good rainfall and 29 per cent of Travancore's sown land is irrigated (Fig. 15).

The central section, the northern part of the plateau which stretches southwards from the Vindhya ranges, is the region most dependent on rainfall as its rivers are not well suited to irrigation, and, unlike the northern plains, it has no great stores of subsoil water. It includes Madhya Pradesh (the old Central Provinces), the Bombay Presidency, Hyderabad, Madhya Bharat (Gwalior), and Bhopal: only 1 to 7 per cent of their sown areas is irrigated. The eastern part of Madhya Pradesh is fairly well off, having a rainfall of 50 to 70 inches: this is ample even for paddy, its chief crop; the north-western section has less, 45 to 55 inches, sufficient for wheat and gram; but the south-eastern section has still less, only about 30 to 35 inches, and here cotton and millet are the chief crops. The Bombay Presidency is worse off. A belt about 100 to 150 miles wide on the eastern side of the Western Ghats is specially liable to droughts. Most of the summer monsoon —which comes from the Arabian Sea—is intercepted by the mountains; some rainfall comes with the so-called winter monsoon from the Bay of Bengal, but it comes erratically and in storms. The annual rainfall has ranged from 14 to 48 inches, the average being about 20 to 25 inches, but 4 inches may fall in one hour.[1] About half the year's rain may come in September and October, and all of it between July and November. Crop production is hazardous: a state of emergency or even of famine has periodically had to be proclaimed. Here India's poverty and malnutrition are seen in all their nakedness.

[1] Bombay had 28 inches in 24 hours one day in September 1949.

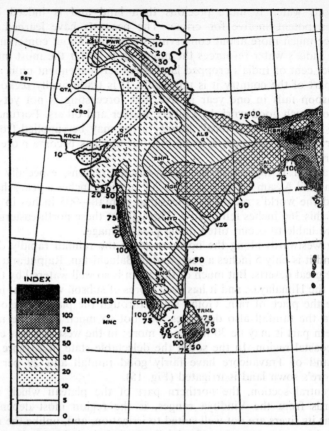

FIG. 15.—Rainfall Map of India (L. A. Ramdas, *Empire Jl. Expt. Agric.*, 1946,
Vol. 14, p. 88)

An effective farming system has been developed. Drought resistant early
maturing varieties of crops are used. The cropping programme is carefully
adapted to the local conditions: deep soils are used for winter (rabi) crops;
shallow soils for summer (kharif) pulses or, if the slope is great, for grass;
soils of intermediate depth for most kharif crops, and special cultural and
soil management devices are adopted.[1] Shallow banks or bunds are put
round the fields to impound rain water and restrain the run off. Ploughing,
if done, is shallow,[2] but neither at the Sholapur nor the Bijapur experimental
farms has ploughing been necessary at all; harrowing has served just as
well. The surface of the soil must be left rough to avoid wind erosion and
to facilitate the sinking in of the rain water. Local experiments are made
to determine the most suitable cultivation process and rotations, and the
possibilities of manuring, especially with farmyard manure. These special
dry farming methods are needed on some 15 million acres of land in the

[1] These methods are discussed by J. K. Basu: 38th Indian Science Congress, Bangalore,
1951.

[2] The older recommendation of deep ploughing and fine surface mulch has been given
up.

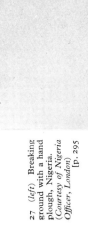

25 (*left*) A Kikuyu settlement, Odongo Reserve, Kenya. *Lady Russell*] [p. 259

26 (*right*) A demonstration farm to teach better methods, Wakemba Reserve, Kenya. (*Courtesy of Public Relations Officer, Govt. of Kenya*) [p. 259

27 (*left*) Breaking ground with a hand plough, Nigeria. (*Courtesy of Nigeria Officer, London*) [p. 295

28 (*right*) Improving the native farming: introduction for the first time of the bullock-drawn plough. Both men and animals had to be taught and the implement designed. (*Courtesy of West African Central Office of Information*) [p. 295

29 (*left*) The barrage at Sansanding, French Niger irrigation scheme. (*Courtesy of Office du Niger, Paris*) [p. 315]

30 (*right*) Irrigating guava trees, Banfora, Ivory Coast. (*Courtesy of Agence Economique de la France d'Outre-mer, Paris*) [p. 315]

31 (*left*) Treading out rice by human labour, Travancore, S. India. (*Photo: author*) [p. 332]

32 (*right*) Making cattle manure into blocks for fuel, Uttar Pradesh, India. (*Photo: author*) [p. 333]

Bombay Presidency, as well as on considerable areas in other States. Even at best they are liable to break down in a year of poor rainfall.

Properly conducted irrigation is the surest means of crop production, and it has been practised from very ancient times in India. References occur in the Rig Veda period (*c.* 2500 B.C.) to irrigation from canals, wells and lakes, and to the skilled craftsmen who "rendered the fields fertile; they led forth the rivers; plants spring upon the waste and water spreads over the low places."[1]

Canals, wells and tanks remain to this day India's sources of irrigation water. Modern developments began in 1865 when the Government of India introduced a system of public loans for financing irrigation works. The British engineers and agriculturists, however, transformed the ancient art into a modern science, and when they departed from India in 1945, they left behind them some of the greatest and most efficient irrigation schemes in the world. The men who did the work had but scanty recognition, and the myriads of people who will benefit by them will never know to whom they owe them. During the present century the irrigated area in the pre-partition provinces increased from 30 million acres in 1900 to over 70 million acres in 1947, the largest in the world. Asia has, indeed, 70 per cent of the world's irrigated land, most of it watered from the Himalayan rivers. The Indian areas are watered as follows:

Canals	Wells	Tanks	Other areas[2]	Total Million acres
20·9	12·6	9·3	6·5	49·3

Government works are responsible for 85 per cent of the canal-irrigated area and about 35 per cent of the rest.

Wells are the simplest and most widely used source of irrigation water though they serve only about a quarter of the irrigated land. The water is lifted either by man power, using a long pole as lever to pull the buckets out of the well, or by a windlass or Persian wheel worked by oxen: the creaking of the wheels as they turn is one of the most typical sounds of the Indian countryside. Wells have the usual advantage that each peasant has his own and can take the water when he wants it; further, the appliances are simple and can be made and kept in repair by the village craftsmen. But they are very inefficient: a pole pump waters only about 4 acres and a water wheel only about 5 to 12 acres. A much better appliance, the tube well, was introduced by Sir William Stampe in 1934 into the United Provinces from California and has proved so successful that by 1937 some 1,700 had been sunk to irrigate about 750,000 acres of crops, an average of about 440 acres each. The average depth of the well is 270 feet and this taps some 80 feet of coarse water-laden sands: the water is under pressure and rises to 40 to 60 feet from the surface whence it is pumped up to the irrigation channels. It can be made to serve several purposes. The issuing stream of water can

[1] H. H. Wilson, *Rig Veda Sanhita*, Bangalore. See also Radhakumud Mookerji, *Indian Civilisation*, Longmans, 1936, and A. K. Narayan Ayer, *Agriculture and Allied Arts in Vedic India*, Bangalore, 1949.
[2] Includes flood irrigation from rivers and some private tanks.

be tapped by the women for filling their pots for domestic use; it flows into a tank where they can do their washing, and thence to a large tank where the men can bathe. A well yields about 30,000 gallons of water an hour, and the pumping is done by electric power generated from the Ganges Canal Hydro-Electric Grid System.

The area commanded by the well is about double the area watered at any one time: it averages about 1,000 acres (roughly $1\frac{1}{2}$ square miles) on which about 500 acres of crop are irrigated.[1] The demand is so great that by 1950 the United Provinces had some 7,000 in operation, about one-third of which were Government owned, while they were also widely used in the Punjab, Bihar, and elsewhere. A British engineering firm is sinking another 1,000 in the Ganges valley.

By 1948 more than 3,000 cusecs[2] were being pumped in the Indo-Gangetic plain, and there was no evidence of any fall in the water level. Stampe considers that it is maintained by an underground river which he equates with the Saraswati of Hindu mythology and of which only the upper level has as yet been tapped; 60 to 80 million gallons per square mile per hour can, he thinks, be safely pumped. If this be so a considerable increase is possible in the number of tube wells along its course.

In other districts, however, extension of pumping systems seems to have lowered the water table: in parts of the Madras Presidency it is 12 feet lower than before the war; it had fallen in the Central Provinces also. A survey of underground water supplies is urgently needed, and the present freedom to sink wells of any depth in any place may have to be curtailed.

Efficient and economic use of the water requires a minimum length of channels and distributaries; this necessitates a rectangular lay-out of the crops. The peasant holdings are commonly irregular in outline; the peasants are often unwilling to correct this by exchange of land. But they are prepared to consolidate their crops into the necessary rectangles in order to get the benefit of the tube well, and they accept further the need for uniformity of variety, cultivation and manuring so as to secure uniformity of growth. This of course is in marked contrast with the ordinary peasant holding, each with its little well and its crops grown in separate and independent patches. Tube well areas stand out as vivid green rectangles against the parched brown of the surrounding countryside, and the villages often have a refreshing look of prosperity. The peasant fully recognizes the value of a tube well.

Most of the irrigation is from rivers by canals. One of India's tragedies is the irregular flow of its rivers. They are in full spate during the monsoon period, and those rising in the Himalayas receive in July and later vast additional quantities of water from the melting snow and ice in the mountains. They tear along, laden with silt, often overflowing their banks and doing much damage to crops, in places eroding the soil or covering it up with sand or silt; at times, as in Bengal in 1943, destroying whole villages with much loss of life. Then when the monsoon ends the rivers shrink; the dry season sets in and the fear is not of flood but of drought.

Hitherto it has not been found practicable to store much of the seasonal

---

[1] Sir William Stampe, *Empire Jl. Expt. Agric.*, 1948, Vol. 16, pp. 47–54.
[2] 1 cusec = 22,500 gallons per hour.

spate of water, but only to divert some of it on to the land for useful crop production. Barrages or diversion weirs have been constructed to deflect some of the water into one or two main canals out of which a network of distributaries carries it on to the fields. The river banks are raised by levees for some distance above the barrage and this leads to some storage of water, but the system ceases to function when the river level falls too low; though the soil may still be moist enough to carry a further crop. There are several of these diversion dams in the north and on the eastern coast, and probably there is little scope for many more.

The proportion of river water used, however, is very small: about 1,356 million acre-feet of water are estimated to flow annually through the rivers of India, but under 6 per cent (only about 76 millions) are taken for irrigation.[1] The utmost that can at present be hoped for the remaining 94 per cent is that it may flow harmlessly to the sea.

In addition to the canal systems fed by rivers there are many tanks and reservoirs to store the rain water for use on the land.

The Food and Cash Crops

Food crops amount to about 262 million acres and cash crops to about 20 million (Table LXXXI). The total is greater than the sown area of land because some of it carries two crops a year.

The chief food crops are rice, millet and wheat, with some maize and barley; these between them occupy 65 to 70 per cent of the sown area. Pulses are next in area, then come the oil seeds, relatively small in area but very important in India's dietary. Fruit—particularly mangoes—and vegetables are grown near the villages, but to a less extent than they should be. The chief cash crops are jute, cotton and sugar-cane, but sugar-cane ranks also as a food crop. Tea and coffee are of great importance in the very limited areas where they grow well; they make considerable contributions to the national income. Tea is confined to the acid soils of the wet hill tracts around Darjeeling, in Assam, and southern India; its cultivation is highly specialized and still largely remains in British hands. Coffee is grown in southern India. Other crops include green manures, green fodder, spices and stimulants (pan), vegetables and fruits, but their area is small.

The chief factor determining crop distribution is the water supply. Rice, jute and tea require most water and are therefore found in the regions of high rainfall, or in the case of rice, of adequate irrigation. At the other extreme come the millets and short-staple cotton which tolerate drier conditions than other crops and are grown in low rainfall regions. In between come wheat, and, often associated with it, gram; also other pulses and oil seeds, sugar-cane and longer-staple cotton: all require good but not excessive supplies of water.

Of all these crops rice is by far the most important: it is India's chief food. As grown it is called paddy; after the husk is removed it becomes rice. Usually 100 parts of paddy give 70 of rice. As a plant it does not appear to be very adaptable to different conditions, but fortunately vast numbers of varieties, wild and cultivated, occur in India, more than in any other country—some 2,000 in Bihar alone; one or other can generally be found

[1] *Report of Planning Commission, 1950.*

TABLE LXXXI. *Areas and production of chief crops, Union of India,* 1949–50

I. FOOD CROPS

Cereals

	Million acres		Million tons	
	1950	1951	1950	1951
Kharif crops:				
Rice	75·4	76·0	23·2	20·3
Maize	7·8	8·0	1·7	1·96
Millets:				
Jowar	37·7		5·8	
Bajra	21·3		2·6	
Ragi	5·4		1·4	
Small millets	13·8		2·2	
	161·4		36·9	
Rabi crops:				
Wheat	24·1	24·0	6·3	6·6
Barley	7·9	7·6	2·2	2·3
	32·0	31·6	8·5	8·9
Total cereals	192·6		45·6	

Other Food Crops

	Million acres	Million tons
Gram	20·2	3·7
Other pulses	26·0	4·0
Oil seeds (edible)	19·0	4·6 (1)
Potatoes	0·55	1·5
Sugar-cane	3·6	4·9
	69·4	64·1

Total Food crops 262

II. CASH CROPS

	Million acres	Output millions
Cotton	11·8	2·6 bales of 392 lbs.
Jute	1·2	3·1 bales of 400 lbs.
Oil seeds (non-edible)	5·1	0·5 tons
Tobacco	0·8	0·2 tons
Tea	0·77	535 lb.
Coffee	0·22	38·6 lb.
Rubber	0·16	33·7 lb.
	20·0	

Total area of crops 282

Sources: *Indian Agric. Stat.*, 1950; *Grain Crops*, C.E.C., H.M.S.O., 1953, for rice, maize, wheat, barley. The International Tea Cttee. estimate the output at 613 m. lb. for 1950 and 622 m. for 1952.

(1) Includes:

	Million acres	Million tons
Groundnuts	9·7	3·4
Rape and mustard	4·7	0·8
Sesamum	4·6	0·4
	19·0	4·6

satisfying the local conditions of soil and climate and the rather fastidious demands of the local markets. Some varieties are almost as tolerant of dry conditions as barley; others can grow in water, and can keep pace with a steadily rising flood; some can grow up to two feet a day in order to keep their heads above water: the straw may finally be 20 feet long. The work of classifying these different varieties, and cross-breeding to produce newer ones, was started in 1913 by G. P. Hector in Bengal and by F. R. Parnell at Coimbatore in Madras and has continued ever since;[1] it is carried on now in each of the states: the experimental rice station at Cuttack, Orissa, is to do international work under the aegis of F.A.O. No experimental work in the whole field of agriculture is more arduous: it involves paddling about in gum-boots in mud and water infested with snakes, leeches and other noisome pests, with no shade from the broiling sun, in regions infested with malarial mosquitoes and annoying insects of every kind. The breeders have produced earlier maturing varieties that can be removed in time to allow a second crop to be sown in the same year; varieties protected from the destructive insect *gundhi* by a leaf sheath that encloses the panicle of grains—otherwise open and exposed to attack; also varieties with purple leaves that the cultivator can readily distinguish from the green leaves of the wild rice growing as a weed in the crop and greatly reducing its yield.

Paddy produces more food per acre than any other grain crop in India. Yields of 1,000 to 1,500 lb. per acre (i.e. 700 to 1,000 lb. of rice) are not uncommon; 4,000 lb. or more have been obtained by suitable manuring with oil cakes and sulphate of ammonia, and in India's most prolific region, the Ambasamu Oram district of the Tinevally River where two crops a year are grown, the record yield is 7,000 lb. per acre for the first and 5,000 lb. per acre for the second, making 12,000 lb. per acre in all. The ordinary cultivator gets nothing like these yields: he has only one crop a year and the average yield for the whole country for the years 1949 to 1951 was 640 lb. of rice per acre.[2]

Next to rice, the millets are the most common foods in India. Like rice they appear to be indigenous and large numbers of different sorts occur: some 36 species and more than 200 varieties are known at the Coimbatore Research Station to be in cultivation and there are probably many others. Jowar or great millet (*Sorghum vulgare*) is the most popular, followed by bajra, pearl or bullrush millet (*Pennisetum typhoideum*): these indeed are often grown as kharif or summer crops in the rainy season. Ragi or finger millet (*Eleusine coracana*) and Indian millet (*Setaria italica*) both tolerate poorer conditions, but the poor man's millet *par excellence* is kodo (*Paspalum scrobiculatum*), most tolerant of all of drought and poverty and grown on poor soil in hilly tracts: these, however, are much less widely cultivated.

[1] Hector's publications began in 1913 in *Mem. Dept. Agric. India, Bot. Ser.*, Vol. 6; his work on classification is recorded in *Indian J. Agric. Sci.*, 1934, Vol. 4. Parnell's work is described in volumes of the *Mem. Dept. Agric. India Bot. Ser.*, beginning 1919, Vol. 9, p. 75 and ending 1922, Vol. 11, p. 185. It was developed by K. Ramiah who summarizes the results in *Empire Jl. Expt. Agric.*, 1952, Vol. 20, pp. 161–74 (jointly with M. Ghose and M. V. Vachhani).

[2] Commonwealth Economic Committee, *Grain Crops*, 1953, H.M.S.O. The Planning Commission puts it at 760 lb. for the period 1939–46.

As the millets are grown in poorer conditions than rice or wheat their yields are naturally lower: the average for jowar is put by the Planning Commission at 418 lb. per acre and that of bajra at 345 lb., the other sorts give still lower yields. So far the plant breeders have been less successful in improving the millets than they have with wheat and rice; but the peasants have had a long start in making their selections.[1]

Millet, being associated with poverty, has a lower social standing than rice or wheat, and as people rise in the social scale they tend to abandon it—not all, however.

Wheat comes between rice and millets in its water requirements and does not tolerate high temperatures; it is largely confined to the drier parts of the north and even there it is a winter or rabi crop: it is usually grown on good soils, and indeed the wheat belt which stretches across the United Provinces and the Punjab includes some of the most productive land in India.

British plant breeders have done much to improve the Indian wheats. The pioneering work of collecting and classifying was done by W. H. Moreland and Bryce Burt: the breeding was started in 1905 at Pusa by A. Howard and his wife Gabrielle; some of their sorts still survive. The work has been diligently continued since and is now being carried on at the New Delhi station under B. P. Pal, and elsewhere.[2] The average yields in lb. per acre of these food grains have been for the ten years 1937 to 1946:

	Average lb. per acre	Range
Rice	759	678–796
Wheat	615	541–671
Jowar	418	322–479
Bajra	315	273–392

The total production of food grains including rice, the millets, wheat, maize, barley and gram, has been for the Union of India:

	1943–44	1944–45	1945–46	1946–47	1947–48	1948–49	1949–50	Average
Million acres	192	202	198	196	191	207	213	200
Million tons	51·7	51·1	45·7	46·1	48·2	47·8	49·1	48·5

(*Planning Commission Rpt.*, 1951.)

There is no sign of increased production of food during the seven years, nor is there for the individual grains. Production of rice, for instance, was 28·8 million tons in undivided India in 1937 and 28·5 million tons in India and Pakistan in 1951. The average overall yield of grain is 540 lb. per acre supplying about 0·9 million calories. There are no signs of yields increasing: if anything, yields of rice, the most important crop, tend to fall:

[1] The plant breeding work is described by R. H. Richharia, *Plant Breeding and Genetics in India*, Patna, 1945.

[2] The Howards' work is described in "Wheat in India," A. Howard and G. L. C. Howard, Calcutta, 1909, in *Mem. Dept. Agric. India Bot. Ser.*, the last being in Vol. 6, pp. 233–66, 1914. Later work is summarized by R. H. Richharia, loc. cit.

		Pre-war	cwt. per acre Average 4 years 1947–50	1951
Rice (1)	Union of India	7·2	6·0	5·6
	Pakistan	7·5	7·4	6·9
Wheat	Union of India	5·6	4·9	5·5
	Pakistan	6·6	7·0	7·3

(1) Milled rice.
(Commonwealth Econ. Cttee., 1953.)

Wheat in Pakistan is an exception: its yield seems to be increasing, but not in India. In contrast with these stationary or shrinking yields of food crops the yield of cash crops, sugar-cane, tea, coffee, etc., which are more efficiently produced, are increasing: output of sugar in 1952 was a record of 1·4 million tons though on account of its high cost of production there were difficulties in disposing of it.

The area under cereals is about 190 to 195 million acres, the largest cereal area of any country in the world. The average quantity of grain produced per head of population is thus about 300 lb.[1] Next in importance to the cereals come the pulses, of which gram (Cicer arietinum) is the chief; lentils, various peas and beans, mung (Phaseolus) and others are also grown: these together with groundnuts supply additional protein in which rice is so deficient. The area is about 46 million acres. They are grown all over India and there are many varieties: one or more can always be found suitable wherever any cereal can grow. (Fig. 16).

Oil is very important for Indian cookery and there are about 19 million acres of edible oil seeds,[2] but it is difficult to give an exact figure because the plants are often grown interspersed among other crops. India grows a greater variety of oil seeds in commercial quantities than any other country in the world: over 125 different kinds, wild or cultivated, are in use.[3] The chief are groundnuts, mustard, and sesame (til). Groundnuts are grown chiefly in the central regions: Madras, Bombay and Madhya Pradesh. They are interesting as being among the few beneficent plant introductions into India, having been brought from America in early times (16th or 17th centuries) by the Portuguese or the Jesuit fathers. This success stands in marked contrast with some of the 20th century introductions which have become pestilential weeds and are proving very difficult to eradicate, especially water hyacinth. In addition a good deal of coconut oil is used.

These three sets of grains between them supply on the average something like three-quarters of the calorie intake of the population. The remaining quarter come chiefly from jaggery or gur, a hard brown mass obtained by evaporating the juice of the sugar-cane; and from milk with smaller contributions from sundry root crops, fruits and vegetables. Spices, "pan," etc., varying in the different parts of India, but popular everywhere, contribute rather to the flavours, stimulants and vitamins than to the calories.

Before the war a number of dietetic surveys were made in various parts

[1] Planning Commission, September 1950.
[2] In addition 5 million acres of non-edible oil seeds are grown, 3·7 million of linseed and 1·4 million of castor (1948–50 figures).
[3] Richharia, loc. cit.

327

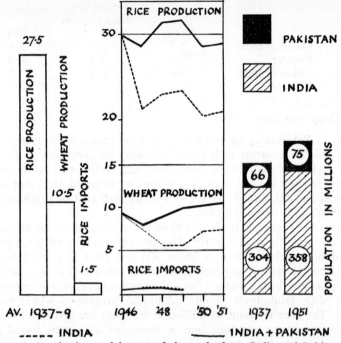

Fig. 16.—Production and import of rice and wheat, India and Pakistan, pre-war and post-war compared with changes in population (Grain date from C.E.C. Reports, Grain Crops, 1953, Population data from *F.A.O.*, *Stat. Yr. Bk.*, 1951).

of India. Good pioneering work was done by the Punjab Board of Economic Enquiry in the 1930's, and the whole subject was put on a sound scientific basis by W. R. Aykroyd at Coonoor, who started the Nutrition Investigation Research Institute which still carries on the investigations.[1] F.A.O. estimates of food supplies are given in Table LXXXII.

India has the largest population of cattle, buffalo and goats in the world, and is second only to Australia in numbers of sheep.

	Cattle	Buffalo	Goats	Sheep	Pigs
1949–50	134	40	44	36	3·6

In spite of their high numbers the animals yield remarkably little human food, they are far too numerous for the very small amount of food available for them. Slaughter of cattle is forbidden by Hindu religious law, the cow being sacred; castration is rarely practised and breeding is uncontrolled; reduction of numbers and controlled breeding are alike impossible. Nor can the animal food supply be increased: land cannot be spared for growing fodder crops; the animals must subsist on straw, weeds, wild grazing or other waste material, and are consequently very inefficient for work or milk production. Norman Wright in 1936 estimated the yield of milk per cow at about three to five pints daily:[2] it is certainly less now. Buffaloes give

[1] He summarized his work in *Special Rpt. No. 16*, Indian Research Fund Assoc., Cawnpore, January 1948.

[2] *Report on the development of the Cattle Dairy Industries of India* (Delhi, 1937).

TABLE LXXXII. *Food supplies. India and Pakistan, lb. per head per year*

	Pre-war Undivided India	1949–50 India	Pakistan	Targets for 1960 India	Pakistan
Cereals	315	262	337		
Starchy roots	18	15	12		
Pulses	48	44	24		
Sugar	31	29	29		
Fats	6·6	6·6	4·4		
Fruits	57	35	68		
Vegetables	55	35	44		
Meat	6·6	4·4	9		
Milk	143	99	161		
Calories	1,970	1,700	2,020	2,000	2,230
Protein, grams per day:					
Animal	8	6	11	7	13
Vegetable	48	38	41	46	46
Total	56	44	52	53	59

(*Second World Food Survey, F.A.O.*, 1952.)

about 50 per cent more milk, and it is richer; indeed in spite of their low numbers they contributed in 1936 about half India's milk supply. Only about one-third of the milk is consumed in liquid form, and in the towns it is commonly adulterated; most of the milk is converted into ghee, a product something like butter but more concentrated. F.A.O. estimate that the whole supply of milk and milk-products amounted on the average in 1949–50 to the equivalent of 4·3 oz. of milk daily, i.e. a little over one pint in five days. Meat is eaten only by few, about 5 lb. a year is the average consumption per head. Still less fish is eaten, and only by some living near the sea, including some high caste Bengalis; the average is about 2½ lb. per year. Widespread poverty and religious beliefs are the chief reasons; beef is forbidden to Hindus by their religious laws; pig is anathema in most parts of India; mutton is eaten only by some, such as the Maratha cultivators. Muslims, however, eat both beef and mutton, though not pork.

The quantities of food produced during the last ten or fifteen years have changed but little while the population has been steadily increasing. In consequence the amount of cereals produced per head has fallen from nearly 15 oz. daily before the war, to 11 oz. daily[1] in 1949–50 and the total calories per day from nearly 2,000 to 1,700 only. The figures are not strictly comparable because the pre-war figures include Pakistan and that for 1949–50 does not, and in any case they are subject to considerable error as Mahalanobis has shown. But a fall has undoubtedly occurred, and is confirmed by dietetic surveys which show that in pre-war days, especially

[1] Note that to provide 1 oz. a day for one million people a year requires 10,184 tons. One million tons of grain could provide the present population with about ¼ oz. per head per day for a year.

*

earlier in the century, more food grains were available per head than now. The effect of the fall is intensified by the circumstance that the range of nutrition levels is rather wide: nothing approaching equality of food distribution has ever existed. There is much real hunger among the poorer people. Not infrequently I have been asked: how many times a day do you eat? And I remember being accosted by a poor Hindu going into one of the very sacred temples from which I was debarred, saying to me: "Give me money, and I will eat for you in the name of God."

On any standard the present dietary is unsatisfactory: it provides insufficient calories, and is ill-balanced, being deficient in fats, proteins (especially animal proteins), vitamins and minerals. In 1944 the Nutrition Advisory Committee of the Indian Research Fund Association drew up a model dietary conforming to their accepted standards and found that it required an increased production of pulses and sugar of about 30 per cent, a five-fold production of fats and oil seeds, four-fold production of vegetables, eight-fold of fish and meat, doubling the milk output and ending adulteration —a programme completely impossible of achievement in any foreseeable future.

At present the chief preoccupation is to maintain the calorie supply which necessitates an adequate supply of grain. As the home production has not increased it has been necessary to import. Before Partition about 1 million tons a year used to come from what is now Pakistan: this has now become an import. Rice also used to come from Burma whenever the need arose, also from Thailand and Indo-China. These sources are now greatly restricted. The result is that India has had to import wheat, much of which has had to come with generous help from the United States:[1]

Imports of rice and wheat, India. Million tons

	Average 1937–39(1)	1947(1)	*Average* 1948–50	1951
Rice	1·54	0·485	0·662	0·749
Wheat	0·087	0·660	1·50	2·97
	1·627	1·145	2·162	3·72

Commonwealth Econ. Cttee,, *Grain Crops*, 1953.

(1) Undivided India.

The problem is old: attempts to deal with it have been continuous since the Famine Commission of 1880 was set up to find some practicable means of avoiding famines or at least of mitigating their worst effects. The Royal Commission on Agriculture in India of 1926 gave in its Report (1928) the

[1] The 1951 imports came from the following countries:

	Rice *Million tons*		*Wheat* *Million tons*
Burma	0·304	United States	1·809
Thailand	0·216	Argentina	0·513
Pakistan	0·158	Canada	0·328
China	0·066	Australia	0·192
Egypt	0·005	U.S.S.R.	0·099
		Uruguay	0·030
	0·749		2·970

most comprehensive account of Indian agriculture yet published, and made a series of far-reaching recommendations which were steadily being put into effect till first the war and then Partition introduced new problems. A "Grow more Food" campaign was organized in 1943 but was not operated till after the war; later, in 1949, when food imports threatened to make a drain on the nation's financial resources, a Self-Sufficiency Campaign was started with the purpose of achieving self-sufficiency by 1952.[1] A Planning Commission was set up which in 1950 prepared a well-thought-out plan. This included the irrigation of 8 million acres of land by major works and 7 million acres of land by minor projects at an estimated cost of Rs. 4,500 million.[2] Four million acres were to be retrieved from fallow and $1\frac{1}{2}$ million acres reclaimed from bush. These additions to the cultivated area would, the Commission estimated, by 1956 increase production of food grains by $7 \cdot 2$ million tons, in addition to $2 \cdot 06$ million bales of jute and $1 \cdot 2$ million bales of cotton: an impressive achievement if it could be attained. The plan involved heavy expenditure and considerable changes have been necessitated by rising costs and scarcity of material, but financial help came in 1951 when the Colombo Plan[3] was inaugurated for "co-operative economic development" in South-East Asia; it had a fund of £1,868 million, about half of which was to be provided by the Asians themselves, about £300 million came from the United Kingdom and lesser sums from Australia and Canada. £1,379 million was earmarked for India, mainly for large multipurpose schemes of the Tennessee Valley type.

There is no lack of high level organization or of scientific and technical higher direction: the Agricultural Research Station at New Delhi is a most impressive organization. But the efforts have not yet shown themselves in higher output of food.

There is plenty of material on which to work. Considerable areas of land and large volumes of water still remain unused as we have seen, but their utilization would be difficult even where it is practicable. Some 90 or more million acres at present waste are classified as cultivable. Of this area about 10 million acres have been in cultivation but were invaded by deep-rooted weeds—particularly kans, a wild sugar-cane, and hariali (*Cynodon dactylon*) which the ryots implements could not tackle; they are destroyed, however, by ploughing with large tractors to a depth of 12 inches and exposing the roots to the sun in the hot dry months. The Central Tractor Organization was set up at Delhi in 1947: in its first three years it had reclaimed 183,000 acres.[4] The remaining 80 or more million acres present greater difficulties: they are often jungle which can be cleared only by large implements, wear and tear of which under the conditions is considerable; malaria is often prevalent, and roads rarely exist. Possibly 20 or 25 million acres could be brought into cultivation, but much of the rest is too steep or badly gullied or eroded.[5] Other reclamation projects deal with the rehabilitation

[1] Described in *Towards Self Sufficiency*, Delhi, 1951.
[2] Rs. 16 = £1. By 1953 $3\frac{1}{2}$m. of these acres had been irrigated.
[3] *The Colombo Plan for co-operative Economic Development in South and South-East Asia*, Cmd. 8080, 1950, H.M.S.O.
[4] *Towards Self Sufficiency*, Delhi, p. 41. In 1952 it ploughed up 235,000 acres.
[5] D. R. Sethi, *Proc. U.N. Sci. Cong. Conservation and Utilisation of Resources*, 1949, Vol. 6, pp. 566–69.

of eroded land of which there are great areas in regions both of high and of low rainfall. Overcutting and overfelling of trees in the high rainfall districts has led to much loss of soil and of subsoil water by increasing the run-off. In dry regions erosion occurs because of the difficulty of maintaining a protective vegetation cover; overgrazing is common, the soil easily becomes reduced to dust and is liable to be carried away by the strong hot winds and especially the violent rainstorms. Fortunately the anti-erosion measures do not conflict with dry farming methods; some of them, bunding, terracing, etc., are used for both purposes.

It is difficult to estimate how much land has been lost by erosion because sheet erosion, the most widespread form, is also the least noticeable; it takes off thin layers of soil perceptible only where careful records are kept, but continuing inexorably till in the end all the surface soil has gone. J. K. Basu[1] estimates that the 70 per cent of the $5\frac{1}{2}$ million acres in the scarcity tract of the Bombay Presidency have been more or less denuded, and about 32 per cent rendered totally unfit for crop production. Much of this loss is recent.

Action on the recognized lines is being taken by the Agricultural Department to rehabilitate this land. The old-established experiment at Sholapur has supplied the basic information and the Land Improvement Enquiry Committee went fully into various aspects of the problem. By 1948 some 722,000 acres had been provided with contour bunds which were later improved by consolidation and the provision of waste weirs to carry off storm water. Grass is being used as a protective agent. But rehabilitation has as yet not nearly caught up with the losses caused by erosion.

More land could come into cultivation if better implements were available. Some 64 million acres of land that have been cultivated are left fallow, partly of necessity to build up a reserve of soil moisture, but partly also because the implements and bullock power are inadequate to get the sowing done in time. (Pl. 31, p. 317.)

More food could be produced if it were possible to store sufficient moisture in the soil during the summer monsoon period to enable it to carry crops during the five or six months of the dry season instead of lying bare as at present. This possibility is being studied by soil physicists. In the meantime, early varieties of crops have been bred or selected which can be cleared away in time to sow another crop before the ground has become too dry. If the winter rains are good two crops can thus be obtained in one year. The plant breeders' chief successes have been with the cash crops, sugar-cane and cotton, and wheat, which was an export commodity when the work began. About 87 per cent of the total area of sugar-cane is now under improved varieties, but only about 20 per cent of the wheat area and probably less of the rice area. For the other food crops, millets, pulses and oil seeds, the area is certainly much less. The position may be better than it looks as no good statistics are available, but the result is a disappointing return for so much devoted scientific work during the past fifty years.

One important reason is the absence of any good link between the plant breeder and the cultivator. While the sugar factories and the cotton ginneries can ensure the use of good varieties, there is no seed trade with high standards

[1] J. K. Basu, *Empire Jl. Expt. Agric.*, 1952, Vol. 20, pp. 326–33.

of efficiency and probity which can take over promising sorts of food crops for multiplication and distribution in pure condition. At present such work as is done is by Government Agency, but it is hampered by the temptation to sell or eat the issued seed rather than await next year's harvest.

One of the most effective methods of increasing output is by fuller use of manures and fertilizers. Cattle manure is produced in large quantity, but it is primarily used as a fuel, as is usual in dry countries where trees are scarce and there is no coal; not more than 40 per cent is estimated to get on to the land. The need for alternative sources of fuel has long been recognized; the Royal Commission on Agriculture in 1928 had recommended the establishment of plantations near the villages for this purpose, but this was not carried out. Oil stoves would provide no solution unless they could be designed to provide the slow, low-temperature combustion needed for the village mode of cooking, the only one the women understand. (Pl. 32.)

Vigorous attempts have been made to induce the towns and villages to convert their refuse into compost. Few of India's towns and none of the villages have water-borne sanitation, and the potential quantity of compost is enormous; only a fraction of this, however, is produced.[1] Fertilizers are much more practicable as agents for increasing yields, particularly nitrogenous, in many cases phosphatic, but rarely potassic or lime. W. Burns, whose knowledge and experience were unrivalled, estimated that by their proper use crop yields could be raised from 30 to 100 per cent.[2] The difficulty is supply. To give only an average of 20 lb. nitrogen per acre to India's 236 million acres of sown land would need 2 million tons. A fertilizer factory set up at Sindhri at a cost of £17 million as part of one of the Damodar Valley schemes came into operation early in 1952, and it is hoped to produce by 1955 about 350,000 tons of sulphate of ammonia a year—containing about 75,000 tons of nitrogen which might be expected to produce about 750,000 tons of grain. A vastly greater need will remain, however, which can be satisfied, if at all, only by imports from the West. Adequate supplies of phosphatic fertilizer are equally difficult to secure: certain quantities of bones are available, but nothing like enough.

The quantities of fertilizer used, and the quantities produced in India, in thousand tons

| | N. | | P_2O_5 | | K_2O | |
	Used	Produced	Used	Produced	Used	Produced
1938	22	5	1·7	0·6	—	—
1948–49	49	13	5·1	5·1	1·0	—
1950–51	65	7	17·0	9·1	4·0	—

But none of these methods can bear full fruit without an adequate water supply. The most important of the schemes are therefore the large multi-purpose dams which not only supply water for farm land and protect it against flood, but provide electric current for agricultural and industrial use.

[1] See A. Acharya, *Bull. 60. Indian Council Agric. Research,* New Delhi, 1950: and also the Compost Bulletins issued by the Dept. of Agric.

[2] W. Burns, *Technological Possibilities of Agricultural Development in India,* Dept. of Education, Health and Lands, Govt. of India, 1944. The experimental material is summarized and discussed by A. B. Stewart, *Rept. on Soil Fertility Investigations in India,* Delhi, 1947, and F. Yates, D. J. Finney and V. G. Panse in *Indian Council Ag. Research Bull. No. 1,* 1953, 20 lb. N. per acre gave an additional 200 lb. of cereals.

One of the most interesting of these schemes deals with the Damodar Valley region. The river rises in the hills of Chota Nagpur at the eastern end of the Vindhya Ranges and flows south-east through Bihar and West Bengal, entering the Hooghly river south of Calcutta. It is notorious for its liability to flood; it has caused the death of millions: the 1943 disaster in the Burdwan region led to a famine in which 1½ million people perished. It is naturally a vicious river, but has been made worse by man. The headwater region has about 50 inches of rain a year, mostly falling between mid-June and mid-September. It was originally covered with forest, but this has been badly overcut and overgrazed, with the inevitable result of serious erosion and flooding. In July 1948, the Central Government established the Damodar Valley Corporation to draw up and carry out a comprehensive rehabilitation scheme. The whole of the catchment area—some 4 million acres—is treated as one unit. In the upland area the erosion damage is smoothed out by bulldozers; terraces, bunds, and other soil and water conservation devices are set up, and gullies are plugged to stop further erosion. Already this region, which had of late carried only meagre crops of millets, is beginning to grow wheat, and what is more significant, the water level in the subsoil is rising. One million acres are brought under direct control; 500,000 acres are to be grass and forest so as to reduce the amount of water run-off and consequently reduce the intensity of flood and soil erosion; 350,000 acres are to be arable land; and the rest is non-agricultural, villages, roads, etc. (Pl. 33, p. 352).

The scheme for the lower part of the valley includes eight dams and reservoirs designed to provide storage for one million cusecs, this being 50 per cent greater than the highest flood recorded (650,000 cusecs); when they are completed, therefore, there should be no repetition of the 1913 and 1943 disasters. The reservoirs will irrigate some 900,000 acres which should yield about 350,000 tons of food[1]; 240,000 kW. will be generated, but as there will be considerable seasonal fluctuations, additional steam plant is to be set up to generate 200,000 kW.[2] The cost of the scheme was estimated at Rs. 680 million, but will inevitably be higher. Already work has had to be slowed down, but it is continuing, and in its comprehensiveness and quality it is an Indian counterpart of the Tennessee Valley Scheme. Work has started on two other great projects: the Hirakud Dam Scheme to control the River Mahanadi, and the Bhakra Nangal Scheme on the River Sutlej: this is the largest of the three and one of its two dams will be little smaller than the Boulder Dam of the United States.

Serious losses of growing crop and of stored food are caused by insect and fungus pests; methods of control are generally found but not widely practised. One of the most spectacular of recent successes has been the destruction of locusts by spraying with B.H.C. dust. India suffers also from large animals; monkeys in particular cause great losses not only by what they eat but by what they destroy, but being sacred animals they may not be killed. Wild pig, deer, birds, and in some places elephants also do damage;

[1] Assuming an average yield of 870 lb. per acre, which is reasonable.
[2] Development of electrical energy is a prominent feature in the plan. Secondary industries are to be established on modern lines: apparently getting away from Gandhi's idea of reviving cottage industries.

they also are protected by the doctrine of *ahimsa* which forbids the taking of life by its adherents.

Experimental farms commonly obtain yields well above the average, showing that India still has considerable possibilities of increasing food production. But the peasants are poor, the holdings are usually small, often scattered and uneconomical to operate. The oxen are inefficient, too ill-fed to be able to work well; implements are clumsy so that cultivations are often delayed and sowing may be late or missed altogether. There is so little fuel that the cow-dung which ought to go on the land must perforce be burned. The widespread poverty not only hampers production, but prevents the building up of reserves. The Famine Commission of 1945 reported that in 1943, the year of the terrible Bengal famine in which over a million people perished, the total food deficit for the whole year was only three weeks supply. The poverty is said to be getting worse.[1]

A contributory cause of the low level of productiveness in some districts has been the system of land tenure based on share-cropping, which often acts as a deterrent. This is to be abolished and replaced by peasant proprietorship and some form of co-operative farming. Consolidated cultivation of sugar-cane, which is a kind of co-operation, has been accomplished in the tube-well areas as already mentioned and may yet be achieved elsewhere for purposes of tractor cultivation. Extension of the idea to the entire group of holdings is proposed and methods for carrying out have been devised;[2] they involve re-arranging the boundaries. Colonies of this kind have already been established in Bombay, and receive loans or grants from the Government enabling them to acquire the large implements needed or to reclaim additional land. If in a specified area two-thirds of the farmers owning 75 per cent or more of the land decide to pool their land or form a society the remainder are compelled to join. The farming may be collective, joint, or tenant. In Madras cultivable land at present waste is assigned to groups of the depressed classes, generally landless labourers, who must undertake to clear it, make roads and wells, build houses and grow crops. Each colonist is given three to five acres either free of cost or at a hire-purchase rent that makes him the owner in twenty years. The area is insufficient for the maintenance of a family and other work must be sought. Full liberty of cropping is allowed, but Government help and expert advice are available. The ultimate goal, as the Planning Commission recognizes, is the change from the old subsistence farming to modern economic farming.

The main difficulty in my view lies in the lack of effective social and agricultural leadership in the Indian villages. Men are trained for the purpose, but they do not take it up. Good agricultural colleges have been operating for fifty years, but the students want Government or similar jobs, not farms. Courses for peasants' sons are well attended, but these young men, too, want jobs, not a return to their fathers' holdings. The fact is that the villages are unattractive, often unsavoury, insanitary and unhealthy; and people who can leave them do so. The result is an almost complete absence of the good

[1] The United Nations estimate is that the national annual income in India is $57 per head compared with $773 in the United Kingdom and $1453 in the United States. The Statistical Institute at Calcutta is studying this question.

[2] Co-operative Farming, Reserve Bank of India, Bombay, 1949.

farmers who in Great Britain have always been the best instructors of their neighbours. Unfortunately it is a vicious circle: the farming cannot improve until the villages are made more attractive, and the villages cannot become more attractive till the farming improves. Much was done by devoted pioneers like F. L. Brayne, Malcolm Darling, Sam Higginbotham and others, but the villagers were apt to leave them to do the work and did not continue it after they departed. The circle can be broken only when the village welfare movement becomes a vocation for India's young people and they realize the truth of Tagore's saying: "In the keeping of the village lies the cradle of the race." The task is enormous for there are some 700,000 villages, and if one may judge from income tax returns, the total middle-class population of India—from which the leadership must come—is only about half a million. It is proposed to continue and develop the work of the pioneers by the American device of comprehensive community projects for improving the living conditions and the agriculture, fostering village industries and in other ways.[1]

The problem of feeding India, however, will remain extraordinarily difficult or even insoluble if the population continues to increase at its present rate. Even to maintain the present low standards of nutrition about 32 million acres of land would need to be added to the cultivated area in the next ten years, or alternatively the output per acre increased by 15 per cent, or some 12 million additional acres brought under irrigation. These extensions may be possible, but would certainly be extremely difficult. India's leaders now recognize this; "family planning" is definitely advocated by the Planning Commission and approved by Pandit Nehru.

PAKISTAN

Pakistan is divided into two parts: East and West Pakistan; a thousand miles of unfriendly country separates them and rapid personal intercourse is possible only by air. Each part borders on the sea: West Pakistan has the large and important port of Karachi, and East Pakistan has Chittagong, which at present is being developed and offers great future possibilities; these ports are 3,000 miles apart. Exchange of commodities between the two Pakistans is therefore not easy.

The two regions differ widely in character. East Pakistan lies on some of the many mouths of the Ganges: it has a high rainfall and suffers from excess of water; its chief products are jute and rice, both of which require much water; its people are rice eaters. West Pakistan has low rainfall and would indeed be almost a desert but for the fact that its rivers are well adapted to irrigation; its chief products are cotton, wheat and millets, all of which, especially the millets, are suited to fairly dry conditions: its people eat chiefly wheat, but also millets, maize, gram and other foods. East Pakistan is one of the most crowded regions of the earth; West Pakistan has large uninhabited areas. West Pakistan was till recently almost unique in the Indian Sub-Continent in producing surplus wheat and rice which were exported—though it is deficient in oil seeds and sugar; of late years it has to import grain. East Pakistan for long had to import rice, though strenuous

[1] The scheme is described in *World Crops*, 1953, Vol. 5, p. 89.

efforts towards self-sufficiency are now being made. The data for the two Pakistans are given in Table LXXXIII.

The population of Pakistan in 1951 was 75·8 millions, of whom 42·0 millions were in East Bengal and 33·8 millions in West Pakistan, 20·7 millions being in the Punjab and Bahawalpur, 5·9 millions in the North-West Frontier Province, and 4·9 millions in Sind and Khairpur.

TABLE LXXXIII. *Areas and production of chief crops, Pakistan* (1949–50)

Million acres

	West	Punjab only	East	All Pakistan
Total area[1]	83·7	37·1	34·3	118
Area of crops	30·7	18·2	25·8	56·5
Including double cropped	2·6	1·3	6·1	8·7
Area irrigated	21·3	11·9	0·2	21·5
Fallow	9·9	2·8	2·3	12·2
Other uncultivated	19·0	9·6	4·2	23·2

Million acres

	West	Punjab only	East	All Pakistan
Cereals				
Wheat	10·62	6·82	0·10	10·72
Rice	2·24	0·85	19·53	21·77
Millet and sorghums	3·50	1·87	—	3·50
Maize	1·00	0·46	—	1·00
Barley	0·55	0·30	0·01	0·56
All cereals	17·91	10·30	19·64	37·55
Pulses				
Gram	2·54	1·62	0·20	2·74
Oil Seeds	1·01	0·40	0·68	1·69
Fodder Crops	—	3	—	—
Sugar-cane	0·52	0·35	0·23	0·75
Cotton	2·81	1·5	0·05	2·86

Million tons

	West	Punjab only	East	All Pakistan
Cereals				
Wheat	3·98	2·94	0·02	4·00
Rice cleaned	0·74	0·51	7·40	8·14
Millet and sorghums	0·60	0·36	—	0·60
Maize	0·42	0·18	—	0·42
Barley	0·13	0·09	0·02	0·15
	5·87	4·08	7·44	13·31
Pulses				
Gram	0·05	0·46	0·65	0·71
Oil Seeds	0·15	0·07	0·12	0·27
Sugar-cane (Gur)	0·73	0·53	0·31	1·04
Cotton (thousand bales)	1,227	718	15	1,242

(*Pakistan Govt. Statistics*, 1951.)

[1] "Classified" to which alone the statistics refer. The geographical land area is 729 million acres, ommitting Kashmir and Jammu.

EAST PAKISTAN

East Pakistan has an area of 34·3 million acres of which about 22½ million are cultivated (2½ million being fallow), but there is a good deal of double cropping so that some 23 million acres of crop are reaped; 20 million acreas are in rice, 1½ million in jute, and the remaining 1½ acres in oil seeds, sugar-cane, pulses, and some minor crops. Practically no wheat, maize, millet or cotton are grown. There is no irrigation—the rainfall is more than sufficient: the problem is to remove the excess of water.

Most of the land is thus continuously cropped with rice. About three-quarters of this (aman paddy) is transplanted from nursery beds in July and harvested in December; the land is then left bare till the following July. The rest, chiefly *aus* paddy, is sown broadcast in April or May and harvested in August. If the soil is moist enough, pulses or oil seeds can then be sown and harvested in January; the fallow period is then reduced to three months. Where irrigation is possible in January flavouring crops, chillies (very important in the peasant's dietary), garlic and onions can be sown and harvested in March. The peasant yields of aman paddy are about 16 or 18 cwt. per acre and of aus about 10 or 11: the general average is about 15, yielding 10 cwt. of milled rice. Yields on the experimental farms are 50 to 100 per cent higher.

Jute is interchangeable with aus paddy and when prices are high tends to displace it, but the area is now controlled by Government; it has in recent years fallen from the war-time peak of 4·7 million acres to 1·3 million acres in 1950. It is by far the leading export commodity, and is the chief source of Pakistan's wealth.

Owing to the density of the population the holdings are very small: more than half of them are less than 3 acres, only about 8 per cent exceed 10 acres. It is impossible to reduce the size further. More land could be made available by reclaiming some of the 2½ million acres classed as "cultivable waste" and including some of the coastal mangrove swamps, which should be productive though they might suffer from deficiency of copper or other trace elements. Some of the 2½ million acres of fallow land might be cropped, but the best hope lies in more double cropping: at present three-quarters of the land lies bare for the six months from January to July and most of it from January to April: it is pitiful to fly over the country during this period and think of the millions of hungry people with so much land unused. Irrigation during this dead period would allow of cropping, fertilizers (at present almost unused) would increase the yields, and the introduction of earlier ripening varieties would often allow a second crop to be sown while the soil was still moist—though the crop might still perish later from drought. All these possibilities are recognized, but funds are inadequate for realizing them.

Considerable losses of crops are caused by wild boars and monkeys; fortunately Moslems afford no special religious protection to these animals. As in India there is a large livestock population. There are far more cattle than can be properly fed; in consequence they are inefficient both as milk producers and for draft purposes.[1] Poultry are more numerous than in West Pakistan.

[1] S. J. Wright reports that 12 man-days are required to plough one acre for aman rice and up to 17 for one acre of jute (*J. Roy. Soc. Arts*, 1951, Vol. 99, pp. 573–83).

The country is not self-supporting in food: the deficits in 1949–50 were roughly:

Grain	Pulses	Oil-seeds	Sugar and gur	
320	1,300	140	100	thousand tons

(S. Hedayetullah, *Pakistan Sci. Cong.*, Dacca, 1951.)

The shortage of pulses is less serious than might be feared owing to the quantity of fish available.

WEST PAKISTAN

West Pakistan has a land area of about 200 million acres but only about 80 million are classified and of these only 28 million are cropped; by reason of double cropping 30 million or more acres of crops are obtained. In addition there are some 10 million acres of fallow. Most of the country is arid, only its eastern part and some of the northern hill districts receive more than 15 inches of rain a year; much of it, including Sind, only about 5 inches, and great stretches of desert have less. The land would, indeed, be practically all desert but for irrigation from the five rivers that traverse it: the Indus and its affluents the Sutlej, Ravi, Chenab, and Jhelum: from these the Punjab ("Land of five rivers" in Sanskrit) takes its name. These are fed by the snows of the Himalayas; they are in full spate in the summer, July to September, but much lower in winter; indeed, many of the water courses are then dry. Some of the summer flood is used for irrigation, but none is conserved and much is lost. Most of the country is a great plain, sloping gradually to the south; the distance from the foothills of Kashmir to the sea is some 600 miles and the fall is about 600 feet; an average of one foot per mile. In consequence, the rivers are liable to change their course and to overflow badly in summer unless properly controlled. But this topography is well suited for irrigation.

In the drier parts the summers are hot; the temperature in the Punjab may exceed 110° F, dust storms occur and may be followed by hail which does much damage. The winters are cool and in the hills frosts are not uncommon.

The Punjab is the most productive part of Pakistan. Of its 37 million acres about 17 million were cropped in 1950, about 12 million being irrigated. Wheat and cotton are by far the most important crops: wheat as the chief food, and cotton, which is of good American type, as the local cash crop; between them they occupy about half the cropped area. The other half is divided nearly equally between other food crops and fodder crops. Grouped according to season: the *Rabi* (winter) crops, wheat, oil seeds and berseem, occupy about double the area of the Kharif crops, cotton, millets, pulses; this makes the best use of the water supply and is convenient for organizing the work of the holding. The wheat yields about 9 cwt. per acre.

Gram is the chief of the non-cereals: it occupied 1·6 million acres in 1950 and produced nearly half a million tons. The chief oil seed is rape.

Five million acres of cultivated land are not irrigated: this is called the *barani* land; it is chiefly in millet—mostly Bullrush millet, bajra, yielding about 450 lb. per acre; some is in barley and some in indigenous cotton.

The irrigated fodder crops are a special feature of the Punjab: no other region in the whole sub-continent grows anything like so large an acreage. The chief of these is berseem (Egyptian clover), which not only provides three cuts of excellent fodder—some 60 tons per acre in all—but greatly enriches the soil in nitrogenous organic matter. The effect on the livestock is very marked: the cattle work better and give more milk than in other parts of India, with the further result that more milk is consumed per head of population in the Punjab than elsewhere. In other respects also the Punjab dietary is better and more varied than in any other part of the country,[1] and the physique of the villagers is strikingly good. Still further improvement in the dietary is being attempted: the cultivation of fish in the canals and tanks is being developed. (Pl. 34, p. 352.)

Up to 1950 the Punjab produced a surplus of wheat for export and of rice for East Bengal, but it had to import oil seeds (groundnuts), sugar and fruit. Attempts are being made to increase home production of all of these. Seed for sugar-cane, however, is not readily obtained as it cannot be produced in the Punjab; it was formerly obtained from Coimbatore in Madras, but this source is no longer available. Unfortunately, too, the surplus grain production has not been maintained: shortage of water, expansion of cash crops and various administrative and other shortcomings have reduced output and in 1951 the Punjab actually had to start importing food.

The livestock population was estimated to be in 1948:

Millions

	Cattle	Buffaloes	Sheep and Goats
East Pakistan	14·7	0·60	4·2
West Pakistan	9·6	5·0	5·9
Punjab	5·4	3·7	2·1
All Pakistan (1948)	24·3	5·6	10·1

(*F.A.O., Stat. Year Book*, 1951.

Some 80 per cent of the population are peasants. On the irrigated land the economic size of a family holding is about 12½ acres though some are smaller, even down to 6 acres; on the unirrigated land the holdings must be larger.[2]

Sind comes next in importance to the Punjab for food production. Without irrigation it would be almost a desert; its rainfall is usually only about 5 inches a year and the greater part of the country carries only desert

[1] The quantities of food crops produced per head of population were in 1950:

	Punjab	West Pakistan excluding Punjab	East Pakistan	All Pakistan
Food crops (million tons)	5·1	1·8	8·5	15·3
Population (millions)	18·8	14·7	42·1	75·7
Food crops lb. per head of Population: total	700	274	452	453

[2] Fuller information is given in *Agriculture in the Punjab*, Abdul Rahman, Agric. Coll. Lahore, 1950.

vegetation. The irrigation is of two kinds: (1) from inundation canals which carry the river flood waters on to an area depending on the volume of the flood and not amenable to human control; and (2) from canals supplied by the Lloyd Barrage at Sukkur. This was finished in 1932, but the canal system is not yet complete: it will ultimately water 5½ million acres; in 1951 the actual area was 3·9 million acres. The scheme of cropping had already been worked out at the Sakrand Experiment Station before large-scale cultivation began: it is in general similar to that of the Punjab except that there is more rice and relatively more millet, less wheat, gram and sugarcane. The *Rabi* crops, wheat, oil seeds, berseem, were originally intended to occupy about twice the area of the *Kharif* crops, cotton, millet, pulses, as in the Punjab, so as to ensure optimum utilization of the water, but this could never be achieved: not more than about 35 per cent of the land is under *Rabi* crops as the cultivator's primitive implements never allowed him to sow his full acreage of wheat in time. In consequence much water runs away unused. The holdings are about double the size of those in the Punjab, many of the peasants are freeholders, but many are tenants on the old hari system.[1]

As in the Punjab, little or no fertilizer is applied. Farmyard manure is used as fuel; any surplus is given to the cotton. The experimental farm has shown that fertilizers give good results: while the cultivator commonly obtains some 800 lb. of paddy per acre the experimental farm obtains 50 or 100 per cent more.

The only other important food-producing area in Pakistan is the North-West Frontier Province which has a classified area of 8·6 million acres, of which 2·45 million are sown, about half being irrigated; some of this is double cropped so that the total cropped area is 2·7 million acres. The chief product is wheat of which there are about a million acres, only about 400,000 of which are irrigated; maize comes next in importance followed by gram; there is very little rice and no cotton. Some sugar-cane is grown in spite of danger of frost damage, also some tobacco: both are valuable cash crops and acreage restrictions have been imposed by the Government to prevent them encroaching too much on the area that should be devoted to food crops. Excellent fruit can be grown, but transport is difficult. Investigations on conservation have long been in progress, but no large-scale application has been achieved: on my visit in 1951, I was given Scotch marmalade and Australian jam and butter. In the hill districts, berseem seed and seed potatoes are producible: both are valuable commodities. Unfortunately the seed potatoes are badly infested with virus disease.

Taking Pakistan as a whole, food production is on a higher level than in India and the average dietary is better. F.A.O. summary[2] for 1949–50 is:

Per day	Pakistan	India
Calories	2,020	1,700
Protein, grams: Animal	11	6
Vegetable	41	38
Total	52	44

[1] For a description see *Report of the Government Hari Enquiry Committee* 1947–48, Govt. of Sind, Karachi (n.d.).

[2] For details see p. 329.

The production of the two chief food crops, wheat and rice, does not appear to be rising in spite of some increase in acreage (Table LXXXIV).

TABLE LXXXIV. *Areas and production of wheat and rice, all Pakistan, for the years 1948 to 1951*

		1948	1949	1950	1951
Wheat	Area, million acres	9·85	10·68	10·72	10·83
	Yield, cwt. per acre	6·7	7·5	7·4	7·3
	Production, million tons	3·32	4·00	3·96	3·95
	Export, million tons	Nil	0·023	0·100	−0·153 (1)
Rice	Area, million tons (Milled equiv.)	21·49	21·77	22·40	22·48
	Yield, cwt. per acre	7·88	7·5	7·3	6·9
	Production, million tons	8·41	8·14	8·19	7·74
	Export (net) million tons	0·017	−0·042 (1)	0·018	0·136 (2)

(1) Import.
(2) Gross export.
(Commonwealth Econ. Cttee., *Grain Crops*, 1953.)

Rice production fell from nearly 8½ million tons in 1948 to 7¾ million in 1951; wheat production rose in 1949 to 4 million tons but has not increased since. Meanwhile the population continues to rise and Pakistan, always regarded as an exporter of grain, has been driven to import wheat: 153,000 tons in 1951, nearly half a million tons in 1952, and it expected to need 1 million tons in 1953. (Fig. 16, p. 328.)

Considerable schemes are in hand or projected for increasing the output of food. The most important is the Lower Barrage under construction in Sind on the Indus, some 250 miles below the Sukkur Barrage; this is intended to command 2·3 million acres at present waste. Associated with it is the Rasul Hydroelectric Scheme, expected to operate 1,800 tube wells, irrigating more than 700,000 acres, and incidentally lowering the water level in some of the Punjab soils. In the north-west of the Punjab the Thal scheme between the Indus and the Jhelum is intended to irrigate 2 million acres of desert; about 100,000 new farms will be set up, supplied with good livestock from an animal development farm which Australia and New Zealand maintain under the Colombo Plan. There are a number of smaller schemes: one in Bahawalpur (a State that produced quantities of food for the armies in the last war) to command about 200,000 acres from the Abbasia Canal; another is the Warsak dam in the North-West Province intended to water 65,000 acres, besides providing electricity for tube wells and for industry. Altogether some 5 or 6 million new acres may be brought into cultivation.

Unfortunately there is another side to the story. Water-logging and salting of the old irrigated land are increasing, throwing many acres out of use every year. The cause is partly that the cultivators take too much water, partly that the canals leak. The largest and most important canal on the Sukkur Barrage Scheme, the Rohri, began water-logging some of the soils within a few months of its completion; by 1950 an adjacent area half a mile wide and some 23 miles long had to be abandoned, and for a further half mile in width yields were below normal: some 15,000 acres were affected in all. The water level in the soil was in 1951 still rising at the rate of 2 or 3 feet a year and the damaged area is bound to increase. In parts of the Punjab salt is coming to the surface and great stretches of land which a decade ago carried good crops of wheat are now sterile, covered with a white layer of salt that gleams in the sun like snow. Some $2\frac{1}{4}$ million acres or more of this salt land are reported in West Pakistan. Accurate figures cannot be obtained, but the area is said to be increasing at the rate of about 30,000 acres a year. Some reclamation is proceeding, but it involves flooding the land with considerable quantities of water that can ill be spared as they are needed for crop production. (Pl. 35.) Under the Colombo Plan some 400,000 acres were reclaimed during the two years 1951–53.[1]

Irrigation schemes are among the most difficult of all agricultural operations; they require continuous supervision by highly competent and absolutely honest experts able to detect the first signs of trouble and to devise means of restoration. Continuous scientific research is necesssry to gain the fundamental knowledge on which alone effective action can be taken. This need is recognized. A Reclamation Research Institute has been set up at Mugal Pura and an Irrigation Research Institute has for many years been established at Lahore; there is also a large and comprehensive Agricultural Institute at Lyallpur.

Meanwhile another very serious problem has arisen for which at present no solution is in sight. The Partition of India not only disrupted trade relations between the various regions but, what was far worse, cut across the irrigation systems of the north. The river Sutlej till recently provided water for about 5 million acres of some of the richest wheat and cotton growing land in the Pakistan Punjab. But before entering Pakistan it flows through East Punjab, which is in India. The Indian Government is now constructing works on its part of the river which enable it to divert the waters from the Pakistan Punjab into its own Punjab: the works at Harike are nearly completed and the great dam at Bhakra Nangal is due for completion in 1958: its height is to be such that it will hold up even the flood water. Already in 1952 the supplies to the Central Bari Doab canal system in Pakistan, controlled at Madhopur in India, were less than before Partition, and the worst cut came in October when wheat was due for sowing. These works are causing great anxiety to the Pakistan Government who fear that much of their Punjab may be reduced to desert. David Lilienthal, the former Chief of the Tennessee Valley Authority, has studied the question and concludes that a satisfactory agreement should be possible: there is enough water for both parties: less than 20 per cent of the water in the Indus Basin is at present used for irrigation.[2] But Pakistan remains anxious and unconvinced.[3]

[1] Cmd. 9016. H.M.S.O., Dec. 1953.   [2] *Economist*, February 28, 1953.

[3] Further information is given in the Agricultural Section of the Report of the U.K. Industrial Mission to Pakistan (Burghley Commission), H.M.S.O., 1950.

Chapter 10

ASIA: II
CHINA, JAPAN, INDONESIA, AND THE RICE-EXPORTING COUNTRIES

CHINA

There has never been much precise information about food production in China, but the fact that it has continued for some four thousand years without apparent deterioration of the land has always had a fascination for Western people. F. H. King of Wisconsin visited the country in 1907 to seek an explanation[1] and later, J. Lossing Buck remained there for some years;[2] his accounts are still the best we have on the subject. One book on Chinese agriculture has been published in English[3] but no official agricultural statistics comparable with those of India are issued. F.A.O. publishes estimates, and as these are the best available, they are used here.

Difficulty arises at the outset from the circumstances that the name "China" has had several different meanings. The old Imperial China covered an area of 4½ million square miles, but lost some of its Provinces so that the China of 1947 was smaller:

	Million acres		
	Land area	Cultivated	Forest
Old Imperial China	2,900		
China of 1947	2,330	225	208
Twenty-two Provinces	1,250	180	
Manchuria	264	35	

The population is estimated by F.A.O. as 452 millions in 1937 and 463 millions in 1950.[4] Less than 10 per cent of the land is cultivated: an average of about half an acre per head; apparently an area of this order has always been regarded as adequate, for the Chinese symbol for "prosperity" is a field with one mouth about it, and the usual size of a Chinese field is about half an acre.

This low utilization of the land is the result partly of topography, partly of rainfall. The rain comes from the east and south-east; only the eastern part of the country receives much: the west is arid, much of it desert. The temperature is almost tropical in the extreme south-east; it is lower in the north; in the drier west the range increases as usual in arid conditions. The wide coastal belt has a good deal of low-lying country suited to agriculture, but further inland come the uplands and the mountains.

[1] F. H. King, *Farmers of Forty Centuries*, 1911; revised edition, 1927.
[2] J. L. Buck, *Chinese Farm Economy*, London, 1931; *Land Utilisation in China*, London, 1937.
[3] T. H. Shen, *Agricultural Resources of China*, Oxford. 1952.
[4] Results of the first Census (June 1953) are not yet available.

Cultivation is mainly in the east. A belt stretching south eastwards across the country from Chahar and Hopei on Manchuria's southern border to Sikang and Yunnan in the south central region has sufficient rainfall for wheat: spring wheat on the western side where the winters are colder, and winter wheat on the eastern side where they are less severe; the block of wetter warmer country to the south-east stretching from Chekian and Hupeh in the north to Yunnan in the south, and eastwards to the sea, is the rice area; while in between is a belt where both wheat and rice are grown, wheat as a winter crop and rice in summer. The wheat belt produces also maize, peas and beans, especially the soy bean of which a considerable acreage is grown in Manchuria, and much cotton. In the drier parts, millets and sorghum replace the wheat; further west come the still drier loess-covered uplands used for grazing sheep and cattle for the production of hides, wool, tallow, etc.

This wheat region comprises rather more than half the cultivated land of China: it has not in the past, however, been self-sufficing in food, but has had to draw supplies from Manchuria to the north and the more productive provinces to the south and east.

The rice region is much hotter: it includes the great river valleys; particularly the Yangtse Valley, one of the most favoured agricultural districts in the world, with rich alluvial soil and ample well-distributed rainfall. This region has been called the "granary of China" and was said to support half China's entire population. The area of rice is less than that of wheat, but the yield per acre is considerably greater so that there is a larger total production. (Pl. 36.) Other crops are barley, rape seed, sweet potatoes as well as some wheat; sugar, tea, cotton and silk are also produced.

In the far south-east is the tropical zone where some of China's special crops, including ginger, cinnamon, and aniseed are grown. The areas and production of the chief crops are set out in Table LXXXV. No fodder crops, cultivated grasses or clovers are grown: there is indeed no room for them. Apart from draft animals practically no cattle, goats, or sheep are kept in the agricultural regions. But most of the holdings have a pig and a few chickens, and the total numbers of each of these exceed those of all other countries excepting only the United States. The livestock numbers are estimated as follows:

Millions

	Cattle	Sheep	Goats	Pigs	Poultry
1937	23	12	22	60	246
1947–48	18	10	14	60	209

(*F.A.O. Stat. Year Book*, 1951.)

Practically no beef, mutton or milk is produced and not much pig meat, poultry or eggs. The holdings are small: mostly about 3 or 4 acres; they are more like market gardens than farms.

The yields per acre can only be described as moderate: they are above the averages for Asia but below those of Japan. They were less in 1949 than before the war: the season, however, was rather poor: 1948 had been somewhat better. In no case is there evidence of increasing yields. Nor had

TABLE LXXXV. *Areas, yields and production of chief crops, China (22 provinces)*

	Million acres		Yield, cwt. per acre		Million tons	
	Av. 1934–38	1949	Av. 1934–38	1949	Av. 1934–38	1949
Wheat	49·5	52·3	8·6	7·8	21·7	22·1
Paddy	49·0	45·8	20·0	19·0	50·1	44·5
Millet and sorghum	30·0	26·7	(M) 9·6 (S) 11·0	8·6 10·0	15·2	12·5
Barley	16·5	15·4	9·4	8·6	7·9	6·6
Maize	11·6	12·4	11·0	10·4	6·5	6·5
Oats	2·6	2·3	6·8	6·2	·88	0·74
	159·2	154·9			102·3	92·9
Peas and beans	20·8	19·5			7·7	6·6
Soya beans	17·8	12·0	9·3	8·2	8·1	4·9
Groundnuts	3·8	4·0	14·4	14·6	2·7	2·9
Sesame	3·6	3·7	4·7	4·5	0·85	0·83
Cotton seed	7·5	5·2	4·1	2·9	1·5	0·82
Sweet potatoes	5·8	7·8	6·4	5·7	18·5	22·8
Manchuria						
Wheat	2·7	1·4			0·9	0·6
Paddy	0·56		14·0		0·41	
Barley	0·36		8·0		0·14	
Maize	3·3		12·0		2·0	
Millet and sorghum	13·6				7·0 10·5	
Soya beans	8·5	5·5	8·8	6·4	3·8	1·8

Other important crops are tobacco (second largest output in the world) and tea.
(*F.A.O. Stat. Year Book*, 1951.)

The Commonwealth Economic Cttee., (*Grain Crops*, 1953) have issued figures for production of milled rice in the 22 provinces:

1947–48	1948–49	1949–50	1950–51	1951–52
32·0	33·2	30·7	32·3	30·6 million tons

45 tons of paddy = 30 tons of milled rice.

production of any of the foods except wheat reached pre-war levels. These reductions in output have not been compensated by additional imports of grain. Before the war there was a small retained import of wheat—251,000 tons in 1938 and 352,000 in 1939, chiefly from Australia—but this probably represented greater ease of procurement by sea than by land in certain localities in view of the poor inland communications; there were also imports of rice of similar magnitude.[1] From 1949 these have been much reduced and there have been exports of rice to Ceylon in exchange for rubber, and of rice, millets and other grains—about 500,000 tons in all to India in 1951: probably with as much political as economic purpose. Fortunately the population appears to have increased only slightly if at all, and so the deterioration of the dietary has been less than it might have been: nevertheless it is bad enough, and it has put the Chinese dietary among the lowest recorded. F.A.O. estimates are given in Table LXXXVI.

[1] C.E.C. *Grain Crops*, 1953.

TABLE LXXXVI. *Average quantities of foods available*
lb. per head per year

	Average 1931–37	1949–50		Average 1931–37	1949–50
Cereals	378	337	Meat	29	24
Sweet potatoes			Eggs	4·4	2·2
and potatoes	66	79	Fish	15	13
Pulses	55	48	Milk	None	None
Sugar	2	2			
Fats	13	15			
Fruit and					
vegetables	125	125			

	Calories per day	Protein, grams per day		
		Animal	Vegetable	Total
Average 1931–37	2,230	7	65	72
1949–50	2,030	6	57	63

(*F.A.O. Second World Food Survey*, 1952.)

By 1960 it is hoped to raise the supply of pulses to 70, of fruit and vegetables to 286, of meat to 32, and of eggs to 7 lb. per head per year: even so the average calorie supply will be only 2,262 per day.

The dietary is deficient in calcium, as shown by the prevalence of osteomalacia, but Vitamins A, B and C seem to be adequately supplied by the numerous fruits and vegetables, some cultivated but many wild, used by the peasants, and Vitamin B is contained in the fermented soya bean drink almost universally consumed in China.[1]

The average yields given in Table LXXXV are not always and everywhere obtained: drought and floods are liable to cause serious losses. Famine has always been on China's doorstep; it is commonly said that three occur during the lifetime of a man: and lives are short in China. There was a serious one in 1949.

What are the possibilities of increasing the output of food? There has hitherto been little sign of increase in the cropped area; for long it remained practically stationary even though the population was slightly increasing: between 1873 and 1933 the population was estimated to have risen by some 30 per cent, but the farm acreage only by 1 per cent.[2] Buck, however, estimated that it could be extended by about 35 million acres, and that another 2½ million could be added if the gravelands were removed. This latter, however, is so utterly opposed to the peasants' views on life and death that it is hardly likely to come about, but some extensions are being effected. New irrigation schemes hold out considerable promise. The Huai river is to irrigate some 5 million acres; and the Yellow River is to water much land in the small Pingyuan Province. These schemes are based on the American multi-purpose model—coming, however, via Moscow—and comprise flood control, hydroelectric work, and afforestation; a forest belt 700 miles long is proposed for Manchuria and extensive planting in China

[1] This question of supplements is discussed in an interesting volume of essays on Chinese country life, *Green Thraldom*, by Tang Pei-Sung (Allen & Unwin, 1949).

[2] Inter. Govt. Conf. of Far Eastern Countries on Rural Hygiene, Bandoeng, Java, August 1937 (League of Nations, 1937).

347

proper. It was indeed high time that afforestation should be undertaken for the amount of soil erosion has been terrible. The Yellow River derives its name from the vast quantities of silt it carries down; some of this forms a delta that will in course of ages be fertile land, much, however, is simply deposited in the bed of the river where in its lower reaches it widens, reducing the speed of the water: the bed is thereby raised, periodically causing disastrous floods.

Much more widespread crop increases would be given by fertilizers, which at present are hardly used at all except in Formosa: H. L. Richardson and others have shown that they raise yields on the average by some 50 per cent.

Composts are, however, used on a great scale. This fact was first brought home to Western agriculturists by F. H. King[1] who attributed the stability of the Chinese system to their practice of systematically collecting all animal and vegetable residues, particularly all human excrements, making them into composts and returning them to the land. The system has a satisfying look of self-sufficiency and full conservation of natural resources, and it found many admirers in Great Britain and America. Later observers, however, have recorded serious defects apart from the great amount of labour involved. Foecal-borne diseases—cholera, typhoid, the dysenteries, summer diarrhoea, round worm, hook worm, blood and liver flukes and others are widespread; they contribute greatly to the prevailing high infant mortality[2] and general death rates besides causing much debilitating illness. Methods of composting are known that reduce the infectivity of the compost, but they also reduce its fertilizing value.[3]

The second weakness is that the process is not in fact self-contained. At its best the compost only returns some of the material taken from the soil: it does nothing to remedy any mineral deficiencies in the soil itself, nor does it return anything like all the nitrogen taken out, for much of this is lost during the process of collecting and composting the excretions. As no restorative clover or grasses are grown and only a relatively small area of other leguminous crops, the nitrogen content of the soil would fall to its low stable level if there were no replenishment. There is, however, replenishment although it was not noted by King: it is brought about by a transfer of soil fertility from the wastes of the hinterland to the remoter farms, and from these to the farms nearer the towns. The towns and villages draw their food supplies from a wide area of the countryside. But their wastes, excrements, night soil, etc., are carried out on to a much narrower belt of land. In consequence, the soils near a town or village are enriched at the expense of soils farther away; these in turn are enriched by soil or organic matter brought in from the outlying forest or waste land, but as this is not so good

---

[1] Loc. cit.

[2] At the Bandeong Conference already referred to it was reported that 45 per cent of the children die before reaching the age of five.

[3] The straw is also returned to the land, being either trodden into the puddled soil between the paddy plants or twisted into small hanks and pushed into the mud between them (R. L. Pendleton, *Proc. U. N. Sci. Cong. Conservation and Utilisation of Resources*, 1949, pp. 258, *et seq.*). For an account of the methods of collecting and utilizing the excreta, and a discussion of the disease problems, see E. C. Faust, *American Jl. of Tropical Medicine*, 1924, Vol. 4, pp. 487–505 and The League of Nations Bandoeng Report (1937) already quoted. See also Tang, *American Journal of Hygiene*, Vol. 50 (1949), pp. 236–62.

as the town compost their yields are lower. H. L. Richardson has pointed out that a traveller can recognize his approach to a town even before he sees its buildings by the higher productiveness of the land—and it is this land that King and other short-term visitors have chiefly described. A further transfer helps to enrich sections of the plains; much silt is brought down on to them by the flood waters of the great rivers from the top soils higher up their course.

The hinterland and forest thus lose what the cultivated soils gain, and a great deal more, for the transfer is extremely wasteful and is possible only because the hinterland far exceeds the cultivated land in area. Soil erosion there is widespread, and drifting sand is covering up land that formerly carried vegetation.

The Government is actively engaged in carrying through a scheme of land reform on the usual Communist lines. Estates are broken up and the land given to the peasants who do not always have either the knowledge or the appliances for working it. This stage is pleasing enough to the peasants and one might expect an increased output of food to result: up to 1952 there were no indications of this, but it may yet come. The next stage, collectivization, is unlikely to be so popular and in any case will be difficult to achieve because of the lack of the reserves of land essential to its success. Collectivization is, however, a fundamental tenet of Communism and for that reason China may be compelled to adopt it. A struggle with the Chinese peasants would, indeed, be a gruesome affair, and for the peace of the world we must hope that it can be avoided.

JAPAN

Japan presents the most serious food problems of any country in Asia. The four main islands are so rugged and mountainous that the agricultural land is little more than one-sixth of the whole area—some $12\frac{1}{2}$ million acres only—and it has stood at about this figure for a long time. The hope expressed a generation ago that another 5 million acres might be added has not been realized. The population is estimated by F.A.O. at $69\cdot2$ millions in 1934–38 and $83\cdot2$ in 1950—a rise of about 1 per cent per annum; the area of cultivated land is thus only about $0\cdot15$ acre per head, the lowest in the world. The position hitherto has been possible only because Japan's long, indented coastline has encouraged fishing, and the average consumption per head of fish before the war was 77 lb. per annum, but was in 1950 down to 60 lb. per head—a quantity, however, exceeded only in Norway and Iceland. The main crop is rice, which occupies about half the cropped land; the remainder carries a great variety of crops: wheat, barley, beans, oil seeds, millets, oats, sweet potatoes, potatoes and other vegetables.

The acreages and production of the chief crops are shown in Table LXXXVII.

There has been a fall in area of rice and of pulses which, however, is more than counterbalanced by increases in barley and in starchy root crops. Yields are high for Asia and have been well maintained; those of rice, sweet potatoes and soya beans have improved.[1]

[1] Japan's rice is grown farther to the north than any other in Asia. Many varieties appear to be photoperiodic and to give higher yields the farther they are from the Equator provided they remain within the proper temperature zone.

TABLE LXXXVII. *Acreage yield and production of main crops, Japan.*

	Million acres Av. 1934–38	Million acres 1950	Cwt. per acre Av. 1934–38	Cwt. per acre 1950	Million tons Av. 1934–38	Million tons 1950
Rice	7·8	7·4	29·0	32·0	11·5	12·0
Barley	1·9	2·5	16·0	15·4	1·55	1·96
Wheat	1·7	1·9	15·0	14·1	1·29	1·34
Sweet potatoes	0·61	0·98	tons 4·9	6·3	3·06	6·29
Potatoes	0·37	0·46	tons 4·3	4·4	1·62	2·44
Peas and beans	0·67	0·29			0·27	0·13
Soya beans	0·80	0·75	7·9	8·7	0·32	0·33
	13·85	14·28				

(*F.A.O. Stat. Year Book*, 1951.)

In consequence the production of grains has increased, and that of sweet potatoes doubled between pre-war days and 1950. Home production has, however, long been insufficient: before the war there was considerable import of rice, averaging 1·7 million tons a year for 1937 and 1938. This fell to only 3,000 tons in 1947, but rose steadily to 878,000 tons in 1951, coming mainly from Thailand, Egypt and Burma, while the import of wheat, which in 1937 and 1938 averaged 125,000 tons, rose steadily from 766,000 tons in 1947 to 1·79 million tons in 1951.[1] The Japanese are thus changing over from rice to wheat.

The total quantities of food available have not sufficed to maintain the pre-war dietary though the fall has not been very great:

	lb. per head per year Av. 1934–38	lb. per head per year 1949–50		Per head per day Av. 1934–38	Per head per day 1949–50
Grain	168	157	Calories	2,180	2,100
Starchy roots	63	66	Protein, grams		
Meat	4	2	Animal	10	8
Fish	35	27	Vegetable	54	45
			Total	64	53

(*F.A.O. 2nd World Food Survey*, 1952.)

Meanwhile, the population continues to increase and food production shows no sign of overtaking it. The deep interest taken by the United States in Japan is an assurance that some solution of the food problem will be found. Japan's chief asset is an enormous supply of very cheap labour which can produce goods for export at prices with which Western countries cannot compete, so that there is always the hope of being able to import grain so long as surpluses are available.

INDONESIA

Indonesia comprises four large and a number of small islands: Java is by far the most important.

Java has hitherto had no food problems comparable with those of Japan or India. The island is very densely populated: something like 900 to the

[1] C.E.C. *Grain Crops*, 1952.

square mile, and in places as many as 4,000—the highest agricultural density in the world—but it contains so much good land and such suitable climate that the Dutch, while they were in charge, made it a model of tropical agriculture, producing not only food but also plantation crops for export— rubber, tea, coffee, sugar, palm nut, cinchona, and others. The population rose by 20 per cent between 1920 and 1930 and was estimated to rise by 30 per cent during the succeeding twenty years:

	1920	1930	1950
Population, millions	49·3	60·7	78

(1920 and 1930 are Census figures: 1950 is estimated: *Statesman's Year Book,* 1952.)

Before the war the area under rice had averaged 10·4 million acres and the production 4·6 million tons of milled rice: in 1950 and 1951 the area averaged 10·1 million acres and the production 4·25 million tons. In addition there were before the war about 5 million acres of maize producing 2 million tons: in 1949 production was 1·8 million tons. Even before the war imports averaging 230,000 tons a year were needed: in 1950 and 1951 they had risen to 327,000 and 402,000 tons respectively.[1] The total food supplies, however, have not kept pace with the growth of population and in consequence there has been a lowering of the dietary: the average quantities per head have been:

	lb. per head per year			*per head per day*	
	Av. 1934–38	1949–50		Av. 1934–38	1949–50
Grain	130	120	Calories	2,040	1,880
Starchy roots	131	118	Protein, grams		
Meat	5	4	Animal	5	4
Fish	9	6	Vegetable	41	38
			Total	46	42

(*F.A.O., 2nd World Food Survey,* 1952.)

It remains to be seen whether the old standards of efficiency of production can be recovered under Java's new management. The output of plantation crops other than rubber has fallen considerably:

			Thousand metric tons			
	Rubber	Coffee	Tea[2]	Cocoa	Tobacco	Cinchona
1940	548	77·6	82·0	1·55	27·4	16·4
1950	523	35·4	35·3	0·87	12·0	5·6

(*Statesman's Year Book,* 1952.)

The experimental stations at Pasoeroean (for sugar) and Buitenzorg (for rubber), formerly known throughout the world for their distinguished investigations, have ceased to function. The Research Station at Bogor is still working, though hampered.

[1] C.E.C. *Grain Crops,* 1953.
[2] Taking out peasant culture the figures become 69·3 and 23·2 respectively. (*Internat. Tea Ctte. Statistics,* 1953.)

Other countries in the Far East are still in various stages of revolution and disorder, and there is no advantage in discussing them in detail. Three of them are of supreme importance for Asia's food supplies as they alone are capable of producing considerable surpluses of rice for export: Burma, Thailand and Indo-China. Thailand alone has maintained her pre-war performance, the failure of the other two to do so is compelling the deficit countries, India, Malaya, Japan and Indonesia to import wheat from Australia and America, and rice from Egypt and Brazil. The production and export of rice from the three countries has been:

Million tons

	Burma		Indo-China		Thailand	
	Av.	Av.	Av.	Av.	Av.	Av.
Milled rice	1937–39	1949–51	1937–39	1949–51	1937–39	1949–51
Production	4·88	3·30	4·05	1·81 (1)	2·90	4·46
Export	2·94	1·20	1·23	0·16	1·38	1·39

(1) Cambodia and South Vietnam only.
(C.E.C. *Grain Crops*, 1953.)

F.A.O. estimates that the export trade in milled rice in the Far East has fallen from the pre-war 9·2 million tons to 3·3 million tons in the period 1949–51.[1]

The net result of all these changes is that the countries of Asia, already ill-fed before the war, are on a still lower dietary now, but while in the aggregate they used to produce the whole of their food supply and even have margins for export, they now no longer do so but have become dependent on America and Australia for the reduced amount of food they are getting.

[1] *Second World Food Survey*, 1952, p. 9. They give the figures as paddy: 13·75 and 4·9 million tons respectively.

33 (*left*) The Damodar Valley project: restoring eroded lands in the head water regions near Hazaripur. (*Courtesy of Damodar Valley Corp.*) [p. 334

34 (*right*) Taking fish from temple tank, Hiran Minar, Nr. Lahore, Pakistan. (*Photo: Lady Russell*) [p. 340

35 (*left*) Former productive wheatland ruined by salt brought up through faulty irrigation, Punjab, Nr. Lahore. (*Photo: Lady Russell*) [p. 343

36 (*right*) Terraces for rice cultivation, Szechwan province, China. (*Photo: Central Office of Information, London*) [p. 345

37 (left) Strip cropping on the contours to prevent erosion, Winona Co., Minn., U.S.A. (Courtesy of Soil Conservation Service, Washington, D.C.) [p. 365

38 (right) Rehabilitating eroded lands: corral on community pasture near Donavon, Sask. (Courtesy of Prairie Farm Rehabilitation, Regina) [p. 384

39 (left) A combine threshing wheat out of the swath, Regina Plains, Sask. (Courtesy of Prairie Farm Rehabilitation, Regina) [p. 386

40 (right) William James Farrer's paddock and field laboratory, Lambrigg, Nr. Canberra, where he bred wheats from 1889 onwards. He died in 1906. (Photo: author)

Chapter 11

THE FOOD EXPORTERS:
I. THE UNITED STATES, CANADA

THE UNITED STATES

The agriculture of the United States may be regarded as a major balancing factor in making up the food supplies of the free world. It is remarkably flexible, and the great development of industry and the ease of transfer from one activity to another, together with the ingenuity of the farmers and of their advisers, make expansions and contractions much easier than in most other countries. The late 19th century and the early years of this century saw a large expansion of output from the farms and ranches; between 1900 and 1904 it rose by 42 per cent to a value of nearly $5 thousand million: an "unthinkable aggregate" as the Secretary to the Department of Agriculture put it.[1] Yet the curve of production has steadily continued to rise, broken only by years of severe drought—especially 1934 and 1936—and still further output is anticipated (Fig. 17). But the position in regard to exports has changed a good deal. The early period had been one of large export of grain, especially wheat, and also of meat, at prices which, though very favourable to an industrial population, put many of our farmers out of business. They were, of course, equally unattractive to the American farmers. Fortunately their home demand was expanding greatly with the enormous development of industry, and so exports fell off rapidly from 1920 to 1932 and remained at a low level till 1944 when they rose rapidly (Fig. 18).[2] Other food exports followed a similar course.

The needs of the allies during the war, however, and the distressful condition of Europe after the war, aroused deep sympathy, and tremendous efforts were made to increase food production. Output of grain was almost doubled, giving large surpluses for export, while the production and export of bacon, pork and lard increased so much that there was now an overall export surplus of meat instead of a net import. Large quantities of eggs, milk products, vegetables, potatoes and dried fruits were exported also. More significant still, the output of oil seeds, especially soya bean, increased so greatly that the United States instead of competing with a hungry Europe for African vegetable oil actually became an exporter—a position which if it is maintained will profoundly affect the supply of margarine for the European countries. The only foods imported on any large scale were sugar, certain fruits and canned fish.

Perhaps even more important than the export of food has been the devising of new methods, especially combinations of methods, and appliances for solving difficult agricultural problems. The knowledge and experience gained is freely put at the disposal of other countries and has been widely drawn

[1] *Rpt. Sec. Dept. Agric., U.S.A.*, Washington D.C., 1904.
[2] From *Foreign Agricultural Situation*, p. 21.

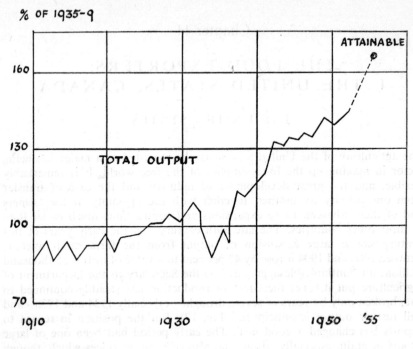

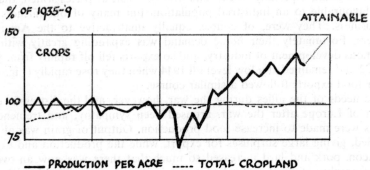

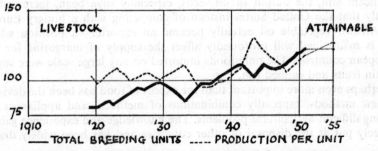

Fig. 17.—Expansion of agricultural output in the United States: pre-war to post-war period (from Ag. Information Bull. No. 88, U.S.D.A. 1952).

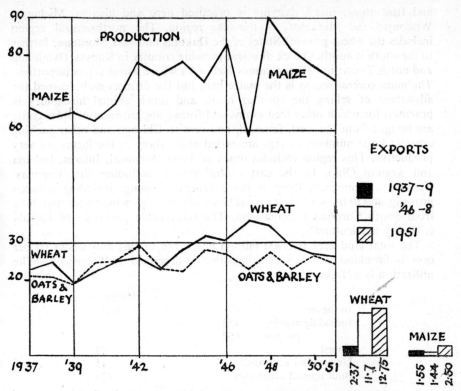

FIG. 18.—Production and exports of grain. U.S.A. 1937–1951 (data from C.E.C. Reports, *Grain Crops*, 1953, and from *F.A.O. Stat. Year Book*, 1951).

upon for dealing with such serious difficulties as soil erosion, salt and alkali troubles on irrigated land, mechanization and other problems.

The great expanse of the country and the wide range of climatic conditions allow the growth of practically all crops, but large home markets—and also the psychology of the American farmer—favour standardization and economy of working, and in consequence there is much specialized farming, based, however, on its suitability to the conditions. The result is a highly complex agriculture which I shall not attempt to describe, nor is this necessary as it has been so fully done before.[1]

The hundredth meridian which runs from the Mexican border through Omaha to the Dakotas divides the country into two great divisions: the mountainous region of the west, and the great plains of the centre and the south, broken in the east by the Appalachian mountains. The rainfall in the eastern regions is good and well distributed, but farther west it is less and there may be long periods with little or none; the mountainous west has great areas of desert. The greater part of the cropping is in the eastern division. The climate of the north-east—the New England States and the lake region—is something like that of Great Britain except that the winters are much colder and their coming and going more abrupt: this is a region of grass

[1] See especially the Year Books of the U.S. Dept. of Agriculture.

and fruit trees; much dairying is practised here and also in Michigan, Wisconsin and Minnesota in the lake region. The north-central region includes the wheat-growing States of the Dakotas and east Montana; farther to the south is another block of wheat-growing country in Kansas, Oklahoma and north Texas; in between comes Nebraska where wheat is less important. The main central region is the maize belt, but the farmers early learned the advantage of selling the corn as meat, and much animal husbandry is practised for which other feed grains and forage are grown also. Store cattle are bought from the west, fattened, and sent to Chicago and other packing centres; large numbers of pigs are raised also. Many of the farms are very productive. This region includes much of Iowa, Missouri, Illinois, Indiana and western Ohio. In the east central region, including the Virginias, Kentucky, Tennessee, there is more general farming, including tobacco growing, and to the south is the great block of cotton-growing States stretching from South Carolina to Louisiana. The remarkable peninsula of Florida is largely horticultural.

The total land area is 1,900 million acres, but of this only about 60 per cent is farmland and less than half that is described as "improved." The utilization is as follows:

		Million acres
In farms		1,133
Including arable	455	
pasture	662	
Forest		624
Unused but utilizable		15
Built up and other uses		128
		1900

(*F.A.O. Stat. Year Book*, 1951.)

The farmland rose from 987 million acres in 1930 to 1,141 million acres in 1945 as the result of the increasing demand for food, but some of this area proved unsuitable and has been abandoned.

The farmland was in 1950 divided into 5,384 holdings; for some years the number has been falling and the average size of the farms increasing:

	1930	1940	1945	1950
Number of farms, millions	6·289	6·097	5·859	5·384 (1)
Average size, acres	157	174	199	210
Farm population, millions	29·45	29·05	24·34	24·43

(1) About 200,000 of the fall in number since 1945 is due to a change in definition of a farm.

Of the 455 million acres classed as arable land, about 255 million were in the chief tillage crops before the war; this was raised to 280 million acres for a time after the war but has since returned to its old level. The areas and production of the principal crops are given in Table LXXXVIII. The remaining arable land (about 200 million acres) is taken up by fallows, rotation

TABLE LXXXVIII. *Areas and production of chief crops, United States*

	Million acres			Yield cwt. per acre			Million tons		
	Average 1934–38	1948	1950	Average 1934–38	1948	1950	Average 1934–38	1948	1950
Wheat	55·5	73·0	61·6	7·0	9·7	8·9	19·5	35·7	27·7
Rye, rice and pulses	6·2	6·1	5·0	—	—	—	2·9	3·5	3·2
Total grain for human food	61·7	79·1	66·6				22·4	39·2	30·9
Maize	93·5	86·1	81·8	11·2	21·2	18·8	53·1	93·5	77·7
Oats	35·0	40·2	40·7	7·9	10·6	9·9	14·0	21·7	20·5
Barley	9·6	12·0	11·2	9·3	11·4	11·7	4·5	6·9	6·6
Sorghum (grain)	3·9	7·3	10·3	6·3	9·0	11·4	1·2	3·3	5·9
Total feed grains	142·0	145·5	144·0				72·8	125·4	110·7
Sorghum for silage and forage	10·7 (1)	5·7	5·1						
Soya beans	2·5	10·4	13·8	9·3	11·5	11·8	1·2	6·1	8·1
Groundnuts	1·6	3·3	2·3	6·7	6·4	8·0	0·54	1·1	0·92
Potatoes	3·2	2·1	1·7	3·1	5·8	6·8	10·0	12·4	11·7
				tons	tons	tons			
Sugar beet	0·8	0·70	0·93	10	12	13	8·1	8·5	12·2
				tons	tons	tons			
Horticultural crops	3·0 (2)	3·5	3·4						
Tobacco	1·5	1·6	1·6						
Cotton	28·3	23·0	17·8						
Total	255·3	275	257·2						

(1) Includes also maize cut for fodder and silage.

(2) A. N. Duckham, *American Agric.*, H.M.S.O., 1952.

(*F.A.O. Stat. Year Book*, 1951.)

grasses and various other crops: the total for the 52 principal crops was in 1950, 339 million acres, but this was lower than in any year since 1941. There are no fodder root crops[1] or kales, and folding in the English sense is not done.

Striking changes in area and output of the chief crops resulted from the war and post-war food situation. Twenty million acres were added to the area of tillage crops in 1948 and 5 million acres formerly in cotton went into food crops; in 1949 a further 5 million acres of land was brought in to restore the cotton acres without trenching on the area of food crops. The production of wheat and of maize went up by more than 80 per cent and the net exports were, in thousand tons:

[1] This absence of root crops has long been characteristic of American agriculture. When Sir Henry Gilbert visited the States in 1882 he expressed surprise that such useful crops should not be grown but he adds: "I was told that no American would bend his back to hand hoe."

357

	Average 1935–39	1947–48	1948–49
Wheat	1,062	13,502	13,962
Maize	152	1,044	2,287
Barley	−22 (1)	512	327
Oats	15	313	87
Rice	218	605	571

(1) Import.

(*F.A.O. Food Balance Sheets.*)

The great increase in production which made these huge exports possible had resulted partly from increased acreages, but partly, and in the case of maize entirely, from increased yields per acre: a new feature in American agriculture. Yield statistics go back to the 1870's: they showed little change till the mid-1930's, improvements in some directions being offset by deterioration in others.

Among the chief factors in bringing about these recent increases in yields have been the use of improved varieties, of better cultural practices, the greatly increased consumption of fertilizers which more than doubled between 1940 and 1950:

Million tons of plant food used in the United States 1940 *and* 1950

	Nitrogen (N)	Phosphate (P_2O_5)	Potash (K_2O)	Total	Liming materials
Average, 1935–39	335	702	352	1,389	
1940	419	912	435	1,766	13,434
1950	1,126	2,071	1,215	4,412	26,536
Target for 1955	2,185	3,485	2,185	7,855	

(Short tons of 2,000 lb. *Fert. Review*, July-September 1952, and October December 1952.)

It is estimated that much more fertilizer could be used with advantage, and a high target has been set for 1955. The United States is self-contained for nitrogen and phosphate, having immense deposits of rock phosphate estimated at 13·3 thousand million long tons.[1] Fertilizers are used most extensively in the eastern half of the States, especially east of the line joining Chicago and the Mississippi delta. Little has hitherto been used in the wheat belt, but more is now being applied.

American farmers are very ready to adopt drastic chemical treatment against pests and diseases.

Another important factor in the increased production has been the spread of more prolific varieties. The new hybrid maize and sorghum varieties in particular have proved remarkably successful, giving 25 per cent or more higher yield than the old ones. Moreover, their value is not confined to the United States: already they or others obtained by similar methods have proved useful in other countries also.[2]

Neither fertilizers nor improved varieties could have been fully effective without the recent great increase in mechanization. The number of tractors rose from 2·21 millions in 1944 to 3·94 millions in 1951, and special implements were widely used for particular purposes such as lifting of sugar

[1] *Fert. Rev.*, April–June 1952.

[2] For an account of hybrid maize see E. S. Bunting, *World Crops*, 1950, Vol. 2, p. 5.

beet even when their use involved some reduction in plant population. The resulting increased speed of working ensured better sowing conditions in the short spring and reduced harvest losses in the short autumn. There are of course fewer horses on the farms; the number fell from 10·6 millions in 1939 to 4·8 millions in 1951, and of mules from 4·2 millions to 2·0 millions: incidentally liberating some 55 million acres previously used for growing their food. But the farmer has become almost completely dependent on petrol coming from outside the farm instead of supplying his own power as before, and it is impossible to foresee what might happen if troubles come.

As a result of these various improvements there has been a great increase in output per man-hour which has gone far to counteract the drift from the land that has been so pronounced since 1941: the farm population, which had then been 29 millions, having fallen to 24·4 millions by 1950, and the total number of workers fell from 11·7 millions in 1940 to 10·4 millions in 1950 and still fewer in 1952 (Table LXXXIX).

TABLE LXXXIX. *United States Population and total employment on U.S. farms*

Year	Total population Millions	Total employment on farms Millions	Population per farm worker Number
1910	92·0	12·1	8
1920	105·7	11·4	9
1930	122·8	11·2	11
1940	131·8	11·7	11
1950	151·7	10·4	15
1952 (1)	157·0	9·8	16

(1) Preliminary estimate. *Fertilizer Review,* October-December 1952.

Their increase in efficiency was such that one worker in 1950 per 15 head of population not only provided almost all the food they consumed, but also a considerable surplus for export, while in 1940 one worker per 11 head of population had supplied less of the total food consumed and there had been only little for export.

Along with the greater mechanization and decreasing farm population has gone a fall in the number of farms and an increase in their average size as already noted.

The area of grass land is put at 662 million acres, but in the arid regions no sharp line can be drawn between pasture and semi-desert scrub. Grassland is usually kept either for permanent hay or for permanent pasture; there is little of the mixed use commonly practised in England. Over much of the northern half of the country grazing cannot usually begin till about May and it ends in October; there is commonly a dry spell in July and August. Dairy cattle and many of the beef animals have to be housed for some five or six months. Feed grains are plentiful, especially maize and oats, and a certain amount of silage is available; the grass land is expected to provide bulky fodder both for the dry period in summer and for the long winter: the protein content is considered less important than it would be in Britain.

Owing to the large areas available, farmers have not usually paid much attention to their pasture land; British visitors have sometimes commented very adversely upon it. American agricultural experts strongly urge the need for pasture improvement. An enquiry by the Department of Agriculture covering the years 1942 to 1946 stressed its importance by showing that hay and pasture provided two-thirds of the nutrients of dairy cows, three-quarters of those for beef cattle, and more than nine-tenths of those for sheep. There has indeed been considerable deterioration of the ranges: R. M. Salter points out that more than 100 million acres of former productive grassland in the south-west have had their carrying capacity greatly reduced by invasion with mesquite and other noxious bush plants. Chemical herbicides are widely and increasingly used against these invaders: at the Southern Great Plains Field Station in Oklahoma beef production was doubled or even quadrupled by killing the sage bush and reseeding. In the areas of higher rainfall Salter estimates that the productivity of more than 230 million acres of grassland could be at least doubled by better use of fertilizer, lime and reseeding.

The numbers of cattle, pigs and to a less extent poultry have increased since pre-war days, but those of sheep and lambs have fallen considerably.

The increase in cattle numbers has been almost entirely in the beef animals and young stock; the changes in meat production follow generally the changes in numbers of animals (Table XC).

TABLE XC. (*a*) *Numbers of livestock, millions, U.S.A.*

| | Cattle | | | | Sheep and | |
	Dairy	Beef	Total	Pigs	lambs	Poultry
1939	24·6	10·0	66·0	50·0	51·3	418·6
1950	24·6	16·8	80·1	60·5	30·7	480·8
1951	24·6	18·4	84·2	65·0	31·5	466·7

(*U.S.A. Bureau Stat.*, quoted from A. N. Duckham, loc. cit.) C.E.C. data in Fig. 19.

(*b*) *Production and export of meat. U.S.A.*

| | Production: million tons | | | Export: thousand tons | | |
	Beef and veal	Pig meat	Mutton and lamb	Beef and veal	Pig meat	Mutton and lamb
Average 1935–39	3·62	3·33	0·40	−53 (1)	43	1
1947–48	5·14	4·69	0·34	110	113	11
1948–49	4·87	4·58	0·31	nil	132	3
1951	4·42	5·13	0·23	−72 (1)	29	3

(1) Import.

(*F.A.O. Stat. Year Book*, 1951, and *Food Balance Sheets*, 1950.) C.E.C. Rpt. for 1951 data.

Culling of sickly or poor-yielding cows is more drastic than in Great Britain. The yield of milk per cow has gone up about 10 per cent since pre-war days: it averaged 4,400 lb. during the 1935–9 period and rose to 4,880 in 1947–48: there has been a small increase in number of cows from 24·2 to 24·4 millions, and the total output of milk had risen from 48·3 million tons to 54·4 million tons. Similar quantities were used for processing in the two cases: 31·0 million tons and 32·0 million tons respectively, so that more became available for human consumption; the quantity consumed per head per year rose from 264 lb. to 304 lb. in spite of the considerable increase in population. Less of the processed milk was made into butter: the Americans denied themselves that luxury in order that more milk might

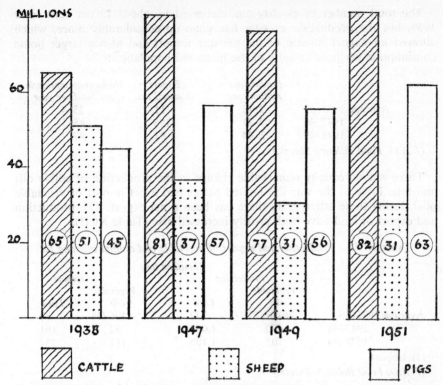

FIG. 19.—Numbers of cattle, sheep and pigs, U.S.A., 1938 and post-war. (Data from C.E.C. Reports, *Meat*, 1952.)

be condensed or dried for export. The consumption of butter per head fell from 15·2 lb. in the pre-war years to 9·4 lb. in 1948–49: in place of a small import there was a substantial export. Cheese also was no longer imported but was exported, and most important of all, the small pre-war export of dried and condensed milk was increased sixteenfold. More than 440,000 tons of these products were exported in 1948–49 as compared with a yearly average of 27,000 tons only during 1935–39, while the net export of cheese rose to 63,000 tons instead of a pre-war net import of 24,000 tons[1] (Table XCI).

TABLE XCI. *Production and export of milk and dairy products*

| | Production: million tons | | | | Export: thousand tons | | | |
	Total milk	Condensed and dried	Butter	Cheese	Liquid milk	Condensed and dried	Butter	Cheese
Average								
1935–39	48·28	1·13	0·984	0·303	Nil	27	−2 (1)	−24 (1)
1947–48	54·27	1·93	0·695	0·504	260	442	24	48
1948–49	54·38	2·00	0·737	0·535	312	384	20	63
1951	55·75	2·30	0·648	0·518		180	3	35

(1) Import.

(*F.A.O. Food Balance Sheets*, 1949 and 1950; C.E.C. Rpts., *Dairy Products*, 1953.)

[1] It should be noted that exports include supplies sent out to American forces overseas.

The total number of poultry has increased by about 12 per cent since 1939, but the production of eggs has gone up considerably more, which allowed an export instead of the pre-war import and also a larger home consumption per head in spite of the increased population:

	Production, million tons	Export thousand tons	Home consumption lb. per head per year
Average 1935–39	2·17	−11	35·4
1947–48	3·41	198	45·5
1948–49	3·44	83	47

(*F.A.O. Food Balance Sheets.*)

There was an equally remarkable change in the production of edible oils and fats. Prior to the war the United States had a net import of vegetable oils: during these latter years there has been a net export. The production and export of land have both greatly increased also (Table XCII).

TABLE XCII.   *Production and export of vegetable and animal oils and fat*

	Production		Export	
	Vegetable oils	Lard	Vegetable oils	Lard
Average 1935–39	261	737	−126 (1)	87
1947–48	490	1,068	52	191
1948–49	705	1,105	111	254

Thousand tons

(1) Import.
(*F.A.O. Food Balance Sheets.*)

This remarkable and rapid change from being a food importer to becoming a substantial exporter is a great tribute to the efficiency of the United States farmers but a still greater one to the unparalleled generosity of the nation. A large part of these exports were given as Marshall Aid, Lend-Lease, or in other ways to the United Kingdom and stricken Europe. When these aids came to an end the importing countries were too short of dollars to be able to buy; but it is safe to assume that further supplies of food will be forthcoming whenever the need justifies the effort required to earn the dollars necessary for their purchase.

HOW MUCH FOOD COULD THE UNITED STATES PRODUCE?

In a country where the possibilities of development and the capacity for achievement are so great as in the United States it would be rash for an outsider to attempt any estimate as to how far this accordion-like expansion of food production could be made to go. R. M. Salter, who in 1952 succeeded the distinguished H. H. Bennett as Head of the Soil Conservation Service, in a kind of inaugural address at Des Moines, Iowa, estimated that if full use were made of existing knowledge and methods the average yields of maize and of cotton could be raised by about 75 per cent, of wheat, other small grains and soya by rather less, and of pasture and hay by 100 per cent—an overall increase of about 60 to 75 per cent. These estimates appear quite sound. The yields of the best farmers are already double the average or more. Certainly the average yields as shown in Table LXXXVIII would strike an English farmer as low: 10 to 12 cwt. per acre of cereals seem to offer scope for improvement, and there is little doubt that this will come as the demand for food increases. Salter emphasizes the need for ending the soil deterioration which is still going on: this he thinks would do more than anything to increase output. The combining of improvements heightens the effects of each: an improved fertilizer scheme would have its effect enhanced if at the same time better varieties, more timely cultivations, more effective pest control and other measures were introduced. But the greatest advance could be made in pasture treatment. He estimated that some 70 million acres of idle and sub-marginal land in the south could be made into usable pasture.

There are still considerable possibilities of increasing the area under cultivation. Much marginal land in the uplands of Wisconsin, New York State, and the Appalachians has been more or less abandoned because of serious deterioration or erosion. Some 70 million acres of the south-eastern States are reported to be in this condition.[1] As in Australia, however, caution is exercised about these marginal lands, and the available resources are used for their development only when the results are likely to be successful. Some 10 million acres in the Eastern States are reported to be in need of drainage. Estimates of possible extensions have always an element of guesswork: a considered view of H. H. Wooten and E. J. Utz[2] is that the 400 million acres classed as crop land in 1945 could be increased by ploughing up 100 million acres of pasture; that a further 80 million acres could be brought into cultivation, 40 million by clearing, 20 million by draining, and 20 million by irrigation. Generally speaking, the land requiring drainage lies east of the 97th meridian, and land requiring irrigation lies west of it.

Where irrigation is practicable some gigantic schemes have been and still are being carried out. By 1952 the area under irrigation was about 25 million acres, chiefly in the Western States: it was estimated that this could perhaps be raised to 45 or 50 million acres on present engineering knowledge. The Columbia River Scheme includes some of the most striking irrigation works yet constructed: among them the Hoover Dam, 726 feet high, the highest in the world, and the Grand Coulee Dam, the most massive; both have spill ways more than double the height of Niagara Falls. When the scheme is completed it will irrigate a million acres suitable for arable and mixed farming besides providing more than $2\frac{1}{4}$ kW. of electricity. The Central Valley of California has a big scheme to make a more even distribution of the natural water supply: at present the San Joaquin section in the north has two-thirds of the total water supply of the whole valley but only one-third of the farm need, while the Sacramento section to the south has two-thirds of the need but only one-third of the supply. The scheme involves setting up 48 dams, including the famous Shasta Dam to regulate the river flow and 20 canals for better distribution of the water; it will irrigate half a million acres of land at present almost unused, and give much-needed supplementary water to another half million acres already in farms. The radiantly optimistic Californians foresee an ultimate addition of $2\frac{1}{2}$ million acres to their present irrigated area of 1 million acres.

[1] W. M. Myers, *Foreign Agric.*, June 1952, Vol. 16, pp. 107–10.
[2] *Proc. U.N. Sci. Cong. Conservation and Resources*, 1949, pp. 602 *et seq.*

The Colorado river schemes include a project (The Big Thompson) in the head water region for driving a 13-mile tunnel through the Continental divide to divert the water from the Pacific side to the Atlantic side where it will irrigate 718,000 acres: a decapitation process that has its counterpart in the Snowy River Scheme in Australia. The Missouri River basin is the scene of other great enterprises: 100 dams are to be constructed and 6 million acres irrigated. Altogether the Bureau of Reclamation had in hand or recent completion in 1952 schemes for irrigating 17·4 million acres. They are opening up new methods of regional development.

These vast enterprises are among the best examples in the world of multi-purpose schemes combining irrigation, generation of electricity, flood control, supply of water to towns and the general development of a whole region. The great prototype and the best known is that under the Tennessee Valley Authority dealt with later.

This and other developments of new methods of solving agricultural problems have been of even greater importance to other countries than the amounts of food actually supplied to the world market; for as the knowledge gained is freely passed on, it has enabled them to cope with troubles that might otherwise have greatly retarded progress or even involved them in serious losses. The agronomic problems of irrigated land have been studied more fully in the United States than anywhere else. The technique has been developed to a high pitch of perfection by the Mormons from the days when they first settled in Utah, and by other farmers who opened up California and other districts. A wide range of problems concerning water supply, drainage, alkali soils, salt damage, soil and crop management have been studied in great detail and the results made universally available. It would be difficult to find any irrigation problem on which these studies have not thrown some light, and many countries having irrigated land have sent their students and experts to study in the United States.

One of the most fruitful of these activities has been in connection with soil erosion. The early agricultural settlers in North America had come mainly from Great Britain and north-west Europe, taking farming methods suitable enough for moist temperature regions, but not for high rainfall hill districts of the eastern States or for the drier grass regions of the west. They cleared the forests and so opened the way to erosion by rainstorms, and they planted great areas with maize and cotton, two of the worst crops for intensifying it. When they went into the drier grass regions of the centre and west they followed an old European rotation of grain and fallow, cultivating the fallow land frequently with disc implements to keep it clean —in accordance with good European practice—and also in the hope of conserving the soil moisture: a false expectation based on the faulty soil physics of the time. The result was to break down the crumbs and reduce the soil to dust which was blown away by the scorching winds of the hot, dry summer. In 1929 Erosion Experiment Stations were set up and in 1933 a Soil Erosion Service was established. It soon received unexpected publicity. A run of dry seasons culminated dramatically in the terrifying dust storm of May 16, 1934, which darkened the sun from the Rocky Mountains to the Atlantic, and made all America aware of the "Dust Bowl" and the need for drastic steps to stop further losses. Surveyors reported that over a billion acres had suffered more or less severely, including some 330 million acres out of 460 million acres of good arable land. The regions most seriously affected were the great wheat-growing plains of Oklahoma, Kansas, north-western Texas, and western New Mexico and Colorado. The resulting devastation has often been described in all sorts of lurid detail.

Once interest in erosion was aroused, it was easy to find other great areas that had suffered and some very alarmist reports were circulated. Africa, according to the Belgian, Jean-Paul Harroy, was a "dying land"; South America a "vanishing continent"; the United States as seen by the Russian agronomist, Lapkes, was well on the road to ruin;[1] Australia was likened by Vogt to a drunken sailor scattering his patrimony to the winds; China was disappearing down the Yellow River—and so on.[2] Characteristically prompt action was taken in the United States. The Soil Erosion Service was reconstituted as a Soil Conservation Service and remedial measures were worked out. The immediate aims were to ensure as complete a vegetation cover for the soil as possible, to check movement of soil and run-off of water, meanwhile to build up a stable crumb structure of the soil. The stopping of soil and water movement was effected by the terracing of sloping land, cultivating and planting along the contours instead of up and down the slopes, the erection of bunds to stop the downflow of water and ensure its soaking in, the alternation of strips of grass and of arable crops to stop soil drifting, the fixing of blowing sands by planting with grass and other suitable plants, protection from wind by shelter belts of trees and other devices. The building up of a good crumb structure of the soil involves scientific problems not yet solved, but can usually be effected by the growth of grass which has the further advantage of providing a protective cover to the soil and the possibility of profitable utilization. The problems in practice, therefore, are first to find the most effective kind of grass for the particular region and then discover how to grow it. (Pl. 37, p. 353.)

The more fundamental purpose of the work was to discover for each area the best way of using the land. Erosion and deterioration had been the result of wrong use: there could be no permanent remedy till a better use was adopted. The aim of the work now is defined as "the use of each acre of agricultural land within its capabilities and the treatment of each acre of land in accordance with its need for protection and improvement."[3] It was early realized that remedial measures cannot be applied piecemeal, they must be carried out systematically over the whole area likely to be affected, commonly the whole catchment area from hilltops to rivers. Successful administrative methods have been worked out for dealing with the personal and social problems thus raised, and these are embodied in Soil Conservation Acts. The farmers and landowners of the area are invited to discuss the practical problems with the Government and State experts; a plan for proper utilization of the land is drawn up based on capability

---

[1] *Social. Selskoe Khoz.*, January 1949, pp. 54–59. A very gloomy account showing the impending fulfilment of Marx's forecast in the 1850's of the inescapable downfall of the country.

[2] A well balanced and useful account is given in G. V. Jacks's and R. O. Whyte's *Rape of the Earth*.

[3] *Rpt. of Chief of the Soil Conservation Service*, 1951, p. 7.

maps prepared by the Government and State Experts after proper soil and other surveys have been made; the farmers are organized into "neighbour groups" in which each knows what part he has to play. Federal grants are available to assist costly work, and technical and scientific help is given by the Department. As it is partly or largely of their own making, the plan is fully supported by the farmers; there is not the automatic opposition that meets a plan imposed from above, and in any case it is backed up by the law. Critical areas such as hilltops, steep slopes, etc., are, if necessary, planted with trees, grass is grown where needed, and the head waters of streams and rivers are adequately protected.

By 1952 there were 2,400 of these Conservation Districts, covering more than 1·3 thousand million acres—76 per cent of all the agricultural land in the country and more than 80 per cent of all the farms. So great was the demand for the grasses specially suitable for preventing soil drift, Suiter's tall fescue, crested wheat grass, and others, that the Department had to take special steps to organize supplies of the seed: this was done so well that, although Suiter's fescue was found on his farm in East Kentucky only about 1940, within twelve years enough seed had been produced for sowing well over a million acres. Rehabilitation of the Dust Bowl States has been so far successful that they were in 1949 producing more wheat than before the Dust Bowl started. The south, especially, has benefited by the soil conservation operations. Its agricultural conditions had been brought to a low level as the result of the soil deterioration and erosion resulting from overcropping with cotton without adequate safeguards. In the New Deal Report of 1937 the South had been called the nation's "No. 1 economic problem." But soil conservation, afforestation, and the use of rivers for irrigation and electricity supply and the control of flood waters have greatly improved the conditions and, together with the post-war industrial developments that have put a better balance into the general economy, have narrowed the gap that formerly existed between the north and the south. The extension of the groundnut area during the war caused a good deal of erosion in the Southern States, but it was dealt with by sowing more blue lupins.

The administrative methods being based on co-operation with farmers have appealed to the member countries of the British Commonwealth, and the Soil Conservation Acts of Canada, South Africa and Australia are largely based on those of the United States, as also are the methods adopted for dealing with the technical problems, with, of course, local modifications.

Soil erosion is always liable to lead to flooding and this causes twofold losses: by washing away the surface soil from the higher land, thereby impoverishing it; and by depositing this soil on the lower land, burying its productive soil under a barren layer of silt and débris. Sensational floods periodically devastate the lower reaches of the rivers, especially the Mississippi, but even more serious though much less spectacular losses occur above the main valleys—75 per cent of the damage is said to be done there—and protection has to begin where the rain falls. These problems of flood prevention and control have been dealt with brilliantly by the Tennessee Valley Authority—always called T.V.A. for short—which was established in 1933 for the control of the difficult Tennessee River and the rehabilitation of the region. It has kept open a navigable channel 630 miles long, set up dams and reservoirs to regulate the flow, provided electricity for new industries, and a fertilizer factory for the purpose of supplying fertilizers to the district and technical information to the industry. In addition it has done much reafforestation of the head-waters region and generally has provided a remarkable demonstration of what should and can be done in controlling an unruly river. Like the soil conservation measures, it has served as a model to other countries: the Damodar Valley Scheme in India quite frankly calls itself India's T.V.A.

Since the war the good custom has grown up of sending groups of British industrialists and others to the United States to study production methods. It is usually found that productivity per man is much higher there than here. Taking a broad average over the whole country this would not be true of agriculture: the output per man is roughly the same in the two countries and the British yields considerably higher. But if the arid regions of the west and the part-time and subsistence farms of the east are left out as being quite unlike anything in Great Britain, and if the comparison is restricted to comparable areas, then the yields are as good as the British and the output per man considerably higher.[1] Strict comparison, however, is made difficult by the fundamental difference in attitude to farming in the two countries. In America farming is a way of earning a living differing only in detail from any other method. The merits of any particular course of action are assessed solely on the extent to which it increases the profits of the whole enterprise. Large farms allow of greater mechanization and reduction of costs than small ones so they increase in number: unlike Western Europe, America sees no social or political advantage in increasing the number of small farms. Nor is there much evidence of the feeling so deeply ingrained in the English countryman that the present owner is only the trustee and therefore must as far as possible conserve the soil and hand it on improved if possible to those that come after him: he is not at liberty to adopt a practice, however profitable it may be for a time, if it will ultimately damage the soil. The American farmer on the other hand feels that he owns the farm and can do what he likes with it: he does not feel bound to stick to rules of good husbandry: if the soil deteriorates he can always go elsewhere. The general standard of husbandry is lower in the United States than in Great Britain, but there is much in the way of organization and labour-saving devices that the British farmer can learn from the American.[2]

A new factor is now coming into American country life the effects of which no one can foresee. Apparently some movement from the city to the country is taking place. In 1950 some 800,000 "residential farms" were reported. Does this mean the introduction of the "gentleman farmer"—the type that did so much to raise the standard of husbandry in Great Britain till high taxation drove them off the land?

[1] A. N. Duckham, *American Agric.*, H.M.S.O., 1952, p. 49. A. W. M. Kitchin, Cambridge Univ. Dept. Agric. Farm Economics, Rpt. No. 36, 1951, and Rpt. of a Productivity Team, 1951. American Council on Productivity all agree on this.

[2] A. N. Duckham discusses this matter fully (loc. cit.). The American farmer must, however, conform to a soil conservation project.

CANADA

Canada is both the nearest and the most important supplier of food to the United Kingdom. Its land area, including Newfoundland, is 2,313 million acres, it is thus larger than the United States or Australia, but most of it for climatic reasons lies outside any present possibility of settlement. Within the habitable area the climatic conditions vary considerably, from Mediterranean summers on the Great Lakes to sub-arctic winters in the northern prairies.

The winter temperatures fall in going inland from either coast to the centre. The January mean temperature at Toronto is 23° F, but at Winnipeg is—3° F; going further west, however, it is 13° F at Calgary. Going northwards it falls more steeply: at Fort Vermillion in Northern Alberta it is —11° F. But the July mean temperature varies much less: at Toronto it is 69° F, at Winnipeg 67° F, at Calgary and Edmonton 62° F, and at Fort Vermillion 61° F.[1]

This extensive region of warm summers includes the greatest part of Canada's agricultural land and of its crop output.

These mean temperatures conceal considerable variation in the daily range. Day temperatures in summer on the prairies may exceed 100° F in the shade, but the night temperatures may be in the 50's; nearer the coast the daily variation is much less.

A still more important difference lies in the rate of evaporation from a free water surface in east and west Canada, and still more in the north and south of the prairies: at Manyberries in the south it is 33·2 inches for the five months period May to September, while at Beaver Lodge in the north it is only 11·9 inches. This dryness of the prairie atmosphere greatly intensifies transpiration: at Swift Current between 1,000 and 3,000 lb. of water are transpired in the production of 1 lb. of wheat grain, i.e. 5 to 16 inches of rain for a 20-bushel crop. Another result of the dryness is to make the low winter and high summer temperatures not only endurable but bracing—provided one is suitably clad.

The rainfall varies in somewhat the same way as the winter temperatures. It is highest in the coastal regions: about 40 to 60 inches a year with much mist and fog in the east, and up to 100 or more inches in the west. It diminishes as one goes inland: at Toronto it is 32 inches, in the eastern prairies about 20 inches and the western prairies about 12 inches; there are stretches of rain-shadow valleys between the Rockies and the Selkirks where the rainfall is equally low. The western slopes of the mountain ranges are wetter than the eastern and the west coast is wettest of all.

The areas suitable for farming form in the main two great blocks: in the forest region of the east, a belt ranging somewhere about 100 miles in width, running inland from Cape Breton Island for some 1,200 miles along the southern frontier, with prolongations on both sides of the St. Lawrence and Saguenay Rivers and round the Gaspé Peninsular; and in the prairie region of the west, a vast triangle with its base of 800 or more miles on the southern frontier, its eastern point near the Lake of the Woods, from which

---

[1] Temperature and rainfall tables are given in the *Canada Year Books*. See also E. S. Hopkins, *Empire Jl. Expt. Agric.*, 1949, Vol. 17, pp. 92–104.

its northern boundary strikes north-westwards at an angle of about 30° for about 1,300 miles in to the Peace River region; its western boundary follows the foothills of the western mountains joining the base about Fernie in Alberta at an obtuse angle. These two blocks are separated by the Canadian Shield, a great tract of pre-Cambrian rock, formerly a mountain range but now greatly worn down by erosion, which so far is mainly uninhabited forest and waste. It contains, however, some millions of acres of heavy clay land, mostly of good quality, much of it peat covered. The climatic conditions make the growing season short, and allow only hardy crops to grow, but settlement in these areas is increasing.

From the point of view of food production, Canada has five widely different sections: (1) Eastern Canada and the Maritime Provinces, with Atlantic conditions of high rainfall and moderate temperatures: a region of grass and forest; (2) the fruit districts of the Great Lakes region: limited areas in its southern part where the temperature conditions are suitable for growing grapes, peaches and other soft tree fruits: outside of these areas mixed farming is the prevailing type of agriculture; (3) the interior continental plain including the prairies, the wooded plains to the north and the semi-arid tracts of the west; (4) the valleys and inter-mountain areas of British Columbia; dry in the rain shadows, mild and muggy in the west; (5) the northern regions with short warm summers and long cold winters. These sections in the aggregate form only a small part of Canada: in the 1951 Census only 174 million acres—less than 8 per cent of the total land surface—were in farms, and little more than half this area—97 million acres—was recorded as improved.

The total population in 1949 was 13·5 millions, an increase of 5 per cent over the 1948 figure, the result partly of a post-war wave of migration from Europe; partly of the unusually high marriage and birth rates of post-war years.

THE EASTERN PROVINCES

Although settlement has gone on for many years a large proportion of the farmland, varying from 40 to 80 per cent in the different provinces, still remains in forest and rough pasture (Table XCIII). The agriculture is extremely varied, ranging from intensive fruit, vegetable and tobacco culture down to subsistence and part-time farming, combined with work in forestry, mining or fishing. The conditions generally favour livestock and mixed farming and this predominates throughout the region; as usually happens in these circumstances, the farms are small.

Ontario

Ontario, though not the largest, is the most varied of the provinces. Only about 10 per cent of its land area is farmed, the rest being forest or rough land, but the farmed area is the most productive in the Eastern Provinces, the result partly of its wide variety of soil and climatic conditions, partly of the good and accessible markets afforded by its many and prosperous towns.

The farms are mostly owned by their occupiers: in 1951 there were 150,000 of them. Nearly 60 per cent were between 70 and 130 acres in size

TABLE XCIII. *Land Utilisation in Eastern Canada: Million Acres,* 1951

	Ontario	Quebec	New Brunswick	Nova Scotia	Prince Edward Island
Total land area	232·5	335·3	17·60	13·27	1·40
Total farm area	20·88	16·79	3·47	3·17	1·09
Improved land					
All crops (1)	8·64	5·79	0·712	0·477	0·426
Pasture	3·23	2·69	0·24	0·155	0·198
Summer Fallow	0·33	0·047	0·007	0·002	0·002
Other use	0·48	0·31	0·044	0·027	0·020
Total improved	12·69	8·83	1·01	0·662	0·646
Percent of total farmland	61	52	29	21	60
Unimproved land					
Woodland	3·85	5·87	2·04	1·84	0·346
Other	4·33	2·08	0·42	0·67	0·103
Total unimproved	8·19	7·96	2·46	2·51	0·449
Population					
(millions) 1941	3·79	3·33	0·457	0·588	0·095
1949 (estimated) (2)		3·89	0·516	0·645	0·093

(1951 Census figures.)

(1) Includes field, garden, orchard and nursery crops.

(2) *Commonwealth Econ. Cttee., 35th Rpt.,* 1952.

and only about 3 per cent exceeded 400 acres. The mixed farms are run by the family with perhaps one hired worker; they have characteristically large barns to house the cattle during the seven cold winter months and to store their food. Dairying is widely practised, especially in the eastern section.

Only about 60 per cent of the actual farm land is "improved"; of the rest nearly half is woodland to provide for farm and household needs and yield some saleable lumber; the remainder is wild grazing. The chief crops are shown in Table XCIV. Grass occupies the greatest area, there being 3·23 million acres of pasture and 3·4 million acres of cultivated hay. This latter occupies about 40 per cent of the cropped land, cereals nearly 50 per cent, other fodder crops about 4 per cent, leaving 6 per cent for all the rest. The rotations generally are based on two years of ley followed by two or three tillage crops, of which the range is wider than in any other province.

The cereals in 1951 included 90 per cent of Canada's winter wheat and maize for grain, and 70 per cent of Canada's mixed grain, usually oats and barley or oats and peas. The fodder crops consist largely of maize grown for silage—282,000 acres in 1951, 70 per cent of all grown in Canada—with some oats and other cereals cut for hay. The large area of "other crops"—nearly 6 per cent of the whole—included 155,000 acres of soya beans—almost all the Canadian area—and, highly important in the economy of the province as a valuable export product, 109,000 acres of tobacco, flue-cured Virginian. Tobacco cultivation was effectively aided by a protective tariff and has brought about the successful development of large areas of poor light soils where ordinary farm crops could rarely do well.

TABLE XCIV. *Areas of chief crops and numbers of livestock in Eastern Canada:* 1951
Thousand acres

	Ontario	Quebec	New Brunswick	Nova Scotia	Prince Edward Island
All cereals (1)	4,131	1,689	199	77	181
Cultivated hay	3,406	3,653	441	345	204
Other fodder crops	337	176	15	15	9
Potatoes	55	92	38	11	30
Other crops (2)	492	74	8	0·7	0·5
	8,422	5,685	701	449	424

(1951 Census Returns.)
(1) Including

wheat	747	12	3·3	1·2	4·7
Oats	1,749	1,396	175	61·6	100

(2) Other crops
include:

Tobacco	109	9·5			
Buckwheat	64	43·7			
Sugar beet	30	10·7			
Soya beans	155	0·5			
Flax	66	2·7			
Others	67	7			

Numbers of livestock, 1950. *Thousands*

	Ontario	Quebec	New Brunswick	Nova Scotia	Prince Edward Island
Cattle	2,105	1,520	153	161	70
Including milch cattle	1,237	1,124	104	99	44
Sheep	504	398	71	132	47
Pigs	2,213	1,250	84	56	68
Poultry	23,460	10,234	1,355	1,969	1,180
Horses	378	288	39	30	22

(*Statesman's Year Book,* 1952.)

Ontario has a larger livestock population except of horses than any other province. The dairy cattle are mainly Holsteins and the beef cattle are Shorthorns; many of them are of very good type. Considerable quantities of dairy produce, bacon and eggs are produced: about half the eggs come from farm flocks of 400 or 500 hens and not from specialized poultry farms.[1] The numbers of livestock, however, show little tendency to expand. Since 1941 pigs, poultry and milch cattle have somewhat increased, but other cattle and sheep have notably decreased, as also have horses. This has happened in Quebec and in the Maritime Provinces except for milch cattle.

In view of the suitability of the conditions to livestock it is perhaps surprising that so much of the 3¼ million acres of pasture should for so long have remained poor. The herbage commonly consists of Kentucky blue grass

[1] In Canada as a whole the proportion is about 75 per cent.

(*Poa pratensis*) red top (*Agrostis*) with a little white clover; methods of improvement that have been worked out on the experimental farms include better management, use of fertilizers, and, when necessary, reseeding. The Department of Agriculture is making vigorous efforts to foster improvements. There is a good deal of wild pasture in the south-west of the province where a considerable area is devoted to stock raising.

On the arable land difficulties arise from summer droughts and from weeds; the fallowing method of control adopted in the prairies is not suitable here, and others have to be used.

Ontario's most impressive district is the wonderful fruit belt along the north shore of Lake Ontario. Its soil is glacial sand overlying clay; it is an old lake bottom varying in width from four to seven miles, and it extends from Niagara River to Burlington thence with some breaks beyond Toronto; it includes a number of attractive and prosperous small towns such as Kingston, St. Catherines and others. The lake greatly mitigates the summer and winter extremes of temperature: in winter the coastal belt may be 30° F warmer than the higher ground twelve miles away. The fruits include peaches, plums, pears and cherries; large quantities are canned but much is sold fresh. Apples are widely grown not only here but in suitable areas throughout Southern and Eastern Ontario and Southern Quebec. Grapes are locally important and a considerable wine industry has developed around St. Catherines.

The fruit is characteristically grown on the sand, but pears and grapes are grown on quite heavy clay soils provided the climatic conditions are suitable.

Quebec

Quebec is the largest and one of the most interesting of all the provinces. Its climatic conditions are comparable with those of Ontario except that it has no fruit region such as that just described. Most of its 335 million acres are forest waste; only 16·8 million acres—5 per cent—are in farms, this being the lowest percentage in Canada excepting only in British Columbia and the Northern Territories. Its special interest lies in the fact that it is basically a French community, descendants of *émigrés* who came to Canada in the 17th and 18th centuries and remained on when the British gained possession. They have retained their language—now, however, very different from the French of Paris or of Tours—their Roman Catholic religion, and many of the old ways of life. The country towns are dominated by the church with its characteristic steeple and by troops of cheerful well-fed children; the windows of the houses have green volets as in France; some of the unspoiled places such as the Ile d'Orléans retain the long houses with squat roofs, and the old "manoirs" still possessing French furniture brought over years ago.[1]

The original settlement was along the rivers, as the only way of transport. The characteristic farm runs from the river to the forest in a strip originally fairly wide but narrowed by subdivision among the descendants. Each year the farm was pushed a little farther into the forest by clearing during the

[1] Some delightful sketches of French Canadian life are given by Georges Bouchard in *Vieilles Choses, Vieilles gens*, Montreal, Libraire d'Action Canad. Francaise, 1931.

winter: a delightful description is given by Louis Hémon in his romance *Maria Chapdelaine*. When all the river land was settled a second tier of farms was opened up along a road or concession parallel with the first set and about a mile from it. Originally the farming was for subsistence, and it still retains much of this character,[1] with timber as an increasingly important adjunct.

Quebec is one of the best examples in the British Commonwealth of a self-sufficing and advanced rural community. It is now, however, rapidly becoming industrialized; one can only hope it will not lose its good qualities.

The best agricultural part of the province lies south of the St. Lawrence, particularly the eastern townships south of Quebec. Cultivation on the other side of the river extends northwards in places; crops and cattle are raised at Lake St. John above lat. 48° N., but timber is the chief product.

The farms are small; there were in 1951, 134,000, three-quarters of them between 10 and 180 acres in size and nearly half between 70 and 130 acres. Little more than half of the farmland (8·8 million acres) was improved; 35 per cent was in forest and 12 per cent unimproved grazing and other land. Sixty-four per cent of the sown land was in cultivated hay and 30 per cent in grain, chiefly oats. Of the remaining 6 per cent about half was in fodder crops: maize for silage, and oats and other grains grown for hay; there were also 92,000 acres of potatoes, the largest acreage in any province though a smaller proportion of the total cropped area than in the Maritime Provinces. The rotations are of the general type, four years ley followed by two years of cereals; the ley is thus more prominent than in Ontario, on the other hand the area of pasture both improved and unimproved is less.

Ontario and Quebec between them have more than half the total cattle population of Canada and about two-thirds of the milch cows and the pigs besides a large proportion of the poultry. Quebec is somewhat less productive than Ontario; it has approximately the same number of cattle and milch cattle per 100 acres of farmland, but fewer pigs and poultry. As in Ontario during the last ten years the numbers of pigs, poultry, and milch cows have increased, but other cattle, sheep and horses have all decreased. Ayrshires predominate among the dairy cattle. Butter is produced for Montreal, and, on the less accessible farms, cheese for export: both are largely summer products obtained off the grass, and the problem of winter feeding is not serious. Potatoes are important; Quebec has a larger acreage and output than any other province, the yields are about 5 tons per acre. A very interesting industry survives in the eastern wooded area: the production of maple sugar from the maple tree.

The life is hard: during the long winter the men are lumbering in the forest, during the summer they farm. Good educational work to raise the standard of farming is done both by Church and State; the priests are much in evidence at the agricultural shows, and the Trappist monastery at Oka is famous for its cheese and its fruits, especially its melons. The State supports also the Macdonald Agricultural College and some good experiment stations.

---

[1] I remember going over the farm accounts with a farmer's wife who kept them. She showed me the receipts from sales of surplus produce and I then asked to see the expenses: "Mais, Monsieur, il n'y en a pas"—"There aren't any"—was the reply.

THE MARITIME PROVINCES

New Brunswick

Settlement in New Brunswick began in 1761, but only 20 per cent of it even yet is farmland, much of the rest is still forest. Moreover, much of the farmland remains unimproved: of its $3\frac{1}{2}$ million acres no less than 2 million are still forest and nearly half a million are rough land: only 1 million acres are described as improved, and of this 243,000 acres are pasture and 701,000 acres are in field crops. The farms are rather larger than in Quebec; about a third of them are between 70 and 100 acres, and about a fifth between 180 and 400 acres; most of them have an area of forest. The main crops are cultivated hay and oats: the hay occupying about two-thirds of the land, oats and other cereals about 30 per cent; of the remainder potatoes are the most important as a valuable cash crop. The climatic conditions are somewhat less severe than in Quebec and the yields are rather higher, oats averaging about 38 bushels per acre in New Brunswick against about 30 bushels in Quebec, and sown grasses yielding about 1·6 tons of hay per acre against Quebec's 1·4 tons;[1] potatoes yield about $4\frac{1}{2}$ tons per acre: some of the good growers can, however, get 7 tons per acre and many of them produce seed potatoes for sale outside the province.

The chief livestock activity is dairying. As in Quebec life is hard, it involves much subsistence farming in summer and as in Quebec, lumbering in the forest during winter to obtain the necessary cash. The general poverty is seen in the unattractiveness of the little towns; there is as yet little industrial development to add to the resources of the people.

Nova Scotia

Nova Scotia was originally settled by the French early in the 17th century, and some of their descendants still remain on the west coast in Digby and Yarmouth counties. Memories still survive in the Grand Pré district of Longfellow's Evangeline, the heroine in his account of the deportations of 1755; she has now become one of the

> "forms more real than living man,
> Nurslings of immortality."

The important modern settlement was by the Scotch who first came over in the *Hector* in 1827, and, as with the *Mayflower*, many of the present inhabitants claim descent from that early group. Nova Scotia being almost entirely surrounded by the sea has a better climate than New Brunswick, and although its land area is 25 per cent less it has nearly the same area of farmland. But this is counterbalanced by the circumstance that the proportion of improved land on the farm is only 20 per cent, the lowest of any of the provinces. The size of the farms is much as in New Brunswick, and, as there, farming is combined with other work, usually lumbering in the forest in winter. Nearly four-fifths of the cultivated land, however, is in grass; the proportion under tillage is the lowest in Canada; this is because of the high productiveness of the grassland: the average yield of hay is about 40 cwt. per acre compared with 32 cwt. in New Brunswick. Formerly there was much beef production; now dairying is more important. But the numbers

[1] 1941 Census.

of milch cattle have fallen since 1941 as also have those of other cattle, sheep and horses; pigs and poultry on the other hand have increased in number. As in New Brunswick potatoes are important and a good seed industry has developed: the yields average 6½ to 7 tons per acre compared with New Brunswick's 4½ tons.

Nova Scotia's richest area is the Annapolis Valley close to the central west shore. Large quantities of apples are grown here, including the McIntosh variety and certain special kinds: Blenheims, Golden Russets and others that appeal to English buyers, but not to those in Canada and the United States. Some are sold fresh; before the war about 1½ million barrels were exported annually to England. Unfortunately shortage of dollars has stopped this trade and trees of some of the special kinds have been uprooted. Some of the apples are dried by a very economical process, the peel, cores and rejects being converted into vinegar and the pomace used for the production of pectin. An experimental farm near the pleasant little town of Kentville deals with the technical problems.

The province is very attractive and its people are greatly attached to it, often returning after years spent elsewhere in earning a living.

Prince Edward Island

Prince Edward Island is the smallest of all the provinces. It is pleasantly undulating and nicely wooded with fertile red soil, more fully utilized than in any other province, no less than 80 per cent being in farms. The proportion of improved land and the average yields are both higher than in Nova Scotia and New Brunswick; in some years indeed they have been the highest in Canada: for oats they have been 39 bushels per acre, for potatoes 10·8 tons and for hay 44 cwt. The cropping systems put about half the land into grass and half into tillage crops, chiefly oats, but with an important area of potatoes. Seventy per cent of the farms are below 130 acres, the average for the whole province is 100 acres. The exports are butter and potatoes, some for table, some for seed.

As throughout Eastern Canada pigs and poultry have increased since 1941, milch cattle have hardly changed in number, but other cattle and horses have decreased. Sheep numbers, however, have remained substantially the same: the island and Nova Scotia are the only two provinces where this has happened.

The island formerly had an interesting and lucrative rural industry in silver fox breeding, but changing fashion has put it out of action, though perhaps only for a time.

The consciousness of this high level of productiveness developed a contented state of mind among the older inhabitants and a widespread reluctance to leave the island. Where better could they be? Unfortunately this feeling seems to be changing. The population is diminishing, while that of every other province except Saskatchewan is increasing. The explanation seems to be that the island has no industries to give greater scope to its young people, no large towns of equal lure with Montreal, Toronto or the cities of the United States. More mechanization, however, would increase the output per man on the land and so make agriculture more attractive.

THE PRAIRIE PROVINCES

The Prairie Provinces are on the great interior plain that lies between the Canadian Shield and Rockies and stretches southwards through the United States; the Canadian part is about 800 miles wide on the frontier (lat. 49° N.), it narrows to about 400 miles at lat. 56° N., the northern limit of ordinary cultivation, and becomes still narrower further north. The southern part is true prairie: semi arid rolling plains, grass covered and treeless except along the streams; the northern part is birch and coniferous forest; in between comes the parklike savannah country with birch, poplar and other deciduous trees. The absence of trees on the prairies is due mainly to the low rainfall, but is partly the result of fires which used periodically to sweep over the countryside. With closer settlement these are now prevented and trees are invading unused prairie from the north. They can be established elsewhere if they are carefully nursed; the Forest Nursery Station at Indian Head has some very good examples showing what can be done to improve the surroundings of the farmhouses.

The prairies are at three levels: the altitude in the eastern section in Manitoba is about 650 feet, in the central section in Saskatchewan about 1,600 feet, and in the western section in Alberta about 3,000 feet. The rainfall is everywhere low, but much of it comes in the summer months when the crops need it; unfortunately it is erratic and may fail badly; two or three dry years may follow in succession completely exhausting the supply of soil moisture. The rainfall is highest in the east—about 21 inches—it is less towards the west: in Saskatchewan it ranges from about 18 inches to 12 inches and in Alberta it is still less. On the whole the lower the rainfall the greater its unreliability. Also the evaporation tends to be greatest in the west where the rainfall is lowest. The winters are very cold but dry and bracing; the summers are very hot, and the transition from winter to summer is sharp, there being only a brief spring. As already pointed out, the mean summer temperature is much the same in the north of the plain as in the south, although the daily range is much less: in the north the summer days are cooler and the nights warmer than in the south; there is less evaporation and more moisture, hence the growth of trees.

Prairie soils are often supposed to be very fertile; this is not universally true. The Manitoba black soils certainly are: they were deposited in the bed of the former Lake Agassiz and are rich in organic remains and in nitrogen. The black soils of central Alberta and the Regina clay plains in Saskatchewan are also very productive. Beyond the old lake Agassiz, however, the Manitoba soils are sands and clays with only such organic matter as could accumulate from the natural vegetation and subject to considerable destruction by ants and many other organisms. Generally speaking the Canadian prairie soils differ from the Russian black earths in having been somewhat leached and this has modified their structure. Usually they are deficient in phosphate, but their stock of other nutrients allows growth up to the limit of the moisture supply so long as this is rather low; more nitrogen, however, is needed where the moisture supply is higher or where better varieties or improved conditions have increased the possibilities of growth. The use of fertilizers began in the early 1930's: a common dressing for wheat is 35 lb. per acre of ammonium phosphate or 25 to 50 lb. per acre of an 11 N–48 P_2O_5 mixture, drilled with the seed: "placed," not broadcasted.

The conditions in the prairies thus differ completely from those in Eastern Canada. The severe winters and the hot dry summers prevent the growth of perennial crops like cultivated grasses and clover though some hardy strains of lucerne survive. The only practicable crops are those which will complete their growth during the four to five months, early May to mid-September, when rainfall and temperature conditions are favourable. Only certain varieties of spring-sown cereals and linseed adequately satisfy these conditions, and the agricultural system is confined to them. Mixed farming is impracticable, monoculture is the rule and the farming is entirely commercial. Only enough animals are kept to work the farm; for them it is necessary to cut some of the cereal crops for making into hay; they are also fed on sheaves of unthreshed oats.

The parklands in the north of the prairie provinces have a wider range of cropping possibilities than the prairies because of their better water supply and lower evaporation. They are not confined to cereals but can be used for mixed farming, and they have proved very suitable for the production of seeds of forage and oil crops; there is also much subsistence or at least semi-commercial farming. The discovery of oil and other mineral resources in these regions may lead to closer settlement and fuller agricultural development.

The best known of the northern agricultural areas is the Peace River Settlement of Northern Alberta, a little north of lat. 55° N. It lies far beyond the original wheat belt in the northern extremity of the triangle already mentioned in which the summer temperatures and long hours of summer daylight—twenty out of the twenty-four in June—permit the growth of northern field crops so long as the varieties are suited to the shortness of the season. Its possibilities were realized some fifty years ago by William Saunders, Canada's first great agricultural expert. The area of possible cultivation has been estimated at about 13 million acres, but the area acutely cultivated at present is only about $1\frac{1}{2}$ million acres. Wheat and cattle are raised and there is a prosperous seed-growing industry producing seed of alskike, sweet clover and lucerne. The inhabitants have great faith in the possibilities of their country. High Prairie, the first town one enters, announces itself as the place "Where culture and agriculture meet"; and another town, Seasmith, describes itself as "The grain capital of the British Empire."

How much further north the cultivation of wheat could be extended is not known. It is grown at Fort Vermillion, in lat. 59°, and with frequent frost damage in experimental plots at Whitehorse in the Yukon Territory and at Fort Simpson in the Mackenzie District, above lat. 62° N.; it has been grown even in lat. 65°. The establishment of an Army Station at Fort Churchill, North Manitoba, gives further opportunities for studying the possibilities. On present knowledge, lat. 62° appears to be the northern limit for the commercial production of wheat in Canada, and then only under favourable conditions of soil and topography.

The unsuitability of the prairies to mixed farming and the narrowness of range of practicable crops made the early settlement of the prairies very difficult, but gave them an extraordinarily interesting history.

The first attempt at settlement was early in the 19th century, when the Earl of Selkirk arranged for a group of Scottish crofters to settle on the land now covered by Winnipeg; they went out in 1812 and attempted to grow wheat. But the methods and varieties available to them proved quite unsuitable, and after four years of terrible hardship and privation the settlement had to be abandoned.[1] The idea grew up that the prairies were suitable only for hunting and trapping, and in 1869 the Hudson Bay Company to whom they had been allotted sold many hundreds of thousands of square miles of them to the Canadian Government for the paltry sum of £300,000.[2]

Serious attempts at settlement began again when the Canadian Pacific Railway pushed westwards across the country in the late 1870's and early 1880's, and fortunately by this time a variety of wheat had been found suitable to the prairie conditions. It reached Canada by an accident that would have been incredible but for the fact that it happened. A Scottish settler in Ontario, David Fife, whose wheat suffered like that of his neighbours from frost and rust, asked a Glasgow friend to send him some other varieties. The seed arrived in 1842 late for sowing, nevertheless it was sown. Most of it failed to ripen, but three ears, apparently from a single plant, not only ripened but escaped rust and gave grain of high quality. Fife saved the seed and sowed it the following year: again it ripened early enough to escape frost and gave high quality grain. Gradually he built up a stock and distributed it to other farmers: it was named after him and being a red wheat was called Red Fife. When the prairies were opened up it proved to be the most suitable wheat to grow there.

During the 1880's and the 1890's there was a great wave of migration from the British Isles and from Europe and the southern section of the prairies near the railway was soon fully taken up. Settlement was pushed farther northwards and westwards; but a northern limit was set by the shortening summers. Red Fife needed 120 to 135 days from sowing to harvest, and above a certain latitude the first killing frost appeared before it was fully ripe. In the meantime the Canadian Government had appointed an agriculturist, William Saunders, to study wheat problems. He realized that the great need was to find or breed early-maturing drought-resistant varieties requiring less than 130 days for completing their growth; and in 1888, he and his sons at the experimental farm, Ottawa, started crossing Red Fife with other varieties, including an early ripening Indian sort known as Hard Red Calcutta. Plant breeding was then empirical and refined techniques were not yet developed; little came of the results at the time, but some of the crosses were preserved in the experimental garden at Ottawa. Meanwhile British millers, who were the chief purchasers of Canadian wheat, were requiring certain milling or baking properties. William's son Charles developed a simple and rapid test for these; he chewed a few of the grains and if the material stuck to his teeth he declared the milling quality good, if not he judged it bad. On the whole the test answered, and he used it

---

[1] This story of grim suffering is told by A. R. Rose in *The Red River Settlement*, London, 1856.

[2] Lord Elton, *Imperial Commonwealth*, 1945, p. 431.

widely, rather to the amusement of some of his colleagues. Applying this test in 1903 to the experimental wheats at Ottawa he picked out one of the 1892 crosses that had been preserved without attracting attention during the intervening twelve years and declared it to be of outstanding quality. It was multiplied and sent out to the prairies in 1909 under the name Marquis. It proved amazingly successful: it needed only 100 to 120 days from sowing to harvest and therefore could be grown further west and further north than Red Fife. It was not rust resistant, but otherwise it was so good than within ten years it had displaced Red Fife and became the dominant spring wheat of Canada and the United States: in its day it was the leading variety in the world.

Red Fife and Marquis brought untold wealth to the Prairie Provinces and established them in the career of prosperity which with occasional breaks, they have enjoyed ever since. Both had descended from that single plant of wheat which David Fife had observed amid the failures from the seed received from Britain. Years afterwards the Canadian Government organized an enquiry as to its origin. No such wheat was known in the British Isles. Search on the Continent showed that it grew only in Galicia, then in Eastern Poland; this was a wheat-growing district and the grain was sent to Danzig for shipment to Great Britain. And somehow, in some way that will never be known, a few grains got into the package sent to Fife.[1]

Once the suitable variety was found the ease of growing wheat on the prairies brought ever more settlers, and it became necessary to push still farther westwards and northwards; varieties of still shorter growing period were required. Systematic plant breeding was started and has been very successfully carried out. First came Prelude and then Ruby which needed only 85 to 105 days for complete growth and so enabled the wheat belt to be still further widened. Other varieties possessing other desirable qualities have since displaced these, but there has been no further shortening of the period of growth. Expansion of the wheat belt has ceased for the present; the area is large enough to satisfy requirements but it could always be widened if necessary.

Meanwhile the rust problem had become acute. The spores apparently blow in from the United States, and the vast area under wheat and the enormous size of the fields facilitate the spread of the fungus once it gets a hold. In 1916 when Marquis was fully established an epidemic of stem rust occurred which was estimated to have caused a loss of 100 million bushels of wheat. Another epidemic in 1927 resulted in a loss of 90 million bushels and a third, in 1935, of 87 million bushels; for the eleven years 1925–35 the average annual loss in Manitoba and Saskatchewan was estimated at 35·5 million bushels. No curative treatment is known nor does any practicable device save the crop from attack; the only safe procedure is to find a resistant variety.

Fortunately resistance genes occur in the durum wheats. It would be no solution to grow these instead of the bread wheats because millers do not like them. Wheat breeders, however, have succeeded in transferring the genes to other varieties of wheat possessing the various qualities desired by farmers

[1] For a full account see the very interesting volume *Essays on Wheat*, Reginald Buller, 1919.

and millers. The work has been done by E. C. Stakman and his colleagues at the University of Minnesota, and by the staff of the Rust Research Laboratory established about 1925 at Winnipeg.[1]

Stem rust or black rust, *P. graminis*, was still recently the most destructive of the wheat diseases in Manitoba and Eastern Saskatchewan, and the problem of finding a resistant wheat was complicated by the circumstance that over two hundred physiological races of the fungus are known and resistance to one does not imply resistance to others. Another rust, leaf rust or brown rust (*P. Triticina*) occasionally causes serious damage in the prairie provinces; about one hundred and twenty physiological races are known. The United States' workers in 1924 were the first to produce a wheat resistant to stem rust: it was called Ceres and was the chief rust resistant wheat in Canada till 1935, but then it succumbed to an attack of physiological race 56 of stem rust. Thatcher was then introduced, also from the States; it is a double cross between two separate Marquis crosses, and is resistant to stem rust but susceptible to leaf rust. The Winnipeg workers in 1939 produced Regent, a cross between Reward and H-44, a United States' strain having mature plant-resistance to the strains of leaf and stem rust prevalent at the time. Later they produced Redman, a cross between Regent and Canus, equal in resistance to rust and better in yield than Regent; this has spread very rapidly and now occupies the leading position in Manitoba; Regent, Thatcher, and Redman are now the main varieties grown in the rust area.[2] Renown, another offspring of the same parentage as Regent, introduced in 1936, is grown on about 9 per cent of the wheat area in Manitoba. But, unfortunately, a virulent race of stem rust, 15B, capable of attacking the otherwise resistant parent H-44, has recently been found in the United States and once in Canada. Will it spread? If so the search will have to be resumed, its labour lightened, however, by the work already done. Fortunately, varieties have been found containing the gene conferring resistance to 15B as well as to other physiological races of stem rust occurring in Canada, and this will be duly introduced into Redman and other useful varieties. But as against this: in the last three or four years races of leaf rust (*P. triticina*) more virulent than those hitherto recorded have begun to appear in Western Canada. The genes conferring resistance have been discovered and will be duly carried into the existing good varieties. And so the work goes on: it is never ending. This, indeed, is the plant breeder's trouble: he may find genes conferring resistance to all the physiological races current at the time he does the work; then suddenly a new one turns up, or a hitherto blameless race becomes virulent, and the search for a new resistant strain must start once more. But the broad success of the plant-breeding programme is unquestioned: it is estimated that in Manitoba and Eastern Saskatchewan alone the use of rust resistant varieties of wheat increased the output of wheat by over 40 million bushels per annum during the period 1938–43.

None of the present varieties, however, can be described as more than

---

[1] For accounts see E. C. Stakman, *Proc. Bot. Cong.*, Stockholm, 1950; also C. H. Goulden and T. M. Stevenson (Ottawa), *Empire Jl. Expt. Agric.*, 1949, Vol. 17, pp. 133–40; J. H. Craigie, *Epidemiology of Stem Rust in Western Canada*, Sci. Agric., 1945, Vol. 25, pp. 285–401.

[2] Searle Grain Co. Ltd., of Canada, *Survey of Varieties*, 1951.

moderately resistant to leaf rust—as yet. But the work goes on. Another plant breeding achievement has been the production of a variety of wheat with a nearly solid stem enabling it to resist the stem sawfly.

This question of disease resistance has for the time being overshadowed the possibility of expanding the wheat area of Canada. For the last twenty years this has been stabilized at about 24 million acres, all that the home

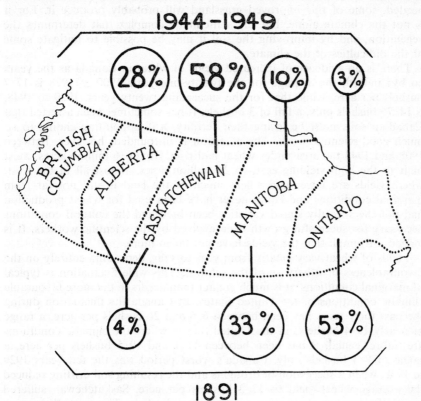

FIG. 20.—Westward expansion of wheat cultivation, Canada, 1891 to 1949; the result of breeding new drought and rust-resistant varieties and of improving farm technique. The acreages are, in millions:

	Ont.	Man.	Sask.	Alta.	All Canada
1891	1·43	0·90	0·12		2·70
Av. 1944–48	0·73	2·47	14·0	6·8	24·2

(Data from E. S. Hopkins. *Empire Jl. Expt. Agric.*, 1949, Vol. 17, page 95.)

demand and the world market has required. During the war (in 1940) the wheat acreage was pushed up to 28·7 million acres, but such an abundance of wheat was produced as to cause great difficulties in handling, transport and marketing, and this large acreage has not been repeated, though in 1949 and 1950 contracts with the British Ministry of Food raised the acreages to 27·6 and 27·0 million respectively. But these are not regarded as permanent increases.

The westward movement of wheat cultivation is shown in Fig. 20. Between about 1926 and 1946 the eastern provinces had lost 200,000 acres of wheat and the west had gained about 2 million acres.

Although the pushing of the wheat belt into still drier regions is for the present at a standstill, this does not mean that the advance of agriculture is stopped. The grassland in these dry marginal areas is now being improved and made more productive, and when the time comes that more wheat is needed, some of this improved grassland will probably produce it. For it is not the climate alone, but the soil-climate complex that determines the vegetation, and by improving the soil it may be possible to mitigate some of the difficulties of the climate.

There is no evidence of increased yields of wheat in Canada as the years go by: indeed, the average for the twenty-one years 1900 to 1928 is 17·7 bushels per acre, while that for the succeeding twenty years, 1929 to 1948, is 14·75 bushels only, a fall of 3 bushels. It has sometimes been asserted that Canadian soils must be losing their fertility, a disappointing ending to so much good scientific work. The assertion is ill-founded, however. Between 1908 and 1948 the area under wheat had risen from 6·6 million acres, most of it in the high yielding east, to 24 million acres, almost all in the west, where yields are lower and where much of the land is still not far from marginal conditions and could never have been used for wheat production had not the specially suited varieties been bred and the cultural conditions necessary for successful growth been evolved by the scientific workers. It is indeed a triumph that the yields have not fallen more.

Yields of wheat vary greatly from year to year, depending entirely on the favourableness or otherwise of the seasons. This wide fluctuation is typical of marginal conditions; it is much greater than occurs in the more favourable climatic conditions of the United States. In Canada the fluctuation during the past forty years has been between 6·6 and 26 bushels per acre, a range of nearly 19·4 bushels; in the United States, where the climatic conditions are more genial, it has been between 11·1 and 19·5 bushels per acre, a range of 8·4 bushels only. Canada's worst period was the ten years 1929 to 1938, when a succession of droughts and the resulting soil drifting reduced the average wheat yield to 12·2 bushels per acre. Saskatchewan suffered most: the average there went down to 9·6 bushels. The most depressing years were 1933 to 1937; the general average was 10·1 bushels and in Saskatchewan 7·6. But Saskatchewan had known worse—in 1937 its average was 2·6 bushels only.[1] (Fig. 21.)

These wide fluctuations in yield can be neither prevented nor foreseen. The individual farmer is helpless against them and no ordinary insurance policy could cover the risk. The great increase in storage capacity has helped to even out the exportable surpluses, also the Prairie Farm Assistance Act established a fund out of which compensation is paid to farmers whenever the yields fall below a specified level. Farmers contribute to this fund 1 per cent of the value of their wheat crop, and the State makes up the balance —over a period of years about two-thirds of the whole.[2]

[1] For a full discussion see E. S. Hopkins, *Empire Jl. Expt. Agric.*, 1949, Vol. 17, pp. 92–104.

[2] The history of the Canadian grain trade has been studied in great detail by Prof. D. A. MacGibbon in his important book *The Canadian Grain Trade*, Toronto Univ. Press and London, Geoffrey Cumberlege, 1952.

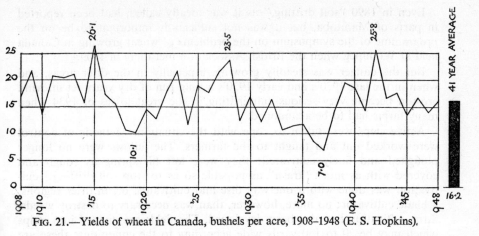

Fig. 21.—Yields of wheat in Canada, bushels per acre, 1908–1948 (E. S. Hopkins).

But the scientific problem still remains: how can these great fluctuations be overcome? In particular: what can be done to improve the very low yields in bad years? That is one of the most urgent problems of to-day.

The immediate reason for the fluctuation in yield is the great variation in the amount of soil moisture in the different seasons. The method adopted for reducing these differences is to fallow the land for a year, keeping down weeds so as to minimize loss of water by transpiration. The fallow is given once in three years so that the rotation becomes—fallow—wheat—wheat, oats, or barley. The effect on the wheat yield is remarkable: some 20 to 22 bushels per acre may be obtained after a properly managed fallow, but only 12 to 14 bushels after a previous wheat crop. Part of this remarkable effect is due to the weeds, among the farmers' worst pests on the prairies. The new herbicides, however, sprayed at the rate of a few pounds per acre, destroy most of them without disturbing the crop. Some 13½ million acres of cereals were sprayed with 2-4 D in 1950, but owing to bad weather 11·3 million only in 1951.[1] Unfortunately, some of the most serious weeds, such as Canada thistle (*Cirsium arvense*), poverty weed (*Iva axillaris*), and wild oat (*Avena fatua*) are not yet amenable to control. But the most important benefit of fallowing is the increased supply of soil moisture consequent on leaving the land bare of vegetation.

It was first supposed that the fallowing would most efficiently conserve soil moisture if the stubbles were ploughed in autumn with a mould-board plough, and the land well cultivated during spring and summer so as to leave a fine layer of soil on the surface. The moisture was assumed to move by capillarity towards the surface, but the fine mulch stopped it before actually reaching there and so saved it from loss. Only after a lapse of years was it found that this view was entirely incorrect and that the continued cultivation, so far from saving moisture, reduced the soil to a fine dust which easily blew away. The continued sequence of cereal cropping and fallow without any rest in grass gradually destroyed the crumb structure, but this persistent harrowing made matters worse.

[1] H. E. Wood, *Proc. 5th Western Canadian Weed Control Conf.*, Vancouver, 1951, pp. 200–205.

Even in 1890 "soil drifting," as it was locally called, had been reported in parts of Manitoba, but it was not sufficiently important to be on the programme of the symposium on the problems of wheat growing in Canada held at Winnipeg when the British Association met there in 1909.[1]

But the danger was steadily growing, especially in the drier areas, and when in the late 1920's and early 1930's a long run of dry years set in, wind erosion became very serious culminating in the great losses of 1934 when many farms had to be abandoned.

Active steps were taken to cope with the situation. Methods of control were worked out and taught to the farmers. The fallows were no longer ploughed and finely cultivated; they were left till spring as rough and covered with as much "trash" as possible so as to stop soil drifting;[2] cultivation was done with a one-way disc and cultivator, or, in drier regions, a blade cultivator: no more, however, than was necessary to destroy weeds. Strip cultivation has also been developed. The fields are divided into strips which may be 20 to 150 yards wide according to the conditions; these are alternately cropped and left fallow. As far as possible they are set at right angles to the prevailing wind so that any particles picked up on the fallow strip may be caught in the crop. The system has been well tested in the Lethbridge area and is very effective. Its drawback is that it favours some of the insect pests, especially the wheat-stem sawfly, which causes serious losses on the prairies: flies emerging from the cocoons in the stubble of the fallowed strips have only a short distance to go to the wheat on the cropped strip. This difficulty is gradually being overcome.

Meanwhile in 1935 the Prairie Farm Rehabilitation Act was passed, setting up an organization to deal with the problems of these affected areas. Where necessary settlement was reorganized and farmers transferred from areas specially liable to erosion to other areas with more stable soil, then grassing down the abandoned land or allowing the native vegetation to reassert itself. The "community pastures" thus formed are regulated by a committee to ensure optimum grazing. Crested wheat grass (p. 40) has proved very successful: out of 1·6 million acres enclosed for improvement in Saskatchewan and Manitoba up to March 1952 about 10 per cent had been sown down. The community pastures have been considerably improved: in the early years around 1938–40, 59 acres were needed per head of cattle, from 1945 onwards, however, 21 acres sufficed. (Pl. 38, p. 353.)

Much has been done to conserve surface water by constructing dams and dug-outs, making channels to connect them with coulees where snow piles up in winter so that the water released on melting may be saved and used for livestock or for irrigation. Rivers also are being controlled to prevent the floods that have sometimes done so much damage and to put the water to good use: a considerable number of irrigation schemes, mainly small, have been set up.[3]

[1] Reported in Supplement to the *Jl. Bd. Agric.*, June 1910, Vol. 17, No. 3, London, H.M.S.O.

[2] One difficulty, however, is that after a dry season the quantity of stubble is too small to be of much use.

[3] Annual Rpt. Prairie Farm Rehabilitation Branch, Canada Dept. of Agric., Regina, 1952. Also L. B. Thomson, Empire Jl. Expt. Agric., 1953, Vol. 21, pp. 289-96.

Even where the soil is not eroded, however, it deteriorates under the continued cultivation required by cereal cropping and fallowing because of the resulting great loss of nitrogen and organic matter. F. T. Shutt long ago showed that after twenty-two years of cultivation the nitrogen content of the soil of the Indian Head Experimental Farm was reduced from 6,940 to 4,750 lb. per acre, only one-third of which had been recovered in the crop:[1] the soil organic matter suffered corresponding loss. This problem crops up throughout the semi-arid regions: in the United States, in Africa and in Australia. In humid climates organic matter is easily returned as farmyard manure or as residues of grass and clover ley ploughed in. In semi-arid conditions these procedures seem to be ineffective: neither farm-yard manure nor ploughed-in straw have consistently increased crops on the prairies. Some farmers burn their straw as the easiest way of getting rid of it, but many now leave it on the ground to provide organic matter, especially where the crop has been combined. Nor has a period under grass in all cases increased productiveness. On several of the prairie experimental farms (but not all) no benefit was derived from periods of one, two or three years in grass and legume, indeed if anything there was a loss, for the yield of wheat was lowered and the crop of hay was so low—only half to one ton per acre—and of such poor quality that it did not recoup the loss on the wheat crop. Similar experiences in South Africa have raised doubts whether in dry conditions grass without legumes (which will not usually grow) can build up reserves of organic matter in the soil.[2] In moister conditions on the other hand the grass ley was beneficial: at Lacombe in Alberta the yield of wheat was increased, in some cases doubled, after a crop of lucerne and timothy in spite of the fact that the soil is black and contains from $0\cdot35$ to $0\cdot5$ per cent of nitrogen. It is, however, possible that the additional yield resulted not from soil enrichment, but from improvement of its texture or through suppression of weeds, notably wild oats, by the ley.[3]

In spite of all this uncertainty it may still become necessary to put some of the wheat lands into grass for a sufficient period to restore the structure and the organic matter.

Many attempts have been made to find some alternative to bare fallow, but none have appealed to the farmers. Intertilled cropping seemed promising at one time and it can be used where the rainfall is sufficient, but, in general it has not proved acceptable. In each of the three prairie provinces the area under fallow is about half that of the cereals, and fallow and cereals between them account for 90 per cent or more of the improved land, indicating that the cropping system is almost universally a fallow followed by two grain crops.

Mono-culture systems are almost always beset by difficulties of organizing labour. Cereal cultivation requires considerable labour in the spring for sowing, and in late summer for harvesting, but very little in between whiles. Formerly workers were transported from the British Islands to gather in the harvest and then brought back, but the development of machinery has made that unnecessary. Some remarkable machines are in use. The disc implement to break up the stubbles may be from 10 to 28 feet wide with two discs per

[1] F. T. Shutt, *Journ. Agric. Sci.*, 1910, Vol. 4, pp. 335–57.
[2] J. J. Theron, *Journ. Agric. Sci.*, 1952, Vol. 41, pp. 289–96.
[3] E. S. Hopkins, loc. cit.

foot width: they can break up to 40 acres a day. The seed drill may sow up to 100 acres a day. For harvesting it is usual to send the swath cutter first followed by the combine to pick up and thresh the swaths; from 40 to 80 acres a day can be done by one unit (Pl. 39). Harvesting is, however, often done by contract at $2½ to $3 per acre for yields up to 20 bushels; for heavier crops a supplementary charge is made. The grain is handled in bulk and is not bagged. This involves some difficulties of transport: the local storage is quickly filled and the railways can only slowly remove the rest; in exceptional cases much grain may wait in heaps in the field for weeks or months. Fortunately the snow when it comes is so dry that it does no damage.

Labour saving devices have now gone so far that one man can manage 600 acres or even more with some supplementary help at seed time and harvest. The result is a tendency for farms to merge, increasing in size but decreasing in number. This makes the countryside more lonely than it was and is raising some serious social questions.

One of the most striking changes in the Prairie Provinces in the years between 1941 and 1950 was the marked decrease in livestock of all kinds, amounting not infrequently to 50 per cent. Even pigs and poultry have decreased, though throughout Eastern Canada they consistently increased in numbers: horses have suffered drastic reduction and are now so few relative to the area of cultivation that one wonders how much longer they will survive. The prospects for mixed farming seem rather remote.

Although the prairie country grows on you it is not at first sight attractive to live in. It is treeless and almost birdless, featureless though resplendent in the growing season with the ripening corn. The white wooden homesteads, white- or green-roofed with neighbouring red barns have usually little garden and often no trees: though one also sees well tended farmhouses with good trees round them. Fences where they exist are untidy: often there are no gates but only strands of barbed wire strung across a gap.

The typical prairie farmer has great courage and will stand up to years of bad harvests knowing that good ones are sure to come again. But he is not, like many of the eastern farmers, rooted to one particular spot. He will praise his farm as the best in this, the best of all localities in this wonderful province: but having said so much he will not infrequently offer to sell it, and would be by no means averse to trying his luck elsewhere. There is a tendency to close down for the winter after the grain is harvested and sold, and transfer to the town or other attractive spot so as to avoid the oppressive loneliness of the farm.

The areas of land utilized and the numbers of livestock are given in Tables XCV and XCVI.

The problems of grain production are similar in general outlines in all three provinces, but with important differences in detail.

Manitoba

Manitoba has more fertile soil and a higher rainfall than the other provinces: the yields are correspondingly higher: in 1948 they were, for wheat in bushels per acre:

Manitoba	*Saskatchewan*	*Alberta*
23·75	13·3	18·5

TABLE XCV. *Land utilization in the Prairie Provinces and British Columbia,* 1951
Million acres

	Manitoba	Saskatchewan	Alberta	British Columbia
Total land area	140·6	152·3	159·2	230·0
Occupied farmland	17·7	61·7	44·4	4·7
Improved land				
Field crops	7·3	23·7	14·4	0·67
Pasture	0·58	1·4	1·1	0·34
Fallow	2·5	12·8	6·2	0·07
Other use	0·3	0·8	0·53	0·06
Total improved	10·8	38·8	22·3	1·15
Unimproved land				
Prairie or natural pasture	5·2	19·9	19·3	2·4
Other ("Forest")	1·8	2·9	2·9	1·2
Total unimproved	7·0	22·8	22·2	3·6
Population, millions, 1941	0·730	0·896	0·796	0·818
1949 (estimated)	0·778	0·861	0·871	1·114

(1951 Census returns.)

TABLE XCVI. *Areas of chief crops and numbers of livestock in the Prairie Provinces
and British Columbia,* 1951 *Thousand acres*

	Manitoba	Saskatchewan	Alberta	British Columbia
All cereals (1)	6,087	22,609	12,603	238
Cultivated hay	399	572	1,206	311
Flax	654	296	135	7
Potatoes	16	16	18	10
Other crops	165	203	448	44
All field crops	7,321	23,696	14,410	610

(1951 Census returns.)

(1) Including:

	Manitoba	Saskatchewan	Alberta	British Columbia
Wheat	2,326	15,634	6,424	101
Oats	1,643	3,815	2,854	103
Barley	2,040	2,449	3,041	32
Rye	53	710	284	2

Numbers of livestock, 1950. *Thousands.*

	Manitoba	Saskatchewan	Alberta	British Columbia
Cattle, including	492	860	1,039	292
milch cows	241	352	308	100
Sheep	117	237	414	95
Pigs	269	434	810	64
Poultry	5,665	449	9,447	3,658
Horses	153	404	319	46

(*Statesman's Year Book,* 1952.)

Greater Winnipeg's population of some 300,000 or more has naturally led to the development of dairying and beef production, potato growing and market gardening. The farm cropping also is more varied than in Saskatchewan or Alberta; cereals occupy little more than half the improved farmland and the fallow rather less than a quarter: the chief remaining crops are linseed and cultivated hay, both relatively more important than in the other two provinces. Of the cereals, barley and oats taken together exceed wheat both in acreage and in tonnage: indeed before the war the output of barley alone was two or three times as great as that of wheat. This greater diversity of the farming and its higher productiveness have meant that one man cannot manage as large a farm; more than 70 per cent of the farms were in 1951 less than 400 acres compared with 47 per cent in Saskatchewan and 60 per cent in Alberta.

In spite of eighty years of settlement some 40 per cent of the farmland is still unimproved pasture, affording, however, a little grazing and wild hay for milk production and fattening of store bullocks brought in from the west.

Saskatchewan

Saskatchewan lies higher than Manitoba; it has a lower and less reliable rainfall, and throughout the farm region it is liable in summer to hot scorching winds harmful to grain crops and especially to grass. In spite of this, however, the westward extension of the wheat crop has made it the most productive of all the provinces; it has 40 per cent of Canada's field crops and 60 per cent of the wheat. The 1951 Census showed an increase since 1941 greater than in any other province both in area of farmland and in the proportion of improved land. Forty per cent of its land area is in farms: no other province except Prince Edward Island has as much. Yet, by a strange coincidence, it is only in these two provinces that the population is falling: in all the others it is rising.

The southern part can grow little but wheat and oats, with winter rye in drier conditions or on lighter soils unsuited to fallowing because of the liability to drift; more of this is grown in Saskatchewan than in all the rest of Canada. A patch in the centre of the province, including Moose Jaw and Swift Current has an average rainfall of 15 inches a year only and is liable to suffer a good deal in dry years because of the high rate of evaporation.[1] To make matters worse, in very dry years plagues of grasshoppers may develop and do much damage before the ground bait finally destroys them.

The northern part is moister park-like country, and though the summers are shorter, grass can be grown and livestock kept; a useful export of beef, pork, turkeys and dairy produce has developed. Further north the grey wooded soils are deficient in phosphate and in sulphur, and need the growth of grass and legumes to make them productive; this belt, however, is but little developed as yet, and it still presents unsolved problems.

[1] This shortage of water complicates living conditions in the drier parts of the province. In a very dry year (1933) I visited a farm to which water had to be carted four miles. I asked "why not sink a well?" and the reply was "I would have to go just as far." Many of the farmers collected ice in the winter and kept it underground to supply table water as long as it lasted. Prairie rehabilitation activities are effecting improvements, however.

Alberta

Alberta is the highest of the three prairie steps; its altitude is about 3,000 feet; its rainfall in the east is about 12–20 inches but lower in the west, at Edmonton it is about 20 inches but less in the south. Alberta has 44·5 million acres—27 per cent of its land surface—in farms, but about half the total farm area is still unimproved prairie or wild pasture. Of the improved land, 90 per cent is in cereals and fallow, almost exactly in the proportion of 2: 1; the remaining 10 per cent is mainly cultivated hay, including 325 thousand acres of lucerne, a larger area than in any other province.

Wheat occupies about half the cereal acreage, the rest being about equally divided between oats and barley. The wheat season is only short: not much more than 100 days; the seed is sown about mid-April and the crop is harvested at the beginning of August. If a really satisfactory 90-day variety were produced the area could be extended. Yields of wheat are better than in Saskatchewan though not up to those in Manitoba; nevertheless, good farmers in a good season may obtain 35 bushels per acre, and even 70 have been recorded. Oats—mostly selections and descendants of Banner—can be sown at the end of April and need not be harvested till the end of September; good quality seed can be obtained, some of which is exported to the United States.

Much of South-Western Alberta is too dry for cultivation and is used for large-scale ranching, beef cattle being raised and either sold fat or sent eastwards and into the United States for finishing.

British Columbia

British Columbia is a region for trees and fish rather than for field crops. It has superb mountains and glorious valleys; in the coastal areas and on the western slopes of the Rockies the rainfall is high and in the south the conditions favour a most luxurious growth of vegetation: Douglas firs grow to a colossal height—they may be 10 feet in diameter and 250 feet high. But the valleys are drier; irrigation is practised in the Okanagan Valley famous for its apples, and in some of the grass valleys used for dairying. The farms are small, 70 per cent of them are less than 70 acres, and those intensively managed are 10 to 50 acres in area. But out of the 230 million acres in the province only 4·7 millions are in farms; 98 per cent of the land is in forest and waste.

Apples and fish are the chief foods exported.

Canada's Output and Export of Food

Adding together the date for the various provinces we obtain the results given in Table XCVII.

Wheat stands first of all food products in economic importance, accounting for 20 to 27 per cent of the total farm cash income in 1951, while cattle and calves provided only 18 per cent and dairy products 13 per cent. As already stated the wheat area has remained fairly stable since about 1928; the production has varied from 8·5 million tons in 1945–46 to 18·7 million tons in 1952,[1] but deliveries are largely smoothed out by Canada's efficient storage

[1] The previous record had been 15·2 million tons in 1928.

389

TABLE XCVII. *Acreages and production of crops in Canada,* 1951

	Million acres		Million acres	Million tons
Total land area	2,313·0	Wheat	25·3	14·8
Occupied farmland	174·0	Oats	11·9	7·41
Improved land		Barley	7·84	5·25
Crops (2)	62·2	Maize (corn)	0·32	0·40
Pasture	10·0	All cereals	47·6	27·9 (1)
Fallow	22·0	Linseed	1·2	
Other land	2·6	Cultivated hay	10·6	
	———	Cereals for hay or		
Total improved	96·8	fodder	1·1	
	———	Potatoes	0·287	
Unimproved land				
Woodland	22·8			
Other land	54·5			
	———			
Total unimproved	77·2			

(1) Not counting a small quantity of mixed corn.
(2) Including field, garden, orchards and nursery.
(Census data and C.E.C. *Grain Crops,* 1953.)

capacity, and 10 to 12 million tons a year may be regarded as Canada's normal contribution to the world's wheat supply. Canada's home consumption of wheat likewise shows but little change; it is usually about 3½ to 4 million tons a year and has not risen with the increasing population because the *per caput* consumption has decreased—a sign of improved standard of living. About 6 to 7 million tons—225 to 250 million bushels—are normally left for export.[1] Over 90 per cent of the wheat is hard spring wheat (Fig. 22).

Next in importance to wheat come oats, of which about 11 to 12 million acres are normally grown and the output is about 5 to 6 million tons—roughly half the acreage of wheat and half the output. The acreage has fallen since pre-war days because horses for which they were grown are no longer as much used on farms and construction work as they were—though Saskatchewan still has large numbers. About 8 million acres of barley are grown, and smaller areas of mixed grain and of maize. The total cereal acreage was in 1951 47·6 million.

Canadian experts recognize that the almost exclusive grain production of the prairies, with its concomitant fallow and the constant drain on the organic matter of the soil, is not a good permanent system, and that a mixed system of agriculture with more livestock and greater opportunities for returning organic matter and plant nutrients to the soil would be better. It would in addition afford more protection against erosion. This would necessitate replacing some of the wheat by barley and oats for feeding to cattle, and some of the fallow by grass, lucerne, clover and other fodder crops. The Department of Agriculture has therefore suggested that the wheat acreage should remain for the present at 24 million, and that as a long-term

[1] 177 million bushels was the average annual export for the pre-war years 1934–35 to 1938–39: 351 million bushels in 1944–45 and 206 million bushels in 1947–48. One million bushels usually weighs 27·2 thousand tons; and 1 million tons usually occupies 36·8 million bushels.

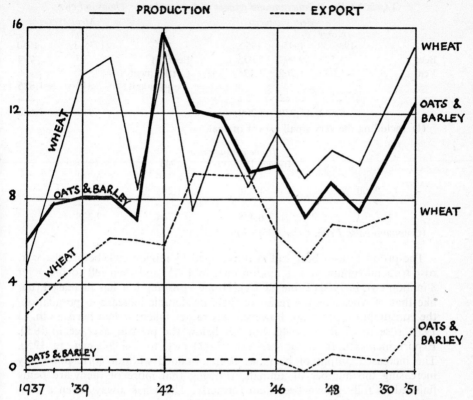

——— PRODUCTION   ------- EXPORT

Fig. 22.—Production and export of Grain, Canada 1939 to 1951. (Data from C.E.C. Reports, *Grain Crops*, 1953). Exports are for August-July years, the values being attributed to the first of the two.

policy it should be brought down to about 20 million so as to allow of considerable extra production of food for livestock.

Livestock Products

The numbers of livestock of all kinds rose to a maximum in the years 1943 to 1945 and have since fallen. In 1950 milch cows were about 10 per cent and other cattle about 25 per cent below the 1935–39 level, sheep also were well below, but pigs and poultry still remain above it (Table XCVIII). In the Prairie Provinces all classes of livestock have decreased: in Eastern Canada only sheep and non-milking cattle as a rule (p. 371).

TABLE XCVIII. *Numbers of livestock, all Canada. Millions*

	All cattle and calves	Milch cows	Sheep and lambs	Pigs	Poultry
Average 1935–38	8·8	3·9	3·4	3·8	57·7
Maximum between					
1943 and 1945	10·8	4·0	3·7	8·1	88·3
1950	6·7	3·6	2·0	5·2	65·4

391

TABLE **XCIX.** *Production and export of beef and veal. Thousand cwt.*

	Meat produced				Meat exported	
	Average				*Average*	
	1935–39	1945	1950		1935–39	1950
Beef	5,523	9,997	7,075	Beef (1)	97	794
Veal	1,039	1,262	1,125	Cattle, meat		
				equivalent	813	1,826
	6,562	11,259	8,200		910	2,620

(1) Including the very small export of veal.

	Home consumption		
	Average 1935–39	1945	1950
Beef	5,402	6,559	6,241
Veal	1,036	1,205	1,137
	6,438	7,764	7,378

(*Commonwealth Econ. Cttee., 35th Rpt.,* 1952.)

The production of beef and veal averaged 6½ million cwt. before the war, rose to a maximum of 11¼ million cwt. in 1945, and then fell to just over 8 million cwt. in 1950 (Table **XCIX**). Home consumption has increased (unlike that of wheat) as the result of the considerable increase in population, the consumption per head, however, has rather fallen: it had been 55 lb. in 1939, rose to 67 lb. in 1946, but fell below the pre-war average in 1950. Export increased from the pre-war 97,000 cwt. to 794,000 cwt. in 1950. The increased output of beef has been obtained without correspondingly increasing the number of animals, showing that more of them are being finished as fully grown beef than formerly. There has always been a considerable export of live animals and this is far greater now than it was before the war: numbers go to the United States where they are fattened for slaughter. The question arises whether it would not be more advantageous to fatten these animals at home: it would of course necessitate an increase in the supply of feeding grains and of green crops for hay and silage.

If the whole of the 1950 supply of beef had come to the United Kingdom as beef it would have satisfied about 12 per cent of our import requirements, if all the cattle had come as well the proportion would have arisen to 40 per cent and much higher if output had remained at the 1945 level. Canada may yet become a very important source of beef for us. The United States market, however, is more attractive than that of the United Kingdom and we are unlikely to get much Canadian beef except where some accident intervenes, such as the outbreak of foot and mouth disease in Saskatchewan in 1952 which temporarily excluded the beef from the American but not from the British market.

Pig meat

In accordance with the change in numbers of pigs the production of pig meat increased from 5½ million cwt. before the war to 12½ million cwt. in 1943 and 13·4 million cwt. in 1944, then fell to 8½ million cwt. in 1950. Home consumption has increased steadily: it was about 4 million cwt. before the war and rose to 7½ million cwt. in 1950; the annual consumption per head rising from 40 lb. before the war to 61 lb. in 1950. This, of course, has led to a fall in exports from the pre-war 1·6 million cwt. a year to less than half that quantity in 1950.

Thousand cwt.

	Average 1935–39	1946	1950	1952
Production	5,540	8,870	8,605	10,000
Home consumption (1)	3,932	5,583	7,519	8,000
Export	1,645	2,695	762	120

(*Commonwealth Econ. Cttee., 35th Rpt.,* 1952.)

(1) The home consumption is greater than is here recorded because in recent years it does not include the canned pork, which in 1950 was 418,000 cwt.

This apparent fixity of production at about 9 million cwt. is due to no natural limitation but to lack of adequate demand. The high output of pig meat in 1943 and 1944 was largely the result of the contract with the United Kingdom coupled with considerable supplies of feed grains for which there was no good alternative market. The total imports into the United Kingdom in 1950 were 4·9 million cwt., only two-thirds of those in 1938; Canada in 1938 had supplied 1·5 million cwt., 20 per cent of the total import, but in 1950 only 0·73 million cwt., 15 per cent. The pig population is largely concentrated in Ontario and Quebec, where the conditions would permit of considerable increases should the demand arise.

Sheep have never been important in Canada. Before the war, production of mutton and lamb averaged 548,000 cwt.; by 1950 it was down to 319,000 cwt., practically all is consumed at home and exports are only small.[1]

Poultry supplied much more meat than did the sheep; the quantities produced averaged 1·4 million cwt. before the war, 2·9 million cwt. in 1947 and 2·6 million cwt. in 1950.

Canned meat

One of the striking post-war changes in Canadian dietary has been the increased consumption of canned meat from the pre-war (1935–39) average of 142,000 cwt. per annum to 1·3 million cwt. in 1952.[2] Home production has been insufficient, with the paradoxical result that Canada exports fresh meat and live animals for slaughter, but imports canned meat from South America for home consumption: a case of selling a high quality product and buying one of lower quality for home consumption.

Thousand cwt.

	Average 1935–39	1950	1952
Production	50	484	1,290
Home consumption	142	506	1,390
Net import	92	23	100

There has thus been a considerable change in Canada's meat diet since pre-war days: somewhat less beef and much less mutton are eaten, but much more pig meat and canned meat, so that total meat consumption per head has increased, though it has not maintained its war-time maximum.

[1] Two thousand cwt. a year before the war, 25,000 cwt. in 1950, none in 1952.
[2] Product weight.

	Average 1935–39	War-time maximum	1950
Total meat consumption lb. per head	128	153	133

The combined effect of this increased consumption per head and of the increase in population has been to raise by 41 per cent the total meat consumption between 1935–39 and 1950.[1] The increased consumption is certain to continue; the question of vital interest to Great Britain is whether increased production can outstrip it to allow of much export.

Dairy produce

The number of milch cows in 1950 averaged 3·9 millions which is somewhat less than before the war, but the yield of milk per cow has increased. In consequence the total production of milk has not fallen but has slightly risen: from the 1935–39 average of 1,484 million gallons a year from 3·9 million cows, it rose during the war under the stimulus of a subsidy to 1,710 million gallons, and in 1950 it was 1,596 million gallons from 3·6 million cows (Table XCVIII). Production of butter, however, has not increased: it has remained steady at about 3 million cwt. a year, the only change being that more and more is made in factories instead of on farms. The factories are decreasing in number but increasing in size; 80 per cent of them are in Quebec and Ontario. Similarly also the output of cheese has remained steady at a little under 1 million cwt. a year. But output of milk products, especially dried whole and skim milk and evaporated milk has increased remarkably: from 823,000 cwt. a year to 2,633,000 cwt., while milk by-products have increased from 278,000 cwt. to 779,000 cwt. in the interval between the 1935–39 average and 1950.

Annual consumption of liquid milk per head was 40·3 gallons in 1938: it rose to 47·3 gallons in 1946, but by 1950 had fallen to about 40 gallons. Before the war consumption of butter averaged 31 lb. per head per annum; it rose during the war but rationing and the introduction of margarine manufacture in 1949 brought it down in 1950 to 23·5 lb. per head. On the other hand there has been a marked increase in consumption of ice cream and of evaporated milk.

Thousand cwt.

	Cheese		Butter		Evaporated milk		Other products (2)	
	Average 1934–39	1950	Average 1934–39	1950	Average 1934–39	1950	Average 1934–39	1950
Production	1030	903 (1)	3182	2772	952	2293	437	750
Home consumption	356	571	3118	2908		2141		
Export	658	563	38	15	241	300	24	198
War-time maximum production	1860		3278					

(1) There were also imports of 11,000 and 91,000 cwts. in these two periods respectively.

(2) Whole milk powder, skimmed milk powder, condensed milk.

(*Commonwealth Econ. Cttee., 35th Rpt., 1952.*)

[1] *Commonwealth Econ. Cttee., 35th Rpt., 1952.*

Eggs

Eggs are produced chiefly in Ontario and on mixed farms with about 200 to 500 head of poultry; there are few specialist farms. In the period 1946 to 1948 Canada supplied us with large quantities; in 1948 one-third of our shell egg imports and three-quarters of our dried egg imports. Since then, however, our imports have greatly fallen.

Exports of Livestock Products: Summary

Canada's exports of beef and processed milk have risen in spite of increased home consumption, but those of pig meat, cheese and butter have fallen off. Production of beef, pig meat and processed milk has considerably increased, but that of butter and cheese has decreased, due not to natural limitations but to lack of incentive.

Canada's exports of food other than wheat to the United Kingdom are considerably less than they were before the war.

Exports to the United Kingdom

	Wheat	Wheat flour	Coarse grains	Bacon and ham	Cheese	Preserved milk	Eggs	Apples
	million tons	million tons	thousand tons	thousand cwt.	thousand cwt.	thousand cwt.	thousand gt. hds.	thousand tons
1938	1·44	0·18	378	1507	678	200	150	150
1950	2·46	0·35	—	732	517	6	13 (1)	44

(1) Dried eggs, however, had increased from 1,000 to 17,000 cwt.

It is reasonable to hope that Canada will continue to cover a large part of the United Kingdom's deficit of about 4 million tons of wheat. There is little doubt also that given the incentive the exportable surplus of beef, pig meat, eggs and dairy produce could be increased. This would necessitate an increased area of arable land and higher yields to provide the necessary fodder grains if the wheat output were not to suffer, also improvement of the pasture so as to raise its present low level of productiveness.

Possibilities of Increased Output

Of Canada's 174 million acres in farms in 1951, 77 million were woodland and rough land leaving about 97 million acres of improved land for crops, fallow and pasture. The farm area was 700,000 acres less in 1951 than in 1941, but the cropped area was nearly 6 million acres greater. The increase, however, was only in the Prairie Provinces: in Eastern Canada there had been a distinct retrogression:

			Million acres			
	All Canada		Eastern Canada		Prairie Provinces	
	Farmland	Field crops	Farmland	Crops	Farmland	Crops
1941	174·8	55·8	49·4	17·1	120·2	38·4
1951	174·1	61·7	45·4	15·7	123·9	45·3
Change in 1951	−0·7	+5·9	−4·0	−1·4	+3·7	+6·9

The farmland lost in Eastern Canada has been taken for expansion of the towns, industrial developments, airfields, roads, golf courses and other sports grounds: almost invariably the more desirable farmland is taken and the rougher land left. The loss is greater than the figures indicate; some new land has come into cultivation, but as already stated this is in the northern "clay belts" of Ontario and Quebec. The 174 million acres of Canada's farmland, however, represent only about 13½ per cent of the total area of the country: some of the remaining 86½ per cent is certainly cultivable. A. Leahey, who is in charge of the Canadian Soil Survey, has estimated[1] that on present methods another 45 million acres could be added to the agricultural land, raising this to about 220 million acres; other experts consider that wider use of improved methods and price incentive could add a further 100 million acres, raising the total agricultural area to 320 million acres—about double the present area,[2] and of the same order as the older estimate of 360 million acres.[3] Much capital would of course be needed, for all the easily developed land is already taken up, and the remainder suffers from some disability which may prove costly to remove. But as the need arises the work will probably be done—at least it has been in the past.

Much is being done to increase the output from land already in farms.

Rust and grasshoppers are perhaps Canada's worst plagues, but other crop diseases and pests are common. The general method of coping with them is to avoid them by breeding resistant varieties: considerable success has been attained.[4]

There are local deficiencies of trace and minor elements in the soils, but they cause less trouble than in Australia. Apples suffer from boron deficiency in all the apple-growing provinces, as also do turnips; magnesium deficiency causes "sand drown" in tobacco in Ontario; copper deficiency affects some of the "muck" soils; lack of iron affects garden trees and shrubs in the Prairie Provinces, but not farm crops. Sulphur is deficient in some of the northern prairie soils; cobalt in parts of Nova Scotia and Central Quebec, and manganese for grain crops in parts of Quebec and Ontario. There may be some 200 million acres of organic soils in Canada capable of some development if the reasons for their present low productiveness can be ascertained.

The method most immediately practicable for expanding Canada's food production is the imrovement of the pasture land. Some 60 million or more acres are included in the farmland, of which over 50 million are classified as unimproved. Much of this is in the arid "range area" of Western Canada, where water supply is a limiting factor, but even here some improvement has already been effected. Considerable areas in other regions offer greater scope. The wild pastures are not naturally rich; none of the native grasses can be described as more than useful: the best of them in the eastern provinces are species of *Poa*, *Agrostis* and *Festuca*. The settlers early

---

[1] Quoted by E. S. Hopkins, *Empire Jl. Expt. Agric.*, 1949, Vol. 17, pp. 92–104
[2] P. O. Ripley, *British Assoc. Rpt.*, 1949.
[3] *Encyc. Brit.*, 1926 Edition, Vol. 4, p. 698.
[4] For accounts of the work see C. H. Goulden, T. M. Stevenson, *et al.*, *Empire Jl. Expt. Agric.*, 1949, Vol. 17, pp. 133–43 and 222–28; and A. W. S. Hunter and F. H. White, *ibid.*, 1950, Vol. 18, pp. 218–26. A full summary (in English) is given in "Applied Mendelism in Canadian Agriculture" (*Zeikschr. f. Pflanzenzüchtung*, 1951, Bd. 30, Heft 1).

introduced cultivated grasses from England and Western Europe, notably timothy, *Poa pratensis*, cocksfoot and bromegrass.[1] Many of these old seeded pastures are worn out and are no better than the wild ones.

The Canadian Department of Agriculture has continuously urged the need for improvement and the Experimental Farm Organization under the able direction of E. S. Archibald and later E. S. Hopkins has shown how it can be done. In the eastern provinces output has been greatly increased by better grazing methods and use of fertilizers: carrying capacity has in some cases been raised from one beast per 3 or 4 acres to one beast per acre. Better ways of making hay and silage have been devised to ensure larger provision for the winter months.[2] Reseeding has often proved the surest way of improvement. Selections of the cultivated grasses have been made for better yield, wider seasonal distribution of productivity, better suitability to local conditions, resistance to disease, etc. So far no corresponding work has been done on the native grasses except reed canary grass (*Phalaris arundinaceae*), slender wheat grass (*Agropyron trochycaulum*), and turf selections of *Agrostis*.

In the Prairie Provinces the native grasses include species of *Andropogon, Agropyron, Stipa, Poa, Bouteloua* and *Buckloe*; the method of improvement involves first the discovery of the optimum carrying capacity (which is usually governed by the amount of water available) and then basing the management on that. Reseeding also is practised in suitable conditions. This necessitates finding a grass that can tolerate the conditions and furnish good fodder for the animals. In the western marginal land one of the best is crested wheat grass (*Cynosurus cristatus*) brought from the Russian Steppe into the United States in 1898. At first it attracted little attention; it was reintroduced in 1906 and found to be very useful in arid conditions in preventing erosion and providing fodder—a warning to agriculturists not to condemn a new plant too soon. A cross between wheat and perennial *Agropyron* grass promises to serve the same purposes equally well.[3] It protects the soils from erosion, it adds organic matter to the soil, and, given time, its roots build up the soil particles into good crumbs, so enabling a combination of grass and arable farming to be effected.

The various problems associated with prairie pastures are studied at the experimental stations at Kamloops in British Columbia, Manyberries in Alberta, and at various places in Saskatchewan by the staff centred on the Swift Current Experiment Station.

Great expansion would be possible if the arid regions of Southern Saskatchewan and Alberta could be irrigated. Unfortunately, Canada is not favourably situated for great irrigation schemes like those of India or Australia. Many of the rivers, like the St. Lawrence, flow through regions where irrigation is unnecessary, few pass through the dry regions where it would be useful. Numerous small schemes have, however, been set up: by 1951 over 600,000 acres of fruit, sugar beet, lucerne and other crops were

[1] In the moister parts of British Columbia, perennial rye grass and cocksfoot have proved valuable as in Great Britain, Western Europe, New Zealand and South-East Australia.

[2] For the silage investigations see P. O. Ripley, *Empire Jl. Expt. Agric.*, 1948, Vol. 16, pp. 237–40.

[3] J. M. Armstrong, *Empire Jl. Expt. Agric.*, 1945, Vol. 13, pp. 41–53.

under irrigation. More schemes are projected. In Alberta, the existing Bow River scheme is being extended to cover a quarter of a million acres. Another on the St. Mary's River in the Lethbridge district is to irrigate over half a million acres. A still larger one in South Saskatchewan is planned to irrigate 800,000 acres besides generating power and providing water for cities. In addition to these big schemes there are a number of smaller ones, much less spectacular but extremely useful, carried out under the Prairie Rehabilitation Scheme already described. Canada has abundant water but it is naturally badly distributed, and this is being rectified as far as practicable.

Vigorous developments are going on in many directions with the aid of the highly competent scientific and technical staffs of the Canadian experiment stations and Universities, and more food can certainly be produced for export. When Britain's financial position improves sufficiently to allow of unrestricted buying the supplies will undoubtedly be forthcoming.

Canada is now in the very interesting stage of expanding industrial output and this involves competition with agriculture for men, land, and financial resources. In Canada, as in Great Britain, it is almost invariably the more desirable farmland that is diverted to industrial and other constructional purposes rather than the rougher land, and so we get the remarkable result that between 1941 and 1951 Eastern Canada, in spite of its large area of unused land, lost 4 million acres of farmland of which 1·4 million was classed as improved. Agriculture's share in the gross values of Canada's output has fallen from 33 per cent in 1921 to 16 per cent in 1951 (Table C).

TABLE C. *Gross value of total production, and of agricultural, manufacturing, pulp and paper, and mineral production in Canada* (1)

		Gross value of production				
Year	Population	Total in Canada thousand $	Agricultural thousand $	Manufacturing thousand $	Pulp and paper thousand $	Mineral thousand $
1921	8,788,483	4,177,836	1,386,126	2,488,987	116,891	171,923
1931	10,374,196	4,132,112	836,441	2,555,126	62,769	230,435
1941 (2)	11,420,084	8,744,662	1,432,601	6,076,308	163,412	560,241
1951	14,009,429	21,241,000	3,488,389	13,817,524*	954,138*	1,228,005

(1) Data from Canada Bureau of Statistics.
(2) Estimated.
* 1950 figures.

Industrial development is inevitable in a young and vigorous country: one can only hope that Canada may succeed in avoiding the losses which Great Britain suffered when the change took place here.

Chapter 12

THE FOOD EXPORTERS
(II) AUSTRALIA AND NEW ZEALAND

AUSTRALIA

Australia is the most sparsely populated of all the continents. Its area is 2·97 million square miles—1,900 million acres—and its population in June 1949 was 7·91 million people: a density of only 2·66 per square mile, allowing 240 acres per head of population. At present the population is increasing rapidly, about 3 per cent per annum of which roughly half is due to immigration and half to natural increase. To the man who has never been there it appears as a land of wonderful possibilities awaiting only proper scientific development. Undoubtedly there are considerable possibilities, but the difficulties are great and only slowly being overcome.

The western half of the country consists mainly of a plateau usually 1,000 to 2,000 feet in elevation broken by a few mountains of 4,000 to 5,000 feet in height, and fringed by a low-lying coastal strip narrow in the west, wider in the north and south. The eastern half is mainly low-lying and is enclosed by a crescent-shaped belt of high land following the east coast and usually 1,000 to 2,000 feet elevation, but with a few higher ridges in the south. This is the Great Dividing Range; it widens out in the south-east and in north where it links on by a narrow bridge with the western plateau. The eastern coastal strip is generally very narrow. Inside the crescent is the great basin of the Murray River and its associates, the largest river system in Australia and the most important because of its possibilities for irrigation; the basin covers some 260 million acres, about one-seventh of the whole area of Australia. Another basin adjoining to the west, and separated by the narrow Main Barrier and Grey Ranges is less fortunate; its rivers flow only intermittently and have no outlet to the sea, but end up in lakes usually salty and dry.

The other rivers flowing to the sea are mostly short and of little agricultural significance because of the narrowness of the coastal strip; those flowing inland are intermittent and dry up, leaving salt in the lower areas.

The rainfall in the southern part of the continent chiefly comes from the antarctic, mainly in the colder months April to September; in the northern parts it is monsoonal and comes mostly in summer, October to March. Storms rising in the Tasman Sea affect the east coast. On parts of the north-east coast rain comes in every month and the yearly fall is the highest in Australia, averaging about 100 inches or more. Round most of the east coast there is a narrow belt of 40 to 50 inches of rain. Much of the south and west coasts, however, are drier; their wettest parts have 30 to 40 inches a year; the Bight region and much of the west coast have 20 inches or less.

Inland from the coast the rainfall decreases and much of the central region has only 5 to 10 inches: this is mostly desert or desert steppe and practically useless; it forms about one-third of the country. Another third has only

10 to 20 inches a year; this is used for grazing and some cropping, but as usual these low rainfalls are unreliable and their periodical widespread failures cause devastating losses of crops and of animals. This liability to drought is one of the major factors in keeping down agricultural and pastoral production.

The rainfall itself, however, is inadequate as an index of productiveness. J. A. Prescott and his colleagues at the Waite Institute, Adelaide, have shown that much better results are obtained by using the ratio of rainfall to evaporation from a free water surface, P/E, suggested by the American botanist Transeau in 1905, or else the ratio of rainfall to the saturation deficit, P/sd, suggested by Meyer in 1926; still better results were obtained when E and sd were raised to the power 0·75. Both indices come to the same thing, for the ratio $P/e^{.75}$ is almost exactly one-tenth of the ratio $P/sd^{.75}$. For approximate purposes the simpler ratio P/E can be used. It is assumed that all rain in excess of one-third the evaporation is useful, so that any month in which P/E is greater than 0·4 may be regarded as effective for crop or pasture production. Where there are five or less such months consecutively pastoral activity is often possible; where more than five, agriculture is climatically possible. For the warmer regions and the tropical north 0·5 is a better figure. Prescott's map based on the index $P/sd^{.75}$ (Fig. 23)

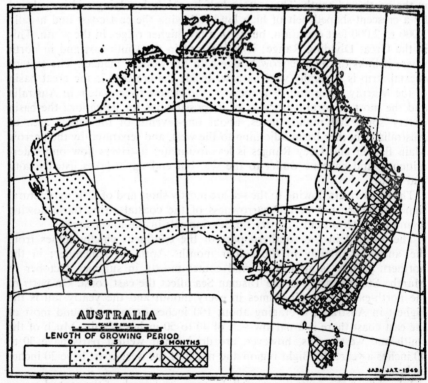

Fig. 23.—Map showing length of growing period in the different regions of Australia (J. A. Prescott and Joyce A. Thomas, *Proc. Roy. Geog. Soc., Australasia*, 1948–1949, Vol. 50, p. 43).

shows how small a proportion of Australia has a growing season greater than five months in the year and how large a proportion has no growing season at all. The actual figures are:

	Desert	Pastoral only	Crops (dry season) possible	No regular dry season
No. of months when P/E exceeds one-third	0	1–4	5–8	9–12
Area, per cent of total	34	42	15	9

In general the soils are not naturally very productive. The plateau of the western half is one of the oldest land surfaces in the world and has in different geological ages several times undergone weathering and erosion, always losing and never gaining plant nutrients; the present soils are therefore very poor especially, unfortunately, in regions of good rainfall. The most obvious deficiency is phosphate, but in recent years widespread lack of some of the trace elements, boron, copper, zinc, manganese, and molybdenum has been found; it is not yet known whether these are the only deficiencies. Considerable areas, especially in the drier districts, are underlain by a calcareous pan which plant roots cannot penetrate and which is difficult to break.

The summer isotherms follow the coast line. Small coastal areas in the south-west have mean temperatures of 65° F, a strip all round the coast has mean temperatures up to 80° F, while in the north the mean temperatures rise to 85° F or more. The winter means range from 50° F–55° F in the south to 75° F in the north.

The native vegetation follows closely these physical characteristics. The coastal region of high rainfall was originally under forest which included many species of hard-wood trees peculiar to Australia, e.g. the Jarrah and Karri found in the high rainfall region of the south-west of Western Australia. Most of those forests have long since gone, and the survivors are largely confined to the slopes too steep for cultivation such as the Blue Mountains of New South Wales or the Darling Range behind Perth. The higher country inland beyond the coastal ranges is mainly rolling plains. Under rainfall of 30 to 25 inches the vegetation is sclerophyllous forest or woodland. In some places there are tree savannahs with grass and eucalypts of various species so closely related to the soil conditions that they give truthworthy indications of agricultural values. The belt with rainfall about 20 to 15 inches is bush savannah with grass and smaller scrub—the so-called mallee. In the southern half of Australia much of this savannah land has been more or less cleared for cultivation or grazing: the clearing was done by rolling down and burning the scrub, felling or ring barking the trees and burning the gaunt dead trunks and branches or leaving them till they finally disintegrated, making in the meantime a very untidy landscape. Some trees are left as shelter for the animals and some of the old sheep stations which have been well tended and long held by families of taste are very attractive and not unlike an English park, with their tall, graceful eucalypts through which the sunshine filters, hiding the slender twigs in its brilliance so that the leaves seem to be suspended by some fairy device. In the still drier regions comes a zone with sage bush and desert grasses varying with the soil type, and finally the desert itself with sand dunes sometimes bearing grasses.

The sequence is the same wherever one begins in the southern part of Australia: a series of belts starting from the moist coastal regions becoming drier and drier as one goes inland, with vegetation which begins in the regions of the wet coast as forest and ends as desert.

The agricultural history of Australia has much in common with that of other new countries in the 19th century. The early settlers (1788–1820) occupied the moist east coastal belt where they tried to practice an agriculture not unlike that of their home country. Great difficulties were experienced owing to the poor quality of the soil and the uncertain rainfall. By a stroke of genius John Macarthur in 1797 had introduced Merino sheep from Cape Colony and later brought in others of pure Spanish stock from the Royal Stud at Kew. The discovery that merino wool could be produced effectively brought more immigrants, and settlements expanded into the drier inland regions. Here the agricultural possibilities were often better, but they varied widely according to rainfall and soil. Wool could still be grown, indeed in the drier regions the pure-bred Merinos did better, and gave finer wool, than in the wetter zones. The expansion of wheat-growing was limited by transport facilities; tree roots also caused great difficulty until stump-jump machinery was developed in the 1880's. As in Canada, the available varieties were unsuitable for the drier inland regions. Wheat-growing became so precarious that Sir William Crookes in 1896 described the possibilities of Australian wheat supplies except from Queensland and a small area in the southern coastal region as simply a "fruitful field for speculation," the yields, especially in South Australia, being so low—averaging for a whole decade less than 5 bushels an acre—as to "cause Europeans to wonder why the pursuit of wheat growing is continued." New varieties better adapted to these dry conditions were needed.

Fortunately with the need came the man. A young Englishman, William James Farrer, threatened with tuberculosis, went out to Australia in 1870, became interested in wheat-growing in the drier regions and proceeded first to select and later to breed wheats specially suited to them. He had no knowledge of plant breeding: he was a mathematician educated at Christ's Hospital and Pembroke College, Cambridge, but he realized that successful sorts must have shorter straw and less leaf in proportion to the grain than the varieties in use, and must ripen earlier. Fortunately, too, he had the artist's eye to see which of his many seedlings to save. At his home in Lambrigg in New South Wales he set up a plant-breeding laboratory; he improvised the necessary apparatus, making forceps out of his wife's hairpins it is said—for in those days Australia could supply none—and in due course produced some highly successful new wheats, including Federation, the best known of them all. (Pl. 40, p. 353.)

For two other problems also a solution was found by the beginning of this century. Reference has already been made to the poverty of many Australian soils in phosphate. In 1882 John D. Custance, the Departmental Professor of Agriculture, showed at the newly established experimental farm at Roseworthy, South Australia, that superphosphate had a remarkable effect in increasing the yield of wheat. By one of those tragedies not infrequent in agricultural history his experiments were not accepted by farmers: indeed, he was distinctly unpopular with them. He resigned in 1886 and was followed by William Lowrie who confirmed the result; this time it was accepted, and Lowrie became regarded as the discoverer. Superphosphate made wheat-growing practicable where otherwise it could not have succeeded: marked crop increases were obtained with even such small dressings as ½ cwt. per acre, which would be considered ridiculous in England; even now one bag per acre, 180 lb., is regarded as a heavy dressing for wheat, except in Western Australia where larger quantities give profitable increases.

The other difficulty was the provision of harvest labour. Canada's method of bringing men over from the British Isles and then returning them after the harvest was obviously inapplicable: instead, labour-saving machinery was devised on a large scale. So effective was the machinery that the total cropped area of 9 million acres in 1900 was raised to 25 million acres in 1929 with but little increase in the farm population.

Meanwhile railway systems were being developed and transport improved. The result of all these developments was that the wheat belt was pushed farther and farther inland into the sheep country and the output rose from 27 million bushels in 1890 to 144 million bushels in 1920; it has gone much higher since (Fig. 24). The wheat did not displace the sheep: the two were combined, and the stubbles with their volunteer herbage provided a fair amount of grazing. A two or three year rotation was widely adopted: wheat; fallow; or wheat; wheat, barley or oats; fallow; the fallow gave an opportunity of destroying weeds and of storing moisture and nitrate for the following wheat.[1] This system still continues.

The moist coastal belt having lost its wheat was put to other and more profitable uses: fat lamb production, dairying, production of apples, onions, potatoes and other vegetables; in addition South Australia developed a wine industry and Queensland grew sugar, pineapples and other tropical crops. Not all the land could be used, however; large areas proved completely unproductive and had to be left in scrub: only in recent years has the cause of the sterility been discovered and the remedy applied.

The vast tract of country—about half the total land area—lying between the moist coastal region and the central desert is largely devoted to sheep stations, Australia's most distinctive and characteristic feature. These may be thousands of acres in extent: the quality of the herbage depends almost entirely on the rain and may be so good that one acre will carry one sheep, or so poor that 5 acres or more are needed. Wool is the chief product: Merino sheep are kept in the drier conditions which they tolerate and under which the finest quality of wool is obtained, while Merino crosses are kept in moister conditions as they have more value as mutton and are less tolerant of drought. Wheat may be grown also but the rainfall is always uncertain, and its effectiveness is diminished by the very high rate of evaporation. Rain may fall during a few months in the year and both crops and grass may

[1] J. A. Prescott and G. R. Piper showed after a fallow the soil on the Waite Institute farm contained 20 to 30 parts nitric nitrogen per million, and after wheat only six or less. Fallowing usually conserves water equivalent to about three inches of rainfall.

then flourish, but the long dry season sets in when they wither leaving the soil apparently bare. The sheep browsing upon it succeed in picking up more food than one would think possible; they feed also on some of the shrubs and on any ephemerals that spring up after a casual shower of rain. But they lose condition; this, however, is less serious for a Merino wool flock than for breeding ewes. Tragedies occur when the rain comes too late or is too small in amount, and a second dry season begins with little or no reserve of food. Ewes are not mated and numbers are reduced in the hope that food supplies may last out, but if they do not, thousands of sheep may perish by starvation.

The inland vegetation being so sparse, and the risk of failure so great, the stocking has to be kept light; the pastures are easily overgrazed, the best plants eaten out and the soils left bare, exposed to erosion. The cost of fencing is so high, and the materials often so scarce that the paddocks are very large and grazing difficult to control. Drinking water is provided by means of artificial reservoirs called dams which are so characteristic a feature of the landscape when seen from the air—another being the dry bed of what in time of rain becomes a river.

The eastern side of the continent is not entirely dependent on the local rainfall for its water supply. Under a large area known as the Great Artesian Basin there is a good deal of water under pressure which when tapped rises to the surface; its depth may be anything up to 7,000 feet. The area covers some 550,000 square miles in Queensland, New South Wales, South Australia and the Northern Territory. More than 3,000 artesian bores have been constructed and the daily free discharge has been estimated at more than 350 million gallons. The water is generally suitable for stock but not for plant life, animals being more tolerant of the dissolved salts than are plants.[1] The water is often "uncontrolled" and gushes out into a pool from which bore-drains are ploughed for miles across country. The stock drink where they will along these channels, and on their sides is some green vegetation, usually coarse, but it supplies a little fresh food which probably enables the animals to digest the coarse dry grass which is otherwise their sole diet for many months during the dry season. How long the water will last is not known. Bores on the lower land appear to supply water permanently, but more than 700 near the edge of the basin have ceased to flow in Queensland.[2] Sub-artesian bores and wells are much more numerous; more than 200,000 have been made. Other artesian basins are known; the Murray River Basin to the south of the Great Basin, the Eucla Basin forming the Nullarbor Plain in the south of Western Australia, the Desert Basin south of the Fitzroy River in the northern part of Western Australia, and two on the west coast of Western Australia, one north and the other south of Geraldton.[3] Comprehensive hydrological surveys have been started to obtain more information about this underground water.

Fortunately for Australia the Murray River and its associates can be used for irrigation. The river basin is divided between New South Wales, Victoria

[1] Water is used for irrigation only at Ayr in Queensland, on an area of 6,000 acres, chiefly sugar-cane.
[2] *The Australian Environment*, 1950.
[3] There is a good map in *Year Book of Australia*, 1951, p. 1,158.

and South Australia which greatly hampered development till Federation, after which the Commonwealth and the three States set up a joint Control Commission which has worked out a comprehensive plan for development and constructed the necessary weirs, canals and other works and is steadily engaged in further extensions.

About 1·35 million acres have already been irrigated (Table CI), more than half of it in Victoria owing partly to more favourable topography, partly to the persistent advocacy of Alfred Deakin, its great Premier in the 1890's.

TABLE CI. *Area of land under irrigation in the different States.* 1948–49 (1)
Thousand acres

	N.S.W.	Victoria	Queensland	S. Australia	W. Australia	Tasmania	A.C.T.	All Australia
Cereals, hay, etc.	166·8 (2)	86·9	18·7			0·14	0·37	241·6
Orchards	19·9	35·9	2·8	9·1	3·6	1·0	0·13	148·2
Vineyards	11·3	40·2		23·8	0·3			
Sugar-cane			49·1					49·1
Other crops	98·7	42·6	20·3	6·1	8·2	1·6		208·6
Total crops	296·7	205·6	90·9	39·0	12·1	2·7	0·49	647·5
Pastures	279·5	517·4	0·5	9·1	13·3	6·8	0·04	826·8
Total	576·2	723·0	91·4	48·2	25·4	9·6	0·53	1474·3

(1) *Year Book of the Commonwealth of Australia,* 1951.

(2) Includes 31,400 acres of rice.

(3) Includes lucerne fed off.

The upper settlements are watered by gravity. The cost of the water (which may be £1 per acre foot) is sufficiently low to allow its use for converting very poor sheep-grazing land into good pastures for intensive fat lamb production in New South Wales and dairying in Victoria, or for setting up orchards of stone fruit. A common size for a fat lamb farm is about 320 to 640 acres with a "water right" for one acre in four; a dairy farm is commonly about 60 to 120 acres; and orchards about 25 acres, with "water rights" for every acre in each case.

Below Swan Hill, however, the land lies above the level of the irrigation canals and pumping is therefore necessary: this considerably raises the cost of the water which may now become £3 per acre foot. Much higher returns are therefore necessary, and the products are mainly citrus or dried vine fruits. Mildura is the centre of this industry: the holdings are usually 15 to 25 acres.

These settlements show up remarkably from the air as densely populated vivid green patches sharply distinct from the surrounding brown and grey arid sheep stations where 20,000 acres or more may be needed to sustain a family.

As commonly happens in irrigation systems some water-logging of the land has resulted from excessive or careless watering, or from seepage from the canals: this in places has caused salt to rise to the surface with destructive effects. Irrigation systems are extremely difficult to manage properly, and many of the early settlers were returned soldiers for whom some provision had to be made, but who lacked the necessary knowledge and experience. Reclamation has been effected by drainage and by more care in irrigation.

The Murray River system provides for over 90 per cent of all Australia's irrigated land. The other river systems allow only of minor schemes: the Hunter River flowing eastwards through New South Wales has a dam at Glenbaum for the irrigation of the lucerne for which the valley is famous, some of the small Queensland rivers are used, also mostly for lucerne, but the Burdekin irrigates the sugar-cane area around Ayr and Home Hill. Tube wells are but little used except on some of the river flats in north-east Queensland: the Burdekin, Fitzroy, Dawson and Lockyer. Elsewhere the geological conditions are in general unsuitable.

Table CI shows the areas of irrigated land in the different States in 1948–49. Of 1·47 million acres irrigated more than half were pastures and about 10 per cent orchards and vineyards.

The Crops

The result of the low rainfall over most of the country is that the area of land suited for crop production is very small. Of the total area of 1·9 thousand million acres about 1 thousand million are in pastoral and agricultural use, but only 21 million acres are cropped, and there are 10 million acres of fallow—together amounting to only about 1·6 per cent of the total land surface (Table CII). Strangely enough this sown area has for many years shown no sign of increasing: it was 21 million acres in 1929 and 20·6 million acres in 1949; there was an expansion to 25 million acres in 1943–44, but it was short-lived, and the acreage rapidly fell back to its old level. This failure to expand will be discussed later.

There are about 250,000 holdings, mostly run by the farmer and his family with but little hired help, though some large companies operate in the north. In the moist coastal belt the holdings are about 150 to 300 acres in size, in the irrigated districts they are much smaller as we have seen, while in the drier interior and in the north the holdings may be hundreds of thousands of acres in size: when the animals are being rounded up the men may be unable to return home at nights owing to the distance, but must camp out. Much of this northern land is leased from the Government, and while the system has advantages it has discouraged costly permanent improvements.

Australia is unique among the continents in that it has no native food plants or animals. All crops, most of its more productive pasture plants, especially clover and lucerne, and all the ordinary farm animals, had to be introduced.

Wheat is by far the most important crop, followed by other cereals: their areas and produce are given in Table CIII. It occupies 60 per cent of the cropped land over the whole country, and 66 and 70 per cent in the three chief wheat-growing States, New South Wales, Victoria and Western Australia. It has remained in the rather dry country; 60 to 70 per cent of it is grown in districts having an average rainfall of 10 to 15 inches during its time of active growth, April or May to October or November. In the west most of the year's rain falls during these months, so that the wheat

TABLE CII. *Distribution of population and of crops among the different States, 1948–49*

	New S. Wales	Victoria	Queensland	S. Australia	W. Australia	Tasmania	Total
Area, million acres	198·0	56·3	428·8	243·2	624·6	16·8	1,900 (1)
population, millions (1948)	3·06	2·11	1·13	0·68	0·53	0·27	7·91
Area of crops, million acres	5·71	4·24	1·95	3·76	4·21	0·34	20·64
Area of wheat, million acres	4·04	3·23	0·61	2·06	2·87	0·008	12·58
Production of wheat, million bushels	64·70	49·06	14·32	26·14	36·25	0·15	190·7
Thousand acres							
Hay	628	657	72	296	229	84	1,970
Green fodder	488	197	511	141	400	116	1,854
Irrigated cereals and hay	166·8	86·9	18·7	—	—	0·14	241·6
Vineyards	16·5	43·7	31	58·8	10·8	—	132·3
Including irrigated	11·3	40·2		23·8	0·3	—	
Orchards and other fruit	98·9	71·5	38·7	28·3	22·0	30·7	290·3
Including irrigated	19·9	35·9	2·8	9·1	3·6	1·0	
Livestock, millions							
Sheep, 1949	50·4	19·2	16·5	9·37	10·9	2·16	108·7
Cattle, 1949	3·25	2·22	6·00	0·46	0·86	0·27	14·1(1)
Including beef cattle	1·99	0·71	4·57	0·18	0·63	0·11	9·26
Pigs	0·37	0·22	0·41	0·07	0·08	0·04	1·20
Meat produced (bone-in) thousand tons	307·6	250·0	247·2	76·0	65·8	19·7	971·4
Factory butter thousand tons	33·3	60·1	47·2	8·82	6·96	4·84	161·2
Factory cheese, thousand tons	2·48	18·52	9·41	11·62	0·86	0·38	43·3

(1) Including Northern Territory's 335·4 million acres and about one million cattle.

TABLE CIII. *Areas, production and export of cereals, pre-war and post-war*

	Million acres			Million tons produced			Million tons exported		
	Average 1937–39	1950	1951	Average 1937–39	1950	1951	Average 1937–39	1950	1951
Wheat	13·8	11·7	10·4	4·94	4·94	4·32	2·70	3·45	2·67
Oats	1·62	1·76	2·16	0·346	0·449	0·621	0·004	0·142	0·232
Barley	0·735	1·08	1·10	0·282	0·510	0·490	0·084	0·272	0·269
Rice	0·024	0·041	0·038	0·028	0·050	0·037	0·013	0·029	0·030

(Commonwealth Econ. Cttee., *Grain Crops*, 1953.)

In Australian statistics wheat is always measured in bushels. The weight of a bushel varies somewhat according to season and other conditions: a usual average is 62·7 lb.: at this rate 1 million bushels weigh 28,000 tons.

407

area is in the belt of 14 to 20 inches annual rainfall, but in the east and south where the distribution is wider it is in a higher rainfall belt of 17 to 24 inches. In all these cases the rain comes in autumn, winter or spring, leaving the summer dry—hence the desirability of the fallow. In regions of summer rainfall wheat cultivation was till recently much more difficult: the rain encouraged so much growth of weeds that the old horse implements could not cope with them, but tractors, large implements and herbicides have now overcome this trouble.

We have seen how the area of wheat was steadily increased by the opening up of the inland districts with the new earlier ripening wheats and the new cultivation technique. It is a striking testimony to Australian agriculture that yields also increased, although much of the expansion was into less productive areas. The yields have been:

		Expansion of area				*Contraction of area*	
	1891–1900	1901–10	1911–20	1921–30	1931–40	1941–47	1947–50
Average yield, bushels per acre	7·3	9·8	10·7	12·0	12·5	12·7	16·4 (10·3 cwt.)

This expansion of the wheat belt continued till 1931 when the acreage reached 17 million. But in many districts the hazards were so great that only the Australian farmers love of taking a chance kept the crop going.[1] The economic crisis of the 1930's eliminated much of this marginal wheat and the sown area began to shrink; this process has continued with a special fall in the very dry year 1944: from this there was some recovery though the fall soon began again (Fig. 24). This shrinkage naturally raised the yield because it was the poorest land that was eliminated. Improvement of varieties and of cultivation technique has still continued raising the yields still further so that the 1930 peak of 220 million bushels was reached in 1947 and 1949, though the acreage had fallen by about one-third.

Drought still remains unconquered, however: in 1944 the average yield was down to 6¼ bushels per acre, the levels of the early days. (Fig. 25.)

Can this production of 220 million bushels of wheat—6·2 million tons—be exceeded, or is it Australia's limit of economic production? Recovery of the lost acreage in the drier regions might be possible if the soil could be left under grass sufficiently long to build up a crumb structure which would retain more of the rainfall. This may result from the pasture improvement now proceeding. But it is a slow process and no one can forecast how far it may go. R. D. Watt, in a critical survey in 1948,[2] made an estimate of 20½ million acres as the ultimate economic acreage: assuming an average of 13 bushels per acre, he arrived at 266½ million bushels, or 7·5 million tons, as an ultimate output. This may be a conservative estimate. In view of later developments an average yield of 15 bushels per acre may perhaps be assumed in which case the output would become 8·6 million tons as

[1] I have been on a farm where a crop could be relied upon only one year in four, but the returns might then make good all the losses and more.

[2] R. D. Watt, *Empire Jl. Expt. Agric.*, 1948, Vol. 16, pp. 187–194.

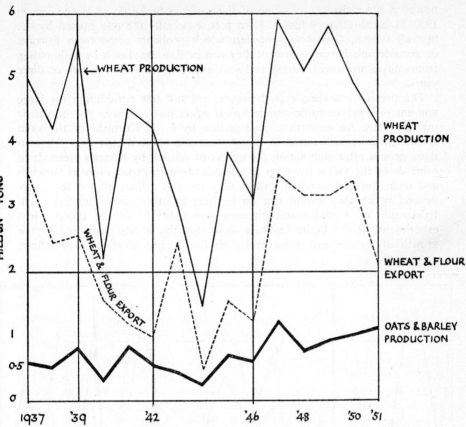

FIG. 24.—Production and export of grain, Australia, 1937 to 1951. (Data from C.E.C. Reports, *Grain Crops*, 1953, and *F.A.O. Stat. Year Book*, 1951.)

against the 6·2 million tons of present-day good seasons. Neither figure may turn out to be correct, but they are at any rate warnings against exaggerated hopes of what Australia can produce.

Australian experts nowadays attach more importance to the development of the regions where the rainfall is reliable than to regaining land in the regions where it is not. Among the steps taken to this end is a better control of fungus diseases. G. Ordish estimates that in 1947–48 they caused a loss of over a million tons of cereals.[1] Plant breeders have had considerable success in producing varieties resistant to flag smut and to stem rust (*Puccinia graminis*), the most important of these diseases[2]—though farmers do not always use them: in 1948 in New South Wales only half a million out of a total of 5 million acres of wheat were sown with resistant sorts, and in consequence some 10 million bushels were lost.[3] Unfortunately,

[1] *Untaken Harvest*, Constable and Co., 1952, p. 38.
[2] See A. T. Pugsley, Back crossing for resistance to stem rust of wheat in Australia. *Empire Jl. Expt. Agric.*, 1949, Vol. 17, pp. 193–98.
[3] *Chemistry and Industry*, December 24, 1949. Lord Bledisloe's Pres. Address 2nd International Crop Protection Congress.

however, the resistance of some of the varieties broke down in the season 1950–51 causing heavy losses. Foot rots, especially the one caused by the take-all fungus, *Ophiobolus graminis* which probably came from Europe, do considerable harm; at present they can be eliminated only by withholding from cultivation wheat, barley and host grasses for a period of two or three years.

The present average yields, however, are still low considering the large amount of good scientific and technical effort that has been put into their improvement. An important investigation by E. A. Cornish[1] of the yield trends on individual farms in South Australia showed that they fell into three groups after eliminating the effects of rainfall by Fisher's method: in some cases the yields went up in accordance with expectation as varieties and technique improved; in others they reached a limit after a few years beyond which they would rise no farther; in other cases they even fell. Exhaustion of available soil nitrogen was indicated as the cause. Field experiments at the Waite Institute show that this is best remedied by the growth of leguminous crops, and their four-course rotation: bare fallow,

INCHES OF RAIN

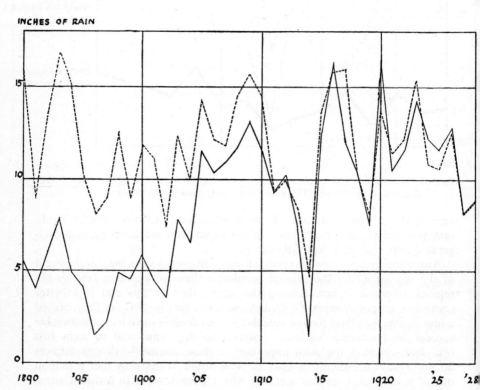

Fig. 25.—Relation of wheat yield to rainfall S. Australia, 1890 to 1951. (A. E. V. Richardson, *Jl. Agriculture, S. Aust.*, Nov. 1929, and *Statistical Register Australia*, per J. A. Prescott). (Upper part.)

[1] E. A. Cornish, Influence of rainfall on the wheat belt in South Australia. *Australian Journ. Scientific Res. Series B*, Vol. 3, pp. 83–137, 1949.

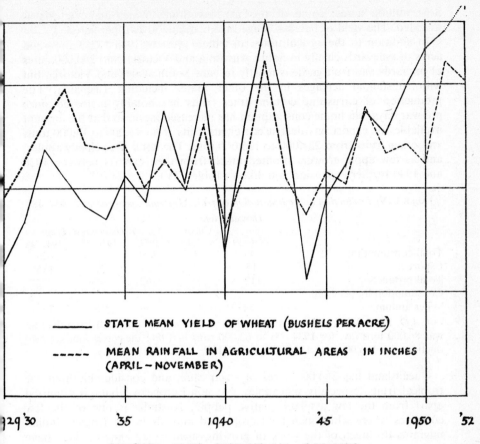

STATE MEAN YIELD OF WHEAT (BUSHELS PER ACRE)

MEAN RAINFALL IN AGRICULTURAL AREAS IN INCHES
(APRIL – NOVEMBER)

1929 '30   '35   1940   '45   1950   '52

COMPILED FROM STATISTICAL REGISTER
FIG. 25. Lower part.

wheat, peas (grazed), and annual Wimmera rye grass, has given an average
yield of 40 bushels of wheat per acre. The average rainfall is 24 inches,
effective for seven months. An alternative method, adopted by some farmers
where the rainfall suffices, is to put down a ley of annual grasses and a
dominant legume such as subterranean clover or species of medicago
(e.g. *M. denticulata* or *M. tribuloides*) and leave it for about four years:
several crops of wheat can then be taken.

The other cereals occupy only about 3 million acres, less than one-third
the area of wheat. Oats and barley are the most important: more could
be grown for export, but present prices are unremunerative and wheat pays
better even where it is less suited to the conditions. Some rice is grown in
irrigated areas; it has the advantage of tolerating a certain amount of salt.
Some sorghum is grown in hot dry districts in Queensland; it tolerates dry
conditions better than other cereals.

The other important agricultural crops are cultivated hay and green
fodder, including wheat, oats and lucerne, of which in 1949 there were

3·67 million acres: some of this in New South Wales and Victoria is irrigated. The yield of hay has ranged from 16½ to 30 cwt. per acre.[1]

In addition to the agricultural crops there were in 1948 132·3 thousand acres of vineyards chiefly in South Australia and Victoria, and 290,000 acres of orchards and fruit gardens mostly in New South Wales and Victoria, but with substantial acreages in the other States including Tasmania. The production of citrus and certain other fruits has notably increased since pre-war days, but home consumption has increased more, so that the amount available for export has decreased: citrus fruits from 15,000 to 13,000 tons, and other fruits from 221,000 to 135,000 tons. The latter were chiefly apples, and as few apple growers profited much from their exports between 1926 and 1940 further expansion is unlikely (Table CIV).

TABLE CIV. *Production and consumption of fruit, Australia, pre-war and* 1947–48

Thousand tons

	Citrus			Other Fresh Fruits	
	1936–39	1947–48	1951	1936–37	1947–48
Total consumption	99	126	149	547	629
Export	15	8	13	221	135
Total production	112	134	162	754	772
Consumption lb. per head per annum	31·7	35	36	133	139

F.A.O. Food Balance Sheets, 1949 and 1950. Exports of apples fell from the pre-war 86,000 tons (av. for 1934–38) to 62,000 tons in 1951; the corresponding production was 196,000 and 183,000 tons. (C.E.E. Rpts., *Fruit,* 1953.)

Queensland has 384,000 acres of sugar-cane, and considerable areas of tropical fruits, especially pineapples. No non-European labour is admitted apart from the few available native people; Australia is one of the few countries where white men tend crops and animals in the tropics. Italian migrants do much of the work of growing sugar-cane; some of them have acquired farms of their own and they largely occupy the wealthy little towns of Tully and Innisfail in North Queensland.

Australian pastures in their natural state are not usually good. They contain few or no leguminous plants—the country is desperately short of these—and in consequence the herbage is deficient in protein, especially when mature and dry, the conditions in which the animals consume it throughout the dry season. In the southern part of the country where the rainfall is less than about 15 or 20 inches a year—the sheep country—the herbage is sparse; in the wet coastal belt of the tropical north—the cattle country—it is very bulky, farther inland the quantity is less but the nutritive value greater. In between the high and the low rainfall conditions come considerable tracts of moderately good pasture such as the plains of the south-east where the rainfall is greater than 20 inches and the herbage includes species of *Danthonia, Stipa* and *Themeda australis,* adequate for wool-production and cattle-grazing, but not for more intense production. Most pastures are improved by dressing with superphosphate and better management of the grazing, and those with the better rainfall are still more improved by sowing better fodder plants from other countries.

[1] *Australian Year Book,* 1951.

The good English grasses and clovers were early introduced and some, especially rye grass, cocksfoot and white clover, have proved extremely valuable in southern districts of adequate and well distributed rainfall. They have not as yet, however, given rise to special strains that have won international reputation as has happened in New Zealand.

For regions of restricted rainfall coming chiefly in winter, some of the Mediterranean plants do better because of their ability to seed early and so avoid the summer drought. Some of the best of these came in solely by accident and were discovered only by chance. Subterranean clover, *Trifolium subterraneum*, now important almost beyond exaggeration, was found in 1888 by A. W. Howard, a farmer near Mount Barker in South Australia; how or when it got there can never be known. It is now widely grown wherever the rainfall is adequate; it needs superphosphate, and then it not only enriches the grazing in protein but builds up the nitrogen content of the soil and so makes possible the growth of grasses more prolific and more nutritive than the native sorts. Another Mediterranean plant, canary grass, *Phalaris tuberosa* came in as an unknown stranger, and was found growing on a rubbish heap at Toowoomba in Queensland about 1900; it was transferred to the Botanic Gardens there and has now become one of the best of the winter grasses. Another of great value is an early seeding annual rye grass of unknown origin discovered in the Wimmera, and bears that name; it is increasingly sown in the wheat belt under a rainfall of 15 to 25 inches. Deliberate introductions have for some years been made by the C.S.I.R.O. with full precautions to avoid any chance of letting in something that may if liberated turn out to be a pest. Some 3,000 or more exotic pasture plants have been tested at the central station at Canberra; those of promise are sent to the regional stations for further trial, and the survivors are subjected to selection for particular characters.

The introductions for summer rainfall regions include *Chloris gayana*, Rhodes grass, from South Africa, which does well in the sub-coastal areas of Queensland. *Paspalum dilatatum* from South America is remarkably successful on the east coastal regions of Queensland and of New South Wales, where in association with *Trifolium repens* it has been a major factor in the development of the dairy industry.

For Australia's wet tropics, Guinea grass (*Panicum maximum*) and molasses grass (*Melinis minutiflora*) have proved useful. Dressings of superphosphate and other necessary fertilizers and good management are essential to the success of the introduced plants.

The search for leguminous plants for the summer rainfall regions has so far been less successful. Two came in some unknown way: *Melilotus indica*, which reached King Island and made dairying possible there, and *Stylosanthes Sundaica*, a tropical lucerne which may do the same for North Queensland.

These exotic plants, however, succeed only where sufficient moisture is available; they are unlikely to become established where the Meyer ratio (p. 400) falls below 75—as it does over much of Australia's pastoral regions. Improvement here must be effected by controlled grazing which necessitates more fencing and more water points, both of which require capital and materials not always available. Further, the animals remain on the land all the year round; the pasture is never rested; and the good grasses tend to be eaten out leaving only the poorer herbage and much bare land on which erosion can start. In many districts, as for example in the Mulga region of Western Australia and the saltbush-bluebush plains of South Australia and New South Wales, the stock-carrying capacity has fallen considerably over the last fifty years and serious problems of rehabilitation have arisen.[1] Superphosphate is extensively used on the pastures: it is estimated that some 10 million acres are dressed annually.

Livestock and their products

The numbers of animals are shown in Table CII and the changes over the years in Fig. 26. Most of the animals are now in the moister regions

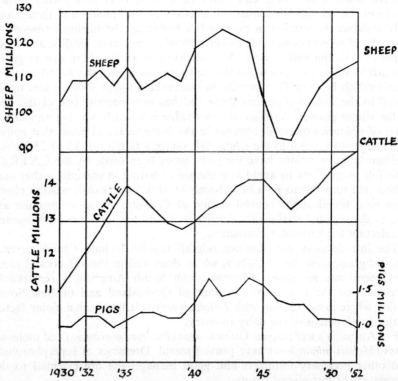

FIG. 26.—Numbers of sheep, cattle and pigs, Australia, 1930–1952 (from S. M. Wadham, *Australian Production at the Cross Roads*, Sydney, 1952).

Years ending March. The data are recorded one year earlier by C.E.C.: e.g. the peak for beef given here as in 1951 is attributed to 1950 by C.E.C.

as the result of the improvement of the pastures, better provision of food in the dry season and better control of diseases, parasites and pests than

---

[1] For a general summary of Australian work on pastures see Trumble, *Blades of Grass* (Georgian Publishing Co.); also Donald and Christian, *Distribution and Characteristics of Australian Pastures*. Both are in the Library of the Imp. Bur. of Herbage Plants, Aberystwyth. The earlier research work is described by A. McTaggart, "Areas in which establishment of exotic plants appears to be practicable," *Journ. C.S.I.R.O.*, 1938, Vol. 12, pp. 151–54, also in *Plant Introductions*, Pamph. No. 114, C.S.I.R.O., 1942, and other papers.

has yet been achieved in the dry interior. Sheep are the most numerous and important, wool being Australia's chief export. Before the war they averaged about 110 million, the highest population in the world: later they rose to 125 million in consequence of the soaring prices of wool, but the terrible drought of 1945 brought them down to 95 million; by 1949 they were back to pre-war level. About half are in New South Wales; Victoria and Queensland come next with 19 and 16 million respectively; South Australia and Western Australia each have rather less than 10 million. Merinos predominate as being most tolerant of dry conditions and yielding high quality wool though the mutton is poor: crossbreds inhabit the moister regions; they are better producers of meat.

Before the war about 205,000 tons of mutton and 116,000 tons of fat lamb used to be produced annually, a total of about 320,000 tons: the mutton chiefly in New South Wales, followed by Victoria and Queensland, the lamb chiefly in Victoria because there the number of crossbreds was largest. Good pastures can produce one fat lamb per acre and maintain the ewe. About 90 per cent of the mutton was consumed at home, leaving about 18,000 or 20,000 tons for export, but only 40 per cent of the lamb was consumed so that the exports were about 70,000 tons, making an aggregate export of about 90,000 tons.

Production of lamb and mutton showed no signs of rising during the 1930's; it went up to a peak of 415,000 tons, however, in 1944, but speedily dropped back to its old level, and the average for the four years 1947–50 was only 324,000 tons: slightly less than for the period 1936–39.

Meanwhile the population has increased, and with it the total consumption of mutton and lamb, so that the exports have gone down:

	Average 1934–39	Average 1947–50 (1)
Mutton	18·1	17·4
Lamb	68·6	46·7
	86·7	64·1 thousand tons

(1) The values for 1951 are exceptionally low because of the drought and hence are not included here.

The 1944 peak shows, however, that considerably more could be produced; the present stagnation in output is attributable to economic rather than to physical reasons.

Cattle numbers have since 1934 fluctuated between 13 and 14 millions, about 4½ millions being dairy stock and 9 millions beef animals; in 1950 the total rose to 14·6 millions and in 1951 to 15·2 millions, beef cattle being responsible for the increase. Beef production (Fig. 27) is almost entirely by ranching; there is very little intensive feeding. Of the 9 million beef cattle about half are in Queensland, about 2 million in New South Wales, 1½ million in the Northern Territory and the north of Western Australia. Formerly there were more in the south, but they have been displaced by dairy cattle and generally have been pushed out to regions unsuited to other pastoral activities.

Four of these regions have become important for beef production. The eastern coastal tract of Queensland is by far the chief. It has good rainfall,

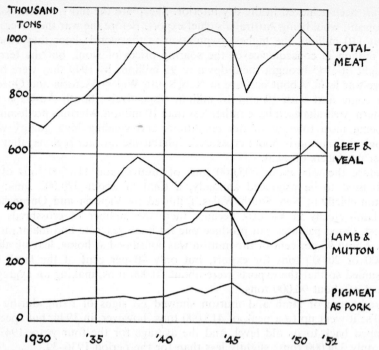

FIG. 27.—Production of meat, Australia, 1930 to 1952 (from S. M. Wadham, *Australia Production at the Cross Roads*, Sydney, 1952), see note on Fig. 26.

and reasonably good transport and slaughter facilities, but it is tick ridden and, except for alluvial flats, its pastures are poor. Then comes the Barkly Tableland, regarded as the best part of the Northern Territory: a tract of about 40,000 square miles of nearly level plains with heavy self-mulching soil; it has most of the best developed cattle stations in the territory, and about one-third of the territory's cattle. There are no rivers, but underground water is tapped by wells 300 or 400 feet deep and lifted by windmills or power pumps. The third region is an area of 30,000 square miles on the western side of the Northern Territory, including the Victoria River and the adjacent eastern Kimberleys of Western Australia; and the fourth, also of 30,000 square miles, is around Alice Springs in Central Australia. Both the latter are liable to suffer from water shortage; they carry a good flush of grass during the rainy months, but a long dry season follows when there is none: also the rain may fail altogether.

Production is on a very low level: over much of the tropical area a usual rate of stocking is ten bullocks per square mile—one per 64 acres—and a holding must be some 1,200 square miles: ¾ million acres: to provide a living, even then the risks are considerable. The average rainfall is high, but it is monsoonal and monsoons are notoriously liable to fail. This happened in 1951, and for two years there was little or no rain in large parts of Northern Australia, with the result that some 1¼ million cattle perished valued at £A 25 million. Bush fires are also a serious risk and may destroy many thousand acres of forage and cause the death of large numbers of animals.

41 (left) Reclaiming the Ninety Mile Desert: two 8-furrow ploughs tandem-fashion turn over 30 acres a day. (Courtesy of Australia House, London) [p. 425]

42 (right) After supplying the missing trace elements and seeding down, the "desert" is converted into good dairy farms. (Courtesy of Australia House, London) [p. 425]

43 (left) Good dairy farms, Pukekohe, N. Island, New Zealand. (Courtesy of the High Commissioner for New Zealand) [p. 433]

44 (right) Airplane being loaded with phosphatic fertilizer for application from the air. (Courtesy of the High Commissioner for New Zealand) [p. 434]

The enterprise is most suitable for large companies with financial resources sufficient to tide over a run of bad seasons and make good in the better ones.

The animals are commonly slaughtered when about six years old; the carcass weight is then about 500 to 600 lb. The total beef production is usually of the order of 600,000 tons a year, but it has varied from 675,000 tons in 1952 to 400,000 tons in 1945; it has shown no very clear sign of increasing since 1937. The output would be much higher but for the large percentage of waste. The meat factories are far from the grazings and there is very little transport; railways are few and inadequate and road trains costly. Many of the animals have to walk hundreds of miles—even up to 2,000 miles—to the slaughter and they may be weeks or even months on the journey, losing condition as they go because of lack of food and water on the way. Labour is scarce and of poor quality: attempts to remedy this are sought in improving the conditions of work and of living.

Before the war about 20 per cent of the total production was exported, but as output has not expanded and the population has increased the surplus for export has shrunk; in the five years before the war it had averaged 107,400 tons a year; in the four years 1946–50 it averaged 88,300 tons only. A much farther drop came later because of the disastrous drought of 1951. The Australians are great beef eaters and are surpassed only by the Argentinians in the amount consumed per head per annum; unless output is considerably increased we are not likely to get even our pre-war supplies, still less any increase (Fig. 28).

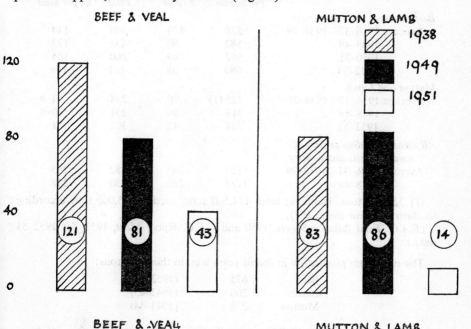

FIG. 28.—Export of meat from Australia, 1938 and post-war, thousand tons. (Data from C.E.C. Reports, Meat, 1952.) Twelve months ending June 30th of year following that stated. In the 1953 Report a Jan.–Dec. year is adopted, hence the figures are not comparable, but the trends are the same.

Pigs are not numerous. They are kept chiefly in Queensland and New South Wales, often on dairy farms where they receive the skim milk; in consequence the fluctuation in output is much less than that from cattle and sheep living only on pastures. About 80,000 to 90,000 tons of meat are produced annually. Most of it is consumed locally and as the output is not expanding the surplus for export is shrinking: before the war it was 12,500 tons a year; during the five years 1946–51 it has averaged 8,900 tons only, mostly frozen pork in each period.

Poultry and rabbits between them supply some 50,000 or 60,000 tons of meat, of which about a quarter is exported. Australia also exports growing quantities of preserved meat; this is almost entirely a post-war activity; the 14,360 tons of 1938 increased to 94,430 tons in 1952.

Taking all forms of meat together the output rose to a little over 1 million tons in 1938, and has varied about that figure ever since except for the catastrophic fall in 1946: there is no indication of any increase. The home consumption has meanwhile risen and in consequence the exports have fallen from the pre-war average of 226,000 tons a year, to an average of 202,000 tons for the years 1946–51; if rabbits and poultry are also included the fall has been from 245,000 to 186,000 tons (Table CV).

TABLE CV. *Meat production and consumption in Australia: and amounts exported.*
Thousand tons

	Production	Export	Consumed in Australia	
			Total	lb. per head
Beef and veal, bone-in weight				
Average 1936–37—1938–39	578	123	449	144
1948–49	582	98	435	123
1950–51	652	69	500	135
1952–53	680	38	464	119
Mutton and Lamb				
Average 1936–37—1938–39	325 (1)	90	234	74·9
1948–49	316	56	251	70·8
1952–53	384	42	302	77
All meat, including preserved meat, rabbits and poultry				
Average 1936–37—1938–39	1127	245	882	265
1948–49	1135	285	850	238

(1) 320,000 tons, including lamb 114,500 tons, mutton 205,000 tons according to *Australia Year Book*, 1951.

(*F.A.O. Food Balance Sheets*, 1950 and C.E.C. Rpts., *Meat*, 1953, for 1952–53 data.)

The maximum production in recent years was, in thousand tons:

Beef	675	(1952–53)
Lamb	260	(1942–43)
Mutton	275	(1943–44)

Dairy production is chiefly confined to the moist coastal regions of New South Wales, Queensland and Victoria: before the war in that order, but now New South Wales and Queensland are falling behind and Victoria has increased its output as the result of increasing pasture irrigation. The output of milk reached 1,100 million gallons in 1930 and except in 1945, the year of severe drought, it has fluctuated between 1,100 and 1,200 million gallons ever since with no certain indication of any increase. The number of milch cows has ranged about $3\frac{1}{4}$ million since 1934, with the usual fall following the drought years of 1945 and 1951. The output of milk is not quite parallel, but it also does not appear to be rising though there is some expectation that it may. The yields per cow are low: they have been:

Average 1934–9	Average 1941–6	Average 1947–51
355	341	383 gallons

(*Qy. Review Agric. Econ.*, October 1951, p. 181.)

The average is brought down by some very low yields in Queensland: Wadham suggests that these districts might be better used for beef than for milk production. Most of the milk is produced on pastures; supplement feed is usually given only by farmers selling fresh milk to the towns.

Before the war about 80 per cent of the milk was used for butter production; this is now down to about 65 per cent; more is being processed, made into cheese or consumed fresh (Table CVI and Fig. 29, p. 440).

TABLE CVI. *Butter and cheese produced and consumed in Australia and amounts exported. Thousand tons*

	Production	Export	Consumed in Australia Quantity	lb. per head per year
Butter				
Average 1936–37				
to 1938–39	191·0	90·0	101·0	32·9
1948–49	165·8	83·4	84·5	24·3
1950–51	165	55·6	109·4	30
Cheese				
Average 1936–37				
to 1938–39	24·9	11·5	13·4	4·4
1948–49	43·0	26·2	17·7	5·1

(*Australia Year Book*, 1951. The quantities for 1947–48 were very similar to those for 1948–49.)

The drop in consumption of butter per head in the early post-war years was due to rationing voluntarily and generously accepted in order to maintain the exports to the United Kingdom. There has, however, been a notable increase in the consumption of liquid milk consumed per head. This amounted to 240 lb. as the annual average for 1936–39, 315 lb. for 1949 and about 280 lb. for 1951 and 1952.

The skimmed milk from the butter making is at present fed to pigs which, however, convert only about 8 or 9 per cent of its protein into human food. Dr. Ian Clunies-Ross has pointed out that if instead it were evaporated it would furnish more first-class protein than is contained in all Australia's production of beef and mutton.

Three facts stand out clearly from the foregoing pages. Australia's production of food shows no clear sign of increasing; the population increases and maintains a good standard of living; the home consumption of food increases: the quantity available for export therefore decreases. Great Britain is the chief buyer and is therefore deeply concerned in the consequences.

The Australian dietary is among the best in the world, but it is not extravagant and is entirely free from reproach. The quantities of meat and of dairy produce have already been given: the amounts of nutrients are estimated by F.A.O. as follows:

	Average 1936–39	1948–49
Calories per day	3345	3165
Grams protein per day: Animal	66·6	64·5
Vegetable	36·7	30·6
Total	103·3	95·3

(*F.A.O. Food Balance Sheets*, 1950.)

The only hope of increasing exports is a considerable rise in production and the question of vital import arises: what prospects are there for this to happen?

The Possibility of Increasing Food Production in Australia

This failure to increase food production in spite of great world need and high prices has caused surprise in view of the excellence of the scientific and educational services and of many of the farmers. It has even been suggested that Australia has reached the limit of development and will henceforth decline through soil deterioration, soil erosion and other causes.[1] There is no evidence to support so pessimistic a view: but equally there is nothing to justify the vision of vastly increased production of food. Drought remains as the great natural factor setting a limit to what man can do at any given time.

The present levels of output do not, however, represent all that could be achieved. There are serious economic and political obstacles. Low prices in the 1930's depleted farmers' financial reserves, and when the war brought higher prices the terrible drought of 1944 and 1945 destroyed crops and caused the loss of some 30 million sheep. There is a chronic inadequacy of transport, shortage of man-power, of appliances such as spare parts, fencing and building materials, all of which have been aggravated in recent years by the Government concentration on industrial development. Like other advanced countries, Australia needs a flourishing export trade, and while markets for agricultural produce are assured it seems improbable that industries could ever export on any large scale owing to the high cost of labour per unit of accomplishment.[2] Their chance of survival is that the

[1] W. Vogt., *Road to Survival*, 1948, p. 235, is very scathing on this subject: his picture is grossly overdrawn.

[2] It implies no lack of respect on my part to quote Mr. Menzies' saying that the fault of the Government lies in attempting too much too quickly and the fault of labour in doing too little too slowly.

primary producers may be willing to pay higher prices for their appliances for the satisfaction of knowing that they are Australian made. Problems of this sort are solved only slowly and generally by the method of trial and error.

Meanwhile the technical problems are being very seriously studied. Much loss has been caused by the prickly pear cactus. This is not a native plant, it was introduced into Queensland in 1815 with the good intention of making hedges and for ornament: by the 1880's it had become a major pest. Fortunately it proved susceptible to attack by certain insects, *Cactoblastus* and cochineal coccid (*Bactylopius indicus*), which are not native to Australia but had to be introduced; and again fortunately they have shown no signs so far of outliving their usefulness by attacking any useful plants.

Rabbits have been even greater pests. They also are not native: twenty-four wild ones were introduced in 1859 at Barwon Park, Geelong, near Melbourne[1] —also with good intentions—and they multiplied prodigiously. Thousands of miles of netting fences were erected to exclude them from the cultivated land and penalties were imposed on anyone leaving open the gates. This proved inadequate and the landowners have been made responsible for rabbit control. Vast numbers have been killed and a trade in rabbit meat and skins has developed, but the returns are far below the costs, and during the war a combination of favourable seasons with shortage of labour and of netting enabled them to multiply enormously. However, a myxomatosis virus liberated in 1950 has had devastating results which give hope for the future.

Soil erosion has caused great losses. As in all new countries where agricultural conditions differ from those of the United Kingdom and Western Europe the earlier settlers made mistakes in soil management which led to soil erosion. No accurate estimate can be made of the losses thus incurred in Australia as a whole, and the problem is further complicated by the fact that natural erosion is always proceeding in the dry desert regions. It is greatest in the hill country of the south-west, when water has caused both sheet erosion and gullying; there is also wind erosion in Victoria and south-east of South Australia.[2] Estimates have been made for New South Wales: in the East and Central Divisions nearly 60 million out of a total of 120 million acres of grazing and farm lands had been affected by wind and water erosion; of these about half were reported to need immediate treatment, while over 1·2 million acres had been virtually ruined. R. D. Watt states that about half the wheatlands of Australia have suffered from erosion.[3] On the Darling Downs, 1·6 million acres of arable and grazing land have suffered and 40,000 acres of former fertile land are now out of cultivation. Upwards of a million acres in the Upper Ord River Valley in the Kimberley district have been badly eroded. C. G. Stephens, R. I. Herriot and R. G. Downes report much loss from wheatlands in South Australia.[4]

As against this, however, there are millions of acres on which soil fertility is increasing under sound farming methods. All four southern States have

[1] See C. W. Hume, *Empire Jl. Expt. Agric.*, 1939, Vol. 7, p. 132.
[2] *The Australian Environment*, 1950.
[3] *Empire Jl. Expt. Agric.*, 1948, Vol. 16, pp. 187–94.
[4] C.S.I.R.O., *Bull.*, 188, 1945.

set up Soil Conservation Branches or Services working under Soil Conservation Acts. An active and well organized conservation programme is being carried out in South Australia: the Acts of 1939 and 1943 empower the Government to limit grazing and to require reduction of livestock wherever necessary. Victoria's Acts were passed in 1940 and 1942. Dookie Agricultural College has established a Research and Demonstration Station to deal with Soil Conservation problems; Downes has done some excellent work in this connection. Western Australia's Act was passed in 1945. Much has been done under the New South Wales Act of 1939 on the same general lines as in the United States: the Government makes the survey, provides advice and supervision free of charge, while the landowners meet most of the other costs.[1] Suitable grasses have been found to aid in controlling erosion and rehabilitating eroded land.[2] The Chief of the Commonwealth Division of Soils, J. K. Taylor, states that the ravages of soil erosion have not yet been definitely checked, but they have been slowed down, and the increasing attention paid to the problem justifies the hope that the losses will in due time be reduced to negligible proportions.

Terrible losses are periodically caused in the hot dry season by bush fires started often by carelessness. The parched vegetation flares up like tinder and vast areas of the countryside may be devastated with great loss of animal and even human life. It is a sickening sight: the sparks and glowing cinders carried ahead of the flame fall on to trees and bushes setting them alight; the flames run from top to bottom with a horrid crackling and hissing noise destroying the tree in a few minutes. I can never forget being out in a terrible fire in 1939. Drought and fire between them cause great havoc; Australia is a wonderful and most attractive and friendly country, but it is at times frightening and can be terrifying. Bush fires will probably always occur, but control measures are steadily becoming more effective. Aeroplane patrols, mobile fire squads equipped with wireless and, above all, a more enlightened public opinion have effected great changes during recent years.

Drought remains, however, Australia's most serious problem. Some great schemes are projected for increasing the area of irrigated land. The most impressive concerns the Snowy River which rises in the Australian Alps on the south-eastern rim of the Murray Basin, but on the wrong side of the watershed so that its waters flow uselessly to the Tasman Sea instead of into the Murray Basin where they would be of great value. This is to be rectified. Its head waters are to be turned back through the Alps into the Basin and decanted into the upper Murray River and the Tumut, a tributary of the Murrumbidgee. The Tumut is also to receive water from the Tooma, a tributary of the Murray, and from the upper Murrumbidgee. This great enterprise must surely rank as one of the engineering wonders of our time: it necessitates the construction of 86 miles of tunnels, one 30 miles long, another 8 miles, a third $4\frac{1}{2}$ miles, in addition to a number of smaller ones, also of seven great dams with an aggregate storage capacity of more than

[1] See *3rd Rpt.*, Rural Reconstruction Commission, pp. 45–61, also L. J. H. Teakle, *Soil Conservation and Land Productivity*, 1948. (*The Valuer*, April 1, 1948, and Univ. Queensland, *Dept. Agric., Reprint*, No. 3) and R. G. Downes, *Bull.* 243, C.S.I.R.O., 1949.

[2] See A. McTaggert, "Grass Types Suitable for Erosion Control," *Journ. C.S.I.R.O.*, 1939, Vol. 12, pp. 155–57.

5 million acre feet allowing the irrigation of more than 1 million acres in addition to generating 2½ million kW of electrical energy—a quantity larger than the present consumption of electricity in all New South Wales and Victoria. On present estimates the scheme will take about thirty years to complete and the cost will be £A 220 million at 1948 prices.

A smaller scheme—but the largest single engineering enterprise actually undertaken in Australia, greater even than the Sydney Harbour Bridge— is to enlarge the Eildon Weir on the Goulburn River in Victoria from its present capacity of 306,000 to 2·25 million acre feet of water, providing also 100,000 kW of electricity. Work has already commenced, but is temporarily curtailed through lack of capital. Unfortunately for Great Britain the contract went to an American firm.

The Hume Weir on the Murray is to have its capacity raised from the present 1¼ million to 2 million acre feet. The State Rivers and Water Supply Commission, which is responsible for Victorian schemes, plans to spend £30 million in the ten years ending 1959: it has in its favour the strong point that the £14 million already spent on water conservation is now giving increased production of £14 million annually, according to its estimates. A dam is to be erected 100 miles up the Burdekin River on the east coast of Queensland impounding up to 5 million acre feet of tropical flood water for the irrigation of about 500,000 acres. Another dam on the Ord River on the north coast has been planned to bring 100,000 acres into use.

If these various schemes mature they will increase the irrigated area from its present 1½ million acres to 5 million acres which will add greatly to the output of dairy produce and fat lamb, fruit and fodder crops, besides considerably enhancing the certainty of production. Unfortunately, the Federal Government in 1952 has stated that it cannot at present raise the capital necessary for many of these and other works. Consequently the schemes must be delayed and some may have to be abandoned.

In any case, the possibilities of irrigation are very limited; the Murray System is the only one of any size: its annual flow of about 10 million acre feet does not begin to compare in magnitude with that of the great rivers of the world.[1] Moreover the flow is variable: the contributions of the Darling, the longest tributary, and the Goulburn, the most dependable, have been, in million acre feet:[2]

	Annual Flow Average	Range
Darling	2·15	0·001–11
Goulburn	2·3	0·567–6

This unreliability has been met by the erection of large storage dams with an aggregate storage capacity of 4·38 million acre feet. The area irrigated is 1·386 million acres. Five million acres is considered to be the maximum area that can be irrigated.[3]

---

[1] Seventy-two million for the Nile and 146 million for the Ganges.
[2] J. A. Aird, in *The Australian Environment, Melbourne*, 1950.
[3] *Commonwealth Econ. Co-op. Rpt.*, 1951, p. 34.

Rectifying Soil Deficiencies

The regions of good rainfall are not yet fully developed, however. Many thousands of acres have been left wild because they were too poor for profitable cultivation; they failed to respond to superphosphate, the fertilizer that had brought so much of Australia's poor land into effective use. Their poverty has now been traced to lack of trace elements, and some of the most remarkable studies yet made of these substances have been at Adelaide by J. A. Prescott and his colleagues at the Waite Institute and H. R. Marston and the C.S.I.R.O. team. Copper, zinc, boron, manganese and molybdenum may be lacking or unavailable. They are needed only in minute quantities, but until they are supplied no ordinary soil treatment is effective. When, however, the missing elements are added the response is immediate and often spectacular. Copper is the usual deficiency on the calcareous shell soils of South Australia and in parts of Western Australia: 7 lb. per acre of copper sulphate is an adequate remedy.[1] Lack of zinc is widespread in the south; on sandy soils in South Australia and on the black soils of the Wimmera: these latter after treatment yield good wheat crops. In many districts irrigated orchards need spraying with zinc salts, as do pine trees in parts of Western Australia. Even more remarkable is the indispensability of minute quantities of molybdenum for clover and lucerne: a few ounces per acre of one of its salts enables these plants to grow where otherwise they fail. Hundreds of square miles of farmland now regularly receive addition of these trace elements with remarkable results; probably nowhere in the world are the effects more striking. Animals suffer equally with plants. H. R. Marston and his colleagues traced the obscure "coast disease" of sheep to a deficiency of copper[2] and of cobalt; and in the light of these studies similar troubles have been recognized and remedied in many other countries. "Steeliness" in wool has been traced to lack of copper, and a Western Australian sheep disease to lack of cobalt.

These various deficiencies are intensified by the circumstance that the animals are out on the land all the year and are not housed. Consequently no farmyard manure is produced. Also no imported foods are used, consequently no elements of fertility are brought in from other countries. Soil deficiencies therefore are not rectified through the animals as often happens in Western Europe, indeed the demands of the animals make them worse. As a result Australia is more than usually dependent on imported fertilizers.

The fuller knowledge of these and other deficiencies of Australian soils gained at the Waite Institute and elsewhere has enabled large tracts hitherto unused to be opened up.

Three hundred thousand acres near Albany on the south coast of Western Australia, in one of the most attractive parts of that attractive State, are to be made into four hundred holdings suitable for mixed farming. There had been earlier group settlement of ex-service men on 100-acre dairy farms

---

[1] Different varieties of the same crop differ in their reaction to deficiencies of copper: D. S. Riceman, *et al.*, found a variety of *Avena strigosa* that was largely resistant, while the Mulga oat was very susceptible (*C.S.I.R.O. Pamphlet 96*, 1940).

[2] On the other hand, some soils contain so much copper that grazing animals are injured thereby. (L. B. Bull, *Proc. Specialist Conf. in Agric., Australia*, 1949. London, H.M.S.O., p. 300.)

in this district in 1920 to 1922, but the pasture plants would not grow, largely because of the unsuspected lack of copper; the farms were neglected or abandoned: they had cost £3,500 each, but were valued in 1939 at £750 only.

Even more remarkable developments are proceeding in the coastal regions of South Australia, in the Eyre Peninsular, Kangaroo Island, and on the Ninety Mile Plain, formerly called the Ninety Mile Desert, a sandy area of 6 million acres south of the Adelaide-Melbourne railway and stretching from near Murray Bridge well into Victoria. All these lands have been hitherto almost waste because of their desperate poverty. The various deficiencies have now, however, been discovered: when they are remedied, certain strains of subterranean clover and phalaris can be grown. Sheep and dairy pastures can thus be made and soil fertility built up.

The most important of these undertakings is that of the Australian Mutual Provident Society which in 1948 took up 400,000 acres of the plain for transformation into clover, lucerne and phalaris farms—wherefore the region is henceforth to be called the Coonalpyn Downs from the little settlement in its centre.[1] (Pl. 41 and 42, p. 426).

In the Eyre Peninsular 98,000 acres of scrub formerly carrying only one sheep to 10 or 20 acres has been made into 70 farms averaging 1,400 acres with a carrying capacity of $1\frac{1}{2}$ to 2 sheep per acre. In Kangaroo Island 280,000 acres of very poor ironstone soil—what Prescott calls "relict laterites"—are being laid out in 200 farms. In Eight Mile Creek on the Victoria border, 4,500 acres of swamp are to make over 30 dairy farms. The opening up of these lands was facilitated when the Crown Land Development Act of 1943 empowered the Government to clear the land and then lease it to settlers, instead of requiring the settlers to clear it themselves. All these developments have been made possible through the investigations of the scientific and technical staffs. Numerous other developments are proposed, including a considerable War Service Land Settlement Scheme for which over 9 million new acres have been set aside; by 1950, $6\frac{3}{4}$ million acres had been allotted in 400 farms.[2]

Considerable developments were proposed in Queensland. The Queensland-British Food Corporation in 1948 acquired 700,000 acres in the Peak Downs district of Central Queensland with the purpose of growing sorghum for shipment to the United Kingdom as a feeding stuff or else used for the production of pig meat or beef on the spot. Had the scheme succeeded, it might have opened the way to the development of 10 million acres of land in that region. But it was carried through hastily, with no preliminary soil surveys, and without even inquiring whether the climatic conditions were suitable. It was abandoned in 1953, having cost the British taxpayer some £540,000.[3]

Investigation is still continuing into the possibility of increasing the output of beef from Australia. All four of the beef regions are being studied: the Northern Territories, the Barkly Tableland, the Alice Springs region, and the Queensland East Coast. A survey team sent out by the Commonwealth

---

[1] For an account of the soils see D. S. Riceman, C.S.I.R.O., *Bull.*, 234, 1948.
[2] *Commonwealth Economic Co-operation Rpt.*, 1951, p. 36.
[3] Cmd. 8760, 1953.

Scientific and Industrial Research Organization is working on 250,000 square miles of the northern regions. A Queensland Royal Commission under W. L. Payne in 1937 had already inquired into the factors hindering development, and showed the need for reducing the holdings to a more manageable size, reforming the system of land tenure, improving the living conditions of the workers so as to attract a better type of men, improving the pastures and fencing them so that grazing could be controlled. The need for increasing the number of watering points was emphasized so as to avoid the present congestion: sometimes as many as 2,000 cattle use the same bore with the result that the grass is killed and the soil rendered liable to erosion. Above all things, improvement of transport is necessary so as to get the stock away more effectively and reduce the fearful wastage of the present system.

Australian experts agree that these are the most serious defects: something has been achieved but much still remains to be done before they are remedied. During the war a great north-south all-weather road was constructed from Alice Springs in the centre of Australia to Darwin in the north; another starting from Mount Isa in Queensland (which has road and rail connections with the coast) traverses the Barkly Tableland. An interesting experiment that might lead to developments has been the establishment of a small abattoir at Glenroy in the interior of the north-west where the animals are killed and carcasses flown to the big meat factory at Wyndham: the enterprise is stated to have been an economic success. The Commonwealth Government plans to spend £1½ million in improving roads and stock routes in the Northern Territory; the work will take some seven to ten years, but it is expected that as the result the output of beef from the Territory will be raised from its present 60,000 tons a year to 90,000 tons.

The supply of labour has always been a difficulty in attempts to develop these tropical regions. The climate is extremely trying during about six months of the year; some of the inhabitants add the degrees Fahrenheit to degrees of humidity and call the result "degrees of discomfort." The supervisors have always been white, but on many stations the actual workers are largely aborigines who, like some of the Africans, are very good cattlemen. But they are decreasing in number and in effectiveness. The importance of improving the living conditions is being recognized and with better quarters more white workers are coming forward. The possibilities of improvement were shown during the war when some 100,000 service men and civilians were stationed in the north, and by dint of much labour made gardens and farms producing vegetables and poultry for themselves. One successful farm at Katherine has become an experiment station, and nearly every cattle station now has its own garden for its vegetable supply.

It is impossible to estimate the amount of beef likely to materialize as a result of these developments. They will necessarily take time to become effective and nothing can happen until transport facilities are improved. After the cattle are born six years usually elapse before they are ripe for slaughter, and often they must be transferred to fattening pastures for finishing. A Federal Cabinet Sub-Committee in 1949 estimated that the following increases over the present outputs could reasonably be expected:

426

	Thousand tons	Time necessary for attainment, years
Northern Territory (Darwin area)	13	15
Barkly Tableland	12	12
Wyndham area, West Australia	10	10
Alice Springs	13	12
	48	

—enough if it all came to the United Kingdom to provide 2¼ lb. per head per annum.[1] Other estimates are much higher: one assumes that Northern Territories could double their present output of about 60,000 tons of beef annually and yet another assumes that it could be trebled. These, however, are little better than guesses, and in any case they are not generally accepted by Australian experts.

More recently (April 1952) the Commonwealth Government recognizing the vital necessity of maintaining and if possible increasing exports, and the fact that agricultural produce constitutes some 85 per cent of all Australia's exports, has formulated a Five Year Plan to break the stagnation in primary production and consequent fall in exports, and to ensure additional exports to the value of £A 100 million annually, as well as saving £A 7 million of imports, chiefly tobacco, cotton and linseed. The plan envisages the following developments:

	Present	Plan
Wheat, million acres	10½	14
Oats and barley, million acres	3	4½
Tobacco, thousand acres	5	30
Linseed, thousand acres	30	200
Meat, million tons	1	1·23
Milk increase		12 per cent.

The additional meat produced will be lamb rather than beef.

There is no physical reason to prevent the attainment of these results, and when the larger development schemes are carried through much higher output may be anticipated.

Each item of the schedule requires for its realization more capital expenditure for farm development, for intensifying methods of production, and for providing better facilities for the transport and handling of goods. It is not easy to see where the capital is to come from. The Australian farmers themselves cannot provide it: indeed many of them remembering the twelve years in the 1920's and 1930's when they were on the verge of bankruptcy because of overproduction are reluctant to incur extra capital indebtedness for the production of goods that may only be saleable at unremunerative prices. In absence of long-term contracts with satisfactory price arrangements many of the farmers producing for export fear that remunerative prices last only so long as a world shortage exists. Until these fears are overcome there is likely to be difficulty in obtaining the necessary capital from those in a position to supply it. The problem is partly psychological, partly economic and political, but it is one for which a solution must be found.

[1] Sir David Rivett, *Advancement of Science*, 1950, Vol. 6 (No. 24), pp. 371–74.

REFERENCES

(1) *The Australian Environment*, Melbourne, C.S.I.R.O., 1950.

(2) *Specialist Conference in Agriculture, Plant and Animal Nutrition in Relation to Soil and Climatic Factors*, Australia, 1950, B.C.S.O.

(3) *Australian Production at the Cross Roads*, Angus and Robertson, Sydney and London, 1952.

(4) *Report of the Rural Reconstruction Cttee.*, I-X, 1944–1946.

(5) S. M. Wadham and G. L. Wood, *Land Utilisation in Australia*, Melbourne University Press.

NEW ZEALAND

New Zealand is agriculturally the most productive of all the new countries, and it is among the most productive in the world. It is a land of small farmers, who have specialized on lines eminently suited to their conditions, and have thereby attained a very high degree of efficiency. Their three lines are dairying, fat lamb production and arable sheep farming; in each they have been extremely successful.

New Zealand consists of two main islands, the North and the South, which together form a crescent about 1,100 miles in length but of no great width, facing westwards and tilted somewhat to the north-west; there are also a number of small islands. The northern extremity is in lat. 34° 25′ S.; the conditions are subtropical and allow the growth of citrus, vines, and other Mediterranean crops. The southern extremity is in lat. 47° 17′ S., and the conditions and crops are in some ways reminiscent of those of Scotland, as indeed are the people: for Dunedin claims to be more Scottish than Aberdeen. The rainfall varies from 250 inches a year in Milford Sound to about 13 inches in Alexandra, but only small areas have these extreme conditions, and most of the country has about 25 to 50 inches a year, well distributed. The western regions tend to be wetter than the east, and the North Island than the South.

The close proximity of all parts of the country to the sea ensures an equable climate. Over most of the North Island there is no great difference between summer and winter temperatures; the summers are not unpleasantly hot, and the winters are so mild that cattle are never housed; some of the in-milk cows, however, are protected by rugs. In the South Island the winters are colder, though here also the cattle are never housed. In some parts the winters are severe; occasionally heavy snow has caused serious loss of sheep. These differences in temperature and rainfall have led to differences in the agricultural systems: the North Island is predominantly grass, for which the conditions are almost ideal, while the South Island, with its drier climate, has proved better for arable farming.

The area of the North Island is 44,281 square miles (28·3 million acres) and of the South Island 58,093 square miles (37·2 million acres), making a total of 65·5 million acres. Steward Island, just to the south, has a further 670 square miles (0·43 million acres), and the Chatham and other outlying islands another 0·435 million acres.

The population in 1951 was estimated at 1·94 millions of whom 0·11 million were Maoris; in 1945 it had been 1·70 millions.

The North Island, although the smaller of the two, is the most populous having two-thirds of the population (1·31 million). Much of it is hill country with only small areas of level land; less than a quarter is below 650 feet in elevation. Its northern sub-tropical part is a narrow peninsular about 200 miles long; the central and southern part is much wider and includes a block of high country with recently active volcanoes and considerable areas of land covered with pumice. The Taupo plateau 1,000–2,000 feet elevation, is one of the largest of these; formerly much of it was waste, but the cause of its infertility is now discovered and it is being rapidly settled. The foothills of the main mountain regions such as the Ruakines are used for large sheep farms producing wool as in Australia. The plains are the country's chief source of wealth: here grassland dairying has been developed to a high pitch of perfection, and the Waikato and other valleys are among the most productive in the world.

The South Island is dominated by the ridge of mountains running from north to south parallel to the west coast and including some very respectable peaks. To the east and south are the important Canterbury and Southland plains where arable farming for cereals and fat lamb production is very efficiently practised.

Thanks to the persevering struggles of Edward Gibbon Wakefield against a reluctant British Government, New Zealand became a British possession in 1840; settlement then began and has continued with fluctuating fortune to the present time. The first products were, as in Australia, wool, wheat and gold. Wool is still very important, but wheat is not; it has virtually disappeared from the North Island and its area in the South Island is greatly reduced. Export of wheat which had begun in 1870 has long since ceased, and for many years the production has been insufficient for the nation's needs so that a considerable import is required. A higher price has now been offered in the hope of diminishing this. New Zealand is an interesting example of a country that lives by exporting agricultural products nevertheless having to import some of its staple foods.

Before the country was settled the native vegetation had been forest and dense scrub with large areas of tussock grass in the low rainfall districts. The early settlers cleared it all by burning; they found that pastures could readily be established by sowing on the ashes of the forest and scrub, and that the young shoots of the fired tussock grass could be eaten by sheep, while the older growth could not. This burning naturally led to erosion in hill districts under high rainfall, especially where conditions did not favour development of secondary growth, or where this had come, but had been reburned.

The land in the two islands was in 1949, utilized as follows:

	Million acres
Improved and farmed	20·13
Occupied but unimproved	23·12
Total occupied	43·25
Forest and scrub	7·66
Reserved for native use	5·80
Non-agricultural use, waste, etc.	8·80
	65·51 (*N.Z. Year Book*, 1950)

429

The improved area of 1948–49 is 1·08 million acres greater than the pre-war average of 1929–34, the grass having increased by 0·50 million acres, the fruit and plantations by 0·53 million acres and the field crops by 0·04 million acres.[1]

This area of 43·25 million acres of occupied land was in 90,192 holdings, 56 per cent of them were less than 150 acres in extent, but they covered only 6 per cent of the occupied land; holdings of 1,000 to 5,000 acres covered 25 per cent, and holdings of more than 5,000 acres 40 per cent; these large holdings, however, are mainly on poor land on steep hills. The details of the agriculturally occupied land were as follows in 1949–50:

Improved and farmed		*Occupied but unimproved*	
	Thousand acres		*Thousand acres*
Sown grasses	18,192	Tussock grass	11,695
Arable crops	904	Other native grass	1,234
Orchard	19		
Market garden and bush fruit	13	Total wild grass	12,929
Plantations	908	Barren and unproductive	1,892
Bare fallow	91	Other non-productive	8,200
		Buildings and gardens	97
	20,127		23,118

(*N.Z. Year Book*, 1950, and *Commonwealth Econ. Cttee.*, 1952, p. 47.)

The crops included:

	Thousand acres
Wheat for grain	125
Oats (53), barley (57), and maize (7)	117
Cereals for chaff, hay, ensilage or fodder	131
Rye grass for seed	55
Other grasses for seed	93
Lucerne (52), grass and clover for hay (494), and for silage (84)	630
Other fodder crops (1)	689

(1) In 1946–47—Turnips and swedes	354
Rape	154
Kale	83

(*Commonwealth Econ. Cttee.*, 35th Rpt., 1952, p. 48.)

The non-productive land includes about 5 million acres of secondary fern and scrub; this was originally forest but was burned and grass seed sown in the ashes; the pasture deteriorated and reverted to wild growth. It is gradually being brought back into use.

Arable cropping is now mainly carried out in the South Island: 96 per cent of the wheat (74 per cent on the Canterbury Plains and 12 per cent in Otago) and 73 per cent of the fodder crops are grown there. As already stated the area of wheat has been greatly reduced: its maximum was 402,273 acres in 1891–92, but by 1937–38 it had fallen to 186,000; during the war it rose, but is now down to 125,000. It remains to be seen whether the new financial

[1] *Commonwealth Econ. Cttee.* 35th Rpt., 1952, p. 47.

inducements will lead to more production in view of the high returns obtainable from grass seed and fat lamb. The area of oats has similarly declined from its maximum of 449,534 acres in 1900 to 53,000 now, and with the steady displacement of horses by tractors a still further fall is possible.

The numbers of livestock before the war and in 1950 are given in Table CVII.

TABLE CVII. *Livestock population, pre-war and post-war. Millions*

	Cattle			Sheep				Pigs		
	Average 1934–35– 1938–39	1950	1951		Average 1934–35– 1938–39	1950	1951	Average 1934–35– 1938–39	1950	1951
Dairy	—	2·86		Ewes	19·09	21·88				
Beef	—	2·09		Lambs		8·26 (1)		0·75	0·55	0·56
				Others		3·72				
Total	4·36	4·95	5·06		30·95	33·86				
Inc. cows in milk	1·77	1·85	1·90							
	(at January 31st)				(at April 30th)					

New Zealand Year Book, 1950 (*C.E.C. Rpt.*, 1953).

(1) By April 30th slaughtering of the lambs is well advanced, the inspectors estimated that 21 million lambs had been produced in 1950.

The numbers of cattle and of cows in milk in 1951 were the highest on record. The dairy cows were formerly Shorthorns, but some 85–90 per cent are now grade Jerseys. The beef cattle are mainly Aberdeen Angus with some Herefords. About 88 per cent of the cattle and 55 per cent of the sheep are in the North Island, the cattle chiefly in the Auckland, Taranaki and Wellington districts.

Since pre-war years (about 1933) the beef cattle have somewhat increased, but there has been no significant change in the number of dairy cows. The average production of butter fat per cow was about 180 lb. in 1917–18, it rose to about 220 lb. in 1926–27, and to 260 lb. in 1940–41; it varies between these limits from year to year according to the summer rainfall with which, as H. E. Annett has shown, it is directly correlated. On the better farms averages of 350 or even 400 lb. per cow are obtained, corresponding to 700 or 800 gallons of milk a year. The total quantities of butter fat processed at the dairy factories, and the total production, were:

	Average per cow lb.	Total production at pail million lb.	Processed in dairy factories million lb.
1940–41	262	466·3	409
1950–51	260	498·3	432·7

(*Rpt. of N.Z. Dairy Board*, 1950–51.)

The results in intervening years are lower, in the worst year by as much as 15 per cent. These figures correspond to a total production of about one million gallons of milk. Although obtained with no concentrated foods and practically nothing but grass, the average yield of butter fat per cow is only about 10 to 15 per cent less than that of Denmark, where considerable quantities of imported grains and cake are fed. Of the material delivered to the factories in 1951 about 76 per cent was made into butter, 22 per cent into cheese, and 2 per cent was condensed or used for whole milk products.[1] More provision is being made for the manufacture of skim and butter milk powders, the world demand for which is growing.

Generally speaking the herds are healthy: the wastage is of the order of 15 to 17 per cent of which about half is due to disease and about one-third to culling. Herd testing and artificial insemination are widely practised.

The sheep are mainly Southdowns and Romney Marsh in the North Island, and Southdowns and Corriedales (Merino × Longwool) in the South Island. The lambs are first crosses, using Southdown rams to ensure the small compact carcasses now required. The numbers of sheep have increased by 2·9 million which is almost entirely accounted for by breeding ewes.

Pigs, on the other hand, have decreased in number; formerly they were kept on dairy farms and utilized the butter milk and skim milk, but these are now more and more being processed. Prices of pig meat have not until recently encouraged its production; in the past farmers turned their attention to pigs only when prices of butter fat fell; indeed, the numbers of pigs were a kind of inverse indicator of dairy prosperity. Pigs are fewer by some 200,000 since pre-war days and are now only 11 per cent of the numbers of cattle: this contrasts strongly with Denmark where the pigs and cattle are almost equal in number.

Horses have fallen greatly in number with increasing use of tractors; in 1938 there were 130,000, in 1951 only 65,000.[2]

THE NORTH ISLAND

The North Island is a remarkable example of man-made productiveness. Nature's gift is the beautiful climate, wonderfully adapted to plant growth. But the soils are poor: some of them, like the pumice soils near the volcanoes, very poor; all are lacking in nitrogen and phosphate, and some in cobalt and copper also. The native vegetation included few good grasses and no leguminous plants except some shrubby ones; for grazing purposes it was necessary to introduce grasses and clovers from England. The favourable climatic conditions give them a very long growing season, and they flourish amazingly when the soil deficiencies are rectified by dressings of super-phosphate and other minerals. Perennial rye grass and white clover now occupy almost all the lowland. Still more remarkable: in the course of years a natural selection has gone on and distinct ecotypes have developed in the

[1] The milk was used as follows in 1950–51:

	Million gallons	Per cent of total
Manufacture	938	87·7
Human consumption	94	8·8
Used in farms and waste	38	3·5
Total production	1,070	

(*N.Z. Abstract of Statistics*, February, 1952, p. 5.)

[2] Draught horses (*Abstract of Statistics*, May 1952).

two islands. Vigorous, perennial leafy strains dominate in the good growing conditions of the North Island plains and valleys where the pastures have long remained unbroken, while in drier and less favourable conditions of the South Island plains where the pastures are ploughed up more frequently, short-lived, less productive strains have appeared. White clover has similarly differentiated into leafy perennial and short-lived ecotypes.

This capacity to produce grass, however, would have helped New Zealand little but for the development of refrigerator transport, which enables New Zealand's products to be offered in the shops of Great Britain in practically fresh condition. The invention came from Australia: in 1873 James Harrison was awarded a gold medal at the Melbourne Exhibition for his method of freezing meat; it was not, however, developed till 1879 and then it was not successful. The first satisfactory cargo of frozen mutton and lamb arrived at London from New Zealand in 1882 in a sailing ship fitted with refrigeration appliances; ten years later the transport was by steamers. Subsequently as the result of investigation at the Low Temperature Research Laboratory at Cambridge and elsewhere, chilling has replaced freezing with great advantage in the transport of beef. But the method works only for fifty days, and it breaks down unless the meat can be on the consumer's table within this period.

Transport difficulties having thus been overcome the grass can be used for the production of dairy produce, lamb and beef; dairying, however, is the chief activity and 75 per cent of New Zealand's dairy cows are on the North Island plains. (Pl. 43, p. 426.)

Pastures once sown in the North Island have hitherto been left down indefinitely. Those for dairy cattle receive 2 to 3 cwt. superphosphate per acre annually and if necessary 5 to 10 cwt. limestone; on much of the lighter lands potassic fertilizer is now becoming necessary and is increasingly applied. Sheep pastures receive less fertilizer, rarely more than $1\frac{1}{2}$ cwt. superphosphate per acre. In 1949–50, 5·73 million acres of grass were top dressed, about 80 per cent being in the North Island. This practice began in 1892 and has been extraordinarily repaying: it has enabled good permanent pastures to be made on land where formerly only poor temporary pasture was possible, and milk production to be practicable on land previously worthless.

The dairy farms are mostly small, many are 50 to 100 acres only or even smaller.[1] The stocking rate is heavy: on the plains and the better flat land 400 to 500 or more breeding ewes are kept per 100 acres—on the best farms up to 800 or 900—and on a typical 100 acre Waikato farm 60 milking cows besides young stock the whole year round. Grazing on the good farms is very intensive. The land is divided into paddocks having 1 acre for every 16 to 18 cows: on a 100-acre farm with 72 milking cows there may be 20 of about 4 to $4\frac{1}{2}$ acres each. These may be further sub-divided by electric

[1] In 1949 the numbers of holdings with cows in milk were:

No. of cows	*Thousand holdings*
4 and less	26
6–50	27
51–100	11
Over 100	2
	66

fences, the cows being allowed only as much grass as they can clear in one day. Frequent harrowing is necessary to spread the droppings.

Excess growth during the flush period in November is made into silage in pits or stacks: the buck rake is increasingly used for collecting the grass. Some hay is made during December. Silage is fed on the bare paddocks during the dry summer months; in winter both hay and silage are used. No purchased or concentrated foods are given: on most of the farms grass has to suffice, though on a few Waikato farms some soft turnips or marrow stem kale are grown for summer feed, and where the winters are colder some swedes and kale for use then. This prolific growth of grass is, however, entirely dependent on regular applications of superphosphate; often distributed on steep hillsides by aeroplane. (Pl. 44, p. 426.)

Further improvements began in 1920 and have continued since. The Grasslands Division has recently developed special purpose pastures containing red clover and H1 rye grass, a vigorous cross between Italian and perennial which under good conditions will last for three or four years making good growth in winter and early spring.[1] From November onwards the pasture is rested to allow the clover to grow and the H1 to seed; the deep roots of the clover enable it to stand up so well during the dry summer months that it provides much good food when other plants are dormant; then when rain comes the H1 seedlings grow quickly and supplement the food provided by the original plants now starting into growth. Perennial rye grass and white clover are frequently included in the mixture to replace the H1 and red clover when they fail.

The usual production of butter fat per acre is about 100 to 150 lb., corresponding to about 200 or 300 gallons of milk; double these amounts are obtained on good pastures, and 400 lb. is the record for a commercial farm. On some of the best fat lamb farms up to 750 lb. live weight increase per acre is obtained, though again the average is much less.

The organization of the work is as efficient as the management of the grass. A farmer and one "boy" will run a 100 acre farm with 55–60 or even 80 cows. It is rare to find more than two men on a farm of 150 acres where 90–100 cows are milked. One man will milk 50 to 60 cows in $1\frac{1}{2}$ to 2 hours. Nowhere else is such a volume of work achieved:[2] the New Zealand dairy farmers are among the hardest workers in the world. The milking, of course, is done by machine, and on most farms there is usually no stripping: further, the animals are out all the year so there is no carrying of food or cleaning out of the sheds. The milk is separated on the farm and the skim milk goes to the pigs while the cream goes to the factory; the milking need not be done at the uncomfortable hours often necessary for an early town delivery of fresh milk.

The processing and marketing are done with great efficiency and economy. The dairy factories are owned by the milk suppliers who must take out shares proportionate in number to the quantity of cream they send in. A number of these factories may be grouped into a larger organization such as the N.Z. Co-operative Dairy Co. Since 1947 the marketing has been

[1] See L. Corkill, *Empire Jl. Expt. Agric.*, 1949, Vol. 17, pp. 157–69.
[2] When Peterson, the American quick milking exponent, visited New Zealand and saw the speed of working there he admitted that he was only a learner.

done exclusively by the Dairy Products Marketing Commission which in each August fixes the guaranteed price to be paid to farmers.[1]

The output of these intensive grass farms has much increased. The average carrying capacity of the Waikato grass farms, richer and poorer, has been, per 10 acres:

	Cows in milk	Breeding ewes
1925	2	1
1930	3	3
1940	4	4
1945	4	6

(Royal Commission on Sheep Farming, 1949), quoted in *Commonwealth Econ. Cttee.*, *35th Rpt.*, 1952.

This steady increase in productiveness is the result of several factors: the fortunate accident that leafy, permanent ecotypes of rye grass and white clover developed in the North Island; the excellent management of the grass, especially the proper adjustment of the number of animals in the rotational grazing to ensure full utilization of the grass and of the animal droppings; and the use of superphosphate and if necessary lime to encourage the clover.

Not all of the plains, however, are fertile. The poor areas of pumice soil in the active volcanic region of Rotorua and the Taupo plateau are in their natural state quite unsuitable for dairying; even beef and wool production were hazardous because of the liability of cattle and sheep to "bush sickness." Much of this land was therefore afforested, chiefly with *Pinus* species. Later it was found that the bush sickness was due to a deficiency of cobalt in the soil[2] and could be avoided by an application of 4 oz. per acre of a cobalt salt along with the superphosphate. As a result the land is now rapidly being put into pasture and the dairy farms are producing as well as any in the Waikato. The physical condition of the soil enables it to retain moisture particularly well. Where water is available settlement is progressing more rapidly than anywhere else in New Zealand, but where there is no water the land is put into forest.

The highlands of the North Island are too poor and too steep for dairying and are used for large sheep farms continuing the old business of wool production: many of the old stations are reminiscent of those of Australia in their size and lay-out, and in the wealth of their owners. The improved herbage consists largely of *Agrostis vulgaris* (brown top), *Anthoxanthum odoratum*, Yorkshire fog, crested dog's tail, plantain, dandelion and others that would be classed in England as weeds, but there is some cocksfoot and *Trifolium dubium*. On the drier hills of the east coast *Danthonia pilosa* is important. Great improvement is effected by superphosphate.

Some reseeding is done through the animals: they are grazed on improved pastures of rye grass, cocksfoot, white clover, lucerne, etc., or alternatively fed on improved hay; some of the seeds pass out with their excreta and, after germination, the young plants being thus supplied with manure, are able to grow and establish themselves. Overseeding with H1 rye grass or

[1] Particulars of the Marketing Organization are given in *37th Rpt. Commonwealth Econ. Cttee.*, 1952, p. 55.

[2] Other cobalt deficient soils have been found in the South Island at Glenhope in the Nelson province, and in Southland.

clover by aeroplane is increasingly practised on the steeper hills to lengthen the grazing season. Where perennial rye grass, white clover, and crested dog's tail become dominant up to 6,000 lb. of dry matter can be obtained per acre, and on better slopes and ridges where stock habitually camp some 9,000 lb. per acre have been recorded. Such pastures can carry 4 to 6 ewes per acre and some cattle. Lower grade herbage consisting of *Agrostis*, Yorkshire fog, *Lotus major*, and subterranean clover with some perennial rye grass and white clover can carry 3 to 4 ewes per acre plus cattle. The unimproved hill pastures may carry 1 to 1½ sheep per acre as well as some store lambs and store cattle.

Although the North Island is best known for its dairying it also produces considerable quantities of fat lamb, especially on the east coast plains and in the Manawatu and Waikato districts. The usual cross is between Romney Marsh ewes and Southdown rams. The lambs are usually killed off the mother; the carcass weight used to be about 32 lb., now it averages about 34 lb. Beef production is closely integrated with sheep production but rather as a by-product, the cattle being regarded as animated mowing machines: it is chiefly carried out in the Wellington, Hawkes Bay, Gisborne and Auckland districts. Some difficulty is experienced in providing winter food.

The eastern upland region—Wairarapa, and the country north of Gisborne —is poor and dry; it is in large sheep stations producing wool and breeding ewes for fat lamb farms. Store cattle are also raised and are useful in keeping down fern and other wild vegetation that would reduce the capacity for carrying sheep; they are finished on good lowland grass.

THE SOUTH ISLAND

The South Island differs greatly from the North. Its farming is much more varied. The valleys and gentle slopes of the northern hills facing Tasman Bay produce fruit, tobacco and hops well; Motueka, Riwaka and others are among the choicest districts in the whole country; nearly half New Zealand's apples are grown here. The uplands are now being developed. The Moutere Hills region, formerly poor sheep pastures carrying about one sheep to four acres, has had its poverty traced to soil deficiencies in lime, phosphate, magnesium and boron. Reclamation has been on good ecological lines: appropriate areas have been sown with good grasses and clovers, others near the sea coast have been planted with apples, and others with *Pinus insignis.* A considerable area had reverted to bracken and much of this must eventually be planted with exotic timber trees.[1]

The Nelson district produces all the tobacco and hops, and considerable quantities of canning crops and of tomatoes grown under glass. The various scientific problems are studied at the Cawthron Institute and associated field stations of the Department of Scientific and Industrial Research. In the Marlborough County where the rainfall is about 24 inches a year, crops are grown for seed including grass, lucerne and other small seeds, choice garden varieties of peas for England; this is a growing industry in New Zealand, the area under small seeds having increased from 66,855 acres in 1929–30 to 213,100 acres in 1950–51 and the production from 20·0

[1] T. H. Rigg, *et al.* "The Moutere Gravels, Waimea County," *Bull. Nelson Catchment Board, N.Z.*

million lb. to 63·6 million lb. Further south is the famous Banks Peninsula renowned for its *Akaroa* cocksfoot introduced by Alexander Hay, an 1843 settler. He received in 1861 two pounds of cocksfoot seed from Edinburgh, gave half away but sowed the rest. It flourished amazingly and ousted the native plants, remaining almost as a pure culture. In course of time it was grown over much of New Zealand, and its seed has long been exported to Great Britain, Denmark and elsewhere. In recent years, however, its production has declined.

Further south and on the drier eastern side lies the great Canterbury Plain 120 miles long, 40 miles wide at its widest, and nearly a million acres in extent with much good land and a rainfall of about 25 inches; it is the most important arable area in New Zealand. It was settled by an English Episcopalian group in 1851 who also established Christchurch and gave it something of a University atmosphere. The plain was first used for wheat production: three or more crops were grown and the land then left for a time to cover itself with grass; later it was broken up again. Temperatures and rainfall are both too low to allow of the almost continuous growth of grass characteristic of the North Island; instead, arable farming with long leys for fat lamb production is widely practised. The cross used is now generally a Southdown ram on Corriedale or half-bred (Merino × Longwool) ewes. A mixture of rye grass, cocksfoot and white clover is left down for three to five years, this may be followed by rape or turnips folded on the land; next may come wheat and then oats in which the new ley is sown.

No concentrated food is given except to the stud flock. The lambs are sold either direct from the mother or from rape. The success of the scheme depends on the ley. There had been a tendency to sow poor strains of herbage, and carrying capacity and subsequent cereal yields were falling in consequence. This was rectified by the use of better strains.[1] The farms are about 300 or 400 acres in size, and are mostly run by the farmer and one or two helpers.

Further south in the Southland district oats are widely grown, but grass-land farming is of great and increasing importance. A considerable acreage of stone fruit is grown in Central Otago.

Yields both in the south and on the Canterbury Plain are very high: wheat usually gives about 36 bushels per acre but 60 or 70 bushels are at times obtained, even 90 bushels on one occasion. A common dressing is one cwt. per acre of superphosphate applied with the seed in the combined seed and fertilizer drill. The nitrogen comes from the ley.

Most of the South Island, however, is hill country and some of it east of the main divide is so dry, having only about 20 inches of rain, that it carried no forest; its native vegetation is largely tussock grass, *Poa caespitosa*, in low-lying wetter parts, and *Festuca novozealandia* higher up. It is wool-growing land suitable for Merino sheep and their crosses; its carrying capacity is low, but as some compensation it produces the finest quality wool.

In less hilly country improvement becomes practicable and then not only wool and store sheep, but also cattle can be produced. The method is to control the grazing and introduce seeds of better plants: *Danthonia, Agrostis* and other grasses, and some clovers; where the rainfall is adequate this can be done by seeding through livestock as on the high pastures of the North

[1] E. Bruce Levy, *Jl. Farmers Club*, London, October, 1949.

Island; good hay is fed to the animals and the seeds pass out with their excreta. Under lower rainfall this method may not suffice: surface seeding and aerial top dressings are then used.

Bruce Levy regards *Agrostis* as the indicator of marginal conditions of fertility and rainfall: wherever it is dominant the pasture can be improved by encouraging white clover and so building up in the soil the stock of nitrogenous organic matter which allows the development of the highly productive rye grass and white clover herbage.

Erosion is less serious in New Zealand than in some of the semi-arid countries, but it has occurred. Some 8 million acres of this tussock land has suffered more or less erosion as the result of overburning and overstocking, combined with damage by rabbits: about 3 million so seriously that much of it has been abandoned. The Lands Department has taken over some of this derelict land and shown that it can be greatly improved by restricting the burning, reducing the number of sheep, and introducing cattle, aerial sowing of grasses, clovers and fertilizers.

Much of the steeper land ought never to have been cleared and should be closed for afforestation, but this necessitates exclusion of livestock and prohibition of burning on the neighbouring grazing land: farmers object to this as burning is their easiest means of controlling bracken, gorse and tea tree. Little as yet is being done: the present policy is to conserve the existing natural forest. In the North Island there has been extensive slip erosion in the Gisborne district and elsewhere: many hillsides are scarred and valley lands have been choked with silt which has caused serious flooding. Elsewhere the increasing attention to soil improvement, the general absence of drought, flood and fire, all tend to keep erosion in check.

A Soil Conservation and River Control Council was set up in 1941 and separate Catchment Boards were established.

The Quantities of Food Produced in New Zealand

The quantities of food produced in New Zealand are set out in Table CVIII. They had all been increasing until the war, then except for cheese they fell

TABLE CVIII. *Food production in New Zealand. Thousand tons*

	Average					Average			
	1931–33 (1)	1937–39 (1)	1949–50 (2)	1950–51 (2)		1931–33 (1)	1937–39 (1)	1949–50 (2)	1950–51 (2)
Mutton and					Butter	147·5	159·6	169	181·9
lamb (1)	251·5	243	332	292·4	Cheese	99·8 (3)	90·5 (4)	105·4	108·5
(inc. lamb)			201	183	Preserved				
Beef and					milk	12·7	15·9	45·7	54·2
veal	115·6	163	185·4	172	Wheat	238	175	131	168 (1)
(inc. veal)			21·2	18·1	Apples	52	51	55	56 (1)
Pig meat	28·9	47	38·9	39					
(inc. bacon									
and ham)			25·3	25·4)					
All meat	475·5 (5)	577·4	530						

(1) *Commonwealth Econ. Cttee.*, 37th Rpt., 1952, and 1953 Rpts.
(2) *N.Z. Abstract of Statistics*, May 1952, pp. 6 and 9. September year for meat.
(3) Average 1933–37. (4) 1938–39. (5) Average 1953–39: *F.A.O. Balance Sheets*.

off, but they have now recovered and passed the pre-war levels. For creamery butter and meat in 1950–51 the increase has been $12\frac{1}{2}$ per cent, for cheese 20 per cent, and for processed milk 250 per cent. Cheese output had risen much higher in the war: it rose to 158,000 tons in 1941–42 at the request of British Ministry of Food, but this proved to be more than the markets could take (Figs. 29 and 30).

Output of wheat and of feeding grains, however, is falling, and for these, as for sugar and fruit, the home production is not sufficient and supplies have to be brought in from overseas. The quantities imported have been in thousand tons:

	Wheat	*Other grains*	*Sugar*	*Fruit*
Average 1935–39 (1)	52·9	17·1	82·5	38·5
1949 (2)	154	9·8	79·5	36·9
1950 (2)	155		127	30·9
1951 (3)	284			

(1) *F.A.O. Food Balance Sheets*, 1949.

(2) *N.Z. Abstract of Statistics*, May 1952, p. 36.

(3) C.E.C. Rpts., *Grain*, 1953.

The imported fruit of 1950 consisted of bananas (12,500 tons) and of oranges, canned and dried fruits in nearly equal proportions; against this was an export of 12,465 tons of apples. Any of the imported fruits except bananas could be grown; even citrus fruits are possible in the northern part of the North Island, but whether in sufficient quantity or at a suitable price is not yet certain.

On the other hand there are large exports of meat and dairy produce; they fell off during the war but have since recovered (Fig. 30). The quantities are shown in Table CIX.

TABLE CIX. *Exports of meat and of dairy produce from New Zealand.*
Thousand tons

	Dairy produce					Meat			
	Average 1935–39	1944	1950	1951		*Average* 1935–39	1944	1950	1951
	(1)	(2)	(2)	(2)		(1)		(2)	(2)
Butter	138	115·3	137	147	Lamb	195 ⎱	136	186	159·5
Cheese	84·6	77·7	99·9	107	Mutton	⎰	54·8	68	49
Dried milk	10·4 ⎱	7·8	29·8	36·8	Beef	58·6	3·0	50·6	36·3
Condensed					Veal	15·8	4·0	8·4	6·6
milk	⎰	0·42	10·85	10·76	Pig meat	27·4	2·0	9·7	8·1
Casein		0·30	5·54	5·89	All meat	301·4	207·8	338	275

(1) *F.A.O. Balance Sheets*, 1949.

(2) *N.Z. Abstract of Statistics*, May 1952, p. 36, calender year for all produce.

1951 was a bad year for lamb and beef production and export, figures for 1952 are higher.

They represent about half to three-quarters of the total output of meat, butter, cheese and preserved milk: New Zealand is the world's largest exporter of butter and cheese and the second largest exporter of meat and

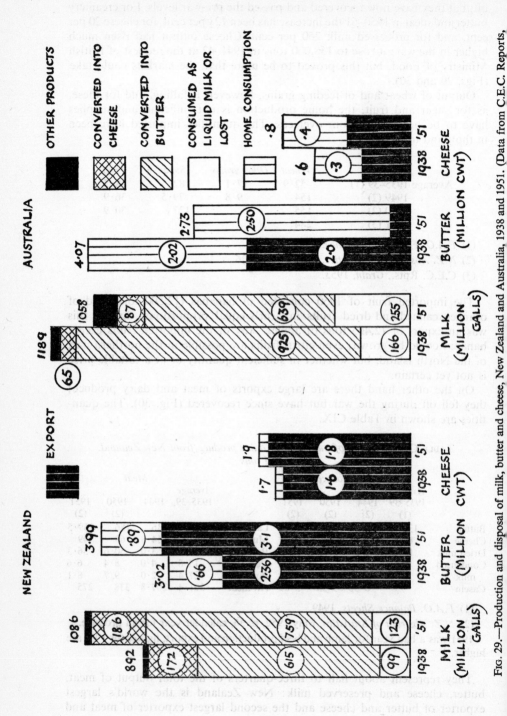

Fig. 29.—Production and disposal of milk, butter and cheese, New Zealand and Australia, 1938 and 1951. (Data from C.E.C. Reports,

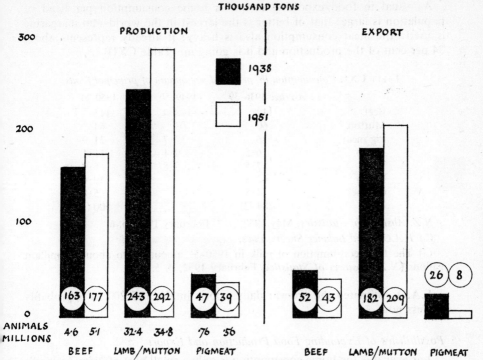

FIG. 30.—Production and export of meat, New Zealand, 1938 to 1951. (Data from
C.E.C. Reports, *Meat*, 1953.)

wool. The direct export of crops is only small, they being largely used as
feeding stuffs and go out as livestock products.

About 90 per cent of these exports go to Great Britain in accordance with
long-term contracts with the British Ministry of Food and the New Zealand
Government Marketing Organization.[1]

Vital as they are to us, they are equally important to New Zealand. Its
external trade is said to be the largest in the world per head of population:
about 80 per cent of the exports are from farms, and they account for a
large percentage of farm income (Table CX).

TABLE CX. *Percentage of gross farm income derived from exports*

	New Zealand Consumption		Export	
	1936–37–	1947–48–	1936–37–	1947–48–
	1938–39	1949–50	1938–39	1949–50
Agricultural produce	89	84	11	16
Pastoral produce	22	13	78	85
Dairying, etc., produce	31	31	69	69
All farm produce	33	29	67	71

(*Commonwealth Econ. Cttee.*, 37th *Rpt.*, 1952.)

[1] Rather surprisingly an export of cheese to the United States and to Canada has begun,
very small as yet, but it will be interesting to see how far it develops.
Particulars of the Marketing Organization are given in 37th *Rpt. Commonwealth Econ.
Cttee.*, 1952, p. 55.

As usual in food exporting countries home consumption per head of population is large: that of butter is the largest in the world—no margarine is used—the meat consumption also is heavy; it already represents about 34 per cent of the production and it is going up (Table CXI):

TABLE CXI. *Consumption lb. per head per annum of principal foods*

	Average 1936–39	1949–50	1950–51
Beef	112	108·4	115
Mutton	60	64	64
Pig meat	26	32·7	31·9
Lamb	6·5	9·1	11·1
Veal	7·5	5·8	5·7
Butter	42·8		39·6
Cheese	4·5		5·8
Milk	284 (2)		500 (3)

N.Z. Abstract of Statistics, May 1952, p. 7. February 1952, p. 6.

(2) *F.A.O. Food Balance Sheets*, 1949.

(3) The total consumption of milk in 1950–51 amounted to about 94 million gallons (*N.Z. Abstract of Statistics*, February 1952, p. 5.

F.A.O. estimated the pre-war daily calorie intake at 3,260: it is probably no less now.

Possibilities of Expanding Food Production and Export

Large as it is the home consumption is only a small part of New Zealand's output of meat and dairy produce and the important question arises: Can this high rate of output continue or is New Zealand, like Australia, near the end of the present stage of development? New Zealand agriculturists consider that more can be produced. Less than one half of the land is as yet improved; a good deal of the remainder is agriculturally unpromising, but both islands, especially the North Island, have considerable areas of land unproductive because of various soil deficiencies: chiefly lime and phosphate, but in places magnesium, boron and cobalt, which can now be rectified.

Some of the hindrances to production can also be removed or reduced. Three weeds carried in from Great Britain had spread with the amazing vigour characteristic of New Zealand conditions and were causing great losses; treatment has, however, now been devised and they are being brought under control. Gorse invaded some of the poor hill land; it has some value for adult sheep if kept under control by burning and close grazing, but once out of hand it is useless and becomes a serious fire risk for the pine plantations now being established on the low quality grazing lands. It is also doing serious damage on Banks Peninsula, where the vigorous strains of cocksfoot grow. Some of the new hormone sprays, e.g. 2. 4. 5 T., however, are proving effective against it. Blackberry has spread terribly in some of the higher rainfall districts of the west coast, indeed parts of the country have been described as one huge blackberry bush. Where the surface of the land is smooth enough to allow the passage of a mower the bushes are cut, a dressing of superphosphate is given and the resulting sward is heavily grazed: no more trouble then arises. Here also 2. 4. 5 T. promises to be an effective control agent. The third serious weed, ragwort, threatened to do much damage in the Waikato region; it is kept down by spraying with sodium chlorate and also by turning wethers on to the land.

There is still considerable scope for improvement of the pastures, good as they are at present. The average rate of stocking is higher than in many countries and has for long been steadily increasing especially in the North Island:

Average numbers of livestock per thousand acres occupied

	Cows in milk	Total cattle	Sheep shorn
1928	30·6	74·5	551
1933	42·7	97·4	587
1949	40·9	111	709
1950	42·7	114	729

(*Commonwealth Econ. Cttee.*, 37th Rpt., 1952.)

But the limit is not reached: these figures are far below those for the Waikato region (p. 435).

Fertilizers are increasingly used. The areas top-dressed with lime and phosphate have been:

	Million acres dressed		Million tons used	
	Lime	Phosphate	Lime	Phosphate
1949–50	1·98	5·14	1·10	0·650
1950–51	2·17	5·68	1·27	0·705

As, however, the acreage of sown grass is 18·2 million and that of wild grass 12·9 million it seems that a considerably larger area could be top dressed with advantage. A difficulty in increasing supplies of superphosphate is that its manufacture requires sulphur, which is severely rationed, or reconstruction of the factory to adapt it to a new process, which would be difficult and costly.

Other fertilizers are but little used: the total quantity in 1949–50 was only 13,000 tons. Nitrogenous fertilizers are not applied to the grassland, and their effect on the yields of arable crops in the South Island has not been fully investigated: at present their cost is very high.[1]

The Grasslands Division of the Scientific and Industrial Research Department at Palmerston North has isolated highly productive strains of good grasses and clovers from which pedigree strains have been bred. Some of the experimental pastures have produced 7,500 lb. of starch equivalent per acre, calculated to yield up to 500 lb. of butter fat or 750 lb. live weight increase and 150 lb. wool per annum.[2] Selected strains of grass have given 14,000 to 16,000 lb. of dry matter per acre, equivalent to more than 7 or 8 tons of hay per acre. Success, however, depends entirely on the clover, for this is the sole source of the nitrogen required by the grass; no nitrogenous

---

[1] In 1952 sulphate of ammonia cost £36 per ton.

[2] Quantities obtained for three years running at the Grassland Research Institute, Palmerston North (E. Bruce Levy, *Jl. Farmers Club*, October 1949). See also his book *Grasslands of New Zealand*. It should be stated that the soil is a deep alluvium and the rainfall good: 45 inches per annum.

fertilizer is given, nor are imported food-stuffs used. In an experiment at Palmerston North a sward of pure high yielding grasses gave 4,000 lb. of dry matter per acre, but the addition of clover raised the yield to 13,000 lb.: doubling the production of grass and adding 5,000 lb. from the clover.[1] The former director, E. Bruce Levy, has expressed the view that the output of beef, lamb and dairy produce from the lowland dairying and fattening country could be doubled in ten years by fuller use of these improved strains, more frequent breaking up and reseeding of the pastures, more use of special purpose pastures to ensure a wider spread of full growth and avoid some of the present wasteful conservation methods, more top dressing and better selection of animals.[2] If nitrogenous fertilizers became available in quantities and at prices to make their widespread use in the South Island possible for out-of-season grass, even higher outputs might become possible.

Although New Zealand does not suffer from drought in the Australian sense of the word there are conditions where irrigation is advantageous. It has been practised for over twenty-five years in parts of Central Otago and it is being increasingly adopted on the Canterbury Plains, where in 1949–50, 106,494 acres were irrigated from the Rangitata river. Even in the higher rainfall conditions of the North Island there are dry periods in summer when the grass gives out and milk yields fall, especially on the light soils of the Waikato, causing heavy financial loss.[3] H. E. Annett has shown that this can be avoided by spray irrigation: 14 acres of sprayed pasture on his 100-acre farm sufficed to keep his 80 cows in full production throughout the dry periods.

The supply of meat could be considerably increased by allowing the lambs to reach a heavier weight before killing them. About two-thirds of them are killed as milk lambs straight off the mothers at a weight of 30–34 lb. The rest are weaned, fed on grass, rape or other fodder crops and killed at 35 or 36 lb. weight.[4] An increase in the supply of milk lambs—which is what the British Ministry of Food has requested—can be obtained only by increasing the number of ewes. If, however, more lambs were kept on the farm to a weight of 40 to 50 lb. additional meat would be obtained without this necessity. Large rams such as the Suffolk would be needed and some changes in management: some of the North Island pastures would have to be ploughed up so that finishing crops could be grown, but they could afterwards be sown down again to better mixtures.

Improvement of the pastures, while a necessary preliminary to more meat production, is not sufficient to bring it about. More killing stations and freezing works are needed, as well as better port facilities. Before the war there was a considerable export to Great Britain of chilled beef which obtained a premium over the frozen beef also sent. But export of chilled beef requires well insulated refrigerator wagons, and prompt loading and dispatch of the steamers; the period between the killing of the animals and

[1] E. Bruce Levy and P. D. Sears, *Proc. N.Z. Animal Prod. Soc.*, 1948.

[2] E. Bruce Levy, *Jl. Farmers Club*, October 1949.

[3] H. E. Annett estimates the loss of dairy income at up to £5 million in a bad season, and during the past eighteen years at fully £70 million: there are further large losses of meat and wool. See *N.Z. Jl. Agric.*, April and May 1951.

[4] The average carcass weight of lamb in 1951–52 was just over 35 lb. (30th Ann. Rpt. N.Z. Meat Producers Assoc., 1952.)

the distribution of the meat must not exceed 50 days of which 30 to 35 are required for the voyage. As the industry was organized before the war these conditions were easily attained; now for various reasons the export of chilled beef has stopped and the less satisfactory frozen meat has taken its place. Attempts are being made to re-start the chilled beef industry,[1] but the difficulties are considerable. Great Britain has offered to buy all the meat New Zealand can produce for the next fifteen years at an attractive price. For the present wool production is more remunerative, but this may not last.

Labour difficulties are more serious, and may set a limit to butter production. As in other advanced countries the supply of labour is becoming the crux of the problem: the number of persons engaged in agriculture fell from 135,909 in 1929–30 to 125,687 in 1950.[2] The output per man has risen and is now among the highest in the world: this has been the result of improving the pastures and the animals, and above all by the extended use of machinery facilitated by New Zealand's wonderful supply of water power suitable for the generation of electricity. But mechanization cannot go much farther in replacing farm workers and in any case it is becoming increasingly expensive.

---

[1] The premium offered for chilled beef is £23 per ton.

[2] *N.Z. Year Book*, 1950. The total farm population had increased from 345,770 to 372,450, indicating that a smaller proportion of the members of the family were working on the farm.

Chapter 13

THE POTENTIAL SUPPLIERS:
THE SOUTH AMERICAN COUNTRIES

South America holds out greater possibilities of additional food production than any other continent. It stretches from the equatorial to the antarctic regions, but the southern subarctic part is narrow and forms only a small percentage of the total area. The larger part of the land mass is within the belt of sub-tropical and temperate production; much of it is in the region of rainfall exceeding 40 inches a year, usually well distributed with no well-marked dry season and no great desert areas comparable with that of the United States and Canada. The native vegetation over large areas is grass or grass savannah, in the northern part there is much tropical forest. Two great river systems, the Plate and the Amazon, occupy a vast area: the Plate system comprises the Pampas already much developed, and the Amazon system, swamp and tropical forest as yet almost untouched.

South America was early colonized by Spain and Portugal, and in the 19th-century migrations from Europe it attracted many Italians, Poles and others from Central and Eastern Europe, but relatively few from the United Kingdom and North-West Europe. An interesting result has been that the stable political institutions characteristic of these countries never got established in South America, and the consequent political instability and irresponsibility have greatly retarded development. Countries with vast potential resources remain undeveloped and many people who have invested in Government and other bonds have had such bitter experiences that they are unlikely to do so again.

The large areas of grass and of deciduous forest make South America eminently suitable for cattle and sheep, and the absence of a regular dry season avoids the set-back in condition which causes so much loss in South Africa and Australia. Moreover the grassland is readily converted into arable land on which according to the latitude all the temperate and sub-tropical crops can be grown. Great droughts occur at times as in 1950 and 1951 in the Argentine, but so do seasons of outstanding abundance; losses from locusts and grasshoppers are less serious than in other continents with considerable desert areas. The troubles of the agriculturist are more often due to man than to Nature.

Usually the populations are mixed: including a considerable number of Indians, many persons of European descent, some of whom, however, have been for generations in the country, and many of mixed Indian and European origin.

During the war money was poured into South America owing to the rapid rise of price of its agricultural and pastoral products, but this did not have the effect of correspondingly increasing output: as in Africa, additional financial inducement did not evoke additional effort. The output of the chief products changed only slightly. In Latin America for example the output has been, in million tons:

	Average 1934–38	1947 (1)
Wheat	8·616	9·212
Maize	17·636	17·600
Meat	5·515	5·158

(1) The Argentine accounted for two-thirds of the wheat, over a third of the maize and nearly half of the meat.

(U.N. Econ. Council for Latin America, Havana meeting, 1949.)

Meanwhile, the population had risen by 23 per cent, but total food production by only 20 per cent and exports only by 16 per cent.

In most of the countries agriculture is primitive with exceptions in the Argentine, Brazil and Uruguay. In Peru, Bolivia, Paraguay, Venezuela, it does not suffice to feed the population, and imports of either grain, meat, or dairy produce or all of them are necessary: in these countries efforts are directed to the production of export commodities, cotton, wool, hides and sugar rather than to that of food. Venezuela has much land suitable for crops and cattle yet not used: about two-thirds of its food is imported, and yet more than half of its population is reported to suffer from malnutrition, while tuberculosis, typhus and syphilis are said to be rife also. Colombia has great areas of fertile soil at present very little cultivated, but lacking roads. Ecuador can almost be described as the Kenya of South America with tropical conditions at its lower altitudes and temperature conditions in the uplands: here dairying and production of European cereals, potatoes and vegetables are all possible. At present the country is mainly a vast forest, but development is beginning; 124,000 acres of good land have been set aside for British and American colonization. Peru has some 30 million acres of potential arable land, but only about 10 per cent is actually cultivated; the output is of cash products for export: sugar, cotton, coffee, wool, hides and skin, and it is necessary to import wheat, rice, fats, oils, meat and dairy produce. Chile has a central zone of about 50 million acres much of it suited to agriculture, but only 5 per cent of it is actually cropped and the cattle number only about 2¼ millions. As in other under-developed regions there is a good deal of soil erosion, this also occurs in Guatemala, a fertile region producing coffee and bananas and apparently capable of a good deal more. In some of the Andean republics, especially Bolivia and Peru, the Indian workers are greatly addicted to *coca* which much lowers their efficiency: some of the most backward areas are here.

Speaking generally, the Governments are endeavouring to improve their agriculture, but this necessitates much more capital and expert guidance and more good labour than the countries themselves can provide. Some of them are more interested in developing industry, which will be very difficult, than in improving their agriculture.

South America contains more potential new land than any other part of the world. Only a fraction of the grasslands have yet been broken up, though great areas could be alternately cropped and laid down to grass or lucerne mixtures. But the greatest area of land awaiting development is the Amazon basin: the greatest not only in South America but in the whole world.

This vast region of nearly 2,000 million acres takes in parts of nine separate

447

countries, few of which could do much development on their own resources: it includes vast areas of swamp in the flood plain of the river and an immense amount of tropical forest. It would be idle to speculate on what this region could produce if it were properly utilized. The luxuriant vegetation gives probably an exaggerated idea of the fertility of the soil, and once it was cleared erosion would almost certainly be intensified unless proper steps were taken against it. The first step is to learn something about the region: nothing invites disaster more surely than opening up virgin country to cultivation without adequate knowledge of all the environmental conditions. In 1947 and 1948 UNESCO organized conferences of experts from the countries concerned, and it was decided to set up an International Institute for making the necessary surveys. It still remains to be seen how far the work can be carried.

Three of the countries of South America play so important a part in the provision of food for the United Kingdom and North-Western Europe that they must be discussed separately: the Argentine, Brazil and Uruguay. A fourth, Paraguay, offers considerable scope for development and is also treated separately.

THE ARGENTINE

The Argentine Republic is the largest food producer in South America and before the war was one of the largest food exporters in the world, having first place with linseed, maize and beef, and second place with wheat.

It has an extraordinarily wide range of conditions, varying from tropical in the north to sub-arctic in the south, and produces a corresponding range of crops. Most of the country is a great plain rising gradually from the Atlantic to the Andes, but broken in the north and south; rainfall and temperature are highest in the north and decrease towards the south and west. The northern section has a rainfall of 60 to 70 inches and mean temperatures about 75° F; it is naturally forest, but with much marsh due to blocked rivers. The middle section has a rainfall of 36 to 24 inches and mean temperatures of about 60° F; it is a great grassy plain, the Pampas. The southern section is much colder and drier and forms the arid steppe country of Patagonia.

The Pampas region is agriculturally and economically by far the most important. Its area is about 200 million acres; it extends for about 800 miles almost from lat. 30° S. to lat. 40° S., and includes the territory of La Pampa and the provinces of Buenos Aires, Cordoba (eastern part) and Santa Fé (southern part). It is treeless, has a deep soil, much of it black (containing, however, only 2 or 3 per cent of organic matter), and is in general the counterpart of the prairies of North America excepting that its climate is more genial, the winters in particular being much milder and the summers cooler. In spite of its great length from north to south the temperatures are not widely different in the different parts: in January they average about 70° F to 74° F, and in July, the coldest month, about 45° F to 55° F; these uniform averages, however, conceal considerable daily ranges of temperature. The rainfall shows more variation: it is about 38 inches a year at Buenos Aires in the east central area, 28 inches at Cordoba in the north-west, but only 21 inches at Bahia Blanca in the south. It comes mostly in summer: the winters are dry. Droughts are liable to occur though they are usually less than on the Canadian prairies and the corresponding country in Australia; nevertheless they do come: one of the worst in modern times was in 1950–51 which was said to have caused the death of something like 10 million cattle—a quarter of the whole cattle population—leaving serious after-effects in the following two years.

The Pampas vegetation varies with the rainfall: in the east and centre it consists mainly of species of *Andropogon, Paspalum, Panicum, Stipa, Bromus* and *Poa*: in the drier west the *Paspalum, Panicum* and *Bromus* tend to be displaced by *Aristida* and *Erogrostis*, but the *Andropogon, Stipa* and *Poa* still persist although the soil is no longer covered, and, being exposed to the sun and wind, is liable to wind erosion. Nowhere are leguminous plants common.

The first stage in the development of the Argentine was of the usual primitive pastoral type: cattle were raised on vast estancias by the picturesque "gauchos," Pampas cowboys, well known to our grandparents. The exports were hides, tallow, some live cattle and some dried meat.

The country became opened up as transport improved: crowds of immigrants from Italy, Poland and other countries flocked in, and grain cultivation expanded; many estancias in the eastern part of the Pampas were broken up into smaller units let off as "chacras" or grain farms to tenants or share croppers. A network of roads, railways and elevators—including the largest in South America—was set up, mainly by British enterprise, to deal with the produce, and the Argentine became the chief exporter of maize and linseed and had second place among exporters of wheat. The quality of the cattle was greatly improved, large, well-equipped packing houses were built, the chilling process developed, and a refrigerator transport organized. The Argentine soon became the world's chief exporter of beef. The arable country remained chiefly in the east, linked with the two ports Buenos Aires and Rosario partly for reasons of transport, but chiefly because the climate here is most suitable for cereal production. The estancias, however, still occupied by far the greater part of the Pampas.[1]

The war has, however, brought about great changes, the end of which no man can foresee.

The total area of the country is 691 million acres, of which about 310 million acres are pasture, and in 1951 about 58 million arable. The chief crops, their output and the post-war changes are shown in Table CXII and Fig. 31.

The arable area had been 60 million acres in 1927: it had risen by 1937 to 67·4 million acres, of which 50 million were cereals and linseed, about one-third being wheat, one-third maize and of the rest half was linseed and the other half oats, rye and barley. By 1951–52 the arable area had shrunk to 59 million acres of which 30 million only were cereals and linseed: of this area wheat occupied rather more than a third but maize was down to one-fifth. The fall was thus unequal: the export grains, wheat, maize, and linseed had suffered most, wheat falling by 37 per cent to 11·8 million acres,

---

[1] An account of the pre-war agriculture of the Argentine is given by Antonio Arena in *Aperçu Agronomique sur la République Argentine, Annales Agronomiques*, 1938.

TABLE CXII. *Acreage and production of chief crops, Argentine*

| | Million acres | | Million tons produced | | | Million tons exported | | |
| | Average | | | Average | | | Average | | |
	1937–39	1950	1951	1937–39	1950	1951	1937–39	1950	1951
Wheat	16·6	12·9	6·5	6·4	5·7	2·0	3·5	2·7	2·4
Maize	10·1	4·2	3·6	6·4	2·6	2·0	4·9	0·78	0·29
Linseed	6·2	2·7	—	1·42	0·55	—	0·41	0·25	0·33 (1)
Oats	2·1	1·54	1·06	0·76	0·72	0·44	0·38	0·38	0·111
Rye	1·21	2·4	0·38	0·29	0·62	0·087	0·096	0·168	0·200
Barley	1·34	1·43	0·88	0·56	0·75	0·34	0·238	0·091	0·152
Sunflower	0·82	4·0	—	0·15	0·95	—	—	0·101	—

(1) As oil.

(Commonwealth Econ. Cttee., *Grain Crops*, 1953, *Vegetable oils and seeds*, 1953.)

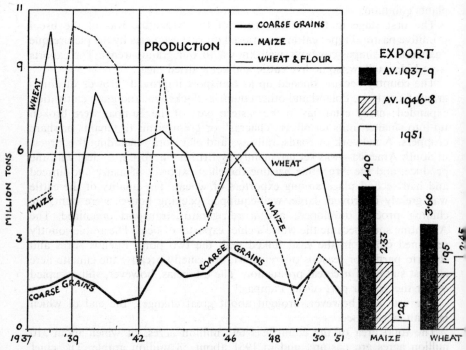

FIG. 31.—Production and export of grain, Argentina, 1937–1951 Million tons. (Data from C.E.C. Reports, *Grain Crops*, 1953, and *F.A.O. Stat. Year Book*, 1951.)

maize by 60 per cent and linseed by 77 per cent; on the other hand, the areas under rye, barley, sunflower and other oil seeds had increased, but even after allowing for this the total acreage of grain crops was 30 per cent less than before the war.

There certainly is no physical reason for the reduction in area of export grains. The potential area of wheat is very considerable, indeed 22·8 million acres had been sown in 1928–29—almost double the area of 1951–52. The western limit for reasonably secure production is set by the belt of 19-inch rainfall, though dry farming methods and irrigation could push it farther if necessary, and the southern and northern limits are set by the temperatures.

Within these limits neither drought nor rust do much harm as a rule, though there may be damage from grasshoppers and locusts.

In the early days the quality of the wheat was low, but much plant breeding and seed selection have been done to improve it and also to find disease-resistant varieties. Maize and linseed are chiefly grown in the warmer parts of the arable country: in the south of Santa Fé, the north of Buenos Aires province, and in Entre Rios. The average oil content of the linseed is high: before the war it was 36·5 per cent with a maximum of 42 per cent. Sunflower also is grown in the warmer regions: it is more tolerant of drought than maize; it was introduced by Russian immigrants in 1900 and has become the chief source of edible oil. No systematic rotations are practised on the Pampas, but when the yields of grain begin to fall the land is put into lucerne for several years, or is left fallow. Fertilizers are little used for farm crops but only for market garden produce, sugar-cane, tobacco, and other special crops.

The average yields are comparable with those in Canada; and they show no signs of rising or falling. For the areas harvested they have been:

Cwt. per acre	Wheat	Maize	Linseed	Oats	Rye	Barley	Sunflower
Average 1934–38 (1)	8·0	14·9	5·3	7·8	5·2	8·9	7·0
1940–43	9·5	15·5	5·5	7·4	5·5	9·4	7·5
1944–46	7·8	11·2	5·3	8·2	4·9	10·3	6·2
1947–50 (1)	9·6	12·2	4·9	9·1	4·8	9·3	7·0
1951 (1)	6·2	11·0	—	8·2	4·5	7·8	—

(1) C.E.C. Rpts., *Grain Crops*, 1953; others from *F.A.O. Stat. Year Book*, 1951.

The lucerne occupies about 13½ million acres: it may last for as long as 10 to 15 years, but it ceases to be productive after about 5 or 6 years and the land then goes back to grain crops. Disease is partly responsible for the "fatigue." Pedigree strains have been produced but are not yet widely known.

The Pampas is the great region for these crops: practically the whole acreage is there.

The sub-tropical and tropical regions of the north are used for the growth of cotton, maté, oranges and other fruits, groundnuts and other crops. Rice is grown in the deltas of the Paraná, Corriente and Tucuman rivers, and sugar-cane in the extreme north-east: some 457,000 acres were grown annually before the war, producing 410,000 tons of sugar; the output has since increased and in 1950 amounted to 613,000 tons.

Vines are grown at the foot of the Andes and the Argentine claimed before the war to be the chief wine producer in America, ranking with Portugal and Roumania as the fourth in the world.

There is some irrigation in the arid north-west of the Pampas, in San José and Mendoza where fruit and other high-class crops are grown.

The numbers of cattle and horses (but not of sheep) fell during the 1930's, but after the war they rose till the disastrous droughts of 1949–50 and May to mid-October of 1951 caused losses variously estimated, but apparently of the order of 10 millions: about a quarter of the total. Sheep, on the other hand, suffered less. The numbers of animals have been, in millions:

	Cattle	Sheep	Goats	Pigs	Horses	Mules and Asses
1922	37·06	36·21	4·82	1·44	9·43	0·91
1937	33·10	43·79	4·87	3·97	8·53	0·90
1947	41·27	50·86	4·93	2·98	7·24	0·50

1947 Census quoted in *S.Y.B.*: no later figures available.

The cattle are chiefly Herefords, Aberdeen Angus, and Shorthorns; they are mainly on the pampas. The sheep live mainly on the cold steppe country in the south; they are kept chiefly for wool; the production of lamb and mutton is only 10 to 20 per cent that of beef.

The average rate of stocking is low: only about one stock unit per 6 acres, but some of the grazing land is very dry and some is very cold.

The population of the country was estimated at 17·88 millions in 1951 as compared with 15·89 in 1947 and 7·88 in 1914. The increase is thus about 3 per cent per annum, one of the highest rates in the world, but it is not all from births in the country; there has been considerable immigration, particularly of Italians. If this increase continues at its present rates the population will, it is estimated, number 21·5 millions in 1959.

The production and export of the chief foods is shown in Table CXIII. Maize and wheat both steadily decreased from their maximum in 1928–29 when the acreage of wheat had been pushed up to 22·8 million and the production to 9·4 million tons; the export was then 6·8 million tons. This was more than the world market then required, and the effort was never repeated. But it shows what can be done. The droughts of 1950–51 years caused a heavy drop which may only be temporary.

On the other hand, both production and export of meat increased. A highly efficient beef industry was built up before the war. The quality of the animals was raised by periodically importing high-class bulls. The Argentine buyers have long been among the most discerning at the British sales of pedigree stock and ready to pay high prices to secure the animals they wanted. Roads and railways were built across the pampas so as to bring the animals to the packing houses with the minimum loss of condition, and a chilling technique was worked out which delivered the meat to the British consumer in an excellent state, far better than was possible with the old freezing method. It had the limitation that it is effective only for a period of about six weeks and it requires specially built ships for the transport. But this was all satisfactorily achieved, and before the war the United Kingdom received about 400,000 tons of meat annually from the Argentine. During the war the chilling process had to be abandoned, the works were closed and the staffs disbanded; the less refined freezing process was used instead, and is likely to be continued until general conditions are more settled. For the present the 200,000 tons of meat coming to Great Britain lacks the quality of pre-war days. The data for production and export are set out in Fig. 32.

Although the export of beef attracts most attention in England it is not the item of chief financial interest to the Argentine: since 1947 when war conditions ceased it has represented only about 10 per cent of the value of all exports, while cereals have accounted for 40 per cent or more.[1]

[1] Data in "A short Report on the Argentine Republic" (Subsecretariat of Information, Argentine Embassy, 1953.)

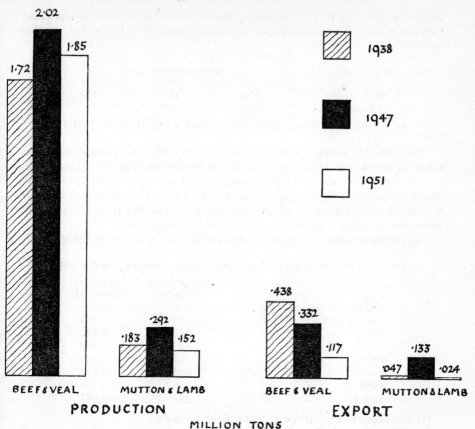

Fig. 32.—Production and export of meat, Argentina, pre-war and post-war. (Data from C.E.C. Rpts., *Meat*, 1953.)

A dairy industry has been started, and although it has not attained large dimensions it has shown that good-quality produce can be obtained. Larger quantities have been produced but consumed at home, so that exports have not increased:

Thousand tons

	Butter			Cheese		
	1941	1947	1951	1941	1947	1951
Production	43·2	51	42	64·5	86·3	105
Export	14·8	17	7·7	12·0	10·6	2·5

(*F.A.O. Food Balance Sheets*, 1949, C.E.C. Rpts., *Dairy Produce*, 1953, for 1951 figures.)

The rapid increase in population and the adoption of an industrialization policy, have aroused fears that the exports of other foods may cease to expand and may even diminish in the future. There is certainly an increased consumption per head of all foods, especially of meat which has reached enormous dimensions, far exceeding the pre-war consumption of the United

Kingdom and even in 1947 exceeding that of New Zealand. Argentine easily tops the world's list of meat-eaters. The quantities available for consumption have been:

	lb. per head per year		
	Average 1935–39	1947	1951
Beef	171	186	200
All meat	235	257	—

(*F.A.O. Food Balance Sheets*, 1949, C.E.C. Rpts. 1953. *Meat*, for 1951.)

Naturally this heavy consumption entails an enormous amount of waste. General Peron has indeed gone so far as to declare that the Argentinians eat or export half the food they produce and throw away the other half. The dustbins of Buenos Aires, he said, would feed a European city. There was no doubt an element of overstatement in this, but it was made with the desire to check this serious and quite unnecessary loss.

The post-war setback in agricultural development is shown in Table CXIII.

TABLE CXIII. *Argentine meat and grain exports: Thousand metric tons*

	Meat and meat Products	Cereals and Linseed (1)
Annual average, 1936–40	618	10,254
Annual average, 1941–45	659	3,303
1946	548	4,882
1947	687	5,679
1948	508	5,689
1949	497	3,611
1950	346	4,366
1951 (2)	278	3,482

(1) Excluding by-products, e.g., wheat flour, linseed oil.
(2) C.E.C. Rpts., 1953.
(*Anuario Estadistica y Sintesis Estadistica Mensual*, 1951 (except 1951 figures).)

It is not the result of soil deterioration or of the war, but more probably of political causes. The Government's price policy has been unfavourable to the farmers: they are said to receive only one-third of the world price for their wheat. The Five-Year Plan set up in October 1946 aimed at fostering industry in order to make the country self-sufficing and to absorb the expanding population. Industry had the preference for capital goods and the farms were unable to get much in the way of equipment. There was a lack of farm machinery, of wire fencing, road-building material, motor transport and high-class bulls. In 1948 there was only 1 tractor per 2,500 acres of cultivated land compared with 26 in Great Britain. Attempts are to be made to supply these wants but the capital outlay will be considerable, and under modern conditions capital is not encouraged to flow from one country to another. In September 1949, however, the Government reversed the order and decided to concentrate on agricultural development.

The natural conditions on the Pampas justify the hope of great expansion of grain and livestock production, and there are considerable possibilities in other parts of the country. It has been estimated that the cultivated area could be doubled or even trebled. Calamities like the droughts of 1950–51 are uncommon; late frost and hail may cause losses and so at times do rust, locust and grasshoppers. Soil erosion has not yet become serious, but there are ominous reports that a "dust bowl" from the arid west is spreading eastwards into the productive country. But the Chacareros of the Pampas have less to fear from these than the grain farmers of the Canadian prairies or of the Australian wheat belt, and all agriculturists who have visited the country agree that it is capable of great agricultural development.

BRAZIL

Brazil has long been regarded as one of the most promising of all lands for agricultural development. "No country in the world," wrote James Bryce in 1912,[1] "possesses so large a proportion of land available for the support of human life and productive industry." Fifteen years later a writer in the *Encyclopedia Britannica* (14th edit.) forecast that "with the immense areas in central and southern Brazil adapted to cattle raising Brazil seems destined eventually to outstrip Argentina, the United States, and Australia, as the greatest purveyor of the world's meat supplies."

More than twenty-five years have since elapsed, but these high hopes have not yet been fulfilled.

Brazil is further important as being the only large tropical country inhabited predominantly by white people and still receiving great numbers of white immigrants. It is thus the most fruitful laboratory in the world for studying the effects of tropical conditions on white people, and the ultimate results of matings of white and coloured peoples. The Portuguese conquerors and colonists of the 16th and later centuries had brought no white women with them and mated with the Indian women; later when negro slaves were imported there were matings with their women. This miscegenation resulted in an "Arianization" or "bleaching" of the offspring as it has been more crudely termed.[2] In recent years there have been constant accessions of Portuguese colonists and migrants have come in from Italy, Germany, Spain, Poland, Japan and elsewhere; but the country still retains its Portuguese language and affiliations although it broke away in 1822, becoming first a monarchy and then from 1889 onwards a republic.[3] The 1940 census gave 63·46 as the percentage of white people, 21·31 brown and 14·64 black; the south being almost entirely white, the north having more Indian blood and the centre more negro. Presumably there was a bias in favour of declaring "white," but the large preponderance simplifies the racial question and makes it sharply distinct from that of South Africa. There is less feeling against miscegenation than in Anglo-Saxon countries, and the aim is to fuse all these different peoples into a Brazilian nation. It will be extremely interesting to see what happens; nowhere else in the

[1] *South America, Observations and Impressions*, p. 404.
[2] T. Lyon Smith, *Brazil, People and Institutions* (Baton Rouge, Louisiana State Univ. Press, 1946, p. 20), quoted by J. A. Camacho, *Brazil. An interim assessment* (Royal Instit. of Internat. Affairs, London, 1952): the demographic and economic problems are fully discussed here.
[3] One of the enviable features of the Constitution as modified in 1946 is that no Income Tax is levied on the salaries of professors or on author's royalties.

world is there quite such a mixing of humanity: Camacho suggests that a fairly homogeneous race predominantly white seems likely to develop at least in the thickly populated area of the south.

Brazil is the largest tropical country in the world. Its land area is 2·1 thousand million acres; roughly half is forest and about 15 per cent is classed as natural grass. In the north the great basin of the Amazon stretches right across from east to west; it is a vast low-lying region some 500 or more miles in width traversed on its northern side by the equator. Most of it is evergreen tropical rain forest, almost impenetrable jungle inhabited by only few Indians including the fierce Chavante tribe. The average annual rainfall is about 80 inches: there is no dry season, but the months July to October tend to be less wet than February to June. As in the African equatorial belt of high rainfall the temperatures are not unduly high: the average is about 80° F, but the humidity is oppressive. The forest yields valuable wood, rubber, palm nuts, Brazil nuts and various other products all collected from the wild: there is but little cultivation. Hookworm and malaria add to the discomforts and difficulties. This low-lying region occupies more than a third of the country.

To the south is the higher land that forms about half of the country; its altitude varies generally from about 1,000 to 3,000 feet, with some isolated mountains of greater height. Except for the low-lying narrow coastal strip, the eastern part is generally higher than the central and the western. The mean temperature is still about 80° F., but the range is greater than in the Amazon forest; the annual rainfall is lower averaging about 60 inches, but the dry season is more pronounced, and in some districts of the north-east severe and even devastating droughts may occur. Much of the land was in forest, but there is a good deal of savannah and in the drier areas of semi-desert scrub; in the west there are considerable areas of swamp. This tract includes the eastern bulge of Brazil and stretches across the great central plateau of Mato Grosso. Its eastern region was early colonized on plantation lines. Sugar-cane and cotton were among the first products; cacao, pine-apples and tobacco came later with manioc, yams, maize and rice as food crops. But even now only a small fraction of the land is utilized.

Further south are the four States that are more developed than any others: São Paulo, Paraná, Santa Catarina and Rio Grande de Sol, the first three in the uplands, the fourth and southernmost lower-lying, chiefly rolling country falling away to the great plains that occupy so much of South America and include the Pampas. The uplands have a genial healthy climate: the rainfall varies in the different districts but averages commonly about 50 to 60 inches a year, usually well distributed, especially in southern São Paulo and the country farther south. The mean monthly temperatures range from about 50° F to about 80° F. Much of the land was deciduous forest except for an area of some 25 million acres in the south where a combination of dry summers and shallow or sandy soils allowed only grass to survive. Much of the forest has now been cleared: it remains only on the steep slopes. This is the most populous part of Brazil: although it forms only 7 per cent of the total area it had at the 1940 census over 31 per cent of the population. It produces all the warm-country crops, coffee, tobacco, maize and wheat; and varieties of cotton are being bred suitable to the conditions. The richest

456

and the most fully developed part is São Paulo, famous for its coffee *fazendas*, while Rio Grande has wheat and good cattle.

Brazil is, however, very undeveloped. Of its two thousand million acres only 45 million—2¼ per cent—are cultivated. Even in São Paulo no more than 20 per cent of the land is cropped and in the other three southern states less than 10 per cent. Most of the land—70 per cent according to Setzer[1]—is poor pasture burnt annually and carrying only small numbers of animals in poor condition: soils, vegetation, livestock and farmers have all alike become impoverished. The cattle are never housed and hence no farmyard manure is available: little fertilizer or lime is used though both are needed, green manuring is not practised. When land is worn out farmers abandon it and move on to a new district.

Brazil's chief food crops are maize, rice, beans and manioc (Table CXIV). Maize and beans are the most widely grown. Manioc is more common in the north and rice and wheat in the south.

TABLE CXIV. *Areas, yields and production of chief food crops, Brazil*

	Million acres		Yield, cwt.per acre		Total production, million tons	
	Average 1934–38	1950	*Average* 1934–38	1950	*Average* 1934–38	1950
Maize	10·0	11·6	11·5	10·2	5·7	5·9 (1)
Rice (Paddy)	2·4	4·9	11·4	12·9	1·4	3·2 (1)
Wheat	0·40	1·7	7·2	6·1	0·144	0·52
Beans	2·3	4·4	7·0	5·7	0·80	1·28
Manioc	0·94	2·4	5·5 tons	5·5 tons	5·2	3·2
Yams and sweet potatoes	0·25	0·29	—	3·3 tons	0·80	1·0
Potatoes	0·16	0·36	2·4	2·0 tons	380	740
Population, million	38·6	52·6 (1)				

F.A.O. Stat. Year Book, 1951.

(1) C.E.C. Rpts., *Grain Crops*, 1953; 3·3 paddy becomes 2·0 rice.

Average yields of all crops are low; for maize they are, however, about equal to the average for South America; for wheat and rice they are somewhat less. There are surpluses of maize and of rice for export, but insufficient wheat is produced and most of it has to be imported. This necessity has been a constant challenge to Brazilian agriculturists. Wheat grows fairly well in the southern regions, but being on the warm edge of the wheat belt, rust is liable to cause considerable losses. Suitable resistant varieties are being sought. Production has more than trebled since the war and in 1950 it exceeded half a million tons. But consumption had also gone up because of the increase in population, and the need for import still remained high: for the five years before the war it had averaged 1 million tons annually, in 1948 it was 715,000 tons and in 1951, 1·35 million tons.[2] It is planned to raise production to a million tons annually, but even this would be quite inadequate. The present yield is so low, however, that considerably more might be expected.

[1] José Setzer, *Proc. Un. N. Sci. Cong. Conservation and Utilisation of Resources*, Lake Success, 1949 (U.N. Dept. Econ. Affairs, 1951, Vol. 6, pp. 136–38).

[2] Grain plus flour, Brazil, 1951. Min. Foreign Affairs and C.E.C. Rpts. *Grain Crops*, 1953.

The wheat is imported from the Argentine where the climatic conditions are more suitable and therefore the cost of production lower, and it is no doubt sound economy for Brazil to send coffee, cotton and other tropical products into the Argentine in exchange for wheat.

Production of all other food crops, maize, rice, beans, manioc, potatoes, yams, has increased considerably since pre-war days, but even so it has only just about kept up with the growth of population. Yields per acre, however, appear to have fallen excepting only for rice; there is a tendency for men to move on to new land when they have worked out the old.

As already stated, Brazil was for long organized on plantation lines, one crop usually dominating; while this lasted Brazil was one of the chief if not the chief producer in the world. Sugar-cane was the first; it was introduced by the Dutch during their occupation of the Pernambuco district in the 17th century, and it flourished so well that Brazil became Europe's chief source of supply and remained so until beet sugar cultivation was firmly established. Brazil has still continued to grow sugar-cane always in the northern districts and the area is now expanding; production in 1948 was 1¾ million tons and Brazil has now the third largest output of cane sugar being exceeded only by Cuba and by India. As an additional outlet some of the sugar is to be used for making power alcohol, for Brazil does not yet utilize her oil or coal deposits but imports fuel.

Cotton was the chief product during much of the 19th century, but lost some of its importance when all slaves were freed in 1888 and labour supplies became difficult. But Brazil is still one of the world's chief producers, being exceeded only by the United States, India, China and Egypt. Formerly, like sugar, it was confined to the north, but its cultivation has now moved southwards and a good deal is grown in São Paulo, suitable sorts having been obtained. The quality is not high: the cost of production is rising and yields are falling, diseases and pests are troublesome. Pakistan, Turkey and other countries produce large quantities of similar type and additional production may not be needed for the present.

Early in the present century the development of the cycle and motor industries created a great demand for rubber and the Amazon forests were almost the sole source of supply. Nowhere else in the world did *Hevea braziliensis* grow, and no other tree produced such good rubber: the trees were wild and it was only necessary to tap them. In 1910 Brazil was supplying 88 per cent of the total world production. Attempts were made to retain the monopoly, but in the meantime some 70,000 seeds had been brought out by an enterprising Englishman, H. A. Wickham (afterwards Sir Henry) and taken to Kew where they were sown and tended: the young plants were despatched to Ceylon where they grew well, and from thence stocks were sent to Malaya and the Dutch Indies. Plantations were started by British and Dutch growers and managed on sound scientific lines, and by 1930 they had almost completely captured the market: Brazil's export was reduced to about 14,000 tons compared with over 800,000 tons produced in Asia.[1] Meanwhile Brazilian coffee was coming more and more into prominence: by 1914 Brazil supplied about 70 per cent of the world's export. Then came the period of high prices during which other countries started production,

[1] *Camacho*, loc. cit., p. 33.

followed by the collapse of the 1930's when thousands of tons of coffee had to be burned because supplies had so greatly exceeded demand. On many of the plantations coffee was given up; some were put into cotton or rice; some were used for pasture, but most of them simply ran wild especially where serious erosion had taken place. For unfortunately the method of clean cultivation commonly adopted by the planters and thought at the time to be sound had as elsewhere led to soil erosion: some of the plantations had to be abandoned, and as the forest had been totally cleared its regeneration was extremely slow.[1] The higher prices of recent years have encouraged some rehabilitation and improvement of the coffee plantations and the use of farmyard manure. Meanwhile a new coffee area has been opened up in the north of Paraná State where, it is said, "the land smells like money." Coffee still remains the chief cash crop, but the present policy is to encourage others as well so as to broaden the basis of prosperity. Cacao cultivation is being extended especially in Bahia and other parts of the eastern region: the area has increased from 450,000 acres before the war to 640,000 acres in 1950: Brazil and Nigeria are now about equally important as producers and are second only to the Gold Coast in output. The cacao plantations are less subject to erosion than those of coffee because the forest is not cleared: some of the trees have to be left for shade. Fruits of all kinds can be grown: Mediterranean varieties in the south and tropical kinds in the north, oranges and bananas in the east. The output of bananas, some 3 million tons a year, is the largest in the world, while that of oranges, about 1¼ million tons a year, is the second largest, being exceeded only by the United States.

Castor bean is one of Brazil's specialities.

The production of all these cash crops except coffee and cotton has increased since the pre-war days; for cocoa the area has increased but not the crop. For coffee and cotton the disturbing effects of the war have not yet been overcome though areas and outputs are now increasing (Table CXV).

TABLE CXV. *Area and production, of cash crops*

	Area. Thousand acres			Production. Thousand tons		
	Average 1934–38	1948	1950	Average 1934–38	1948	1950
Oranges				1172	1226	1252
Bananas	63	96	109	1479	2726	3169
Sugar, raw	463	819	815	1031	1751	1750
Cocoa beans	450	640	642	124	128·5	128·6
Coffee	860	610	690	1446	1037	1079
Tobacco	255	356	350	92·7	117·6	106·4
Cotton	2118	1650	1902	389	332	336

(*F.A.O. Stat. Year Book*, 1951.)

Most of the agricultural production is by manual labour and the chief implement is the hoe: in 1950 there were only 15,700 tractors in the whole country.[2] Rice was the crop on which they were most used, but a start had been made with wheat and cotton; coffee plantations are not very suitable,

[1] For an account see Pierre Gourou, *Les pays tropicaux*, Presses Universitaires de France, Paris, 1947. (English translation, Longmans, 1953. *The Tropical World*.)
[2] *F.A.O. Stat. Year Book*, 1951, p. 181.

however. Mechanization is bound to be increasingly adopted as more and more labour is attracted to industry.

The broadening of the basis of Brazil's agricultural exports is shown by comparing the composition of the 1925 list with that of 1948:

Per cent of total value of all exports

	1925	1948		1925	1948
Coffee	72·0	41·6	Cotton	3·2	16·5
Animal products	3·7	6·2	Timber	0·7	4·5
Cocoa	2·6	5·0	Rubber	4·9	0·2
Rice	Nil	3·4			
Fruit	0·4	1·5			
Vegetable oils and seeds	0·4	4·4			

(J. A. Camacho, Brazil, an interim assessment, *Roy. Inst. Internat. Affairs*, 1952, p. 92.)

Livestock

The recorded numbers of animals have steadily increased and by 1951 were:

Cattle	Pigs	Sheep
54	28	16

(C.E.C. Rpts., *Meat*, 1953.)

Both cattle and pigs are more numerous than in the Argentine though sheep are fewer. Nevertheless the production of beef is far less and the export is very small: unlike the crops, meat production has not increased since the war (Table CXVI).

TABLE CXVI. *Production and export of meat: pre-war and post-war*

Thousand tons

	Production						Export		
	Average 1934–39		1948	1949	1951		Average 1935–		
	Total	including commercial	Total	including commercial	com-mercial	com-mercial	39	1948	1951 (1)
Beef	1275	836	1265	910	955	987	107	63	4·8 (2)
Pork	491	240	454	225	233	137	3	2	0·3
Mutton and lamb	48	12	58	30	30			1	
	2031		1974	1165	1218		110	66	

(F.A.O. Stat. Year Book, 1951, and Food Balance Sheets, 1950.)

The total includes an estimate of the slaughterings in the farm for home consumption: the commercial is for slaughtering in registered places.

(1) C.E.C. Rpts., *Meat*, 1953.

(2) Chilled and frozen only. The corresponding figure for 1938 was 42,300 tons.

The low export compared with the Argentine is due to the circumstance that Brazil has three times the population of the Argentine and also a lack of transport facilities and packing houses. If these were provided considerable areas in the centre and the west could be used for cattle raising. Considerable areas in São Paulo, Minar Gerais and Bahia have been sown with *Coloniãs* grass (*Panicum maximum*) producing pastures that can carry and fatten about 0·7 mature beasts per acre.[1] The pig population—23 million—is extraordinarily large: far greater than that of any other country in South America and exceeded only in China and the United States. This suggests that the conditions are well suited to them and that a considerable increased production of pork, bacon and lard might be expected if larger food supplies became available. An American organization has undertaken the growth of hybrid maize in the south for this purpose and it will be interesting to see the result.

The value of the annual agricultural and pastoral output has increased considerably in the last twenty-five years, but the percentage exported has not changed: the figures have been, at 1939 prices:

| | *Million cruzeiros* | | | |
Average	For home consumption	For export	Total	Percentage exported
1925–29	4137	1615	5751	72
1945–49	6295	2668	8963	70
1949	7212	2702	9914	72

(*Economic Survey of Latin America*, 1949: U.N. Econ. and Social Council, Chapter VIII.)

Food Supplies

It is extremely difficult to assess food supplies in a country with so large a peasant population as Brazil. F.A.O. estimates place Brazil among the under-nourished countries, but suggest that the intake of calories is improving, though that of animal protein is deteriorating. The figures per head are:

	Average 1935–39	1948
Calories per year	2152	2343
Fat, grams per day	51·5	50·0
Protein: animal	31·5	25·1
vegetable	36·4	38·3
Total	67·9	63·4

Only three significant changes were recorded in the dietary: a fall in the consumption of meat from 110 lb. per head per year to 87 lb.; a rise in the consumption of manioc from 50 to 107 lb.; and of fruit from 150 to 180 lb. The latter is an improvement: the two former changes are not. No food balance sheet later than 1948 is available. It is possible that 1949 might show better results as production of maize and rice was higher and exports were less, leaving more in the country, also both production and imports of wheat were higher. Whatever the actual value of the figures may be there seems little reason to doubt Camacho's statement that "Malnutrition and

---

[1] I am indebted to Dr. Leme da Rocha for information on this and other matters in this chapter.

disease undermine the energy and productive capacity of too large a proportion of the population."[1]

The hopes of fifty years ago that Brazil would become a great source of world food supplies have not yet materialized. Production has increased, but has apparently only kept pace with the growing population. Exports of foods are low, and show no signs of increasing: they are given in Table CXVII.

TABLE CXVII. *Exports of food from Brazil, thousand tons*

	Average 1935–39	1947	1948	1949
Maize	33	166	111	0·002
Rice (as paddy)	92	328	216 (1)	1
Manioc flour and tapioca	7	100	29	1·28
Oranges	154	59	100	72
Bananas	169	132	163	168
Sugar	46	62	361	39
Meat	110	63	48	37
Cocoa beans	120	99	72	132
Coffee			1050	1162

(1) As rice; equivalent to 310 paddy.

(*F.A.O. Food Balance Sheets* for 1935–39 and 1947: Brazil, 1951 Min. Foreign Affairs, pp. 52 and 53 for 1948 and 1949.)

The saddest feature in the list is the fall in export of meat at a time when further supplies are so badly needed for the world market. Economic and political factors are no doubt responsible to some extent for this low level of food exports, but efforts are being made to increase agricultural production. In accordance with prevailing custom a Plan—the Salte Plan—was drawn up and approved in 1950 for the improvement of health, nutrition, and energy supply;[2] it was to be completed by 1954 at a cost of 20 thousand million cruzeiros (nearly £400 million). Fifty-six per cent was to be spent in improving transport, 14 per cent on improving agricultural production and 15 and 13 per cent respectively on power and health. Already by 1951, however, curtailment had become necessary.

The high proportion devoted to transport can be justified from experience in the British Commonwealth: it has been shown repeatedly that successful agricultural development demands good transport facilities. A system of agricultural and veterinary research and education is in operation co-ordinated under a national central organization.

It must be admitted that the difficulties are considerable. More than a third of the country is taken up by the Amazon basin, a most seductive region for the planner but extremely difficult for any practical achievement. The Ford Motor company obtained a concession of 5,000 square miles on the River Tapajos, one of the tributary streams, for the purpose of estab-

[1] Loc. cit., p. 17. He quotes also the statement of the Joint Brazil-U.S. Commission of 1949 (p. 130) that about 20 per cent of the children die in their first year. It is only right to add that much good work has been done on tropical sanitation by Dr. Oswaldo Cruz and others: the city of Rio de Janeiro is said to be clear of malaria and yellow fever.

[2] Its name is a compound of *Saudé* (health), *alimentação* (nutrition), *transporte* and *energía* (power).

lishing rubber plantations. They were able to show that tolerable living conditions for the staff could be secured, but the main object was not achieved and the concession was given up. The Agronomic Institute of the North at Belém is investigating the possibilities and, as already stated, UNESCO has proposed a systematic scientific study of the whole basin. But no important practical results can be expected in the near future.

The upland regions to the south offer greater possibilities but with serious limitations. The extensive and luxuriant tropical forest gave the earlier travellers the impression of rich soils and no doubt helped to foster visions of a Land of Promise. Subsequent sad experience in many places has shown that tropical forest soils are often poor and acid, and very liable to erosion once they are cleared for cultivation. Brazil has been no exception to the rule. The low levels of yield, and the practice of shifting to new land when the old is exhausted, are the natural consequences of this poverty, which is borne out by such chemical evidence as is available. Large quantities of lime and of phosphate are probably needed to produce the conditions in which good rotations can become effective: it is not clear that natural deposits of phosphate are included among Brazil's many mineral riches. The productive soils of São Paulo and Paraná are on pancakes of erupted material forced up through fissures, but the great surrounding areas of soil are poor. The cropping systems are exhausting; there are only small proportions of recuperative crops: lucerne, clovers or sown grasses; even beans, the most widely grown of leguminous crops, occupy only about one-tenth of the cultivated land; there is no green manuring and little farmyard manure is used. Fertilizers were almost unknown till after the war; they are, however, gradually being used; in the season 1950–51 it was unofficially estimated that consumption had risen to:

N	P_2O_5	K_2O
12	30	12 thousand tons

Although these quantities are still only small they are larger than in any other country in South America.

The most urgent problems appear to be the devising and adoption of cropping methods that will build up soil fertility in areas of good climatic conditions, and ensure soil conservation in areas where erosion threatens to be serious. The introduction of suitable grasses would almost certainly lead to great improvement, and some of the large holdings might with advantage be broken up into smaller and more productive units. There are also difficulties of other kinds. According to Setzer[1] practically all the money raised in taxes in the countryside has been spent in the State capitals and little or nothing has been done for conserving or improving the soil or making good roads: so the vicious circle has started: the poverty of the soil has kept the farmers poor and they in turn have still further impoverished the soil. Further, he urges the need for protecting farmers against dishonesty of merchants and others and of improving education and health services.

[1] José Setzer, *Proc. U.N. Sci. Cong. Conservation and Utilisation of Resources*, 1949. U.N. Dept. Econ. Affairs, 1951, Vol. 6, pp. 136–38.

URUGUAY

Uruguay is a small country on the east coast of South America lying between lat. 30° and lat. 35° S. It is shaped rather like a pear with the narrow end pointing northwards; the Atlantic and the estuary of the River Plate bound it on the east and south, and the Argentine and Brazil on the west and north. It is mainly a low-lying plain broken in the north; its southern part is geographically an extension of the Argentine Pampas with similar deep black soil and grass vegetation. There is no dense forest, but trees grow in the river bottoms.

The climate is genial. The rainfall averages about 35 inches and is less inland than near the coast: it is well distributed and there is neither a dry nor a wet season. The temperatures average about 70° F. in summer (January and February) and about 50° F. in July, the coldest month. The conditions are healthy for men and animals and very favourable for livestock production and arable farming.

The population in 1950 was 2·38 millions on 72,000 square miles: it had been increasing over the previous thirteen years at the rate of more than 1 per cent per annum. There has been a good deal of immigration, especially from Italy and Spain. The area of the country is 46·2 million acres used as follows in 1950:

	Million acres
Grazing	34·2
Cropping	3·9
Forest	1·0
Non agricultural	7·1
	46·2

(F.A.O. Stat. Year Book, 1951.)

The cropped land is mainly in the southern pampas-like part of the country, and the same crops are grown as in the Argentine. Wheat and maize predominate, occupying about half the arable area; the wheat is for human consumption and the maize for the animals. Sunflower and linseed come next in importance and then oats and barley, the latter chiefly for fodder, but about one-third to one-half is for malting: this proportion tends to increase. There are smaller areas of rice, groundnuts, and an unusual crop, bird seed.

Of these crops wheat, maize, linseed, oats, barley and bird seed are old established, but the others are more recent. Groundnuts came in about 1930, sunflower, rice and malting barley about 1936. Sunflower has been the most successful of these, its area rose to 390,000 acres in 1950. As in the Argentine, citrus and other fruits are grown and grapes for wine making. The area and outputs of the chief crops are given in Table CXVIII.

The yields are lower than in the Argentine: in the case of maize much lower; though they show some signs of rising: they have been, in cwt. per acre:

	Average				Average		
	1934–48	1943–46	1948–50		1934–48	1943–46	1948–50
Wheat	6·0	6·4	7·5	Oats	4·1	5·0	4·9
Maize	5·0	5·2	5·6	Barley	6·1	7·1	7·1
Linseed	4·8	5·9	5·5				

(F.A.O. Stat. Year Book, 1951.)

TABLE CXVIII. *Area and production of chief crops, Uruguay*

	Area: million acres				Production: million tons			
	Average				Average			
	1937–39	1949	1950	1951	1937–39	1949	1950	1951
Wheat	1·26	1·28	1·22	1·44	0·374	0·45	0·43	0·47
Maize	0·54	0·40	0·47	0·87	0·134	0·083	0·088	0·27
Sunflower	0·02	0·25	0·26	—	0·005	0·041	0·098	—
Linseed	0·45	0·39	0·39	—	0·110	0·074	0·089	—
Oats	0·23	0·27	0·16	0·14	0·046	0·058	0·034	0·037
Barley	0·046	0·081	0·068	0·054	0·015	0·027	0·024	0·018

(Commonwealth Econ Cttee., *Grain Crops*, 1953, and *Vegetable Oils and Oil Seeds*, 1953.)

The farms are small; a usual size is about 250 acres, about half are owned by the occupier and the rest are let to tenants or worked by a manager.

The area of grazing land is about ten times that of the cropped. The numbers of livestock have been, in millions:

	Cattle	Sheep	Pigs
1924	8·4	14·5	
1937	8·3	17·9	0·308
1946	6·8	19·6	0·420
1951	8	23	

The cattle have changed but little in numbers, the sheep have increased considerably. There was an export of 50,000 tons of beef in 1947 and 74,000 tons in 1948. Sheep are the most important of the animals, and are grown for wool, which is the chief export of the country, not as yet for lamb or mutton. The average rate of stocking is about one stock unit for three acres, which is considerably better than in the Argentine and results from the absence of any important extent of arid or cold pastures.

	Production thousand tons		Export thousand tons		Home consumption lb. per head		
	Average		Average		Average		U.K.
	1935–38	1948	1935–38	1948	1935–38	1948	1935–38
Beef and veal	267	206	140	74	151	125	55·6
Mutton and lamb	64	85	9	5	65·2	76	25·1
All meat, including poultry and offal	372	331	150	84	263	234	133

F.A.O. Food Balance Sheets, C.E.C. Rpts. give export of beef in 1951 as 61,200 tons and in 1952 as 42,600 tons.

A generation ago cereals for human consumption had to be imported, but home production was encouraged so effectively that before the war there was an export of wheat averaging for the 1935–38 period 95,000 tons a year. In 1947, however, 125,000 tons of wheat had again to be imported as well as 11,000 tons of maize, but exports were resumed in 1948. Imports of food still continue: chiefly sugar, bananas and potatoes, but they are more than counterbalanced by exports of arable products, the value of which has in some years (e.g. 1949 but not in 1950) been greater than that of the meat. The consumption of meat per head, although high by British standards even those of pre-war, is less than in the Argentine, leaving proportionately more for export, nevertheless the quantity exported is less than before the war.

A better balanced dietary would liberate still more meat for export.

In earlier days there was considerable political mismanagement, greatly retarding development of the country. This is now proceeding vigorously. The cattle are being improved, especially in the south. An experiment station has been set up and there is an active farm advisory service. Few countries offer greater possibilities of agricultural and pastoral improvement at the present time than Uruguay.

PARAGUAY

Paraguay is entirely inland, and lies between lat. 20° S. and lat. 27° S. Much of it is grassland, an extension of the Argentine plain, but there is a good deal of forest in the uplands and much marsh on the lower ground. None of the uplands exceed about 2,200 feet in altitude. It is both hotter and wetter than the Argentine or Uruguay. The mean temperature during the summer months December to February is about 80° F and during the winter months about 65° F: the average rainfall at Ascencion is 62 inches, fairly well distributed. The soils in general are productive. Both soils and climate fit the country well for livestock and crop production.

Until 1938 Paraguay consisted of an area 61·7 thousand square miles lying between the rivers Paraguay and alto Paraná: it then took from Bolivia another 95·3 thousand square miles making a present total of 157,000 square miles, 100·5 million acres. The old part is called the Oriental and the new the Occidental section. The population of the old part had been 800,000 in 1926; that of the present enlarged country is estimated at 1·27 millions.

The cattle population is equally sparse. In 1928 old Paraguay had about 5 millions, in 1949 the enlarged country had about 4·1 millions. Exports of meat and meat products have improved since a few packing houses were set up by Argentine and Uruguyan organizations, but they are still small: they have been:

	Old Paraguay	Present Paraguay	
	Average 1934–38	1946	1947
Thousand tons	7·36	21·3	13·4

The agriculture is primitive, and does not even provide all the food for the inhabitants although the average area of land per head of population is about 80 acres. The chief food products are manioc (about 1 million tons annually) and maize (about 100,000 tons from about 190,000 acres); only little wheat is grown and practically no barley or oats. The crop exports are maté, cotton, tobacco and various fruit and timber products; citrus fruits especially tangarines are commonly grown, grape fruit have been exported to England. Sugar-cane is grown, but much of the sugar is made into spirit; sugar for consumption is imported. There are small areas of rice, bananas and groundnuts, sufficient to show that these could be produced.

The possibilities of development are very considerable, but how or when they will be realized no one can say. The men of the country are said to be indolent, and since August 1948 immigration has been restricted to citizens of American countries: the Italians who used to be encouraged and who can work well in these conditions are no longer admitted. Nor will it be easy to attract the necessary capital for development: a considerable communist element among the mine workers propagates the idea that foreign capital is "the enemy," yet until it can be induced to come in the great potential agricultural resources must remain largely undeveloped.

Chapter 14

TRENDS IN WORLD FOOD SUPPLIES

In 1952 F.A.O. published its second survey of the world's food production.[1] This showed a distinct improvement on the position since 1946, but many countries were still producing less food than before the war, and where there had been an increase it had only in few cases kept pace with the growing population. (Table CXIX).

TABLE CXIX. *Estimated world population, also quantities of food and numbers of livestock produced in the world* (*excluding U.S.S.R. Pre-war* (1934–38) *and* 1950).

	Population, millions		Grains (1) million tons		Potatoes million tons		Oil seeds million tons	
	1937	1950	Pre-war	1950	Pre-war	1950	Pre-war	1950
Europe	371	394	117	107	135	141	0·7	1·8
North and Central America	179	216	112	171	{ 12·1 (3) 2·5	14·6 2.3 }	7·1	14·6
South America	84	110	27	25	{ 2·8 1·4	4·9 1·8 }	3·3	3·3
Asia	1,139	1,273	258	255	{ 8·1 25·5	9·7 35·5 }	27·3	25·8
Africa	169	198	25	29	{ 0·6 —	1·0 9·3 }	2·8	3·6
Oceania	11	13	5·4	6·5	0·5	0·5	—	—
Part World (2)	1,953	2,204	545	594	{ 159 (3) 39	172 49 }	41·5	49·2
U.S.S.R.	189	203						
Total World	2,142	2,408						
Percentage increase			12·7		9·0		11·0	18·5

(1) Wheat, rye, barley, oats, paddy, millets, and sorghums.
(2) Excluding U.S.S.R.
(3) Sweet potatoes and yams. Also for other continents. Pre-war African value assumed to be 10 for assessing the total production.

	Numbers of livestock, millions					
	Cattle		Sheep		Pigs	
	Pre-war	1950	Pre-war	1950	Pre-war	1950
Europe	102	98	119	101	78	69
North and Central America	101	114	61	38	64	76
South America	107	133	97	123	30	35
Asia	227	217	127	121	85	83
Africa	76	88	105	110	3	4
Oceania	18	20	143	147	2	2
Total (exc. U.S.S.R.)	631	670	652	640	262	269
Percentage increase		6·2		−1·8		2·7

(*F.A.O. Stat. Year Book*, 1951.)

[1] *Second World Food Survey, F.A.O.,* Rome, November, 1952. The first was in 1946.

Europe had suffered most. Grain production in the period 1949–51 was still 6·5 million tons a year below pre-war and potatoes were down by 7 million tons although the population had increased by 23 millions. Output of oil seeds had increased and so had that of sugar. The numbers of livestock which had fallen heavily during the war were not yet back to pre-war levels: sheep were nearly 18 per cent down and pigs 12 per cent.

Asia also suffered badly, especially the Far East. Output of grain in 1950 was about 1 per cent less than pre-war; there was a fall in output of 3·6 million tons of rice—the principal food—there was also a loss of oil seeds and of sugar. Sweet potatoes and yams had, however, increased by 10 million tons which would go some way towards counterbalancing the losses of grain. The number of animals also decreased. Against all this was an increase of nearly 12 per cent in the human population.

South America's production of grain was down by 2·8 million tons in 1950 and by 4 million tons for the period 1949–51; that of sugar had risen from 2·5 to 4·1 million tons; output of potatoes had also increased somewhat. The livestock population, however, increased more than in any other continent without, however, helping the food supplies as grain instead of being exported was fed to the animals; cattle rose by 24 per cent, sheep by 27 per cent, and pigs by 17 per cent. The human population also had the highest rate of increase: it went up by 30 per cent. In Oceania food production and population have just about kept even.

Only in North America did food production outstrip the growth of population: grain production rose by 50 per cent, that of oil seeds doubled, but the human population increased only by 20 per cent.

Within these great continental areas there are, of course, considerable differences. In Europe the United Kingdom, the Netherlands, Denmark, and Switzerland all increased their output of food relative to the population. New Zealand has done the same. Some countries, however, have fallen behind greatly in output of food per head. The result has been to widen the difference between the dietaries of the different nations; some of the richer ones have improved their dietary, some of the poorer ones are worse off. According to the estimates of F.A.O. the number of persons in the United Nations on the very low dietary of less than 2,200 calories a day has nearly doubled while the numbers on the satisfactory dietary of 2,800 or more calories a day has fallen by 22 per cent:

	Number of persons Millions			*Per cent*	
Calories per day[1]	*Pre-war*	*1949–50*		*Pre-war*	*1949–50*
Above 2,800	367	286		23	16
2,800–2,200	631	378		38	22
Below 2,200	617	1,114		39	62
Total	1,615	1,778		100	100

(F.A.O. Stat. Year Book, 1951.)

[1] The chief countries are:
(1) *Above* 2,800: the United Kingdom, North West Europe, Switzerland, Canada, U.S.A., Australia, New Zealand, the Argentine.
(2) 2,800–2,200: France, Central and Eastern Europe, S. America (except Argentina), Israel, S. Africa, Egypt.
(3) *Below* 2,200: China, Japan, S.E. Asia, Indonesia (about 1950).

Four of the countries that before the war were in the first group have now fallen into the second: France, Germany, Austria, and Yugoslavia; Denmark still remains in the first group but at a lower level. On the other hand the South American countries have greatly improved their position; the Argentine has stepped up from the middle to the first group. Brazil, Peru, Venezuela, and Colombia have risen from the lowest to the middle group. In Asia the situation is worse than in Europe. The crowded countries, India, Japan, and China, already on a low-level dietary, have all fallen back; China, indeed, has dropped from the middle to the bottom group. (Fig. 33.)

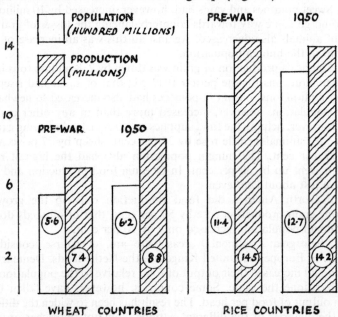

FIG. 33.—Population and food grain production (million tons) in wheat- and rice-eating countries, pre-war and 1950. (*F.A.O.*, *Stat. Yr. Bk.*, 1951.) The wheat countries are Europe (exc. U.S.S.R.), North America and Oceania, the rice countries are Asia (exc. U.S.S.R.). Rice is estimated as paddy.

The 1953 Report showed some advance, chiefly in North and South America and in Oceania.[1]

This widespread failure of food production to keep pace with the growth of population might easily lead to disaster. As we have seen in the preceding chapters great efforts are being made in many countries to cope with the problem. Possibilities of extending the area of cultivation have been examined. This had, indeed, been the method used during the fifty years of rapid expansion, 1870–1920, when the white population increased by 225 millions and brought 450 million new acres into cultivation.[2] The process still continued after the first war; during the period 1910 to 1930 the cultivated area increased by 110 million acres. Since then very little has been added. And yet, even now, less than 10 per cent of the world's 33½ thousand million acres of land is

[1] F.A.O. Rpt., *State of Food and Agriculture*. 1953.
[2] A. D. Hall, *Rpt. British Assoc.*, Oxford, 1926, p. 255.

cultivated, another 15 per cent is more or less used for grazing but some three-quarters of the world's land area is at present yielding little or no food:[1]

Total land surface		Cultivable land (2)	
thousand million acres		*thousand million acres*	
Cultivable (1)	10	Cultivated	3
Forest	10	Grazing land	5
Arid and desert	6	Utilizable but unused	1
Inhabited and waste	8		
	—		
	34		

(1) C. B. Fawcett, *Geog. Jl.*, 1930, Vol. 76, pp. 504–9.
(2) *F.A.O. Stat. Year Book*, 1951.

The three thousand million acres at present cultivated allows on an average 1¼ acres per head. Our present British dietary can be produced on about 1·3 or 1·4 acres at British yields. The Indian vegetarian dietary requires at Indian yields 0·6 acres per head. More than half of the world's population consumes so little meat or milk that an area of 0·6 to 1 acre per head suffices at present for them. But the better fed people require two or more acres per head at current yields.

In the preceding chapters we have seen how in many countries the cultivated land has, where necessary, expanded on to the grazing land by removal of some limiting factor either by irrigation, by replacement of the wild herbage by better grasses which under proper grazing management gradually make the soil cultivable, or by other ways. It is not possible to say how much of the grazing land could be brought into cultivation. Savannah country outside the tropics can be fairly easily converted to arable. In the tropics the difficulties are greater especially if the soil is lateritic. There have been some sad experiences in Africa: our groundnut scheme among them. Grass regions outside the tropics, the prairies or pampas have been mainly brought into use already, but the difficulties increase as the conditions become drier and the rainfall less reliable. If such expansion became necessary special financial measures would be required to cover the risks: irrigation is very costly and dry farming methods uncertain. Australian experience shows that the enterprise is not one for the ordinary unaided farmer. In the hotter regions the difficulties are still greater: experience being gained in Africa will show what is practicable.

Expansion into the tropical forest is possible but difficult and costly. It is being done by the Belgians and ourselves in West Africa by substituting food-yielding trees such as oil palm and cacao for the native trees, clearing only the minimum amount of land for food crops so as to avoid leaving the soil bare and exposed to erosion. The poverty of the soil necessitates frequent recourse to bush fallows. Insects are a constant menace carrying diseases and causing great discomfort; and the climate is enervating. Reference has already been made to the possibility of exploiting the Amazon forest region, but the very considerable difficulties, political and physical, are not easily surmounted.

[1] It should be added that less than 20 per cent of the world's land area has been topographically mapped; a further 5 per cent has been the subject of reconnaissance surveys (T. D. Weatherhead, *J. Roy. Soc. Arts*, 1951, Vol. 99, pp. 848–64, discussing surveys by aeroplane.

Some of the cold forest can be cleared and used; the clay belt of Northern Ontario is coming into use; the soils are not particularly good but they are being courageously tackled. How far north cultivation can be pushed cannot be predicted; the Canadian method of combining summer visitation to the farm and winter residence in more genial surroundings makes utilization of the land less unattractive, and the efforts of plant breeders to produce earlier ripening and more frost resistant varieties of suitable crops make it more practicable. The Finns, the most northerly farmers of the world, are contributing valuable experience. Trustworthy information about the activities of the U.S.S.R. is not available but sources of labour can be drawn upon there that are not open to the Western countries. Whatever the future may hold there seems little prospect of much expansion northwards nor into the tropical forest except for special tree crops.[1] In the middle latitudes the obviously cultivable land is mostly taken up and the only land left is subject to some disability, which can now, however, usually be diagnosed with considerable certainty. In some instances it can already be overcome economically as in the Ninety Mile Desert in Australia already described; more usually the difficulty is the lack of water, and this threatens to become the factor that will finally limit expansion of food production and settlement in these otherwise habitable regions. So far this question of water supply has not received the attention it deserves.

For the moment the chief importance of expansion of the cultivated area is to counteract the losses of land due to erosion and to encroachment of the cities, of military, transport, and sporting activities.

A more hopeful method of improving food supplies is to intensify output from land already used, much of it producing at present far less than it is capable of doing. In all the advanced countries and in African countries associated with the United Kingdom, France, and Belgium teams of agricultural experts are devising and demonstrating improved methods of crop production. In the more advanced countries a considerable proportion of the farmers use these methods and have raised their output accordingly; some, indeed, have reached the stage where higher output can be obtained only at considerably higher levels of expenditure but many are, as yet, nowhere near this standard. Even the best farmers are still far from the possible limit as shown by the extremely high yields sometimes obtained; the $3\frac{1}{2}$ tons of wheat per acre for example (p. 68) as compared with Great Britain's average of 20 cwt.; the secrets of these exceptional yields are, however, not yet known. But in the less advanced and poorer countries only few of the farmers practise the better methods. Good crops may be grown on the experimental farm, but the peasants outside may obtain only about half the yields. You ask them why they do not use the better methods and the answer commonly is: the experimental farm is run by the Government; they can do such things, but we cannot.

In almost every country methods are known by which output of food could be greatly increased; in many cases experts will declare it could be doubled. Why is it not done? One of the main reasons, perhaps the chief one, is that in

[1] This question of regional development is discussed by L. Dudley Stamp in *Our Undeveloped World*, Faber, 1953; he also concludes that the middle latitudes offer the best prospects.

almost every country farmers operate only on a small scale. Ranching, it is true, is done on the large scale, but its products are wool and meat produced on wild herbage; it is sharply distinct from farming. The vast majority of farms in most countries are family affairs, run by the farmer and his family with at most only two or three additional regular workers and some extra help at busy times. In many districts, indeed, farming is not even a full-time occupation: it may be combined with fishing, with forestry, or with mining and is then usually run jointly with the women. Over a large part of the world farming is literally only a cottage industry; in spite of its overwhelming importance it has never yet been brought within the ambit of companies operating on the large scale. And yet every human being is an unresistant customer, the demand for agricultural products is absolutely regular and accurately predictable, and there is never the slightest need for salesmanship or advertising. From time to time men who have acquired wealth in business or industry have taken to farming and attempted to do it on proper business lines; in many cases they became lawful plunder for half the supposedly simple-minded countryside, and sooner or later gave up their operations. Nor have companies or committees usually fared better; one could cite many instances of public bodies starting in at farming with high hopes and after a time quitting because the losses were too high. Our African groundnut scheme and the less-known Queensland sorghum scheme are likely to become classic demonstrations of the difficulty of running large-scale farming enterprises by corporate bodies.

The reason for the unsuitability is mainly that the conditions of production are not under complete control. The best laid plan of field operations may be completely upset by a heavy rainstorm or an unexpected drought. A cow is responsive to a kindly human touch, but she doesn't understand a committee. The health and management of a herd may be almost perfect, but suddenly out of the blue may come foot-and-mouth disease, or swine fever, or some other disease and the whole herd may have to be destroyed. The risks cannot be calculated, and so they cannot be covered by insurance except at speculative rates.

This small scale of operations means, of course, that the farmer has very little capital to spare for effecting improvements even when he can see their advantages. He knows that no two fields are quite alike; a result obtained in one place is not necessarily obtainable in another; he knows that his old methods and appliances work after a fashion, and he does not know that the new one would do so. In general he cannot take the risk.

On the other hand he does not usually crash in bad times as a company might do. As returns diminish he simply spends less, and hangs on hoping for better times.

We must presumably accommodate ourselves to this fact of food production as a small-scale industry and seek means to raise its efficiency and give it the advantages—or some of them—that it would have if organized on big business lines. The classical method is by co-operation. As already pointed out this was first developed in Denmark and is still more fully and efficiently carried out there than anywhere else. As practised there it gives the small man the advantage of skilful business organization which can buy cheaply and sell dearly—reversing the order under which isolated small farmers usually work.

473

He is enabled to obtain a high output from the land and an enviable standard of life for his family. The method has been adopted with equal success in Norway, Sweden, Finland, Holland, and various other countries. But it requires for success high standards of intelligence and integrity, and a deep sense of responsibility to the community. Attempts at cheating, at palming off defective produce, or failure to play the game, would undermine the system and make it unworkable. For this reason co-operation has not been as successful as was hoped among the peasant farmers of India or Africa where the responsibility of the individual is to his family or himself rather than to the community; societies have been started but have been gravely hampered by the habit developing among some of the officers of embezzling the funds.

Another system, co-operative farming, was devised in Italy. A group of peasants acquire a large farm and either work it as such or break it up into smaller units so arranged that much of the work can be done co-operatively, as is also the buying of appliances and the processing and marketing of the produce. Alternatively, a group of adjoining peasants will agree to boundary adjustments and exchange of land so that the holdings can become adjacent rectangles which are then cropped in transverse belts, the tractor implements working along the belt and across the holdings. This allows of very efficient tillage, the use of high-class fertilizers and seeds, and timely harvesting. Unfortunately, peasants are often reluctant to make the necessary exchanges, fearing that they may be cheated, and the system has not spread as widely as it deserves. The outstandingly successful example is the Sudan Gezira scheme already described.

Collective farming has been developed in the U.S.S.R. Here all the land of the village or local unit is worked as one large farm; it is owned by the State, but operated by a committee elected by the workers and guided by a chairman and party representative not freely elected. Big tillage and harvesting operations are done by Government-owned machine and tractor stations. All produce belongs to the group; all outgoings are paid in kind. The Government claims a considerable share, the tractor station must be paid, provision made also for replacements, extensions, social services and other things. The balance left over is distributed to the workers in accordance with the work they have done; they can either eat or sell their share of the produce as they wish. No other wages are paid; there is a small cash allocation but no cash basis for remuneration. In addition, each worker has an area of land varying from half an acre up to two and a half acres on which he can grow what he likes and keep such animals as he and his family can look after, but he must not engage paid labour.

The system looks well on paper, and where it suits the natural conditions and the psychology of the workers it can be made to work well; but independent-minded peasants find it very irksome. The Russian Government has succeeded in imposing it throughout the U.S.S.R., but difficulties have arisen in the satellite countries, and there is no evidence of it working anywhere without rigorous and continuous compulsion.

Several of these schemes are being worked in Israel under conditions in which some sort of comparison will be possible; it will be extremely interesting to see the results.

Under the old system in many parts of the world the farmer had not only to produce food but to sell it, and commonly it had to go to a middleman from whom he had borrowed money and who was, therefore, in a position to squeeze him badly. This often happened in India, in Eastern Europe, and other peasant countries. The difficulty has been met in parts of the British Commonwealth by establishing marketing boards, which take the whole of the disposable produce, arrange for its grading, bulking, processing, storage, and sale and are able to secure much better prices than the farmer himself could obtain. The Milk Marketing Board of England and Wales and the Cocoa Marketing Board of West Africa have proved very useful in widely different conditions. The Cocoa Board has established an equalization fund, keeping back a proportion of the receipts in years of plenty so as to give the producer something more than the market price in seasons when this is low. Their lack of reserves puts farmers in a difficult position in seasons of poor financial returns and it greatly curtails their activities in following seasons. It may result from low yields or from low prices. One of the agricultural problems most in need of solution is to find some way of avoiding the fluctuation of yields to which farmers are liable in marginal or difficult conditions. This may be achieved. Low financial returns due to widespread price depressions like those of the 1930's present greater difficulties. Farmers suffer severely as the result; many in England even went bankrupt during those years because they refused to discharge their men or let down their farms; Australian farmers recalling those times are loth to expand their output. Price equalization or supporting schemes worked by marketing boards or other organizations are widely adopted. The United States Government started in 1933 the Farm Produce Price Support Scheme as part of Roosevelt's "New Deal"; under this, minimum prices are fixed for specified basic commodities, wheat, butter, etc., and whenever prices reach this level the Government buys the produce to prevent them falling further. The farmer is thus relieved of the worst anxieties and can plan for plenty, while the consumer is assured of continuous supplies. The Government may, however, have difficulty in disposing of the produce and embarrassingly large quantities may accumulate. In April 1953, 455·8 million bushels of wheat, nearly 500 million bushels of maize, 70 million pounds of butter (this was increasing) and large amounts of other foods were said to be held, and there was a likelihood of further large additions. There were, of course, wishful buyers, but the prices asked were considerably higher than the United Kingdom, the chief of them, felt disposed to pay, and the accumulation may continue. The prices are fixed to cover not only the cost of production but also to afford the farmer an adequate standard of living—which is quite a different matter from standards elsewhere. Aid in disposal is possible under a section of the Act whereby a sum equal to 30 per cent of the Customs receipts may be used to subsidize sales, and it has been argued that as a considerable part of the Customs receipts are paid by the United Kingdom this should be brought into account in the negotiations. Holland also has a price support system but its purpose is limited to protecting the farmer against loss. The British systems vary somewhat with the commodity; for barley the price guarantees against loss; for milk a "pool price" is paid with some Government support for welfare milk; for wheat and eggs (so long as they are supported) the price aims at encouraging production.

This difficulty of dealing with stocks accumulated under price-supporting schemes became acute in the 1930's and no solution was found; large quantities of food were in consequence burned or otherwise destroyed. John Boyd Orr proposed the establishment of a World Food Bank which would take over these stocks and distribute them to the under-fed nations but the method was considered impracticable. No other has yet been found.

Whatever is done in the way of farm organization or of marketing schemes the farmer still remains an operator without large capital reserves. Many of the expansions of production made possible by advances in science and technology require large capital outlay, and although they would yield large quantities of food the actual financial returns may be unsatisfactory from a business point of view, especially where costly ancillary services are needed; better roads, more railways, houses, supplies of water, and electricity. Governments have themselves in many countries undertaken the developments. In free countries where the electorate is largely urban the tendency since the war has been to develop industry or commerce rather than agriculture or the pastoral industry; this has happened in Queensland, where better transport would have mitigated some of the terrible cattle losses caused by the drought of 1951–52, and in the Argentine, where the meat output is now reduced. In non-industrial countries—such as East and West Africa and in Asia the Governments have not the money to spend even though they recognize the needs. The territories under British administration receive grants from the Colonial Development Fund maintained by the United Kingdom, while India and South-East Asia are aided by the Colombo Plan financed by the United Kingdom, Australia, and Canada and by the countries concerned. Before the war large private corporations were prepared to undertake great reclamation schemes and developments; the Sudan Plantations Syndicate is a good example. In the post-war period the Volta Scheme of the Gold Coast is also privately organized. For the success of these enterprises it is absolutely essential that all commitments should be duly honoured, and unfortunately post-war nationalism does not seem to postulate the integrity of the Government in this matter. The action of the Persian Government, and the speeches of some of the African politicians, are likely to check what might have been a valuable flow of capital to their countries.

Assuming these problems of organization and of capital supply to be solved (and given honesty and confidence there is no reason why they should not be) there is no reason to fear any shortage of materials needed on the farm. Fertilizers can be produced to an almost unlimited extent. Phosphates, which are used in the largest amount, are derived from rock of which prodigious quantities are available in North Africa, the United States, and the U.S.S.R., and there are smaller deposits, including some less suitable for present-day processes, in various parts of the Commonwealth. The limiting factor at present is the supply of sulphur, but manufacturing methods are being studied which do not require it. Nitrogenous fertilizers, used in increasingly large quantities, need only gypsum as raw material but their manufacture demands high standards of chemical engineering and also supplies of energy; the equivalent of five tons of coal for each ton of nitrogen fixed. Potash supplies are also indefinitely large. There is, therefore, no need to fear shortage of fertilizer. Potential supplies of materials for control of pests and diseases are likewise almost unlimited. Like fertilizers their manufacture demands highly efficient chemical and engineering technology, but the raw materials required are abundant.

Assuming all these problems solved the vital question still remains; can the present surpluses of food in the exporting countries be expected to continue?

THE SURPLUSES OF FOOD: PRESENT QUANTITIES AND FUTURE PROSPECTS

Wheat

The United States is the largest producer of wheat in the world; the output had been 35·75 million tons in 1948 but this proved too much for the markets and the area fell from the 73·3 million acres at which it then stood to 61·6 million acres in 1950 and the output to 27·74 million tons. China comes next in area and output, followed closely by India in area but not output as the Indian yields are, for climatic reasons, considerably lower than Chinese. Neither China nor India now has any surplus; India, formerly an exporter, has, indeed, to import wheat to make good shortages of rice. Before the war the Argentine grew 17 million acres of wheat, producing 6·6 million tons; in 1950 there were only 13 million acres yielding 5·7 million tons. Australia's pre-war figures were 13 million acres and 4·2 million tons, falling in 1950 to 11·7 million acres but an output of 5 million tons. The area shrunk further to 10·2 million acres in 1952. The shrinkage may not be permanent: it is attributed to the high price of wool, the shortage of fertilizers, and of machinery—all temporary causes. Australia's yields have in recent years gone up.

European production suffered greatly during the war and even by 1950 had not fully recovered. (Table CXX.)

France and Italy are the largest European growers, each producing in 1950 about 7·7 million tons, but this was not sufficient and each had to import. France, however, is striving to become an exporter, and Italy aims at reduced imports. If the European East–West trade in grain could be fully resumed Europe, apart from Great Britain, could become self-supporting in wheat.

The United Kingdom is and is likely to remain the largest importer of wheat. The total requirement is about 7½ million tons a year and the import about 5½ million tons or about 200 million bushels. Most of this has, in recent years, been bought through the International Wheat Pool, into which exporters undertake to put certain quantities which are then allocated to purchasing countries at a specified price. The British quota for the season 1951–52 was 177 million bushels.[1] Any requirements above this have to be purchased at a free-market price. The exportable surpluses for 1950–51 were, in million bushels:

U.S.A.	718	France	54
Canada	425	Pakistan	24
Argentine	124	Russia, Danubian and	
Australia	189	minor countries	16

Total, 1,550, about 42 million tons.
1 million bushels = about 27·2 tons.
1 million tons = about 36·8 million bushels.

(*Economist*, November 4, 1950, from Broomhall's *Corn Trade News*.)

[1] In 1953 Great Britain did not sign the agreement, as the price demanded was too high. For Government measures affecting cereals in the United Kingdom and other countries, see C.E.C. Rpts., *Grain Crops*, 1953, Appendix I.

TABLE CXX. *Area and production of wheat, pre-war and* 1950

	Area, million acres		Million tons	
	1934–38	1950	1934–38	1950
America				
United States	55·4	64·6	19·5	27·7
Canada	22·6	26·9	7·2	12·6
North and South America	103·1	110	35·2	48·6
Europe				
Italy	12·5	11·7	7·25	7·62
France	17·8	10·7	8·14	7·70
Spain	11·3	9·9	4·36	3·38
United Kingdom	1·87	2·47	1·74	2·65
All Europe	73·7	70·5	42·3	41·4
Asia				
China (2)	49·9	52·7	21·7	20·6
India (3)	27·0	24·0	7·42	6·32
Pakistan (3)	9·3	10·7	3·18	4·02
Turkey	8·5	11·1	3·41	3·87
All Asia	113	118	43·0	46·0
Africa	14	15	3·8	4·3
Oceania	13	12	4·4	5·2
World (1)	317	325	129	145·5

(*F.A.O. Stat. Year Book*, 1951.)
(1) Excluding U.S.S.R.
(2) Twenty-two provinces. The figures in both second columns are for 1949, the 1950 data not being available.
(3) The pre-war data are for 1937–39.

The details vary from year to year according to yields but the general picture alters little. The chief buyers are ourselves, Germany, Italy, India, and Japan; all are trying to produce more of their own grain, and certain other countries driven to import wheat in the lean years after the war have already ceased to do so. The largest exporter is now the United States—quite a different position from pre-war days when the exports were only small. Britain's chief source of wheat beyond the Pool allocation is Australia, payment being in sterling; if Australia cannot supply all, the rest comes from Canada bought with dollars. Apart from currency difficulties it seems improbable that any shortage of wheat can arise in our time; Australia's home demand is only about 80 million bushels and Canada's only about 35 or 40 million; both are far below their export surpluses.

Rice is of special importance as the staple food of Asia. Well over 90 per cent of the world's output is produced there; the largest areas are in India, China, and Pakistan but even so these countries are not self-sufficing but have to import from the surplus countries, as also do Japan, Malaya, Ceylon, and Indonesia. On the other hand, Burma, French Indo-China, Siam, Formosa, and before the war Korea, were exporters. In the pre-war period Asia as a whole had an export surplus of about 2 million tons of milled rice a year. This is so no longer; indeed, Asia has ceased to be even self-sufficient. Its total output had averaged 145 million tons before the war; in 1950 it was less than 142 million tons; the population, however, had greatly increased meanwhile. Burma, Siam, and Indo-China, which before the war had supplied the needs of South-East Asia, produced in 1950 only 16½ million tons in place of the former 18 million; Burma, the leading producer, grew 5·2 million tons only instead of 7 million. Asia was saved from starvation only by heavy shipments of grain from the United States. Fortunately for Asia the United States and Brazil have greatly increased their output of rice and have become considerable exporters. But even with these imports Asia is short of rice and is likely to remain so until Burma, Siam, and Indo-China increase their output so that they can once more export to their neighbours on the pre-war scale or better.[1] There is no physical reason why they should not; the cause is disorganization resulting from their political changes, but it is not at all clear when they will be able to play their former part in the feeding of Asia. (Table CXXI.) (Fig. 34.)

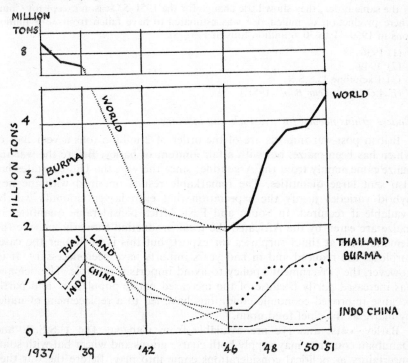

FIG. 34.—World chief exporters of rice and their exports, pre-war and post-war. The other two and their exports were:

	Million tons		
	1937	1938	1939 *and later years*
Korea	1·00	1·11	None
Formosa	0·684	0·653	None

(Data from C.E.C. Rpts., *Grain Crops*, 1953.)

[1] World exports of rice before the war were of the order of 8 million tons per annum; they had fallen to 1 million tons by 1945; thereafter they began to recover, but by 1951 had reached only 4·5 million tons (*C.E.C. Grain Crops*, 1953, p. 97).

TABLE CXXI. *Areas and output of rice (paddy) in Asia*

	Area, million acres			Production, million tons	
	Average 1934–38	1950	1951–52 (C.E.C.)	Average 1934–38	1950
China	49·0	45·7	45·4	50·0	47·0
India	62·3 (1)	75·4	73·6	34·2 (1)	31·0
Pakistan	18·7 (1)	22·4	22·5	11·2 (1)	12·5
Burma	12·2	9·5	9·1	7·0	5·2
Thailand	8·3	13·1	14·5	4·36	6·78
Indochina	13·8	11·1 (2)	5·5	6·5	4·6 (2)
Java and Madura	9·6	9·4 (2)	10·4	6·08	6·07 (2)
Japan	7·8	7·4	7·4	11·5	12·0
All Asia	203	217		145	142
World (3)	212	233		151	152

For conversion to milled rice deduct 30 per cent.

The C.E.C. (*Grain Crops*, 1953) figures differ somewhat from the above but are of the same order; they show little change for the 1951–52 season except for China where production of milled rice was estimated to have fallen from 32·3 million tons in 1950–51 to 30·6 million tons in 1951–52.

(1) 1936–38.
(2) 1949.
(3) Excluding U.S.S.R.
(*F.A.O. Stat. Year Book*, 1951.)

Coarse grains needed for livestock and industry

British post-war imports are of the order of 2 million tons a year half of which has been maize, but with a fair amount of barley. Before the war the maize came mainly from the Argentine; since the war, the United States has also sent large quantities. The remarkable results obtained with the new hybrid varieties justify the expectation that even larger amounts will be available if required. In South and East Africa considerable quantities of maize are eaten by the Africans; the local production formerly met the full demand with at times surpluses for export, but this is no longer the case; surpluses are reduced and in bad years imports have been necessary. It is, however, the Government's policy to avoid imports if possible. The demand has increased partly because of the increased native population, and partly because improved economic conditions have led to a replacement of millet by maize as the chief food grain.

Barley, oats, and rye are available from Canada. The U.S.S.R. and Danubian countries may supply both coarse grains and wheat but with some uncertainty as political considerations come into play. Before the war they served a useful purpose in making up shortages in years when yields in the main exporting countries were low. About three-quarter million tons of coarse grains—barley, maize, and oats—were received in 1950, 676,000 from the U.S.S.R. and the rest from Yugoslavia and Roumania; 840,000 tons came in 1951 from the U.S.S.R.

Future supplies are likely to be available if we can afford to buy them; they are now dollar commodities to a larger extent than they were. By 1948 world production was about 10 per cent greater than before the war; it has since shrunk somewhat. The distribution of the crops, however, has changed greatly since pre-war days; the United States in 1950 grew 50 per cent of the whole against 44·6 per cent in pre-war days; Western Europe 13 per cent compared with 18 per cent, and Eastern Europe 9 per cent against the pre-war 12 per cent.[1]

Oils and fats

World production of all fats had by 1950 risen to 23 million tons which was 6·5 per cent above the pre-war output of 21·6 million tons.[2] Consumption in the different countries varies greatly and is closely related to the national income per head:

		Per head per annum		
National income, $	*Below* 100	100–300	300–500	*Over* 500
Consumption of edible fats, lb.	7·9	16·2	29·1	42·7

(United Nation's Secretariat, quoted by Sir Geoffrey Heyworth, Chairman of Unilever, 1952 meeting, *Economist*, June 28, 1952.)

Supplies of vegetable fats are more easily increased than those of animal fats.

The large quantities of oil cake used before the war were obtained partly by import, partly from linseed, cotton seed, palm kernels, and other oil seeds imported into Great Britain and crushed by very efficient processes. Some reduction in quantity is probable but not certain. More of the seeds are likely to be crushed in the country of origin which would then export only the oil, keeping back the cake either as cattle food or as manure. The French already think this may happen in the savannah regions of Senegal where cattle can be kept and fattened on groundnut cake; the position is somewhat different in wet forest regions where cattle do not thrive. Cultivation of oil seeds is likely to increase; they are important as the chief source of fat in all countries that are largely vegetarian, especially hot countries where animal foods are lacking; they help to make the rather unattractive basic foods more palatable. They are of growing importance to European countries as the raw material for the manufacture of margarine and cooking fats. The oils differ in suitability for this purpose and although modern chemical technology has succeeded in making some modifications by hydrogenation and other methods it has not made the different oils interchangeable. Makers of margarine, however, do not rely on one source of vegetable oil only but use a blend, and by proper scientific control are able to obtain almost any desired consistency, colour, or taste within limits; some brands are almost indistinguishable from butter. Margarine can also be enriched with vitamins and other accessory foods to make it nutritionally equal to butter: it is really a triumph of modern chemistry.

The chief sources of oils for making margarine are palm[3] and coconut, but groundnuts, sunflower, cotton seed, and maize are also very suitable; soya bean somewhat less so. Rape is the chief source in Germany and Sweden but it is not certain that the fat is as easily utilizable in the body as the others.[4]

[1] *Grain Crops*, Commonwealth Econ. Cttee., 1953.   [2] *Economist*, June 23, 1951.

[3] Some palm oil (not, however, kernel oil) is used for making soap; the quantity may diminish if synthetic detergents come sufficiently widely into use.

[4] For further discussion see T. P. Hilditch, "World Fat Supplies," *Advancement of Science*, 1949, Vol. 5, pp. 322–328. Nearly half of the fat consists of the 22 carbon atom erucic acid, while the more usual vegetable fats are of the 18 carbon atom oleic and linoleic acid types.

With the exception of rape all these oil seeds are warm country products and cannot be grown in the British Isles or in Northern Europe. Sunflower is grown in the Danubian countries, Hungary, Bulgaria and Rumania, and also in the Ukraine and the Argentine; soya bean in the more genial conditions of the southern United States, in parts of China and in Manchuria; groundnuts and cotton are products of the savannah and good grass regions of the tropics; palm and coconut of the tropical forest regions. The result of this distribution is that the United Kingdom and Europe, except the Danubian countries, are very largely dependent for vegetable oils on imports; before the war the United Kingdom had to import 0·6 million tons annually and Europe 2¼ million tons. Canada and the United States imported just under one million tons. This total net import of about 3¾ million tons was supplied chiefly from South-East Asia (one million tons from Malaya, Netherland Indies, the Philippines, etc.), China, India, and Ceylon (1.1 million tons), Africa and the Middle East (0·8 million tons), South America (0·5 million tons), there were also half a million tons of whale oil. During and in the early post-war years supplies fell off greatly, amounting in 1946–47 to 2½ million tons only. Asia, in particular, exported but little and, in view of the growing populations, it looked as if world supplies would shortly be very inadequate. Ministers became nervous and their fears caused the groundnut scheme to be put into the hasty execution which ended in its failure. The fears proved to be exaggerated; output of oil seeds as of other agricultural commodities increased, and by 1951 were 10 per cent above their pre-war value. (Table CXXII, Fig. 35.)

TABLE CXXII. *Production of vegetable oils, pre-war and* 1950–51
Thousand tons of oil equivalent

Edible oils	Average 1934–38	1950–51	Industrial	Average 1934–38	1950–51
Ground nut	2,750	3,150	Linseed	1,150	1,085
Soya bean	1,840	2,655	Rape seed	1,350	1,745
Cotton seed	2,450	2,180	Others	340	380
Olive	880	580			
Sunflower	630	1,140		2,840	3,210
Coconut (1)	1,575	1,535	Edible	12,050	13,335
Palm (1)	810	925			
Others	1,115	1,170	Grand total	14,890	16,545
Total	12,050	13,335			

(1) Some for industrial use
(C.E.C. Rpts., *Oil Seeds*, 1952).

The relief from the anticipated shortage came chiefly, as with grains, from the United States which increased its production of soya bean by 950 thousand tons[1] and has now outstripped China, formerly the largest producer. There was also an increased output of groundnuts in Asia, United States, and West Africa, and of sunflower in South America.

Exports of oil have not run parallel with production: they increased in the

[1] Production of soya beans in United States: 1·66 million tons in 1938–39 and 8·02 million tons in 1950. Assumed yield of oil: 15 per cent. (C.E.C. Rpts., *Oil Seeds*, 1953.)

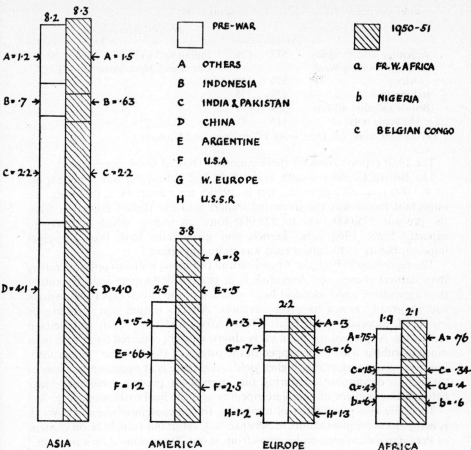

Fig. 35.—World's chief producers of oil seeds, pre-war and post-war. Million tons oil equivalent. (Data from C.E.C. Rpts., *Oil Seeds*, 1953.)

hard currency areas; the Americas (excluding the Argentine and Uruguay), Belgian and Portuguese Africa, but decreased in the soft currency areas. In 1948 and 1949 the exports had been, compared with pre-war:

Exports, thousand tons oil equivalent

	Pre-war	1948	1949
Hard currency areas	740	1,272	1,835
Soft currency areas	5,089	2,732	2,896
	5,829	4,004	4,731
Including animal fats and oils	1,463	1,127	1,457

The main increase was from the United States, the values for which were:

	Pre-war	1948	1949	
	100	277	954	thousand tons

Q*

483

The chief decreases have been, in thousand tons:

Probably recoverable	Pre-war	1949	*Probably irrecoverable*	Pre-war	1949
Argentine and Uruguay	577	189	Indian and Ceylon	589	206
Africa, excluding West			China and Manchuria	630	(70)
Africa	510	340			
Indonesia	529	375			
British Oceania all fats	369	309			
Oil seeds only	115	45			

(*Economist*, June 24, 1950, from Lever Bros. and Unilever.)

The 1950 exports from all these countries showed some increases.

The British Commonwealth as a whole had before the war a net export of 493,000 tons oil equivalent, but in 1950 a net import of 61,000 tons. An important factor was the increased import into the United Kingdom from the pre-war 575,000 tons to 928,000 tons, an import which is likely to expand.[1] Since 1940 palm kernels and groundnuts have been the chief imports: before 1940 cotton seed was more important.[2]

The regression in both the Argentine and Indonesia is due to political rather than natural causes; the Argentine is at present developing industry rather than agriculture and Indonesia has lost much of the Dutch expert help which had so greatly raised its productiveness. Africa's output can certainly be increased, especially from British West Africa and the French and Belgian territories. At present the palm oil is almost entirely collected from wild trees much as rubber used to be tapped in the forests of the Amazon; plantations, however, give considerably higher yield. Also there is at present much loss of oil due to decomposition during the interval (at present sometimes long) between the moment of complete ripening and the final extraction. (Fig. 36.)

There are also possibilities of improving the oil content of the seeds. Work is being done on groundnuts in Senegal. S. C. Harland raised the oil content of Peruvian cotton seed on his plots from about 20 per cent to 29·4 per cent.[3] The very promising work on rape seed in Sweden is described on page 114.

The prospects for future supplies of margarine and of cooking fat, therefore, seem reasonably good.

Dairy produce

Unfortunately, we cannot say the same for butter. Our home production was never great, and our imports have fallen sadly: the total annual supplies have been:

	Thousand tons		
Pre-war	1950	1951	1952
500	373	324	241

(C.E.C. Rpts., *Dairy Produce*, 1953.)

In consequence our consumption per head which before the war had been 24 lb. per annum fell during and after the war to 10 or 11 lb. a year; it was

[1] C.E.C. Rpts., *Oil Seeds*, 1952.
[2] E. G. Woodroofe, *Jl. Roy. Soc. Arts*, 1953, Vol. 102, pp. 77–90.
[3] S. C. Harland, La Vida Agricola, Peru, 1945, quoted by him in *Four Thousand Million Mouths*. Ed. Le Gros Clark and N. W. Pirie, 1951, p. 100.

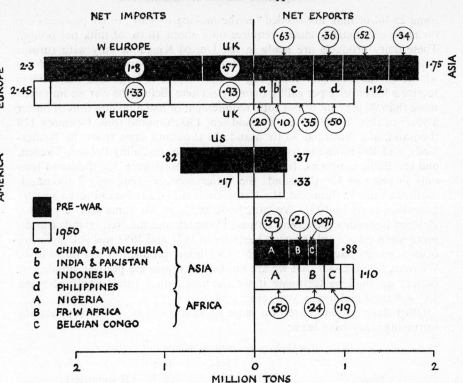

FIG. 36.—World's net exports and net imports of oil seed, million tons oil equivalent, pre-war and 1950. (Data from C.E.C. Rpts., *Vegetable Oil Seed*, 1952, p. 11.) Japan is a net importer, hence the net export from Asia as a whole (1·75 million tons) is less than the sum of the net exports from the four countries shown. Note the great fall in imports by the United States; this is becoming more pronounced.

higher in 1951 but lower in 1952. Consumption of margarine then reached the record amount of 19 lb. per head per year.

This replacement of butter by margarine occurs in other European countries and elsewhere—not, however, in New Zealand, Quebec, or certain other countries: the world production has been:

	Million tons	
	Pre-war	1951
Butter	3·93	3·30
Margarine	1·25	2·33
	5·18	5·63

(Sir Geoffrey Heyworth, Unilever Annual Meeting, June 1952.)

The falling off of butter production is not the result of any diminution in milk supply; on the contrary the world output of milk has increased, but the utilization has greatly altered: less is made into butter, more into other products: cheese, evaporated, condensed, or dried milk or used in making infant and invalid foods, chocolate, etc. Butter has the disadvantage that some 25 lb. of milk are needed for the making of 1 lb.; other products are far more economical: cheese requires only about 10 lb. of milk per pound. These dairy products are made in the United Kingdom only with surplus milk that cannot be sold for liquid consumption—about 14 per cent of the whole. In the countries supplying us the surplus is large and the farmers receive a lower price per gallon than is paid here. Before the war we imported more than 90 per cent of our total requirement of half a million tons of butter a year: of this, in 1938, New Zealand sent 130 thousand tons, Denmark 118 thousand, and Australia 90 thousand; 36 thousand came from the Netherlands, and 100 thousand tons from other sources including Poland, Sweden, and the Baltic countries. In 1951 our total imports were 308 thousand tons only in place of 476 thousand; the "other sources" sent only 2 thousand, Australia only 33 thousand, the Netherlands only 18 thousand; even smaller quantities came in 1952. We can, however, hope for some recovery: New Zealand is steadily increasing output, Denmark and the Netherlands can do more when we are able to pay, Australia in 1951 and 1952 was still suffering from a wholly exceptional drought. Our home production has fallen also. We must face the fact that we are unlikely to regain the pre-war supplies of butter; we shall be fortunate if we can maintain a total supply of some 350–400 thousand tons a year. (Fig. 37.)

Other dairy products are in a more hopeful position. World supplies are increasing; they have been:

World diary production, million cwt.

	1938	1951	
Cheese	29·8	39·3	(21 countries)
Condensed and evaporated milk	35·0	51·7	(11 countries)
Milk powder	7·2	14·2	(13 countries)
Butter	56·9	48·4	(24 countries)

(*Dairy Produce*, C.E.C. Rpts., 1952.)

It is not certain how far supplies of cheese to the United Kingdom will increase. Before the war our average annual consumption was 188 thousand tons a year of which 44 thousand tons were made at home and 144 thousand imported; the consumption increased somewhat as meat became scarcer, rising to 204 thousand tons in 1948–49[1] and about 230 thousand tons in 1951: home production fell somewhat, however, and may not fully recover. World supplies are available, but Canadian and American cheese can be purchased only with dollars. New Zealand, however, is increasing output and is not only our chief supplier but is having to seek markets in America: in 1951, 96 thousand tons were shipped to the United Kingdom and 10 thousand tons to other countries, chiefly the United States and Canada, thus earning much-needed dollars. Unfortunately there has been a sad lowering of quality. Ration cheese became almost a byword; some of the famous English cheeses made by the skilful womenfolk in farm houses of Cheshire, Yorkshire, Somerset, and elsewhere are threatened with extinction: Stilton survives as a factory product but our children are unlikely to have the range of pleasing varieties that we have enjoyed. (Fig. 38.)

[1] *F.A.O., Food Balance Sheets*, 1950.

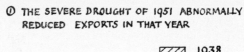

① THE SEVERE DROUGHT OF 1951 ABNORMALLY REDUCED EXPORTS IN THAT YEAR

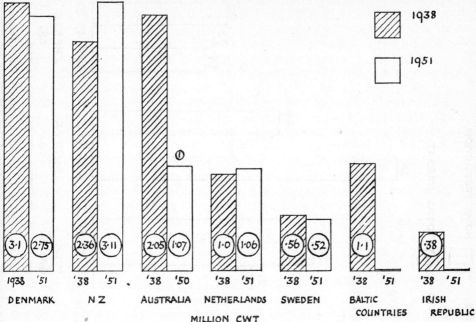

FIG. 37.—World's chief exporters of butter, 1938 and 1951. (Data from C.E.C. Rpts., *Dairy Products*, 1953.)

Meat

There is a good deal of uncertainty about our future meat supplies. Before the war our annual consumption was about 2·8 million tons a year of which about 2·2 million were beef,[1] mutton, pork; about 0·3 million tons were bacon and ham; and 0·32 million were poultry, other meats and offals. Of this total 1·5 million tons were imported. During the war home production fell drastically as we have seen, but imports increased so long as Lend-Lease arrangements were functioning; they then fell off and in 1950 the import was only 1·15 million tons and home production 1·25 million making a total supply of about 2·4 million tons, a shortage of about 400,000 tons compared with pre-war days.

The main reduction had been in beef and pig meat; total supplies of lamb and mutton fell but little. This steadiness of lamb and mutton supplies at about half a million tons a year is the result of increasing imports from New New Zealand; home production has fallen and as we have seen is unlikely to reach pre-war values owing to shortage of shepherds and fear of worrying by dogs. New Zealand is the chief source of supply, and more may be expected from there. Australia also sends large quantities, reduced in the post-war period by the very high prices of wool. (Fig. 39.)

Supplies of pig meat fell drastically from the pre-war 830 thousand tons a

[1] Throughout this section "beef" includes veal and "mutton" includes "lamb."

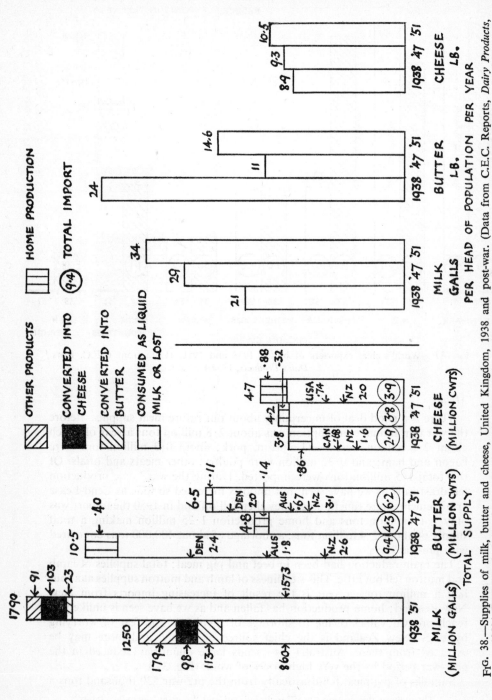

FIG. 38.—Supplies of milk, butter and cheese, United Kingdom, 1938 and post-war. (Data from C.E.C. Reports, *Dairy Products*, 1953.) Butter and cheese figures do not add up to total supplies because of changes in stocks. Import figures are for retained

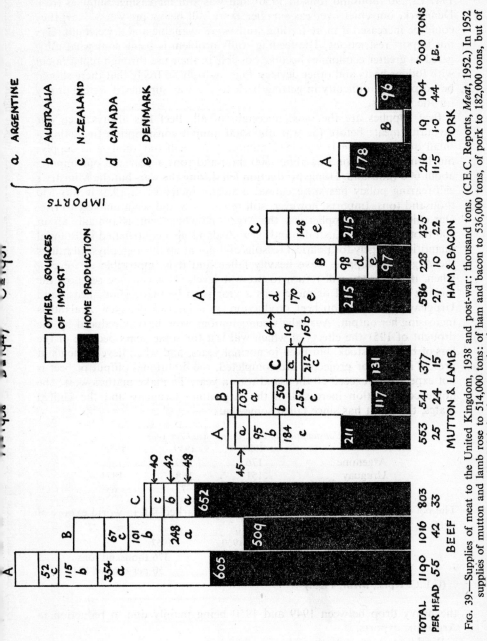

Fig. 39.—Supplies of meat to the United Kingdom, 1938 and post-war: thousand tons. (C.E.C. Reports, *Meat*, 1952.) In 1952 supplies of mutton and lamb rose to 514,000 tons: of ham and bacon to 536,000 tons, of pork to 182,000 tons, but of beef fell to 727,000 tons, 607,000 being home produced.

year, and even in 1948–49 were still half a million tons down. But recovery was proceeding rapidly: home production rose from 113 thousand tons in 1947 to 290 thousand tons in 1950[1] and was still increasing. Supplies from Denmark, our chief overseas supplier, were still below pre-war values; they could be increased if more feeding stuffs were available and if we could relax our import restrictions. The feeding stuffs problem is being somewhat mitigated as greater economies become possible in their use through replacement with fodder beets and other devices. Pigs multiply so freely that there should be no physical difficulty in getting back to pre-war supplies if we could pay for the imports.

Beef supplies are the most uncertain of all. Beef has always been our favourite meat: before the war our total annual consumption (including a small quantity of veal) was 1·15 million tons—half our total meat supply; our home production was about 600 thousand tons a year and our imports about 600 thousand. Home production fell during the war, but the Ministry's calf-rearing policy has since caused a steady increase; in 1950 it was 630 thousand tons. Imports, however, still remain low and seem unlikely to rise. Our chief pre-war supplier was the Argentine which sent us annually about 400 thousand tons. Australia and New Zealand also contributed substantial quantities. Largely for political reasons and not at all through physical causes the Argentine supplies have heavily fallen and it is impossible to forecast when, if ever, they will return to pre-war levels. Nor can one see how the missing 300 thousand or more tons a year is to be made good. Brazil and Uruguay could develop beef production on a large scale, New Zealand is increasing her output, Australia's contributions were heavily reduced by the drought of 1951 the effects of which will last for some years because of the loss of breeding stock, but even in normal years, and when developments at present in hand or projected are completed, the additional output of beef is not expected to exceed 50 thousand tons a year. To make matters worse the home consumption increased in the Argentine, Uruguay and the United States, though it has since fallen somewhat:

Consumption of beef, lb. per head per year

	1938	1949	1952
Argentine	176	209	183
Uruguay	151	168	187[2]
United States	62	72	68

The net result of all these changes has been a marked fall in world export of beef:

1938	1949	1950	1952
748	624	467	376 thousand tons
100	83	62	50 per cent of 1938

(C.E.C. Rpts., *Meat*, 1953.)

the heavy drop between 1949 and 1950 being mainly due to reduction in Argentine exports.

World production both of beef and of pig meat has, however, increased since the war (Fig. 41), but exports have fallen, excepting of canned meat

[1] *Annual Abstract of Stat.*, 1951.   [2] 1951

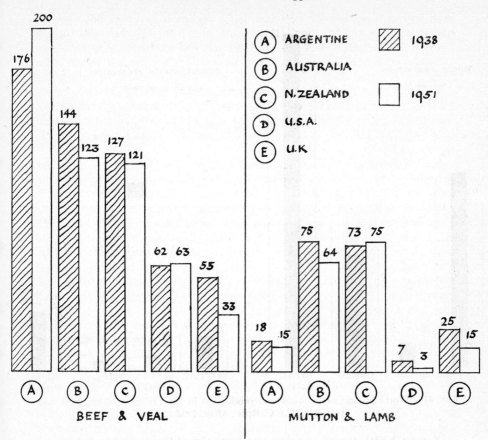

Fig. 40.—Consumption of beef and veal, lamb and mutton, etc., per head per year in the chief consuming countries, 1938 and post-war. (Data from C.E.C. Reports, *Meat*, 1953.)

(Figs. 42 and 43), and the United Kingdom as the largest buyer has suffered most. (Fig. 44.)

The position in regard to our imports of meat is shown in Table CXXIII. A shortage of some 300 or 400 thousand tons of meat compared with pre-war supplies is indicated and unless the Argentine returns to its previous levels of supply a good part of this may be permanent. Some of this could be supplied by raising more cattle ourselves. Our present home production of about 600 thousand tons of beef a year necessitates the slaughter of some two million mature animals. Another 1¼ million head of cattle, however, never grow up, being slaughtered within four days of birth as necessary but unwanted concomitants of the dairy herds of the country. By arranging that they should be produced from a beef bull some of these could be fully reared. More calves could also be raised on hill farms. In all, W. A. Stewart has estimated that an additional 660 thousand cattle could be raised yielding about 220 thousand tons of beef.[1]

[1] W. A. Stewart, *Jour. Roy. Soc. Arts*, 1953, Vol. 101, pp. 395–402.

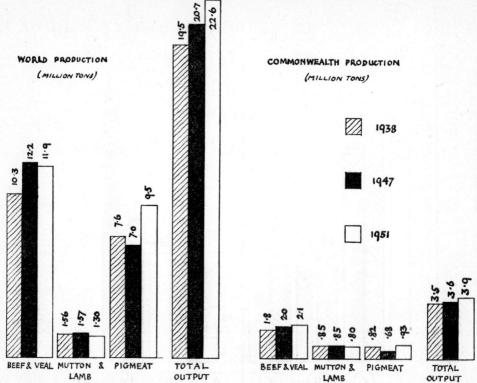

FIG. 41.—World production of meat and production in the Commonwealth, 1938 and post-war. (C.E.C. Rpts., *Meat*, 1952.)

TABLE CXXIII. *Imports of carcass meat into United Kingdom. Thousand tons*

	1934–38 Average	1951	1953 (estimated)
Argentina	436	87	238
Australia	195	67	140
Canada	7	Nil	—
New Zealand	257	275	360
United States	11	Nil	Nil
Others	134	86	
Total imports	1,040	515	780
Home production	1,063	941	1,020
Total supplies	2,103	1,456	1,800

Trade and Navigation Accounts and Ministry of Food (*Economist*, January 3, 1953.)

Naturally, there has been much casting about for other possible supplies. Africa seems at first sight promising but as we have seen (p. 237) the difficulties imposed by the dry season and the disease-bearing insects are very great. Our best hope lies in increasing outputs from a number of the smaller

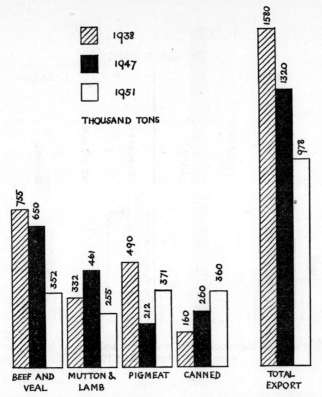

FIG. 42.—World export of meat, including canned meat, 1938 and post-war. (C.E.C. Rpts., *Meat*, 1952.)

suppliers including Eire, but always with the hope that South America will once more expand its production.

This heavy fall in world export of meat emphasizes the need for developing fish resources. This is outside the scope of the present work, but it should be pointed out that fish has not replaced meat in our dietary to anything like the extent it might have done: consumption of meat including game, poultry, and offals has fallen by over 40 lb. per head per year since pre-war days, while that of fish has increased only by 3 lb. per head:

	Consumption, lb. per head per year		
	Average		
	1934–38	1948–49	Change
All meat	133	91	−42
Fish	27	30	+ 3

(*F.A.O. Food Balance Sheets*, 1951.)

Fish culture for food has hardly begun in the United Kingdom, though in some countries, e.g. Poland before the war, an acre of water was said to be as profitable as an acre of land.

493

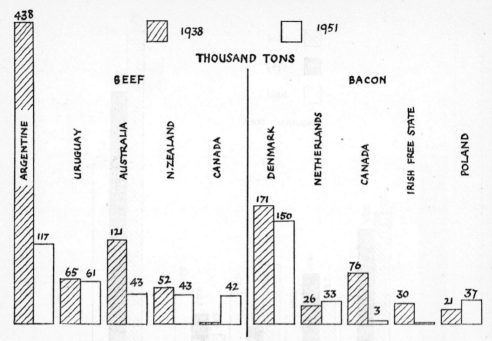

Fig. 43.—World's chief exporters of beef and bacon and ham, 1938 and post-war. (Data from C.E.C. Rpts., *Meat*, 1952.)

Sugar

Sugar is probably the safest of all the foods. The world production is about thirty million tons a year, a third of which is beet sugar and two-thirds cane sugar; output could easily be increased. Both crops are being studied very fully by scientific and technological workers, their yields are already good and in many countries are rising. Sugar beet is mainly confined to Europe and the U.S.S.R. but sugar-cane is grown widely in the tropical and sub-tropical belt of South America, South and East (but not West) Africa, Asia, and

TABLE CXXIV. *World production of sugar. Thousand tons*

	Beet			Cane	
	1937–38	1948–49		1937–38	1948–49
Germany	2,213	1,283	India and Pakistan	3,240	3,200
France	969	950	Australia	810	944
United Kingdom	426	615	British West Indies	401	609
All Europe	7,180	6,737	South Africa	452	544
U.S.S.R.	2,500	2,400	All Commonwealth	5,609	6,090
Other countries	1,374	1,324	Cuba	3,018	5,146
			Brazil	985	1,550
Total beet	11,054	10,506	Total non-Common-	12,421	13,860
Total cane	18,030	19,950	wealth		
Total sugar	29,084	30,456	Total cane	18,030	19,950

(Messrs. C. Czarnikow, Ltd., in *Economist*, August 20, 1949.)

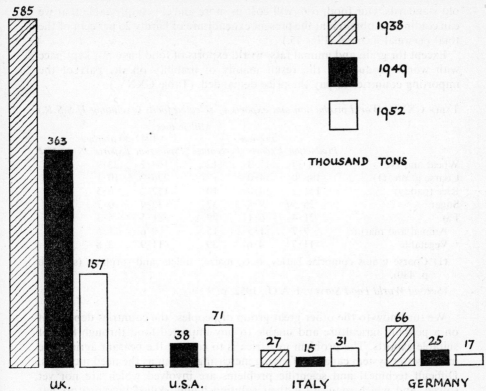

FIG. 44.—Imports of beef by the chief importing countries, 1938, 1949 and 1951. (Data from C.E.C. Rpts., *Meat*, 1952.)

Australia. The largest producer is Cuba, followed by Brazil and India; for some of these countries: Cuba, Mauritius, Barbados, the Leeward Islands, it is almost the only export, for many of them the chief fear is of over-production and a slump in prices. The Commonwealth countries have made export agreements to prevent this. The United Kingdom uses about 2 million tons a year and produces on the average about 550 thousand tons, though the output has been up to 700 thousand tons. The cost in 1952 was about £5 per ton greater than that of foreign sugar.[1] Rationing was retained till 1953, not because supplies were unobtainable, but because Cuban sugar, of which there was abundance, was a dollar commodity. (Table CXXIV.)

The future of food supplies

Summing up the future of food supplies for the United Kingdom we may feel hopeful about bread grains, margarine, milk, bacon, pork, and mutton at present levels of consumption, also sugar, fruit, and vegetables. But we cannot rely on pre-war supplies of butter or of beef however much we may hope for them. Also, but probably of less importance, we cannot expect pre-war quality in our food: neither beef nor cheese is likely to be up to the

[1] Minister of Food, House of Commons, October 22, 1952.

old standards. Our food, too, will cost us more and it is improbable that we can continue to obtain it at the present expenditure of hardly 20 per cent of the total personal income. (Fig. 45.)

Except for grain and animal fats, world exports of food have not kept pace with world production, the result mainly of inability on the part of the importing countries to pay the price demanded. (Table CXXV.)

TABLE CXXV. *World production and exports of selected foods (excluding U.S.S.R.)*

Million tons

	Pre-war			1949–50 *average*		
	Production	Exports	Percentage	Production	Exports	Percentage
Wheat and rye	149·7	17·3	12	163·2	23·9	15
Coarse grains (1)	196·0	14·0	7	226·2	10·1	4
Rice (paddy)	151·2	14·8	10	152·2	6·5	4
Sugar	26·5	9·8	37	32·9	10·7	33
Fat	21·4	6·1	29	21·5	5·3	25
Animal and marine	9·7	1·5	15	9·6	1·5	16
Vegetable	11·7	4·6	39	11·9	3·8	32

(1) Coarse grains comprise barley, oats, maize, millets, and sorghum (see also p. 480).

(*Second World Food Survey*, F.A.O., 1952, p. 9.)

We turn now to the other great group of peoples: the countries dependent on a peasant agriculture and unable to buy imported food through lack of suitable exports. The problem in Africa is to convert the peasant agriculture into a better system capable of giving increasing output as the need increases. Difficult technical and scientific problems are involved which are not yet solved, and which require for their solution highly skilled investigators left to work in peace and security. They cannot be adequately dealt with by visiting experts remaining for a few months only, but with no permanent interest in the country; nor could they be solved by people who have merely learned something at a college and got a degree. Scientific acumen of a high order is needed; it cannot be imparted but only developed in those in whom it is inborn. Such men can only be attracted, not produced.

When the better methods are elaborated there still remains the problem of getting them widely adopted. The necessary equipment and appliances cannot be made by the village craftsmen as can those needed by the old peasant agriculture; they are producible only in countries where there is a network of interlocking engineering, chemical, electrical, and other industries, highly efficient and highly organized, and directed by able business men to ensure the optimum utilization of all available resources. There must equally be the network of highly efficient schools, colleges, and research organizations to provide the flow of scientific and technical staffs to deal with the many problems continuously arising. Such complex systems grow up only slowly; they cannot be created by any waving of political wands—though they may be so destroyed. It is highly improbable that any such system can be set up in Africa in any foreseeable future; neither capital nor men are available. Nor need Africa dissipate its resources by trying to set up its own systems. Existing manufacturing countries are fully able to supply the materials, and the higher scientific institutions of the Commonwealth, Western Europe, and the United

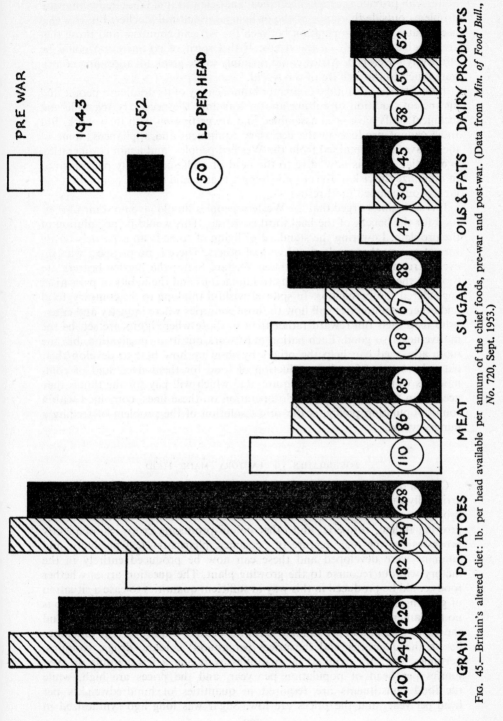

FIG. 45.—Britain's altered diet: lb. per head available per annum of the chief foods, pre-war and post-war. (Data from *Min. of Food Bull., No.* 720, Sept. 1953.)

PRE WAR

1943

1952

LB PER HEAD

50

DAIRY PRODUCTS 38 50 52

OILS & FATS 47 39 45

SUGAR 98 67 88

MEAT 110 86 85

POTATOES 182 249 238

GRAIN 210 249 220

States, can provide the higher technical and scientific guidance in dealing with problems outside the range of the ordinary agricultural teacher. But this also necessitates close co-operation between the African countries and those that are capable of supplying the needs. If this spirit of co-operation could be effectively developed, Africa could certainly make great advances and contribute much to the welfare of the world.

India has the advantage of greater homogeneity of its dominant people and an ancient tradition of culture and of learning; the necessary scientific and technical staffs have been assembled and are getting on with their work. But India cannot produce all the necessary equipment and appliances, some of them have to be obtained from the Western peoples, and again co-operation is essential. India is now alive to the need of a planned family pattern so as to minimize the risk of the chronic hunger that would result if population too greatly outstripped food resources.

It is sometimes urged that the Western peoples should give up some of their food for the benefit of the backward countries. This would be no solution of the problem. Lowering the standard of living of some is an extremely costly way of raising the standard of living of others. There is no prospect whatsoever of running the world as a huge Welfare State; the burden-bearers are too few, the claimants for benefits too numerous and the habits of parasitism engendered too pernicious. In spite of wishful thinking to the contrary, food and other commodities will flow to those countries where industry and enterprise reap their full reward rather than to those where limits are set, be the motive never so good. Each nation must work out its own salvation, but the more advanced can help the others by showing how best to develop their natural resources for the production of food for themselves, and of commodities which other people require, and which will pay for the things they need from the outside world. Co-operation on these lines, combined with a sound population policy, is the surest solution of the problem of feeding a hungry world.

POSSIBILITIES OF FACTORY MADE FOOD

One of the first triumphs of chemical technology was to manufacture artificially the dye-stuffs which formerly had been extracted from plants: this proved so successful that it put an end to the old and profitable industry of growing indigo, turmeric, and other colour-producing crops. Subsequently processes for the manufacture of perfumes, pharmaceutical products, and vitamins were developed and these can now be produced entirely in the factory without recourse to the growing plant. The question arises whether foods could be produced in this way in sufficient quantities to ease a situation of growing scarcity should it arise. In principle some of them could: there is no fundamental difference between the substances already manufactured and the sugar, starch, and protein that form the basis of our foods. The difference lies in the quantities and the prices per pound: colours, drugs, vitamins, perfumes, etc., are required in quantities averaging a few pounds or even ounces per head of population per year, and the prices are high, while the food constituents are required in quantities of hundredweights per head per year, and the prices are low. Sugar was long ago synthesized in the laboratory, but no process has yet been devised for producing it in a factory at prices comparable with the cost of production from sugar beet or sugar-cane.

Some very competent chemists believe, however, that synthetic production of both sugar and starch may still be possible. Fats have already been manufactured by the Germans in the last war starting from propylene prepared from coal and then converted into glycerine. Even under the stress of dire necessity, however, and in conditions where economic factors were entirely eliminated, they could never make as much as 2,000 tons of edible fat a year; while the United Kingdom would need over 10,000 tons a week to provide an 8-oz. ration for its people. This difficulty would in time no doubt become less, but a more serious one remains. The fats constitute a series of compounds of the same chemical type but with different numbers of carbon atoms. Natural fats contain even numbers, usually 16 or 18,[1] and the human body is attuned to these and can utilize them. But the synthetic product is a mixture in equal molecular proportions of fats with odd and with even numbers of carbon atoms, and the evidence, though conflicting, indicates that the human body cannot deal with the fats containing odd numbers of carbon atoms: they may be assimilated but they are unutilized. Also, some of the synthetic fats are iso-bodies, i.e., have side chains, and these also the body cannot utilize.[2]

Proteins cannot, as yet, be made synthetically.

Both fats and proteins, however, can be built up from carbon-dioxide and simple salts by some of the micro-organisms. Again the Germans led the way: during the first war when their protein supplies became very short they cultivated certain yeasts, using home-produced beet sugar and synthetic nitrogen compounds as food. The yeasts built these up into proteins which were valuable both for human and for animal food. The method has been developed in Great Britain and provides considerable quantities of protein generally used in soups and gravies. Considerable expansion of this yeast-food industry has been made at Frome in Jamaica, using molasses and waste sugar—of which large quantities are available—as the food for the organism. Development has been slower than was hoped but the difficulties have not all been technical.[3]

One of the fresh-water algae, chlorella, is remarkably effective in synthesizing fats and proteins. Like other green plants it needs as its raw materials only carbon-dioxide and a nutrient solution of simple salts, but it excels the ordinary plant in two ways: none of the light it receives is reflected: all is absorbed by its chlorophyll; and it can vary the proportions of proteins and fats in its composition according to the conditions in which it is living. It has been much investigated by H. A. Spoehr and H. W. Milner at the Stanford Research Institute, California (Carnegie Institute of Washington) and by later workers; cultures have been obtained in which the dry matter contained

---

[1] The heavy preponderance of even numbers suggests that natural fats are in the main synthesized from units of the 2-carbon atom acetic acid. It has been shown at the Shinfield Dairy Research Institute that this is true for butter fat.

[2] *Synthetic Fats, Their Potential Contribution to World Food Requirements*, F.A.O., Washington, D.C., March 1949.

[3] A. L. Bacharach and T. Crosbie-Walsh, in *Four Thousand Million Mouths*, ed. Le Gros Clark and N. W. Pirie.

50 per cent of crude protein and 25 per cent of lipoids, but the protein content can vary from 7 to 78 per cent and the lipoid content from 4·5 to 96 per cent of the dry matter. The fatty acids are mainly of the 16 or 18 carbon atom groups and should be suitable as food. The protein contains all the essential amino acids, and unusually large amounts of several vitamins are present.[1] Mass cultures can be grown in tanks or in glass tubes or pipes; temperature and light conditions can be completely controlled and high yields are obtainable. Chlorella can yield 50 to 100 times more food per unit area than ordinary agriculture. Investigations have been made under I.C.I. and other bodies to see if the process can be worked commercially. Present indications are that the costs are much higher than in ordinary agriculture.

The underlying principle is not unlike that of the cultivation of glass house crops in culture solutions—the "hydroponics" of which a good deal was heard in the 1930's; public interest has died down, but the investigations of R. H. Stoughton of Reading University are showing its possibilities for certain horticultural products: tomatoes, sweet peas, carnations, etc.

Vast quantities of protein synthesized by plants are unused because they are mixed with substances of unpleasant taste or harmful nature, or, as in the case of grass, accompanied by large quantities of indigestible fibre. The protein can now be extracted free from these undesirable accompaniments and made into a kind of cheese which can be suitably flavoured and presented in an attractive form. The percentage of protein in the leaf can be increased by the use of nitrogenous fertilizers. The process is not yet on a commercial basis, but the scientific problems are mainly solved.[2]

The sea contains more vegetable matter than the earth and has hardly been touched as a source of vegetable food. Some of its plants are edible, but in general they would need to undergo considerable changes before they could be used for human or animal food. This, however, should not be difficult in principle though at present it is uneconomic in fact.[3]

These various methods are for the future: they constitute a strong second line of protection against world starvation should the time arrive when world agriculture is insufficient to feed the world population. But, meanwhile, world agriculture is developing and its possibilities are vividly emphasized by the circumstances that at present (1) less than 10 per cent of the earth's land surface is cultivated: the rest is largely waste; (2) only about one-tenth to one-half of 1 per cent of the sun's radiation received at the earth's surface is fixed as organic material: the rest is lost; (3) only about half or less of the organic material ultimately reaches the table as human food, much of the rest is wasted. Taking the earth's surface as a whole, for each million calories of energy received from the sun only one calorie is converted into human

---

[1] H. W. Milner, *Jl. Amer. Oil Chemists Soc.*, 1951, Vol. 28, pp. 363–367. Extrapolating from laboratory data (admittedly a hazardous process) he calculates that 1 acre of chlorella could produce 40 tons of dry matter containing 20 tons of protein and 3 tons of fat—which is something like 50 times or more the output per acre from a good British farm. See also H. A. Spoehr, *Proc. Amer. Phil. Soc.*, 1951, Vol. 95, pp. 62–67; W. H. Pearsall and G. E. Fogg, *Food Sci. Abstracts*, 1951, Vol. 23, p. 1.

[2] R. E. Slade, *British Association Rpts.*, 1937. N. W. Pirie in *Four Thousand Million Mouths*.

[3] See an admirable summary by Prof. Lily Newton, *Advancement of Science*, 1949, Vol. 6, pp. 275–286.

food.[1] And lastly, little attention has yet been paid to the conservation and most efficient use of water, the factor finally limiting food production.

The problem of improving our utilization of these natural resources is being studied in many countries and it offers our best method of increasing the total supply of human food.

[1] This remarkable calculation was made by H. W. Milner of the Stanford Research Institute (*Jl. Amer. Oil Chemists Soc.*, 1951, Vol. 28, pp. 363–367). It refers to the temperate zone and the average radiation received is estimated to be 7,300 million kilo calories per acre. See also H. A. Spoehr, loc. cit.

LIST OF FIGURES

CHAP. FIG.   PAGE

I   1. Land, people and grain production in the six continents.   15

II   2. Agricultural land and livestock in England and Wales: pre-war and post-war.   28

3. Utilization of home-grown wheat and barley, United Kingdom, pre-war, war-time, and post-war.   33

4. Production and import of wheat and coarse grains, United Kingdom, pre-war and post-war.   34

5. Increasing output of milk per cow and rising fat content, England and Wales, 1925 to 1952.   67

IV   6. Map showing reclamations in North Holland, 1608 to 1952.   85

7. Grain production, Netherlands, Denmark and Sweden: 1937–1951.   100

8. Grain imports, Netherlands, Denmark and Sweden.   105

9. Production and disposal of milk, butter, and cheese, Netherlands, Denmark and Sweden.   117

10. Finland's recovery of agricultural production after loss of territory to Russia in the last war.   123

11. Northern extension of spring wheat cultivation in Finland resulting from the breeding of new varieties and developments in agricultural technique.   125

V   12. Post-war changes in agricultural production, France.   137

13. Increasing importations of wheat by Mediterranean countries.   154

VI   14. Production and export of maize, Union of South Africa.   202

IX   15. Rainfall map of India (L. A. Ramdas).   320

16. Production and import of rice and of wheat, India and Pakistan, compared with changes in population.   328

XI   17. Expansion of agricultural output, United States.   354

18. Production and export of grain, United States.   355

19. Numbers of livestock, United States.   361

20. Westward expansion of wheat cultivation, Canada, 1891 to 1949; the result of breeding new drought and rust-resistant varieties and of improving farm technique.   381

21. Yields of wheat per acre, Canada, 1908–1948 (E. S. Hopkins).   383

22. Production and export of grain, Canada.   391

XII   23. Map showing length of growing period in the different regions of Australia (J. A. Prescott and Joyce A. Thomas).   400

24. Production and export of grain, Australia.   409

25. Relation of wheat yield and rainfall in South Australia, 1890 to 1952. (A. E. Richardson: J. A. Prescott.)   410–11

26. Numbers of livestock, Australia (S. M. Wadham).   414

27. Production of meat, Australia (S. M. Wadham).   416

28. Export of meat, Australia.   417

29. Production of milk, butter and other dairy products, Australia and New Zealand.   440

30. Production and export of meat, New Zealand.   441

XIII   31. Production and export of grain, Argentina.   450

32. Production and export of meat, Argentina.   453

XIV   33. Population and production of wheat and rice in wheat and rice-eating regions respectively.   470

34. World's chief exporters of rice and their achievements.   479

35. World's chief producers of oil seeds.   483

CHAP. FIG.   PAGE

XIV   36. World net imports and net exports of oil seeds.   485
      37. World chief exporters of butter, pre-war and post-war.   487
      38. Supplies of dairy products, United Kingdom, pre-war and post-
          war.   488
      39. Meat supplies, United Kingdom, pre-war and post-war.   489
      40. Consumption of beef and veal, mutton and lamb, lb. per head
          per year in the chief consuming countries.   491
      41. Production of carcass meat, World and Commonwealth, pre-war
          and post-war.   492
      42. World export of meat, pre-war and post-war.   493
      43. World's chief exporters of beef, and bacon and ham, pre-war and
          post-war.   494
      44. World's chief importers of beef, and the quantities they took,
          pre-war and post-war.   495
      45. Britain's altered diet, pre-war, war-time and 1952.   497

NAME INDEX

Acharya, A., 333
Adriaens, E. L., 280, 281
Ady, P., 299
Aird, J. A., 423
Åkerman, Å., 114
Altona, R. E., 208
Annett, H. E., 77, 431, 444
Archibald, E. S., 397
Arena Antonio, 449
Armstrong, J. M., 397
Ashton, E. D., 67
Ashton, Hugh, 212
Avid, J. A., 423
Avis, P. R. D., 68
Ayan, E. G., 147
Ayer, A. K. N., 321
Aykroyd, W. R., 235

Bacharach, A. L., 499
Bailey, M. A., 177
Baird, J. C., 53
Baker, R. E. D., 262
Baker, V., 62
Balbo, Marshal Italo, 156, 157
Balfour, Col., 246
Balls, W. Lawrence, 177, 181
Banego, Squiss, 287
Barlow, H. W. B., 237
Barnes, A. C., 198
Barrachina, J. B., 147
Basu, J. K., 320, 332
Beckley, V. R. S., 236, 258
Begtrup, H., 97
Bennett, H. H., 362
Biffen, R. H., 250
Binns, A. L., 182
Binns, Sir B. O., 134
Blagburn, C. H., 42, 44
Blake, A. J. Jex, 260
Bledisloe, Lord, 409
Blewett, W. V., 305
Bloom, Alan, 64
Bonsma, J. C., 200
Bouchard, Georges, 372
Bouffil, F., 313
Bovill, E. W., 260
Boyd, D. A., 31
Boyko, E., 171
Brayne, F. L., 336
Brown, C. H., 174, 179
Bruin, P., 91
Bryce, James, 455
Buber, M., 161
Buck, J. Lossing, 344, 347
Buddin, W., 36
Bull, L. B., 424
Buller, Reginald, 379
Bunge, V. A., 262
Bunting, A. H., 245
Bunting, E. S., 358
Burnet, Dr. Etienne, 235
Burns, W., 333

Burt, Bryce, 326
Burt, Cyril, 18
Buxton, P. A., 238

Caffrey, M. J., 56
Camacho, J. A., 455, 458, 461
Cameron, J. F., 245
Capell, J. E., 245
Carrington, Lord, 59
Carr-Saunders, A. M., 17, 18, 19, 20
Castle, M. E., 74, 101
Chamberlain, F. P., 36
Christian, C. S., 414
Church, B. M., 65
Church, R. J. Harrison, 315
Clarke, John, 48
Clothier, J. N., 231
Clunies-Ross, Ian, 419
Collett, L. H., 213
Cooper, M. M., 67
Corkill, L., 434
Cornish, E. A., 410
da Costa, J. Botelho, 272
Craigie, J. H., 380
Crookes, Sir Wm., 5, 402
Crosbie-Walsh, T., 499
Crowther, E. M., 286
Cruz, Dr. Oswaldo, 462
Culwick, G. M. (Mrs.), 269
Curd, F. H. S., 238
Custance, John D., 402
Czarnikow, Messrs. C., 494

Daladier, Edouard, 280, 312
Dalgas, E. M., 107, 108
Darling, Sir Malcolm, 160, 173, 336
Davey, D. G., 238
Davey, T. H., 296
Davies, Dr. J. N. P., 262
Davies, W., 60, 75
Dawe, C. V., 44
Deakin, Alfred, 405
Dean, R. F. A., 262
Debenham, F., 217
Delamere, Lord, 250
Demolon, A., 141
Dent, J. M., 308
Donald, C. M., 414
Donaldson, Frances, 64
Dougall, H. W., 57
Downes, R. G., 421-2
Drexler, A., 68
Duckham, A. N., 357, 360, 367
Dudley, Rowland, 64
Dugard, J. H., 211
Dumont, R., 132, 140
Dyke, G. V., 68

Eastwood, C. G., 302
Ede, R., 96, 109
Edwards, D. C., 252

Elliot, Walter, 235
Ellison, W., 61
Elton, Lord, 378
Engledow, Sir F. L., 225, 229
Evans, E. Estyn, 58
Evans, I. B. Pole, 206–10, 215, 217, 230–1, 247
Evelyn, S. H., 239

Faber, Harald, 97, 109
Fabricius, 108
Farrer, W. J., 402
Faulkner, O. T., 286, 295
Faust, F. C., 348
Fawcett, C. B., 14, 471
von Feilitzen, Hj, 110
Fenelon, K. G., 41
Fife, David, 378, 379
Finney, D. J., 333
Fisher, John, 210
Fjord, N. J., 109
Fogg, G. E., 500
Foot, A. S., 74, 101
Forde, Daryle, 293
Fortes, M., 299
Fortescue, Earl of, 62
Fox, F. W., 202, 205
Frederiksen, Lars, 109
Freeman, T. W., 57, 58
Frumkin, G., 20
Fuggles-Couchman, N. R., 241, 242

Gaitskell, A., 217
Galley, R. A. E., 302
Garrett, S. D., 36
Garstin, Sir Wm., 265
Ghose, M., 325
Gilbert, Sir Hy., 357
Gilbert, S. M., 241
Gilks, J. C., 235, 257
Gillman, Clement, 241
Gillman, J. and T., 211
Godden, W., 31
Gordon, James, 52
Goulden, C. H., 380, 396
Gourou, Pierre, 459
Grafton, Duke of, 63
Greenwood, M., 289, 292
Gregor, J. W., 61
Griffith, Sir Wm., 299
Griffiths, Moses, 61
Grove, A. T., 284, 286, 298
Grundtvig, N. F. S., 97
Guillaume, Maurice, 311, 316

Haarer, A. E., 252, 277
Halain, C., 281
Halcrow, Sir Wm., 305
Hall, A. D., 235, 470
Hall, T. D., 205, 208
Hamilton, R. A., 74
Hammond, J., 67
Hardy, G., 280, 312
Harland, S. C., 484
Harrison, James, 433
Harroy, J. P., 365
Hartley, K. T., 292

Hay, Alexander, 437
Hay, W. D., 74
Haylett, D. G., 206
Hector, G. P., 325
Hedayetullah, S., 339
Hemon, Louis, 373
Henderson, G., 64
Herriot, R. I., 421
de Hevesy, P., 153, 178
Heyworth, Sir Geoffrey, 481, 485
Higginbotham, Sam, 336
Hilditch, T. P., 481
Hopkins, E. S., 368, 381–3, 396–7
Hopkins, J. M., 74
Hornby, H. E., 238
Horne, F. R., 64, 66
Howard, A. and G. L. C., 326
Howard, A. W., 413
Howes, F. N., 287, 299
Hume, C. W., 421
Humphrey, N., 258
Hunt, K. E., 41
Hunter, A. W. S., 396
Hurd, A., 42
Hutchinson, H., 215
Hutchinson, J. B., 261
Huxley, Elspeth, 250

Irvine, F. R., 299
Issawi, C., 174
Iveagh, Earl of, 63

Jacks, G. V., 365
Jackson, J. H., 211
Jackson, J. K., 264
Jenkin, T. J., 75
Jewitt, T. N., 237
Joseph, A. F., 267
Jungers, E., 276

Keay, R. W. J., 284
Kennedy, K., 73
Kernohan, J. T., 74
van Keulen, B. W., 245
Khama, Tschedi, 217
King, F. H., 344, 348
Kirk, Dudley, 17, 20, 21
Kitchener, Lord, 263, 265
Kitchin, A. W. M., 367
Knight, John, 62
Knight, R. H., 267
Kokot, D. F., 216
Korkman, Nils, 115, 128
Kuczynski, R. R., 21

Lapkes, Ya, 365
Laubscher, F. X., 239
Laudelout, H., 280
Leahey, A., 396
Leitch, I., 31
Leplae, E., 273
Levy, E. Bruce, 437, 443–4
Lilienthal, David, 343
Line, R., 61
Linehan, P. A., 74, 75
Little, K. L., 306
Livens, P. J., 273

Lomberg, M., 192, 212
Longobardi, C., 155
Lowe, J., 74
Lowrie, Wm., 403
Lynn, C. W., 304

Macarthur, John, 402
MacBride, J., 245
McCullock, W. E., 293
MacDonald, Sir Murdock, 265
MacGibbon, D. A., 382
Mackie, J. R., 286
McTaggart, A., 414, 422
Mahalanobis, P. C., 317
Malthus, 5
Manniche, F., 97
Marston, H. R., 424
Martelli, G., 63
Masefield, G. B., 236, 239, 260
Massee, A. M., 70
Massey, R. E., 267
Matheson, J. K., 260
Mathison, I., 65
Mayer, Colin, 249, 253, 256
Mayer, E. J., 171
Mead, W. R., 122
Mellanby, Kenneth, 298
Menzies, R. G., 420
Meredith, D., 208
Mill, J. S., 21
Milne, Geoffrey, 244
Milner, H. W., 499–501
Milton, W. E. J., 76
Mitchell, Sir Philip, 260
Monnet, Jules, 140
Mookerji, R., 321
Moreland, W. H., 326
Morgan, W. B., 239
Morrison, J., 53
Müller, P. E., 108
Mundy, H. G., 221–2, 228
Murray, G. W., 180
Muskett, A. E., 52, 53
Mussolini, Benito, 157–9
Myers, W. M., 363

Nash, T. A. M., 296
Nehru, Pandit, 336
Newton, Lily, 500
Nilsson-Ehle, H., 114
Northcott, C. H., 257
Nye, P. H., 299, 304–6

Ordish, G., 71, 409
Orr, John Boyd, 235, 257
Orwin, C. S., 44, 62
Østergaard, P. S., 109

Packman, J. A., 294
Pal, B. P., 326
Panse, V. G., 333
Parnell, F. R., 325
Payne, W. L., 426
Pearsall, W. H., 500
Pei-Sung, Tang, 347
Pendleton, R. L., 348
Pereira, H. C., 256, 258

Perón, Gen., 454
Pihkala, K. U., 130
Piper, G. R., 403
Pirie, N. W., 500
du Plessis, A. J., 202
Posnette, A. F., 301, 305
Post, L. Van der, 217
Praeger, R. Lloyd, 58
Prescott, J. A., 400, 403, 410, 424–5
Pugsley, A. T., 409

Rahman, Abdul, 340
Ramdas, L. A., 320
Ramiah, K., 325
Ravnholt, H., 97
Rennell of Rodd, Lord, 301
Riceman, D. S., 424
Richards, F. W., 184
Richardson, A. E. V., 410
Richardson, H. L., 348–9
Riche, Le, 211
Richet fils, Ch., 280, 312
Richharia, R. H., 326–7
Rigg, T. H., 436
Ripley, P. O., 396–7
Rivett, Sir David, 427
Robertson, G. Scott, 52
da Rocha, Leme, 461
Rose, A. R., 378
Rose, C. J., 208
Ross, J. C., 205, 208–10
Rounce, N. V., 243
Rowland, S. J., 101
de la Rue, I. H., 225
Russell, E. J., 71, 77, 157

Salter, R. M., 360, 362
Sampson, H. C., 286
Samuel, L., 167
Saunders, Chas., 378
Saunders, Wm., 378
Sayce, Roger, 63
Scott, Richarda, 293
Schwartz, E. H. L., 216
Schwetz, J., 281
Sears, P. D., 444
Segni, Antonio, 158
Selkirk, Earl of, 378
Sethi, D. R., 331
Setzer, José, 457, 463
Shawki, M. K., 264
Shen, T. H., 344
Shortt, H. E., 238
Shutt, F. T., 385
Sillery, A., 217
Simmonds, N. W., 262
Simonart, P., 280
Sjollema, B., 76
Skrine, Sir C., 171
Skrubbeltrang, F., 97
Slade, R. E., 64, 77, 500
Smit, R. J., 202
Smith, T. Lyon, 455
Somerville, W., 73
Speyer, F. C. O., 65
Spitz, Geo., 315
Spoehr, H. A., 499–501

Stakman, E. C., 380
Stamp, L. Dudley, 59, 61, 472
Stampe, Sir Wm., 321–2
Stapledon, R. G., 60–1, 75–6
Staples, R. R., 219, 225
Steel, R. W., 299
Stephens, C. G., 421
Stevenson, T. M., 380, 396
Stewart, A. B., 333
Stewart, W. A., 491
Stocks, Percy, 19
Storey, H. H., 233, 238, 244
Stoughton, R. H., 500
Strampelli, N., 152
Svärdström, K. F., 116–17

Tagore, Rabindranath, 336
Tang, C. C., 348
Taylor, J. K., 422
Teakle, L. J. H., 422
Theiler, Arnold, 200
Theron, J. J., 206, 395
Thomas, A. S., 261
Thomas, J. F. H., 61
Thomas, Joyce A., 400
Thomson, G., 18
Thomson, L. B., 384
Thornton, R. W., 213
Thorpe, H. C., 251
Tihon, L., 281
Todaro, F., 152
Todd, J. McA., 301
du Toit, P. J., 201
Tondeur, G., 277, 282
Tothill, J. D., 184
Trapnell, G. G., 231
Trehane, W. R., 67
Trist, P. J. O., 64
Trought, T., 177
Trowell, Dr. H. C., 262
Trumble, H. C., 414
Turner, R., 288
Turner, R. R., 74
Turrell Bros., 68

Utz, E. J., 363

Vachhani, M. V., 325
de Valdivia, J. M., 147
Valle, Otto, 122, 124–5, 127
Vine, H., 284
Virtanen, A. I., 77, 127
Voelcker, O. J., 301
Vogt, W., 365, 420

Wadham, S. M., 414, 416, 428
Wakefield, A. J., 245
Wakefield, E. G., 429
Walker, Sir Gilbert, 319
Wall, G. van de, 202, 205
Wallace, D. B. Johnstone, 73
Waters, H. B., 300, 304
Watt, R. D., 408, 421
Weatherhead, T. D., 471
Wellington, J. H., 217
White, F. H., 396
Whyte, R. O., 365
Wickham, H. A. (Sir Hy.), 458
Wigglesworth, V. B., 70
de Wildeman, E., 280, 282
Willatts, E. C., 161
Williams, C. B., 70
Williams, E., 262
Williams, H. T., 38
Williams, T. E., 75
Wilson, D. Bagster, 235
Wilson, H. H., 321
Wood, G. L., 428
Wood, H. E., 383
Woodroofe, E. G., 484
Wooten, H. H., 363
Worthington, E. B., 263
Wragg, F. C., 38, 43
Wright, E. J., 235, 309
Wright, Norman, 30
Wright, S. J., 338
Wyllie, J., 44

Yates, F., 31, 65, 333
Yates, P. Lamartine, 134

INDEX

AFRICA, Agricultural and food conditions, 182–5, 232–9
Agricultural research in, 254
Chief foods produced, 233–4
Diets, mostly unbalanced, 234
Eastern central regions, 232–70; Western central, 271–316
Equatorial regions, 184
European countries associated, 185
Political agitators retarding development, 244, 255, 263
African reluctance to farm, 259
African reluctance to redistribution of population, 244, 255, 263
Alcohol from potatoes, 90, 113, 126
Alcohol from wood pulp (sulphite liquor), 113
AMERICA, SOUTH, Agricultural conditions, 446–8
ANGOLA, 271
Animals, Farm: efficiency as converters of fodder into human food, 31
ARGENTINA, 448–55
Chief crops, area yields, production and export, 450–1
Industrialization, effects of, 453–4
Meat, production and export, 452–4
AUSTRALIA, 339–428
Bush fires, 422
Butter, production, consumption and export, 419
Crops, areas of chief, 407
Food production, possibility of increasing, 420–7
Fruit, production, consumption and export, 412
Grain, production and export, 407–11
Growing period, length of, 400
Irrigation, 405–7
Livestock, numbers, 407, 414
Meat production, consumption and export, 414–19
Pastures, improvement of, 412
Rabbit pest, 421
Reclamation and development schemes, 424–6
Soil, conservation and erosion, 421–2
Soils, deficiencies, 401
Trace elements, 424–5
Wheat history, 402–3
Wheat, production and export, 407–11
Yield and rainfall, 408–11

Bambarra beans, 303
Bananas (plantains), export from Cameroons, 289
Important in diet: Belgian Congo, 277
Uganda, 261
Barley in U.K. How used, 33
Barley production (see the different countries)

BASUTOLAND, 212–14
Food supplies, 213
Soil conservation, 213
BECHUANALAND, 215–17
Food supplies, 216
Improvement schemes, 216–17
Beef, production and export: Argentine, 452; Australia, 415–18; Brazil, 460; Canada, 392; Eire, 55; U.K., 38, 49; Commonwealth and world, 487–93; U.S.A., 360
Beef supplies to U.K., 38, 49, 490–1, 495
BELGIAN CONGO, 272–83
Corridor system, 279
Crops, area and production, 274–9
Native diet, 280–2
Natives, position of, 272
Possibility of further exports, 282
Soil erosion, 279
Benniseed (see Sesamum)
BRAZIL, 455–63
Crops, areas, yields and production of chief, 457–60
Effects on white people of tropical conditions and mixed marriages, 455
Development, possibilities of, 463
Food, supplies, 461
Export, 462
Burma: Rice from, 352
Butter production: Argentine, 453; Australia, 419; Denmark, 107; Eire, 55; N. Ireland, 50; Netherlands, 94; New Zealand, 438; Sweden, 117; World supplies, 485
Butter: consumption in U.K., 29, 484, 486

Cacao tree, introduction into Africa, 287
CAMEROONS, 285, 289, 291
CANADA, 368–98
Agricultural land, loss of, 398
British Columbia, 387, 389
Crops, area and production of chief, 390
Dairy produce, 394
Egg production, 395
Foods exported to U.K., 395
Food production, possibility of increasing, 395–8
Fruit: Nova Scotia, 375; Ontario, 372; British Columbia, 389
Grain production and export, 390–1
Irrigation, 397
Meat production, consumption and export, 392–4
Pasture improvement, 396–7
Eastern Provinces, 369–75
Crops, areas of chief, 371
French Canada, 372–3
Fruit belt, Ontario, 372
Livestock numbers, 371
Prairie Provinces, 376–89
Black soils, characteristics, 376

CANADA—*Prairie Provinces—continued*
Crops, areas of chief, 387
Early settlement, attempts at, 378–9
Livestock numbers, 387
Prairie farm rehabilitation, 384
Soil erosion, 384
Wheat, cultivation: northern limits, 377
Fluctuating yields, 382–3
Production and export, 390–1
Rust problem, 379–80
Weed control herbicides, 383
Westward shift, 381
Capital for expansion of food production, provision of, 476
Cassava: Angola, 271; Belgian Congo, 275; 277, 280; Gold Coast, 302–3; Kenya, 250, 255; Nigeria, 284, 291; Senegal, 311, 313; Sierra Leone, 307, 309; Sudan, 269; Tanganyika, 243; Uganda, 261
Cassava, Virus resistant, 238
Cattle as "brideprice" (Africa), 237, 257
Cheese production: Argentine, 453; Australia, 419, 440; Finland, 129; Netherlands, 94; New Zealand, 440–1; N.W. Europe, 117; World production, 486
Cheese: supplies for U.K., 486
CHINA, 344–9
Composts and disease, 348
Crops, area and production of chief, 346
Food supplies, 347
Livestock and products, 345
Possibility of increasing food production, 347
Soil erosion, 349
Chlorella: possible source of food, 500
Cocoa production: Belgian Congo, 276; French Africa, 312–13; Gold Coast, 299–302; Nigeria, 287
Coffee production: Angola, 271; Belgian Congo, 276; French Africa (Ivory Coast), 312–13; Kenya, 249–50; Uganda, 261; Tanganyika, 241
Collective farming, 72, 474
Co-operation in farming, 473–4; Denmark, 96; Eire, 58; Finland, 122; Israel, 172; Italy, 158; N. Ireland, 52; Sudan, 265–9
Cotton cultivation: Belgian Congo, 277; Brazil, 458; Egypt, 177–8, India, 324; Nigeria, 288; Pakistan, 337, 341; Sudan, 265–9; Uganda, 261; U.S.A., 357
Cultivation, shifting, attempts to improve: Belgian Congo, 279; Nigeria, 295
Cultivation, World area, possibilities of expansion, 471–2 (*see also* the different countries)

DENMARK, 96–109
Butter, bacon and egg production, 103–4
Co-operative Organizations, 96
Crops, areas, yields and production of chief, 99–101
Fertilizers, consumption of, 102
Folk High Schools, 97

DENMARK—*continued*
Food, production, export and consumption, 107
Food units (for animals) produced, 102
Grain imports, 105
Land reclamation, 107
Land utilization, 97
Livestock numbers, 103
Milk and its utilization, 103
Seeds, export of, 101
Smallholders, difficulties of, 109
Diets: *see under* each country
Digitaria exilis, 291, 307
Diseases of animals, losses caused by and protection against, 71, 188, 200, 238, 256, 293, 303
Diseases of crops, 36, 69–71, 238, 250, 301, 279–80
Diseases of crops, protection against, 69, 238, 301

EGYPT, 174–81
Crops, areas, production and yields of chief, 177
Food, supplies of, 180
Irrigation, 175, 180–1
Land distribution, 176
Livestock, 178
Eire: *see* Irish Republic
Ensilage, 77, 95
Erosion, Soil, *see* Soil Conservation
Ethiopia, birthplace of some food plants, 182; *Eragrostis tef*, 198
EUROPE, food production and imports, 79–83
Recovery programme, 81
Western fertilizer consumption, 82

Factory-made food, possibilities, 498–500
Fats, world production and export, 496
Fertilizers, world supplies, 65; *see also* different countries
FINLAND, 121–31
Crops, areas and production of chief, 124, 126
Fertilizers, consumption of, 127
Foods: imports and exports, 129–30; quantities available per head, 130
Land utilization, 123, 131
Livestock, numbers and products, 128–9
Recovery, remarkable post-war, 123
Fish, consumption of, Basutoland, 213; India, 329; Portugal, 150; U.K., 493
Fish culture, Israel, 170; Pakistan, 340; Southern Rhodesia, 230
Food production, methods of increasing, 59–77, 472; *see also* the different countries
Food units (Scandinavian), 109
Food, world supplies, 468
World production and exports, 496
FRANCE, 132–41
Crops, areas, yields and production of chief, 135–6
Farming, types of, 134
Food, production, imports and quantities available per head, 138

FRANCE—*continued*
Land utilization, 133, 135
Livestock, numbers and products, 136–7
Monnet Plan, 134, 140–1
Peasant system, effects of, 134, 139
Statistics, Note on, 135
Wheat, production and import, 135–8, 141
FRENCH AFRICA, EQUATORIAL, 310, 315–16
FRENCH WEST AFRICA, 310–15
Assimilation of Africans, 311
Crops, area and production of chief, 313
Development schemes, Sansanding, 314–15
Foods, exports, 313
Groundnuts, 311–13
Nutrition studies, 312

GAMBIA, 309–10
GOLD COAST, 298–306
Cacao cultivation, 299–302
Swollen shoot disease, 301
Development schemes, 304–5
Livestock, 303
Native diet, 302–4
Grains, coarse, for livestock: world supplies, 480, 496; *see also* the different countries
Grain, total world production, 468
Grass drying, 77
Grass: better species sought, 412–14 (Australia); 397 (Canada); 252 (Kenya); 206–7 (S. Africa); 366 (U.S.A.)
Improved strains, 75–6, 434
Soiling by animals, 73
Grassland, improvement of: Great Britain, 71–7; Netherlands, 90–1; *see also* Pasture improvement
Grazing, rotational, 74, 433 (New Zealand)
Groundnuts, Angola, 271; Belgian Congo, 278; French W. Africa, 311–13; Gambia, 310; India, 325; Nigeria, 288; Portuguese Africa, 246, 271; Sierra Leone, 307; S. Africa, 196; S. Rhodesia, 226; Sudan, 269; Tanganyika, 244

Herbicides, 36, 71, 408 (Australia); 383 (Canada); 442 (New Zealand); 205 (S. Africa); 361 (U.S.A.)
HOLLAND, *see* Netherlands
Hydroponics, 500

INDIA, 317–36
Composts, 333
Crops, areas and production of chief, 324, 326
Improvement of, 332
Development schemes, 331–6; Damodar Valley, 334; Bhakra, Nangal Dam, 343 (Planning Commission)
Dry farming, 320
"Family planning," 336
Fertilizers, use of, 333
Food crops and supplies, 323–30
Improvement of villages, difficulty of effecting, 335–6

INDIA—*continued*
Irrigation, 321–3
Land utilization, 318
Livestock, difficulty of improving, 328
Manure, cattle, burnt for fuel, 333
Nutrition studies, 327–30
Rainfall distribution, 319–20
Soil erosion and conservation, 331–2
Tube wells, 321
Water of rivers, low utilization, 323
INDONESIA, 350–2
Insect attacks on crops, possibility of forecasting, 70
Insecticides, 70, 302
Insects, harm done in Africa, 235, 237, 264
IRELAND, NORTHERN, 44–53
Chief crops, areas and production, 46
Food, quantities shipped, 51
Livestock, numbers and production, 49
Potatoes, Ulster varieties, 48
IRISH REPUBLIC, 53–8
Co-operative Creameries, 58
Crops, areas, yield and production of chief, 54
Depopulation problems and development schemes, 56
Food, quantities shipped, 55
Livestock, numbers and production, 54
Irrigation: Bechuanaland, 216–18; Canada, 397–8; China, 347; Egypt, 175; Gold Coast (Volta Dam), 305; India, 321–3, 334; Israel, 162–6, 170–1; New Zealand, 444; Niger (Sansanding), 314; Pakistan, 340–3; S. Africa, 210; S. Rhodesia, 230; Sudan (Gezira), 265–9; U.S.A., 363–4
ISRAEL, 160–74
Crops, areas and production of chief, 163–5
Development plans, 169–72
Fish culture, 170
Food supplies, 167–9
Grapes, 166
Land reclamation, 161–2, 170
Land utilization, 163
Livestock, 166
Negev, 171
Oranges, 165
Producers' organizations, 172
ITALY, 150–60
Co-operation, peasant methods, 158–60
Crops, areas, production and yields of chief, 151–4
Foods, quantities produced, imported and available per head, 152
Fertilizer consumption, 155
Fruit, 153
Land reclamation and colonization, 155–8
Land reform, 158
Land utilization, 151
Livestock, numbers and products, 154
Wheat problem, 151–4
Ivory Coast: *see* French W. Africa

JAPAN, 349–50
Jute, 323–4, 338

Kaffir corn (*Sorghum vulgare*); *see* Millets and Sorghums
KENYA, 247–60
  African cattle, 257
  African diet, 257
  African farming, 254–9
  British farming, 249–50
  Crops, areas, production and yield of chief, 250
  Indian population, 259
  Livestock and products, 252–3
  Soil erosion, 253, 256
  Kola nut, 284, 302, 304
  Kwashiorkor, 234, 262

Land: area under cultivation in different continents, 15
  In relation to population, 14–16
  Loss of agricultural, Canada, 398; U.K., 59
Leguminous crops, need of new, for dry conditions, 206
Libya, Italian colonization, 156

Maize: Angola, 271; Argentine, 450–1; Belgian Congo, 278, 280; Brazil, 457; Egypt, 176–8; Gold Coast, 302–3; Kenya, 250, 255–7; Nigeria, 291; S. Africa, 190, 193–4, 202; S. America, 447; S. Rhodesia, 227; Uganda, 261; United States, 355, 357
Malaria, losses from, in Africa, 235
Malnutrition: in Africa, 234–5
Manure, cattle, burnt as fuel, Africa Basutoland, 212; E. Africa, 237, 255; India, 333
  Cattle, prejudice against use, 215, 244, 255, 263
Margarine, production, 114, 127, 481, 485
Marketing Boards, 475; Cocoa: Gold Coast, 300; Nigeria, 290
Meat, world production and export, 487–95. *See also* different countries
  Consumption per head in chief consumer countries, 490–1
  Yield per acre of grassland: U.K., 75–6; of veld, 208, 225
Mechanization, progress in Europe, 82; U.K., 57
Mediterranean countries: increasing wheat imports, 154
Milk, food required for production, quantities, 67
  Yield per acre of grassland, 74, 90, 434
  Yield per cow, 68 (U.K.); 90, 103, 116, 128, 136, 167, 178, 199, 208, 252, 262, 293, 328, 360, 431 (N.Z.)
Milk products, world production, 484–6
Millets and Sorghums: Africa, 176, 191–5, 203, 205, 213, 226–7, 239–44, 255–63, 269, 278, 280, 284, 290, 311; Asia: India, 325–6; Pakistan, 337, 339; China, 345–6; U.S. (hybrid sorghum), 358
MOZAMBIQUE, 245–7

Native Reserves: Union of S. Africa, 210–12; S. Rhodesia, 225–6
NETHERLANDS, 83–96
  Crops, areas, production and yield of chief, 90–94, 100
  Fertilizers, consumption of, 92
  Food supplies, 94
  Grain, imports of, 105
  Grassland, intensive management, 90
  Horticulture, 91–2
  Intensive cultivation, 88
  Land reclamation, 84–7
  Land utilization, 89
  Livestock numbers and production, 92
  Milk yield, production and utilization, 92–3, 117
NEW ZEALAND, 428–45
  Cobalt deficiency, 435
  Crops, areas of chief, 430
  Herbicides, 442
  Irrigation, 444
  Land utilization, 429–30
  Livestock numbers, 431
  Meat and dairy products consumption per head, 442; production and export, 438–41
  Meat and dairy products, possibility of expansion, 442–5
  Milk yields, 431–4
  Pastures, 432–8
Ngana in cattle, 237
NIGERIA, 283–98
  Cash crops: cocoa, 287–8; cotton, 288; groundnuts, 288, 297; palm oil and kernels, 286–7, 297
  Development plans, 294–8
  Exports of agricultural products, 297
  Food crops, 292
  Livestock, 292
  Native diet, 294
  Soil erosion, 298
Nitrogen fertilizers, 65; India, 333
NYASALAND, 239–40

Oil palm: Belgian Congo, 275–6; French Africa, 312; Gold Coast, 299, 302; Nigeria, 286; Portuguese Africa, 246; Sierra Leone, 306
Oil seeds: Europe, 90, 95, 113; India, 327; World supplies, 468
Oil, vegetable, world supplies, 481–5
Organic matter in soil, losses and replacement: Canada, 385; E. Africa, 252; S. Africa, 206; S. Rhodesia, 222
Ova, transplantation of, 67

Paddy, *see* Rice
PAKISTAN, 336–43
  Crops, areas and production of, chief, 337
  Irrigation in, 339, 342–3
  Soil deterioration, 343
PARAGUAY, 466–7
Pasture improvement: Australia, 412–14, Canada, 397; Kenya, 253; New Zealand, 433–5, 443–4; S. Africa, 206–8; U.S.A., 366

Peasant farming, difficulties of improving, 496

Phosphatic fertilizers, 65; in Australia, 402–3, 412, 424–5; Gold Coast, 304; New Zealand, 433, 443; Nigeria, 288–9, 292; S. Africa, 205

Piassava, 306

POLAND. Crop production in, 83

Population; African, Asian and Latin American countries, 23; European countries, 20–1; Great Britain (Royal Commission), 18; rate of growth in different countries, 17, 18; relation to land and grain cultivation, 15

World and continents, 13–15, 468

PORTUGAL, 148–58
  Foods, quantities available per head, 150
  Wheat, production and import, 149, 154

Potatoes, production, world and continents, 468

Price-supporting schemes, 475

Pyrethrum culture, Kenya, 249

Rape family, promising for cold climates, 127

RHODESIA, NORTHERN, 231

RHODESIA, SOUTHERN, 218–31
  African farms, output from, 225–6
  European farms: Crops, areas, yield and production of chief, 221–3
  Dairy products, 225
  Foods, quantities produced, 226–8
  Green manuring, 221–2
  Land utilization, 219–20
  Livestock, numbers and products, 224
  Possibilities of further developments, 228–30
  Tobacco, 223

Rice: Africa, 278–80, 290, 296, 303–5, 307–9, 310, 314–15; Asia, 323–5, 338, 345, 349, 351, 352; Europe, 143, 153; S. America, 457, 462, 464, 466; World exports, 496; World production, 478–80, 496

SAKUMULAND, development scheme, 243

Sansanding, irrigation scheme, 314–15

Sea plants, possible foods, 500

Senegal, *see* French West Africa

Sesame (Benniseed), 269, 285, 289

Sheanut (vegetable butter), 284, 304

Sheep, losses due to dogs, 39

Sisal, Kenya, 249, 256–7; Tanganyika, 241

SIERRA LEONE, 306–9; Rice, 307–8

Soil conservation, erosion: Australia, 421–2; Belgian Congo, 279; Canada, 384; China, 348; Commonwealth Africa, 209, 213, 215, 230, 253, 256–7; India, 331–2; New Zealand, 438; United States, 364–7.

Somaliland, 260

Sorghums, *see* Millets

SOUTH AFRICA, UNION OF, 186–210
  Crops, areas of chief, 193
    Yield, compared with other countries, 205

SOUTH AFRICA, UNION OF—*continued*
  Eragrostis (teff grass), 198
  Fertilizers, 205
  Fodder crops, 198
  Food supplies, 201–4
  Fruit, 196–7
  Grasses, introduced, 206–7
  Increased production, possibilities of, 204–5
  Irrigation, 210
  Kaffir corn (*Sorghum vulgare*), 195
  Land utilization, 192–3
  Livestock, numbers and products, 199, 200–8
    Diseases, 200
  Maize, area, yield and production, 194, 202
  Native reserves, 211
  Organic matter, loss from soil, 206
  Phosphate deficiency in herbage, 188
  Soil conservation, erosion, 209
  Soil deterioration, 206
  Sugar, 197
  Tobacco, 198
  Veld, improvement of, 207, 208
    High, 186, 189
    Middle, 191
    Low, 196
    Bush, 186
  Wheat, area, yield and production, 189, 191–5
  Winter rainfall districts, 191

SPAIN, 141–8
  Crops, areas and production of chief, 143
  Colonization schemes, 146–7
  Fertilizers, 145
  Food supplies, 145
  Land improvement, 145–7
  Land utilization, 144
  Livestock numbers, 143–4
  Oranges, production, 143, 148
  Scientific services, 147
  Wheat, production and import, 143, 148, 154

Statistics, agricultural, limitations, 7, 68, 135, 317

SUDAN, 263–70
  Food crops, 269
  Gezira scheme (cotton and sorghum), 265–8
  Scientific services, 270

Sugar production: Europe, 79–80; Denmark, 107; France, 138; Netherlands, 94; India, 323–4, 327; Natal, 197–8; Uganda, 261; Queensland, 412; U.K., 29, 35, 41, 79; World, 494

Sun's radiant energy, low utilization, 500–1

SWAZILAND, 214–15
  Food supplies, development grants, soil conservation, 215

SWEDEN, 109–21
  Crops, areas, yields and production of chief, 110–15
  Fertilizer consumption, 115
  Food exports, 120
  Food supplies, 119

SWEDEN—*continued*
Food units produced (for animals), 113
Land utilization, 111
Livestock numbers, 115
Meat production, 118
Milk, yield, production and utilization, 116, 117
Plant breeding in, 114
Small farms, economic difficulties of, 120
Synthetic foods, possibilities of, 498–500

TANGANYIKA, 240–5
Difficulty of relieving congestion of population, 244
Groundnut scheme, 244
Wheat, 242
Tea culture: Africa, 239, 249, 276; China, 345; India, 323–4; Indonesia, 351
Thailand, rice production and export, 352
Tobacco culture: Canada, 370–1; Nyasaland, 239; S. Rhodesia, 223; U.S.A., 256–7
Tsetse fly control, 237, 241, 296
and cattle population, 293, 303

UGANDA, 260-3
Chief crops, 261
Difficulty of relieving congestion, 263
Native diet, 261–2
UNITED KINGDOM
Agricultural holdings, numbers and size, 43
Agricultural production, value of, 39
Barley, utilization of, 33
Bacon and ham production, 489
Beef consumption per head, 491; Import, 492, 495
Beef supplies, 29, 489
Butter supplies, 488
Changes in agriculture caused by the war, 32–6
Cheese supplies, 488
Crop production, wartime peaks, 35
Crop yields, increasing, 68
Crops, areas and production of, chief, 27, 28
Diet, pre-war and post-war, 25, 40, 497
Effort expended to raise production by 50 per cent, 42
Fertilizer consumption, 65
Food imports, pre-war, 29
Food production, pre-war, 29; post-war, 40, 41
Food production, animal products, 38
Food production for livestock, 30, 31, 38
Food supplies per head per annum, 25, 497
Food supplies, future prospects, 495
Grains, coarse, production and import, pre-war and post-war, 34
Land, agricultural, loss of, 59, land reclamation, 60–4
Land utilization, 27
Livestock numbers, 32, 38
Meat imports, 491–2
Meat production, 29, 491
Meat supplies, 489, 491–3
Milk production, 38–9, 44

UNITED KINGDOM—*continued*
Milk supplies, 488
Milk: improving yields per cow, 66–8
Mutton consumption per head per year, 491
Mutton supplies, 489
Nutrients, starch equivalents and calories produced per acre, 31
Oil seeds import, 485
Pork supplies, 489
Potatoes, area and production, 27, 36
Rough grazing, 60
Self sufficiency, percentages of: pre-war, war-time and post-war, 35, 41
Sugar beet, area and production, 27, 37
Sugar supplies, 79, 80, 495
Wheat, area of, 27, 36–7
Wheat production and import, pre-war and post-war, 34, 478
Yields, some record, 68
UNITED STATES, 353–67
Agriculture, comparison with British, 367
Agricultural output increasing, 354; further possibilities, 362–4
Crops, areas and production of chief, 357
Eggs, production and export, 362
Farm workers, falling numbers, 359
Fertilizer consumption, 358
Irrigation, 363–4
Livestock numbers, 360–1
Maize production and export, 355, 357–8
Meat production and export, 360
Milk production and export, 361
Oils and fats: production and export, 362
Pasture improvement, 360
Soil, conservation and erosion, 364–7
Wheat production and export, 355, 357
Urena lobata, Belgian Congo, 277; Nigeria, 289
URUGUAY, 464; Crops and meat, 464–6

War of 1939–45. Effect on British Agriculture, 30–6
Effect on World Food Production, 469
Weeds, control of, *see* Herbicides
Wheat, diseases of: Eyespot, 36; rust, 250; 379–80; Take all, 36
Wheat production: Argentine, 450; Australia, 409; Brazil, 457; Canada, 391; China, 345; Commonwealth Africa, 195, 227, 250–52; India, 326; Pakistan, 327, 339–41; United States, 355–7; World (chief countries and continents), 478
Wheat world supplies, present and future, 477–8
Wheat, U.K. Utilization, 33–4
Workers, agricultural: falling numbers U.K., 42; U.S.A., 359
World food production and exports, 496
World food production and population, 468–70

Yams (W. Africa), 278, 291, 303

Zuyder Zee, reclamation of, 85

GEORGE ALLEN & UNWIN LTD
London: 40 Museum Street, W.C.1

Auckland: Haddon Hall, City Road
Sydney, N.S.W.: Bradbury House, 55 York Street
Cape Town: 58–60 Long Street
Bombay: 15 Graham Road, Ballard Estate, Bombay 1
Calcutta: 17 Chittaranjan Avenue, Calcutta 13
New Delhi: Munshi Niketan, Kamla Market, Ajmeri Gate, New Delhi 1
Karachi: Haroon Chambers, South Napier Road, Karachi 2
Toronto: 91 Wellington Street West
Sao Paulo: Avenida 9 de Julho 1138–Ap. 51